A Pictorial Record of L.N.W.R. Signalling

Crewe South Junction photographed shortly after the commissioning of the new signal Cabin and the 'Crewe System' all electric signalling in 1906 (Chapter 14 and **Plate 14.4***). The very large locking room windows were a feature of the large Crewe system cabins which were of composite construction. A drawing and details of the impressive signal gantry appears in Chapter 6 (***Figure 6.10***). The crosses on the arms at the far right denote that they are not in use. A strip of wood nailed across the signal arm was introduced for this purpose on the LNWR in 1886 and this was replaced by a cross in November 1897, a system still used by British Rail today (although they are generally painted white).*

A PICTORIAL RECORD OF

L.N.W.R. SIGNALLING

by

Richard D. Foster B.Sc., C.Eng., M.I.C.E.

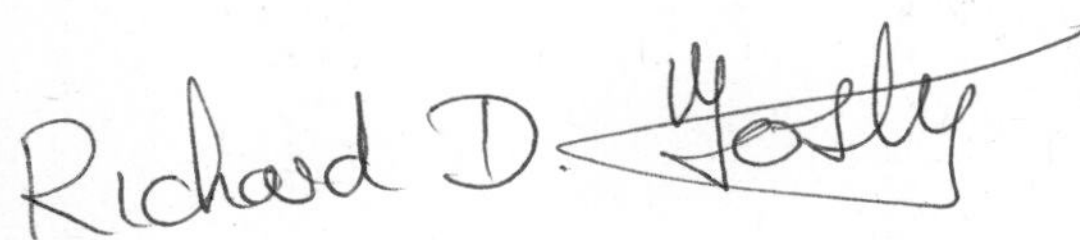

Oxford Publishing Company · Oxford

SBN 86093 147 1

To the memory of the men of the LNWR Signal Department, and their successors, this book is respectfully dedicated.

Printed by Blackwell's in the City of Oxford

Published by:
Oxford Publishing Company,
Link House,
West Street,
Poole, Dorset.

Contents

Page

Introduction iv

Chapter 1 — Early Days 1

Development of fixed signals, disc signals, semaphores, auxiliaries, time interval system, abolition of disc signals, Clark two-mile telegraph, introduction of interlocking, Telegraph Department, introduction of absolute block system, Saxby and Farmer.

Chapter 2 — The Signal, Electrical and Telegraph Departments 14

Formation of Signal Department, staff structure, Heaton Norris and Crewe Offices, resignation of Edwards, appointment of Dick and Thompson, District Inspectors, Telegraph Department, Amalgamation of Signal and Telegraph Departments, formation of Electrical Department, organisational changes, Signal Department staff.

Chapter 3 — Signals, Pre-1883 Designs 26

Contractors signals, two and three position signals, development of LNW designs, '1874' and '1876' signals, pinnacles, distant signals, signal sighting and lamps, slots, calling-on, bridge and disc (ground) signals.

Chapter 4 — Standard Signals 1883 to 1928 39

Development of 1883 design, colours of signal lights, signal sighting, co-acting signals, heights of signals, signals on multiple track lines, signal ladders, distant signals, painting.

Chapter 5 — Bracket Signals 58

Standard types, S62 and S61 designs, arrangement of signal arms, special designs.

Chapter 6 — Gantry Signals 72

Need for, wood and iron gantries, special designs.

Chapter 7 — Ground, Subsidiary and Special Signals 85

Disc and miniature signals, lights in discs, bridge, calling-on, and shunt ahead signals, new type call-on and shunt signals, loop line, route indicating, and colour light signals.

Chapter 8 — Level Crossings 101

Types of crossings, development of methods of control, Board of Trade Requirements, first LNW gates, standard LNW gates and equipment, gate stops, principles of operation, key system, painting.

Chapter 9 — Signal Cabins — Pre-1874 Designs 113

Development of shelters for Policemen, raised cabins, development of designs by contractors, divisional designs, types 1 and 2 standard designs.

Chapter 10 — Signal Cabins — 1874 to 1930 123

Development of standard designs for construction by the LNW, Type 3 hipped roof design, Type 4 gable roof design, standard windows, standard sizes, composite and wood construction, determination of sizes, siting and heights of cabins, special cabins — narrow and overhead, extension of cabins, type 5 design, fires, painting, coal and ash pens, standard huts.

Chapter 11 — Interlocking Frames and Ground Frames 148

Philosophy of design for LNW, first Webb design, cam-head and tumbler types, construction of, overhead frames, addition of tappet locking, tappet frame, construction of, fate of Saxby frames, ground frames, right angle, key interlocking (SK446) and SK80 type, Annett's keys.

Chapter 12 — The Block System and Signalmen's Instruments 173

Early types of block instruments, tell tale instrument, 1-wire three position experiments, adoption of 3-wire system, Fletcher combined instrument, Stockport Works, arm and light indicators, standard repeaters, route (train) indicators, Fletcher electric lock, signalmen's reminders, signing the register, link or lever collar, Fireman's call box, Northampton Locks, track circuits, Train on Line indicators.

Chapter 13 — The Working of Single Lines 191

Development of Pilot and Staff systems, staff and tickets, 2-wire block, tablet and Webb and Thompson electric train staff systems, licence for manufacture, miniature staff, staff exchanging and switching out.

Chapter 14 — The Crewe All-Electric Signalling System 200

Needs, developments, choice of system for LNW, Webb and Thompson system, Gresty Lane, construction and operation of indoor and outdoor equipment, improvements, overhead apparatus, installations made, Camden Junctions, fires, licence for manufacture, subsequent changes.

Chapter 15 — Miscellaneous Equipment 213

Turntable bolt, point rodding, facing points, clearance bars, midway release, lineman's boards, bells, gongs, face discs, wire adjusters, multiple lever distant signals, fog machines.

Chapter 16 — Signalling Layouts 228

Kenilworth, Staveley, Sedbergh, Alsop-en-le-Dale, Thrapston, Oxford, Bethesda, Penygroes, Bletchley.

Chapter 17 — Signalling on the Associated and Joint Lines 235

Introduction; LNW and GW Joint; Shrewsbury and Birkenhead Joint; Vale of Towy; Welshpool; West London and West London Extension; North London; Manchester, South Junction and Altrincham; Whitehaven, Cleator and Egremont; Carlisle; LNW and GN Joint; Leeds (New); LNW and L&Y; Ashby and Nuneaton.

Appendix I — LNWR Signal Department — Senior Staff 1873 to 1923 258
Appendix II — LNWR Telegraph Department Staff 1897 260
Appendix III — LNWR Rules for Sighting Signals and Signal Department Regulations 261
Appendix IV — Signalling Costs 267
Appendix V — Regulations for Working Fletcher's Electric Lock for Intermediate Sidings, 1884 269
Summary of Contents 270
Acknowledgements 272

Introduction

Under the leadership of Richard Moon, its able and powerful chairman, the London and North Western Railway evolved, during the 1870's and 1880's, into the most important of the pre-grouping companies. Although not the largest in terms of route mileage it was the largest in financial terms and for many years it claimed to be the largest Joint Stock Company in the world. The backbone of its operations was the main line from London to Birmingham, Liverpool, Manchester and Carlisle, probably the most important and heavily trafficked main line in Britain. Under these circumstances the Company was justified in describing itself as the 'Premier Line'.

In compiling this book I have tried to put together a selection of photographs which will illustrate as wide a cross section of LNWR signalling equipment and practices as possible. These are supplemented by scale drawings and diagrams which should assist readers in understanding how the equipment worked and was put together. For the modeller the many scale drawings should enable accurate models to be made of this characteristic and essential LNWR lineside equipment.

Where it is appropriate, each Chapter is laid out in such a way that the standard equipment, designs and methods are described first. These were used in most instances and are the most representative and typical of LNW practice. Variations and special items were, however, inevitably required to suit particular site and traffic conditions. The Chapters therefore go on to describe some of the more common and interesting variations which occurred and the reasons for them. Where designs and practices varied with time (such as signal cabin design) the chapters are set out chronologically so that the development processes can be followed.

The London and North Western Railways had a signalling system including both equipment and practices that was highly standardised. The reasons for this lay in the Company's strong and centralised organisation and policies. The designs and practices of any organisation always owe as much to the personalities and facilities available as they do to the duties required and the LNW was no exception to this. Chapters 1 and 2 describe the evolution of the LNW Signal Department and explain how its course was influenced by circumstances and personalities.

Richard Moon believed that the most important objective of the organisation was to make a good profit for the shareholders. He therefore objected to contributing to other people's profits (as he felt happened when work was put out to contract) at the expense of his own, and encouraged the idea that the LNWR should, wherever possible, do the work itself at a lower cost. It should be noted of course that this would only occur where there was a good and continuous work load to keep the men and machines occupied and gain from economies of scale, hence one off work would always be better suited to contract. As a result of this philosophy, over the years, Crewe Works developed into the largest engineering works in the world, capable of turning out practically anything that might be asked of it. F W Webb was appointed Chief Mechanical Engineer in 1871. He was of the same school as Moon, and was well versed in the economies to be gained through standardisation and mass production. He was well aware of the pitfalls of this approach in poor quality and increased maintenance costs. Quality at Crewe was important and was never sacrificed on the altar of reduced first costs. The facilities at Crewe were ideally suited to the mass production of the vast amount of signalling equipment required.

Something of the scale of the operation of the Signal and Telegraph Departments can be understood from some 1906 statistics. The LNWR then had some 1500 signal cabins containing between them 37,500 levers controlling 20,000 signals. The Company employed about 3,000 signalmen, plus 700 men to repair and maintain the mechanical equipment, 900 for the telegraph work and 150 for electric lighting work.

The Company's Officers, particularly those concerned directly with operating the traffic, were also deeply committed to the philosophy of standardisation. They were concerned about operating practices and procedures and the appearance and performance of equipment rather than reduced construction costs. From long and sometimes bitter experience they had learnt that diversity of practice could spell disaster. The men who had to operate the trains were not always the most intelligent of people and could easily be confused by equipment or practices which were different in one place to those in another. As far as possible they tried to achieve a situation where all the equipment was of similar design and could be operated in as nearly as possible the same way, no matter where it was on the system. Throughout this book evidence of the operation of these standardisation policies will be found. In general they were extremely successful and produced a uniform, simple and workmanlike system both from the operating and maintenance points of view. Occasionally things could go wrong. This was true, to some extent, in the attempts to standardise block working where, due to several unfortunate decisions, it was the late 1890's before the degree of standardisation aimed at was actually achieved. This situation is fully described in Chapter 12.

The grouping of 1923 made little real difference to the LNW Signal Department (the LMS had far too many other things to do than to interfere in areas where things were perfectly satisfactory) and as far as the Western Lines of the LMS (as the LNW had become) was concerned, signalling practice continued unchanged from LNW days. The only real difference was that LNW equipment began to appear on some of the smaller lines which had come into the Western Lines organisation. On the Central Lines (the old Lancashire and Yorkshire Railway), LNW style cabins began to appear (but not signals or lever frames). It was not until 1928, when the LMS began a determined campaign to shake up the management structure, in order to break down the inter-departmental and inter-constituent rivalries and bickerings, that things began to change. A new man with new ideas and no obvious sectional biases (A F Bound) was brought in from the LNER to superintend the signalling for the whole of the LMS (See 'A Pictorial Record of LMS Signals'). Therefore, for the purpose of this volume, LNW signalling practice is taken to continue until 1928.

In a book of this sort it would obviously be impossible to illustrate and describe every item of LNWR Signalling equipment. To do so would require a book perhaps ten times as long as this. A further constraint is the availability of photographs of sufficient quality to be suitable for inclusion. The vast majority of LNWR signalling equipment existed at a time when 99% of railway photographs were of engines and trains. The majority had disappeared before even the handful of enlightened enthusiasts came along who recognised that there were other things to railways (like carriages, wagons, buildings, road delivery vehicles, let alone signals!). Even so, the author has had to do a great deal of heart-searching in choosing the illustrations and many fine pictures have had to be left out because of the limitations of the space available.

This volume sets out to describe and illustrate the signalling equipment used by the LNWR. Because of the limited space available it has been necessary to assume that the reader has a reasonable knowledge of the geography of the LNWR system. Similarly it has not been possible to describe signalling rules and regulations and operating procedures or their development. Readers may obtain further information from publications such as the 'Pre Grouping Atlas' for the location of the places mentioned in the text. 'British Railways Signalling' by Kitchenside and Williams (both Ian Allan Ltd.) is a good guide to signalling principles and practice. In general LNW spelling of place names is used as are the names the LNW used for the various items of equipment described. Similarly the units of measurement and money are those in use in LNW days, all dimensions being in yards, feet and inches and money being in pounds, shillings and pence. (Conversion factors are given in Appendix 4).

While a good deal of documentation about engines has survived, because of this locomotive orientation of enthusiasts, much valuable material about other aspects of railway operation has been lost. A vast amount of work has been necessary, over the last ten years or so, to piece together, from many sources, remaining scraps of evidence in order to produce the overall picture presented here. Some gaps remain to be filled and the author would be delighted to hear from anyone who is able to add to the picture.

Richard D Foster

Kenilworth station cabin, this was erected in 1883 in connection with the doubling of the line (see also Chapter 16). A tall structure was provided to enable the signalman to see the whole of the layout under his control. There were sidings at the far end of the station and the signal cabin was positioned so that they could be seen from the cabin windows over the footbridge (the cabin operating floor was elevated approximately 25 feet above rail level). Even so clearance or fouling bars were fitted to the main line trailing points as an additional safeguard. The LNW made a special effort to produce an attractive station for its customers at Kenilworth and the lower portion of the cabin has been finished in a matching style to the remainder of the buildings. Above station canopy level the cabin is constructed in the ubiquitous and cheaper 'Crewe' bricks. Presumably the LNW thought that the gentry did not look upwards!

Photo: B E Timmins

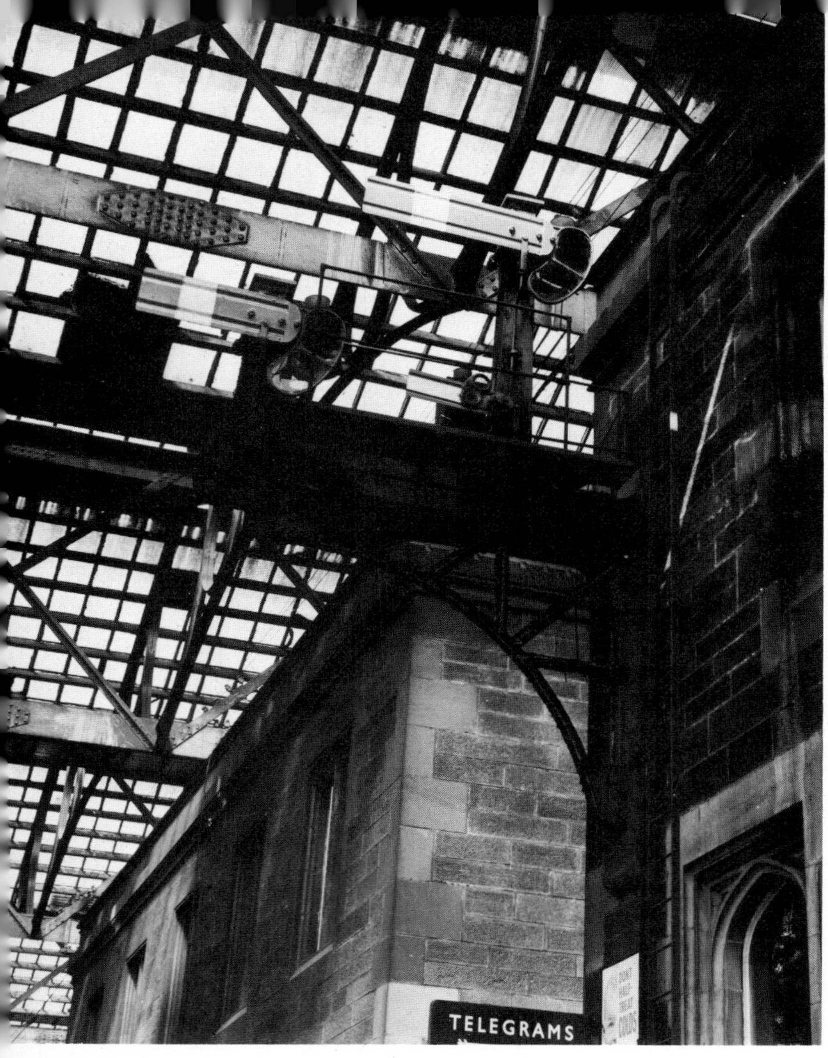

This signal was attached to the wall of the station buildings on No. 1 Platform at Carlisle. It protected the scissors crossovers situated near the centre of the platform which were used for joining and dividing trains or changing engines. The main arm controlled movements along the platform road ahead while the call-on arm (Chapters 3 & 7) allowed an engine to proceed cautiously forward along the platform line when this was occupied ahead by standing vehicles. The lower left hand arm controlled movements over the crossover road to Siding A. The signal structure is made up from standard S61 bracket signal parts (Chapter 5) adapted for this special situation. Note the access ladder up the side of the building.

Photo: British Rail

Despite the use of a signal gantry, the dolls could still be quite tall in order to give adequate sighting as in this example at the south end of Preston Station. The photograph, taken in 1953, shows how the dolls applying to each line are grouped together for clarity. The group on the left apply to the Down Slow and the right hand group to the Down Fast line. The speeds allowed through the station were low and so the distant arms were fixed at danger. Of interest is the way in which the left hand end of the gantry is supported by a small stool on top of the bridge girders. This saved the cost of, and space required by, a separate leg. Note also the arrangement of the signal wires in the middle of the gantry structure. A LNW three arm miniature semaphore signal is visible between the up and down lines. Framed under the right hand end of the gantry is the former Park Hotel which was LNW and L&Y joint property.

Photo: British Rail

Chapter One　　Early Days

The signalling system on the London and North Western Railway did not evolve overnight. It developed in stages as needs arose, with experience and as a result of increasing traffic and higher speeds.

DEVELOPMENT OF FIXED SIGNALS

Almost as soon as the Liverpool and Manchester line opened it became evident that some means was required of controlling trains at stations and junctions. The Company police were given the task and were provided with suitable flags and lamps. Many of these men were allocated to particular positions on the line at which they had to provide a signal to every train that passed (**Figure 1.1**). Problems arose, of course, if the policeman had to leave his post for any reason. To overcome this fixed signals (i.e. a moveable target or arm and a lamp on a permanent *fixed* post) were improvised by the engineers or superintendents at a few places.

The use of rotating signals originated considerably earlier than the adoption of semaphore signals and the earliest recorded instance of the former type was on the Liverpool and Manchester Railway in 1834. A wooden or metal flag was introduced to get over the difficulty that the visibility of ordinary flags or flag-poles was dependent on the force and direction of the wind in the vicinity. The development of mounting the wood or metal flag 'across' the post, rather than it projecting from one side of the post in the way that an ordinary fabric flag is carried from a flag-pole, opened the way to the adoption of a circular target or 'disc' rather than a rectangular flag.

The target or disc faced the driver to indicate danger but in their original form the signals showed no indication when turned to 'clear', as they were rotated (turned off) so that the disc was edge on to the driver. It was the Great Western Railway, under the instigation of Brunel, that adopted the practice of fixing a crossbar at right angles to (and below) the disc, so that the crossbar showed when the disc did not, thereby giving a positive signal in both positions. Moreover, the GW practice was to use the *crossbar* as the 'stop' indication, the action of rotating the signal to hide the crossbar and display the disc thereby denoted 'clear' (see 'A Pictorial Record of Great Western Signalling').

On the LNWR development followed a different course. At the time the absence of a signal in the 'clear' position was not considered a deficiency and displaying the disc face-on to the driver denoted 'stop' or danger. What was of concern however was that it was often difficult for drivers to distinguish easily between those signals which applied to them and those which applied to the other line. Although the discs were painted red on the front face and white on the rear, at a distance, or when seen against a sky line or in poor light it was practically impossible to be sure which was which. In order to overcome this problem, particularly in the case of signals showing 'on' or danger, a horizontal crossbar was added under the disc (and in the same plane as it). The crossbar had projections on its ends which pointed upwards for an up line signal and downwards for a down line signal (**Figure 1.1**). The signals thus continued to show no indication when at 'clear' and these LNW signals were therefore in reality disc signals with a symbol (the crossbar) on the post to signify the line to which they referred. Needless to say, they were often referred to as disc and crossbar signals although it should be emphasised that they were not the same as the better known and longer lived disc and crossbar signals employed on the GWR. As will be seen from **Figure 1.1** the disc signals worked only to two positions, and trains were cautioned verbally by the policeman or by the use of the green lamp or flag (**Figures 1.1 and 1.2**).

Semaphores had been introduced for transmitting signals across long distances over land, many years before there were railways in the modern sense. The first railway semaphore signal was put up in 1841, both as an improvement on the disc type and to enable the signal to show three indications as distinct from the two that were possible with disc-type signals. A slot was cut in the signal post and a wooden arm worked in it. This showed three positions, stop (arm horizontal), caution (arm inclined downwards at about 45°) and clear (arm vertical and hidden inside the post). The virtual absence of a visible signal again denoted 'clear'.

The introduction of semaphore signals to railway working was an engineering and traffic matter and originated out of a suggestion made by Mr Rastrick of the London and Brighton Railway, the first example appearing on the Croydon Railway (see 'The London, Brighton and South Coast Railway' (3 volumes), by J T Howard-Turner). The semaphore type of signal was found to work reliably and to be satisfactory from a traffic point of view and gradually began to supersede the disc (and crossbar) signals for new work and renewals, particularly in the Northern Division.

These first fixed signals were provided at stations to protect stationary trains and those crossing from one line to another at junctions. Because the signals had to be worked at the posts it was usual for all the signals to be placed together near the centre of the station or junction so that they could be controlled by one man. The signals were therefore often in advance of the 'fouling point'. For instance, the signals at a junction were usually placed at the facing points and a 'station signal' near the centre of the platform. A train standing in the station could have half its length projecting behind the signal. Drivers were expected to be familiar with the location of the points and the likely positions of trains and be able to stop clear of them if the signal was at danger. Inevitably with these centrally placed signal posts the temptation to mount all the signal arms (for all the lines and routes) on the same post was too much and some began to look rather like Christmas trees!

It was essential that drivers (and brakesmen) obtained a good and early sight of the station and junction signals so that they could bring their train to a stand with the rather primitive brakes then available. In fact it was often necessary to stop a considerable distance before reaching the signal. Many of the station and junction signals had to be raised a considerable height above rail level to give drivers a distant and unobstructed view above buildings, bridges and cuttings. It was also found that it could be difficult to positively identify the position of a signal arm at a distance when it was seen against a confusing background of colours, buildings, trees etc. as it tended to blend in with the scene. Where possible an attempt was made to find a clear background for the arm, the best of all being the sky. Obtaining this often resulted in tall signals, and this became something of a tradition on the London and North Western.

It soon became clear that the station and junction signals alone could not provide adequate protection. Most companies adopted the use of 'auxiliary', 'distance' or 'distant' signals placed some distance in the rear of the station or junction and operated by wire from it. These provided an advance warning for drivers of the state of the line ahead. 'Auxiliary' signals appeared on the LNW in the 1840's.

SIGNALS.

RED is a Signal of **DANGER—STOP.**

GREEN „ CAUTION—PROCEED SLOWLY.

WHITE „ ALL RIGHT—GO ON.

These Signals will be made by **Flags** in the Day-time, and by **Lamps** at Night, and in Foggy Weather.

In addition to the above, *any* Signal, or the arm **waved** violently, denotes danger, and the necessity of stopping immediately.

11. When the Line is clear, and nothing to impede the progress of an Engine or Train, the Signalman on duty will stand erect, with his Flags in hand but showing no signal, thus—

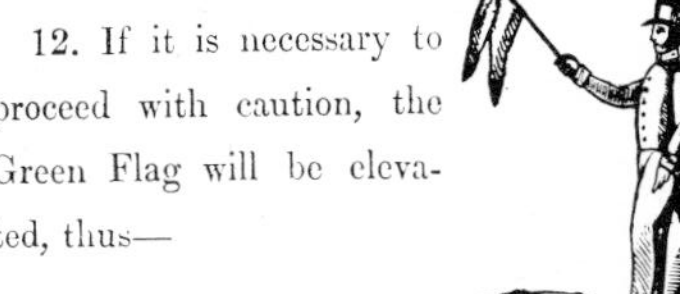

12. If it is necessary to proceed with caution, the Green Flag will be elevated, thus—

13. If it be necessary to proceed with Caution, from any defect in the rails, the Green Flag will be depressed, thus—

14. If an Engine or Train is required to stop, the **Red** Flag by day, or Red Light by night or in Foggy weather, must be shown, the Signalman facing the engine.

15. Every Signalman and Pointsman will be responsible for having his **Lamps** properly trimmed, and his **Signals** in good order, and shewing a distinct and clear light.

16. Hand Lamps and Flags when used as Signals must always be held in the hand and not placed upon or stuck into the ground. Care must also be taken that the person sent on any occasion to use a Signal be practised in the same, and understands its meaning.

17. It is the duty of every person on the Line who is intrusted with Signals, to observe every passing Engine or Train, and if within five minutes any other Engine or Train follows on the same Line, not only must the proper Signal to Stop be shewn, but every effort must be made to attract attention to it. If there be an **interval of more than five** minutes, and less than ten, the Signal to Caution **must be made.**

18. As regards Signals, it is the duty of every servant of the Company to prevent danger, and if from accident, the proper servant or officer cannot perform his duty, any other servant on the spot must give the Signal required.

STATIONARY SIGNALS

Are either Disc or Semaphore.

Semaphore Signals are constructed with either ONE or TWO Arms for day Signals, and Coloured Lamps for night and foggy weather.

The Signal is *invariably made* on the **Left-Hand** side of the post as seen by the approaching Engine-Driver.

19. The **all right** Signal is shown by the Left-Hand Side of the Post being clear, the Arm being within the Post, thus:

Or by a White Light.

20. The **caution** Signal, to **slacken speed,** is shown by the Arm on the Left-Hand Side being raised to an Angle of 45 Degrees, thus:

Or by a Green Light.

21. The **danger** Signal, always to stop, is shown by the Arm being raised to the Horizontal position, thus:

Or by a Red Light.

DISC SIGNALS are generally constructed of circular form with a Cross Bar underneath, either with two ends turned downwards, or upwards, as the case may be.

22. Those with ends turned **downwards** thus:—

Denote the Down Line, and relate only to Down Trains.

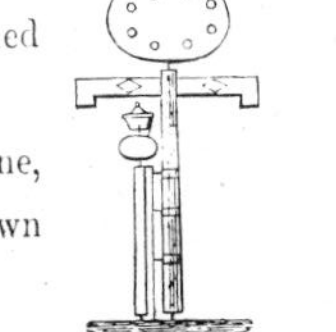

23. Those with ends turned **upwards** thus:—

Denote the Up Line, and relate only to Up Trains.

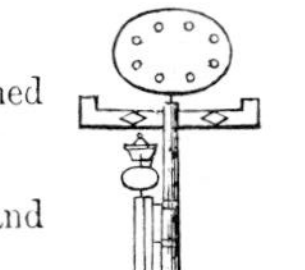

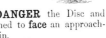

24. When at **DANGER** the Disc and Cross Bar are turned to **face** an approaching Engine or Train.

25. When **All Right** the Disc and Cross Bar Signal are turned Edgeways to an approaching Engine or Train.

26. As precautionary Signals, the **Red Signal** will be shewn for **five minutes** after the departure from an intermediate Station of any Ordinary Train, in order to stop any coming Engine or Train. After this time has elapsed, the **Green Signal** will be exhibited for **five minutes more,** to complete the ten minutes' precautionary Signal.

27. On a Train entering a long Tunnel, the **Red** Signal will be turned on until the Signalman shall have received Telegraphic Notice that the Train has emerged from the other end, when the **Green** Signal will be turned on, to complete the precautionary Signal.

JUNCTION SIGNALS.

Where the Junctions are provided with Two Semaphore Signal Posts, corresponding with the two meeting Railways; the *Signals* for each line are shown on the *Signal* Post appropriated to it, in the same way as on the Station Signal Posts.

28. The Signals at the Junctions are always set at **DANGER,** and no Engineman is allowed to pass until the arm is lowered to **CAUTION,** or the **Green** Light is shewn.

29. When two Trains are seen approaching a Junction from different Lines, the Signalman must keep his Signals on at Danger to **both** Trains, and not allow either to pass until one of the Trains has been brought to a stand.

AUXILIARY SIGNALS.

30. Auxiliary or Distant Signals are to shew the same as the Main Signals; that is, when the Main Signal is **All Right** the Auxiliary Signal is to be **All Right,** and when the Main Signal is at **Danger** the Auxiliary Signal is to be at **Danger,** *except* in cases where the Main Signal is temporarily lowered to allow an Engine or Train to pass through the Station, during which time the **Auxiliary** or **Distant Signal** will remain at **Danger.**

When the Main Line is clear after the departure of an Engine or Train from the Station, the *Precautionary* Signals described in Rule 26, page 14, must be shewn on the *Main Signal only*, the Auxiliary Signal being lowered after the Train has got sufficiently clear of the Station.

31. When a Train is stopping at a Station, or when there is any obstruction thereat, the **Main** and **Auxiliary** Signals must be at **Danger**; and **any coming Engine or Train must be brought to a Stand at the Auxiliary Signal,** when the Engineman will open his Whistle; and afterwards proceed with caution towards the Station.

If the Auxiliary Signal is out of order, a person must be stationed not less than 200 yards beyond the Auxiliary Post with Hand Signals and Detonators, and act under the instructions of the man in charge of the Main Signal Post.

Figure 1.1 *A reproduction of the portion of the 1860 LNWR Rule Book covering the types of signal in use at the time. Interestingly the 1847 edition showed the semaphore only and did not mention the disc signals.*

One of the first mentions of the Auxiliary Signal was in a curious instruction of 24th February, 1846, although a few such signals had clearly been in use for a while.

> 'The fan or arm of the auxiliary signal at Cheddington, Leighton, Roade, Blisworth and Weedon are re-painting to a yellow colour which will be more discernable than green, the ground colour is obliged to be nearly red, the signal will however, continue to be shown for the assistance of the drivers, although it is not intended they should stop thereat but come on as heretofore as far as the stationary post, when the policeman will tell them why the train has been stopped.'

One hopes that the drivers understood exactly what they were supposed to be looking out for! It would seem that the arms of the auxiliary signals had originally been painted green to conform with their 'caution' function. In retrospect, it is perhaps a pity that the LNWR did not continue to paint the auxiliaries yellow.

The Company was not really sure how the auxiliaries should be used and in 1848 a number were removed and it was agreed that the majority of the remainder would only work in poor weather as this abstract from the 1849 Rule Book indicates:—

> *'Auxiliary Signals'*
>
> 'At many of the principal stations Auxiliary Signals worked by a wire are placed 500 yards in advance of the station signal posts. These Auxiliary Signals are intended to warn the enginemen and guards in thick weather (when the main signal cannot well be seen at the usual distance) of the RED being turned on at the station and for this purpose a GREEN signal is shown at the Auxiliary Post. Except when the red signal is shown at the station no signal whatever is shown by the Auxiliary. The enginemen are not to depend solely on the Auxiliary Signals but they may always depend on the RED signal being on at the station whenever the GREEN is seen at the Auxiliary.'

However a few signals at difficult places continued to be worked for all trains and one at Weedon which protected the canal drawbridge stood normally at danger and was only 'turned off' on the approach of a train.

All this was bound to cause confusion and slack working and a number of accidents occurred because the working of the auxiliary had been neglected or had not been attended to properly.

In November 1854 the working of the auxiliary signals was modified:—

> 'Auxiliary signals are now made to show a red as well as green. In all ordinary cases of the main signal showing red in order that an engine is to stop at the main signal, the auxiliary as heretofore is only to show green it being understood that when the auxiliary is green the main signal is red, but when a train is stopping at the station and extending beyond the main signal, or any other obstruction on the main line between the main signal and the auxiliary, the auxiliary is to be made a positive signal and turned on to red, and when necessary the policeman is to go back with his hand signal to give the drivers of following engines verbal instructions.'

The Auxiliaries were thus made a stop signal in their own right and gave protection to trains standing at stations or junctions ahead. The principle that the Auxiliaries should generally show the same as the main signals was not introduced until the 22nd November, 1856 when Rules 30 and 31 in **Figure 1.1** came into force. The 'stop and proceed' portion of Rule 31 reduced delays and the risk of a following train running into one that would otherwise be waiting at the auxiliary. This 'stop and proceed' rule remained in force at a number of distant signals in South Wales well into this century due to the steep gradients.

It took time to get the modified regulations across to the men on the ground however and Mr Bruyeres made the following caustic comment about what he found a few weeks later when he made a night journey on his district.

> 'Now let me ask you how the auxiliary signal can show a red light same as the main signal if the lamp is not lighted.'

The circular sent out regarding the working of the auxiliaries had contained no instruction about the necessity of lighting the lamp!

THE TIME INTERVAL SYSTEM

The system of controlling the trains in use was the 'Time Interval' system. Here it was endeavoured to maintain a distance of time between successive trains. The station and junction signals played a fundamental part in the regulation of the time-interval system. In order to prevent fast trains from catching slower ones the station signals showed a caution signal for a predetermined period to indicate that another train was only a short distance ahead. The 'caution-only' signal was found to be inadequate and the method of working was altered in January 1846:—

> 'The trains including luggage and ballast are now so close upon each other, to avoid risk of collision, the police regulation to turn on the green signal for 10 minutes on the passing of a train will be cancelled and the following order substituted. On the passing of a train the red signal is to be turned on for 5 minutes then turned off, and the green turned on for 5 minutes longer, at the expiration of those 10 minutes the line is considered clear and no precautionary signal shown. The green signal only will be sufficient to turn on on the passing of an engine without a train.'

This basic regulation with its stop and precautionary signals remained in use, with minor modifications from time to time, for the remainder of the life of the time interval system.

The majority of the signals stood normally at 'clear' and the system allowed several trains to occupy the section of line between two stations at the same time.

The operation of the signals at junctions was somewhat different. By 1849 the signals were semaphores and only showed two positions — 'danger' and 'caution' — and were normally set at danger. They were lowered to caution for the passage of each train (Rules 28 and 29, **Figure 1.1**). There was no all-right position, primarily because it was necessary to pass over the points at reduced speed. Later, when interlocking began to be applied, it was not possible to interlock three position signals.

The time interval system with station and junction signals was adopted on many lines from the time of opening. This occurred on the Chester and Holyhead line for instance where in 1846 it was ordered that the 23 semaphore signals required between Chester and Holyhead should be of the LNWR type supplied by Stevens and Sons of Southwark Bridge Road, London. The signals were placed at the Shrewsbury and Chester Junctions, Mold Railway Junction, at all the stations, on either side of the Conway and Foryd Bridges and at the tunnels.

ABOLITION OF THE DISC (AND CROSSBAR) SIGNALS

The disc and crossbar signals began to disappear in the late 1850's and were replaced by semaphores. For example, in November 1862 it was decided to convert the existing disc signals on the Bedford to Bletchley line to semaphores in order to make them consistent with those on the remainder of the line. October 1863 saw a decision to replace the disc signal at Eccles, the only one remaining on the Liverpool and Manchester Line, with a semaphore. On the lines to Leeds the disc signal at Grotton was ordered to be replaced by a semaphore in June 1864, while one at Saddleworth was replaced with a semaphore on a new site in August. July 1865 saw authorisation given to replace all the remaining discs between Leeds and Stalybridge with Semaphores. By 1867 disc signals only remained in use on the Southern Division main line. Here a complication had arisen which delayed the changeover. The up 'third' or goods line had been opened in stages from July 1858 onwards until it reached as far out as Bletchley. Semaphore had been adopted on this line so that they would not be confused with the passenger line signals which remained of the disc type. The signals were generally placed side by side although there were no auxiliary signals on the third line. This arrangement did not assist the drivers at night of course and on the 1st July, 1858 an additional regulation was introduced:—

> 'At night the goods line signal post is distinguished by a fixed green light placed immediately below the lamp, that will show either a red or a white light accordingly as the trains are to stop or proceed.'

It will be noted that the 'caution' signal was not used (See **Figure 1.1**). The retention of the disc signals was not satisfactory however and it was decided to make the third line signals of distinctive form by fitting rings to the arms and so allowing ordinary semaphores to be used on the main lines. This had been done by 1867 and the work of removing the disc signals was put in hand.

THE CLARK TWO-MILE TELEGRAPH

The basic idea of using the electric telegraph to regulate the working of trains had been suggested very early on in the history of railways. Indeed, the LNW was involved in its evolution. The section of the London and Birmingham Railway between Euston and Camden was the venue of some experiments shortly before the opening of the line. On June 25th, 1837 successful trials took place of Cooke and Wheatstone's electric telegraph, in which Robert Stephenson with his usual acumen had taken a keen interest. The instruments were of the five needle speaking type. Satisfied with the experiments, Stephenson was anxious for the telegraph to be installed throughout from London to Birmingham. The Directors however were only prepared to do this if the Grand Junction, then about to open its line, would also consent to do so. This they were not willing to do and the London and Birmingham forfeited to the Great Western the distinction of being the first railway to install the electric telegraph.

There could be no doubt about the usefulness of the telegraph as a means of general communication and it spread rapidly throughout the country for both public and railway work. The majority of the telegraph was provided and maintained by the telegraph companies and many of the town to town public telegraph wires shared the same lineside pole routes as the wires used for railway work. The railway telegraphs could be and were used for passing information on the working of the traffic but generally the circuits in the early days only operated between the larger stations and were of little use to the staff at intermediate stations and junctions.

In January 1854 Edwin Clark of the Electric Telegraph Company sent a report to Captain Huish, the General Manager of the L&NWR, in which he outlined proposals on which the trains could be regulated by use of the telegraph. The principles outlined formed the basis of the block system as finally adopted in Britain.

Clark indicated that separate wires running between adjacent signal stations only would be necessary for controlling the trains. The wires were only to be used for indicating the state of the line and not for conversing or sending other messages. He envisaged that the line would be divided into sections of a convenient length, say from one to five miles to suit the traffic, the existing stations and junctions being used in most cases. Each signal station would have a signal for each line and two telegraph instruments, one referring to the pair of lines on the up (London) side of the station and the other to the pair on the down

Plate 1.1 *A Block Instrument of the type devised in 1854 by Edwin Clark for use on the LNWR. Two three-position needles were provided, one for the down line and one for the up line, the descriptions of the needle positions which were adopted for use on the LNWR are shown. The 'line blocked' position was only used as an emergency signal and indicated that the wires had been cut to give warning that a mishap had occurred in the section or that the instruments had failed. The needles were controlled by the drop handles below them and these could produce momentary dial signals by moving the handles to the right or left as necessary. As explained in the text, the block signalling needle operations were carried out partly from the forward end of the section (as was entirely the case in later practice) and partly from the rear end of the section and so both handles could be pegged over to one side or the other to give a continuous signal. Handles at both ends of the needle circuit were also necessary to convey, or reply to, dial beat messages used in the signalling process since bells were not provided at first. The metal pegs used to hold the handles over can be seen attached to chains on the front of the instrument. These pegs were, of course, the origin of the expression 'Peg up the Block' (or 'pegging up' for a train) and the description of block instruments as pegging or non pegging types. Like most early telegraph and electrical instruments, large terminals were provided on the outside of the instrument case for the wire connections.*

Photo: Courtesy Science Museum

TRAIN TELEGRAPH SIGNALS.

44. Between **LONDON** and **RUGBY** Signals have been erected at intervals of about two Miles apart, at which Electric Telegraph Instruments have been placed; the **Red** or Danger Signal is to be shown until the Line is telegraphed clear; and any Engine or Train arriving within this period is to be stopped, and the Driver and Guard told by the Policeman on duty that the Line is blocked according to the indication of the needle.

GENERAL INSTRUCTIONS.

1. There are two Telegraph Instruments in each Signal Station, generally in the same Hut; one being devoted to the Down Line, and the other to the Up Line—the Line to which they refer being marked upon them. Each Instrument has two dials, one communicating with the Up Station, and the other with the Down Station, as engraved upon the Instruments.

2. A Signal is made by permanently holding the needle over to the right or left, and attention is called by continually moving the needle to the signal required.

3. If the needle suddenly becomes vertical, and no motion of the needle takes place on moving the handle either to the right or left, it indicates either that the Telegraph is broken down, or that the wire is disconnected by the Guard of some Train travelling upon the Line, to warn the Signalman that the Line is blocked. Under such circumstances, no other Train must be allowed to proceed on that section of the Line without being stopped, and the Engineman and Guard warned of the danger:—

Each needle, therefore, makes three Signals:—

1. Needle to the left, signifying "Train on the Line."
2. Needle to the right, signifying "Line Clear."
3. Needle vertical, signifying "Line blocked and impassable."

4. On the approach of an Up Train, the Signalman is to ring the bell of the next **Up Station**, to call attention, and to continue moving the needle backwards and forwards until he receives a response. Upon hearing the Bell, the Signalman at the other, or **No. 2 Station**, holds the needle over for a moment, to show that he is in attention. **No. 1 Station** Signalman then gives **two** slow and very distinct ticks with his needle to the left, if it be a Passenger Train, or Single Engine; or **three** slow and distinct ticks if it be a Goods, Coal, or Cattle Train that is passing his station. **No. 2 Station** Signalman repeats the signal, to show that he understands it correctly, and then blocks his needle over permanently to "Train on Line," and leaves it there until the train arrives at or passes his Station.

5. If another train arrives at **No. 1** before the previous one has been Telegraphed as having passed **No. 2 Station, No. 1** Signalman is again to ring the bell, and call the attention of the man at **No. 2 Station**, and Signal the Second Train in precisely the same manner as previously directed; and similarly, if a third or fourth train should pass his Station.

6. On the man at **No. 2 Station** receiving notice that another Train has arrived at **No. 1 Station** before the first Train has passed his Station, he is to acknowledge the Signals, as before described, and to enter on his slate the description of both Trains which are still on the Line between him and No. 1; and similarly, if a third or more Trains be announced to him as having entered his length.

7. As the Trains pass his Station, he will cross them off his slate one by one, and be careful not to Telegraph the Line as clear, *until the last of the Trains has passed.* When all the Trains have passed **No. 2**, and the length between him and **No. 1** is clear, he calls **No. 1**, by ringing his bell, and shaking his needle, which is to be acknowledged by **No. 1**, as before directed. **No. 2** Signalman then holds his needle over to the right for a moment to denote "Line Clear," which **No. 1** Signalman is to repeat, and then to block his needle over to the same signal. **No. 2** is not to take his eye off the instrument until he sees that **No. 1** has blocked his needle over correctly.

8. Down Trains are to be telegraphed in precisely the same manner as described in the Rule for "Up Trains."

9. The dials show at all times, and at every Station, whether there are any Up or Down Trains, between the next Up and Down Stations.

10. **No** obstruction to be allowed on the Line, if the dials indicate the approach of either Up or Down Trains.

INSTRUCTIONS TO SIGNALMEN.

11. The Telegraph Station Policemen will keep their Needles held over to "Train on the Line," until a Train has **completely** passed by; and should they observe from the appearance of the passing Train that it is going slowly, or likely to fail, they will still keep their Needle in that position, and not give the Signal back "Line Clear," until time has been allowed for the slow Train to make some progress over the succeeding link.

12. The Needles are not to be worked too quickly, each movement is to be made slow and distinct.

The Man receiving the Message is not to leave the Instrument until the Needles have become steady.

13. On a Train passing a Telegraph Post without the Tail Lamps on the last Carriage, the Policeman on duty will telegraph onwards "Train on Line;" but he will not telegraph back to the last post "Line Clear," but continue his Needle blocked "Train on Line," until the next Train passes him complete, that he may feel satisfied the Line is clear.

14. The Police in charge of the Train Telegraph Instruments and Signals, when they have to caution Enginemen on passing, are to use the same words as indicated on the Instruments—that is, **"Train on Line,"** or **"Line blocked,"** as the case may be.

Every Engine is to stop at the Danger Signal, and every Engine passing the Red Signal without stopping, unless the Driver receives verbal Orders from the Policeman in charge, is to be reported.

15. The Police at the Telegraph Posts **between** Stations, are not to have any Hand Lamp in their hand except during a Fog, when they are to use the Hand Lamp, in addition to their Signal, taking care that the Hand Lamp shows the same as the Main Signal.

16. In case of any uncertainty as to a Signal, or if the needle which belongs to the next Station is vertical, keep your Signal Post to danger, and warn the Enginemen and Guards that the Telegraph denotes that a Train is standing on the Line, and that the Line is impassable somewhere between you and the next Station.

17. The Auxiliary or Distant Signals are always to show the same as the Main Signals—that is, when the Main Signal is at **"Danger,"** the Distant Signal is to be at **"Danger;"** and when the Main Signal is **"All right,"** the Distant Signal is to be **"All right."**

Figure 1.2 *'Two-Mile' Telegraph Regulations as set out in the 1860 Rule Book.*

Figure 1.3 TWO MILE TELEGRAPH STATIONS BETWEEN LONDON AND STAFFORD

Euston	Bourne End	Weedon	Baddesley Colliery Siding
Chalk Farm Canal Bridge	Berkhamsted	Brockhall	Polesworth
Chalk Farm Engine Crossing	North Church	Buckby Bank	Amington Sidings*
South End Primrose Hill Tunnel	Tring	Crick	Tamworth (South Box)
North End Primrose Hill Tunnel	Tring Cutting	South End Kilsby Tunnel	Tamworth (North Box)
Kilburn Station	Cheddington	North End Kilsby Tunnel	Coton Level Crossing*
West London Junction	Horton Siding	Hillmorton	Hadesmoor Level Crossing
City Junction	Leighton	Rugby Loop Siding	Lichfield
Willesden†	Leighton Ballast Pit	Rugby (South Bridge)	Elmshurst Level Crossing*
Brent	Stoke Hammond	Rugby (Trent Junction)	Armitage
Wembley	Bletchley	Cathiron Crossing	Cannock Junction
Harrow	Loughton	Brinklow	Rugeley
Pinner	Wolverton (Blue Bridge)	Shilton	Bishton Level Crossing*
Bushey Station	Wolverton	Bulkington	Colwich
Watford, St. Albans Junction	Hanslope	Attleboro' Stone Siding*	Tixall Level Crossing
South End of Watford Tunnel	Ashton Bank	Nuneaton	Queensville Level Crossing
North End of Watford Tunnel	Roade	Nuneaton (Midland Junction)	Stafford (Trent Junction)
King's Langley	Blisworth	Hartshill Siding	
Nash Mills	Banbury Lane	Mancetter Level Crossing*	
Boxmoor	Bugbrook	Atherstone	

* Open during daylight only.
† Signalled 'Third Line' only.

Figure 1.3 *List of the 'Two-Mile' Telegraph Stations between London and Stafford in 1860. In addition, subsidiary posts, equipped with indicators to show the position of the 'Block' existed at Merivale, Amington and Lichfield Level Crossings, and signals only were provided at Sudbury to protect goods trains shunting there. The spellings of some of the place names have changed somewhat over the years.*

(country) side. Each instrument had two telegraph dials and two handles one for each of the up and down lines between the two adjacent signal stations (**Plate 1.1**). As originally proposed the dials were to be marked 'Line Clear' on the top right and 'Line Blocked' at the top left. The vertical or neutral position was intended to be a danger signal indicating to the man in charge that something was wrong.

The needles were to be kept 'blocked over' either to one side or the other by means of the handles which were fixed in position by a block or wedge of wood placed under them. The system of working proposed was a little different from that which evolved in later years. The block needles were to stand normally at 'Line Clear' this being done by the signalman at the rear end of the section blocking over his telegraph handle. When a train entered the section the signalman released the handle and vibrated the needle to indicate to the signalman at the advance end that a train had entered the section. That signalman indicated that he had received and understood the message by blocking his telegraph handle over so that the needles remained at 'line blocked'. When the train had passed him he released the needle and vibrated it to attract the attention of the first man who then blocked his handle over to 'Line Clear' again.

In the main part of his paper Clark did not go as far as to recommend that the system should only allow one train in each section at any one time. Instead he simply proposed that the signalman at the rear end of a section would exhibit the caution signal after a train had entered the section until he received an indication from the man at the other end that the section was again clear. The danger signal was exhibited if necessary for a short period of time just after a train had passed. The system was thus the old 'time-interval' with the addition of the telegraph to provide further information.

Clark did however venture to suggest the adoption of an 'absolute block' system:—

> 'It will be observed that in the system described it has not been thought desirable to forbid two trains entering on the same length of line between the signal stations, it is however evident that if the stations are placed sufficiently near together to avoid delays from stoppages, that by such an arrangement all accidents from collisions will be quite impossible, and in this case the caution signal will be entirely cancelled.'

The directors decided to adopt Clark's basic proposals and in 1855 work began installing the system on the Southern Division main line. The 'Two Mile' train telegraph system was brought into use on the first sections of the line about the end of the year. The 'permissive' form of the 'block' was adopted and one or two minor modifications were made to Clark's proposals. The lettering on the telegraph dials was made to read 'Train on Line' on the left and 'Line Clear' on the right. The term 'Line Blocked' was used for the vertical position of the needle. The regulations for operating the 'Clark Two-Mile Telegraph' as they existed in 1860 are reproduced in **Figure 1.2**.

To assist in communicating the occurrence of an accident or failure within a section Clark recommended the adoption of a scheme whereby trainmen could cut the appropriate block wires to give an early indication of the blockage to the men at the train telegraph stations. This was adopted in the initial LNW installations:—

> 'Should your train break down and obstruct either the up or down line, you will immediately proceed to the nearest telegraph post, having white porcelain insulators, and by disconnecting both the railway wires in the manner that will be explained, you will give notice of the obstruction so that all other trains will be cautioned: but you will not neglect in addition the usual precautions taken in such cases to stop approaching trains. You will observe that every

Figure 1.4 PORTIONS OF L.N.W.R. WORKED ON PERMISSIVE BLOCK – 1869

London to Nuneaton
Walsall, Cannock Junction, Park Street and Bridgeman Place
Bescot, Dudley Junction and Bodley's Crossing (down line only)
Wednesbury and Wednesbury Junction (up line only)
Great Bridge and Horseley Fields
Dudley Port and Horseley Fields
Sheepcote Lane and Bushbury Junction
Adderley Park and Marston Green
Aston and Vauxhall
Colwich and Stafford
Stafford and Earlestown
Worleston and Crewe
Liverpool and Kenyon Junction
Ditton Junction and Birdswood
Preston and Preston Junction
Oxheys Cattle to Barton (up line only)
Wigan to Eccles
Manchester, Ardwick to Hyde Road
Manchester Victoria (No. 3) and Old Salford Junction
Longsight and Levenshulme
Levenshulme and Heaton Norris Junction
Stockport, South end of tunnel and Edgeley Junction
Sandbach, North Stafford Junction to Crewe main signal box (up line only)
Manchester, Salford Junction and Ordsall Lane Junction
Manchester, Oldfield Road Goods Yard and Ordsall Lane
Manchester to Weaste
Patricroft and Barton Moss Junction
Barton Moss and Astley
Astley and Bury Lane
Kenyon Junction and Bury Lane
Shrewsbury and Wellington
(Chester and Holyhead – this section almost ready for use)

Figure 1.4 *List of the sections of the LNWR worked on the Permissive Telegraph (Time Interval plus Telegraph) system in 1869. As can be seen an appreciable proportion of the line was worked on this system.*

Figure 1.5 PORTIONS OF THE L.N.W.R. WORKED BY THE ABSOLUTE BLOCK SYSTEM – NOVEMBER 1869

Primrose Hill Tunnel
Broad Street to Victoria (North London etc)
Watford Tunnel
Kilsby Tunnel
Birmingham, Edgbaston to New Street (North End) (Tunnels)
Birmingham, New Street (South End) to Banbury Street Ticket Platform (Tunnels)
Dudley Port (Lower) to Sedgley Junction (down line only)
Dudley Port (Upper) to Sedgley Junction (up line and down loop lines only)
Brownhills to Anglesea Siding (down line)
Walsall, Bridgeman Place to Bodleys Crossing (up line only)
Manchester, Hyde Road to Longsight Main signal cabin
Stalybridge Tunnel
Grotton Tunnel
Grotton Station to Greenfield Junction
Diggle Tunnel (Single) (Standedge)
Huddersfield Tunnels
Morley Tunnel (between Howley Park and Morley Station)
Dewsbury to Thornhill Junction
Liverpool Tunnels
Bolton and Kenyon Branch (Single)
Sutton Oak to St. Helens (Single)
Preston, Wyre Junction to Oxheys Cattle Siding
Whitehaven, Bransty Junction to Harrington Junction
Whitehaven, Bransty Junction to Corkickle (Single tunnel) (Furness)
Chester Station to Saltney Junction
Conway Marsh to Pendyffryn and Penmaenmawr (Tunnels)
Tal-y-bont to Penrhyn Junction and Penrhyn Junction to Bangor (Tunnels)
Bangor to Carnarvon Junction (Tunnel)
Carnarvon to Cwm-y-glo and Llanberis (Single)
Craven Arms to Llandovery (Single)
Abergavenny Junction to Brecon Road (Single)
Brecon Road to Govilon, Gilwern and Clydach
Clydach to Brynmawr (Single)
Beaufort to Ebbw Vale Junction

Figure 1.5 *List of the sections of the LNWR worked on the Absolute Block system in 1869.*

alternate post has a special description of insulators, easily recognised for the purpose of disconnecting the wires.'

To further assist with this process the block wires were placed as the lowest wires on the posts, the 'up' wire on the up side of the posts and the 'down' wire on the down side. Loops of thin wire which could easily be broken were brought down the posts to assist the men in cutting the wires. Temporary repairs could be made by twisting the wires together to restore communication when the obstruction had been removed. The system was only installed on a large scale on the Southern Division main lines although it appeared on the Shrewsbury and Wellington Joint line. A short lived experimental section was also provided on the Joint line between Chester and Mollington. In practice problems occurred with this system of disconnecting the wires through breakages and other faults while it was found to be expensive to maintain and was eventually abandoned.

Edwin Clark was one of those rather versatile characters which the Victorian era seemed to produce from time to time. He was born at Marlow in 1814, the son of a pillow lace manufacturer. After two years at Cambridge he was mathematics master at Coombe Wood and then Brook Green, Hammersmith, schools between 1839 and 1845. His life then changed direction and he became resident engineer on the construction of the Britannia and Conway Tubular Bridges from 1846 to 1850. He became Chief Engineer to the Electric Telegraph Company in August 1850, a post he held until about 1860. It was during this period that he prepared the block signalling report and in this context it could perhaps be seen as something of a sales exercise!

Clark invented the hydraulic graving dock and canal lift and constructed docks in Bombay, Malta and London. He was also responsible for the design of a number of swing bridges and laid a telegraph cable from Dungeness to Holland, while in 1856 he laid out a general plan of railways for Russia! He retired in 1876 and finally died of cancer in 1894.

Use of the Clark block revealed a number of defects, the principal ones being that the signalman at the advance end of the section had no control over the trains approaching him and he could not prevent or regulate their passage. The practice of allowing more than one train to enter the

Figure 1.6 SOME PORTIONS OF LNWR WORKED UNDER SPECIAL REGULATIONS – 1869

Section	Method of working
Manchester Nos. 2 and 3 boxes Victoria Station	Gong and disc.
Ordsall Lane and Oldfield Lane Goods Siding	Electric Gong.
Heaton Norris Junction and Station Box	Gong and disc.
Eccles Junction and Patricroft Junction	" "
Patricroft and Clifton Crossing	" "
Clifton Crossing and Eccles Junction.	" "
Middlewich Junction and North Stafford Junction Sandbach	" "
Macclesfield North and South ends of Station	Gong.
Saddleworth and Delph Branch Junction	Gong and disc.
Diggle Station and Goods Yard	" "
Morley and Morley Goods (North)	Gong
Stockport North and South end of Station	Gong and small arm
Leeds Copley Hill Junction and Copley Hill Sidings South	Gong and disc
Leeds Copley Hill Junction to Whitehall Junction	Telegraph Bell communication
Shap Summit and Tebay	Up trains are telegraphed from Shap Summit to Tebay. No train is allowed to follow down the incline at less an interval than 10 minutes.
Stations between Bangor and Carnarvon	Single wire telegraph at these stations by means of which the departure of each train from each station is notified to all other stations in each direction.
Walsall Bridgeman Place to Bescot Dudley Port Lower to Sedgeley Junction	Up lines only, bell communication to appraise staff that train is coming.

Figure 1.6 *The Block System (in the Permissive or Absolute form) was not flexible enough for working in busy station and yard areas. Alternative means which would provide the signalmen with more information had to be used. This table lists some of the sections of line involved and the methods of working in force.*

section also caused problems. The signalman had no ready means of recording how many trains had entered or left the section and erroneous 'Line Clear' indications were often given.

Messrs. Martin and Newman, district officers of the Electric Telegraph Company, assisted in efforts to overcome the problems. Slates were introduced for the men to record the passage of the trains each one being crossed off as it passed (**Figure 1.2**) while a few signal cabins were issued with small pegboards. However the basic form of the Two-Mile telegraph and the Time-Interval system remained in use for many years and its use was gradually expanded particularly on the busiest portions of the system. The three position semaphore signal was generally used, working to two positions at junctions and busy places.

THE INTRODUCTION OF INTERLOCKING

Despite the introduction of the Time Interval system and the Two Mile telegraph the points and signals continued to be worked by hand levers, usually placed at or adjacent to the points and signals themselves. Misunderstandings between the various pointsmen employed to work the points and signals around large stations frequently caused minor accidents. The Board of Trade strongly advocated the concentration of the working of the points and signals at one place where they could be under the control of one man. Some limited work was done in this direction although in most cases it consisted simply of bringing the levers together at one point. Accidents, therefore, still continued through the men pulling the wrong levers!

Some attempts were made to interlock the points and signals, the most significant steps being achieved perhaps by Gregory at Bricklayers Arms in 1843 where the signals were interlocked to prevent conflicting signals being 'off' at the same time. Atkinson in 1852 and C F Whitworth in 1853 patented some point and signal detectors. In 1856 John Saxby of the London Brighton and South Coast Railway patented a system whereby the points and signals at a junction could be worked simultaneously and so prevent collisions through the points being set for one line and the signals cleared for another. The firm of Stevens and Sons took an early interest in signalling matters and had begun supplying signals and related gear about 1840. This firm did quite an appreciable amount of work for the LNWR in the early days.

In October 1859, the LNWR gave notice of its intention to open the new line from Kentish Town Junction (Camden Road) on the North London Railway to Willesden. The signalling apparatus, of the old stirrup and lever design had been provided by Stevens, but did not give a sufficient degree of interlocking protection, in Colonel Yolland's (the B.O.T. Inspector) opinion. It was possible, if the attempt were deliberately made, to clear conflicting signals. Permission to open the line was therefore withheld and an employee of the NLR, Austin Chambers, who some years later, after a period in business, became Signal Superintendent of the Metropolitan Railway, added some mechanism which gave the desired result. The line duly opened from the 2nd January, 1860. Chamber's device introduced the principle that related lever movements should not be possible once the first movement had commenced and until it was complete. This important principle still applies in interlocking today. Saxby and Farmer purchased Chambers patent for £2,000 in 1867.

In 1860 John Saxby introduced a new form of locking frame (Patented in July), where the points and signals were worked by separate levers and the true principles of interlocking were applied. The interlocking was set in motion immediately a lever was moved but not completed until the lever had moved the full distance. Not long afterwards he attended a LNWR Board Meeting and demonstrated a model of his apparatus. As a result he was asked to signal Birmingham New Street Station and it was found that only two men were required to work it as against the 10 or 12 expected. Saxby had had a small works where his apparatus was made for some years but in the same year he and John Stinson Farmer (both men were working for the LBSCR at the time) obtained a 10 year lease of some LNWR owned land at Kilburn (adjoining Kilburn Lane, later Canterbury Road). A new works was constructed there during 1861 and 1862. Saxby resigned

Plate 1.2 *Crewe North Junction in the early 1860's. This view, looking south from the works area, shows the North Junction cabin standing in the 'V' between the Liverpool and Manchester lines which pass respectively in front of and behind the carriage shed on the extreme left. The Chester line sweeps round to the right foreground. The tiny junction cabin only controlled the two double junctions and the junction signals can be seen positioned just in front of the cabin. These illustrate the classic arrangements, used in the early days, for such signals. There are three posts, each containing two arms, one applying to the up, and one to the down, line on each of the three routes. Thus the arms on the left hand post apply to trains coming off the up Manchester line (left hand arm) and to down trains requiring to pass onto the down Manchester line (right hand arm). The tall centre post applies to trains from the up Liverpool line and those requiring to pass onto the down Liverpool line. The right hand signal, fitted with distinguishing rings, applied to the Chester lines. As can be seen from the short length of the slotted section of the posts these signals were only worked to two positions (Danger and Caution) as was usual at large stations or places where there were facing points. None of these signals were, of course, at the fouling points for the lines they controlled and drivers approaching them had to be prepared to stop clear of the points or any conflicting lines if their signal was at danger. In most cases this would involve stopping 100 or more yards before reaching the signals. The lamps are mounted lower down the posts than the arm and the same lamp serves to illuminate the spectacles for both up and down lines. Just in front of the hut, situated between the Up and Down Chester lines, are a set of levers which worked the various siding connections (concentrated but not interlocked!). Something of the rudimentary nature of railway operations and signalling practices of the time can be appreciated by studying the photograph. The sidings in the foreground all connect directly with the down and up Chester lines and no trap safety points are provided, although wooden scotch blocks have been placed across the ends of the two sidings (occupied by carriages) nearest the main line. Only one signal is provided to control movements from all the sidings in the centre of the photograph to the down Chester line, presumably drivers were, again, expected to know when it had been lowered for them. The area to the right of these sidings appears to be used as a store ground for materials and rubbish. Behind the pall of smoke from standing engines two huge engine sheds can be made out. Even at this early date Crewe was, obviously, of considerable importance in locomotive matters. The engines in the foreground are presumably awaiting attention in the works, those with squared off spectacle plates are Trevithick types and those with rounded plates are Ramsbottom 'DX's and 'Problems'. All have painted numbers rather than the later standard cast number plates.*

Photo: Courtesy National Railway Museum

his post on the Brighton Line in 1862 and went into partnership with Farmer in 1863. Almost from the start they did quite considerable quantities of work for the LNWR.

Steady progress was made from this time onwards in the concentration of the points and signals and with the installation of interlocking throughout the system.

FORMATION OF THE TELEGRAPH DEPARTMENT

The rapid expansion of the telegraph system on the LNWR brought problems in supervising and administering the work of the telegraph contractors. It was therefore decided to appoint someone to superintend the work and in 1864 Mr Samuel M Martin of the Electric Telegraph Company was appointed as the first Telegraph Superintendent of the LNWR. The new work and maintenance continued to be carried out by the contractors however, Martin and his staff simply organising the work and ensuring that the installations were carried out to an adequate and uniform standard.

In 1870 the telegraphs forming the national town to town communication system were taken over by the state and incorporated into the Post Office. At this time Mr Martin indicated his wish to resign his post and return to the field of contracting. This provided an opportunity to reconsider the Company's telegraph arrangements and following the general LNWR policy of 'do it yourself if you can' it was decided that in future the Company would install and maintain its own telegraphs. Martin's resignation was to take effect from the 30th June, 1870 and in preparation for his new role he offered, in April 1870, to contract for the maintenance of the LNWR telegraphs and instruments. This offer was declined however and the Company continued with its preparations to take on the maintenance itself.

INTRODUCTION OF THE ABSOLUTE BLOCK SYSTEM

Returning to block working, in 1869 the Board of Trade enquired of the various railway companies as to the methods they had adopted for working the trains and how much progress they had made with the introduction of the absolute block system (where only one train is allowed in any section at one time). The report on the LNWR makes interesting reading and gives an insight into the way the Two Mile telegraph was being used in the last few years of the Permissive Time Interval era.

Mr Cawkwell of the LNWR wrote to the Board of Trade in July 1869 to explain their system.

> 'We state that though our trains are not worked on what is known as the Absolute Block system, with certain exceptional cases a considerable portion of the line for some years has been worked with the aid of electric telegraph posts within a short distance of each other and at each of which drivers are warned of any preceding train in the next section and the time by which it is in front. It has worked well and is to be established on other portions of the main line.'

Colonel Yolland, who was appointed to look into the question, remarked from the above that the Company appeared to have an ingenious method of indicating at the telegraph posts the distance and time between trains. He thought however that the system was not as good as the space interval provided by the absolute block. He was somewhat disillusioned when he visited the line to see operations for himself and found that the principles set out by Mr Cawkwell were not in fact adhered to.

The Company's revised regulations of 1867 showed that the object aimed at was to inform the driver by means of the signals whether or not the section ahead was occupied. There was no verbal communication as to the time since the last train had passed unless this was less than 3 minutes (originally 5 minutes) in which case the signal was maintained at danger and the following train stopped and warned before being allowed to proceed. Yolland concluded that the whole thing was no more than a very elaborate and expensive system for warning drivers and then giving them all the responsibility! He also found that it was quite impossible to see many of the signals in time to stop at them with the brakes normally available on the trains. Distant signals were still not provided at many of the smaller telegraph posts. The system of recording the number of trains which had entered a section on a slate and crossing them off was also not adhered to and few records were actually kept.

Colonel Yolland concluded that the system was not satisfactory and he did not approve of its being extended. No other company was using a similar system, although the Great Northern had had something very much the same in use on its lines in the London area for some years. As can be seen from Figure 1.5 only a small portion of the line was worked on the Absolute Block system at this time. Most of the installations were over quite short sections of line where there were especial difficulties of some kind (such as tunnels and sections of single line).

The LNWR, perhaps sensing impending troubles, concluded their submission of November 1869 by remarking that it had been decided to carry out a trial installation of the absolute block between Edge Hill and Ordsall Lane. It was hoped that this and an installation on the Stour Valley Line would be completed on the 1st December 1869. In practice only the latter line was converted and the Liverpool and Manchester installation was postponed until the signal cabins were complete and some further investigations had been carried out. There were some difficulties on the Stour Valley line at first but by March 1870 – after some modifications had been made – the system was working satisfactorily.

The results of the BoT enquiry were quite clear, while the Stour Valley experiment had shown that the absolute block system was a practical proposition for adoption on the line. The LNW Directors therefore resolved to install a proper block telegraph system, the work to be concentrated initially on the main lines between London and Manchester, Liverpool, Holyhead and Carlisle. At the same time consideration was given to the best methods of signalling the stations and the regulations to be adopted for the use of the block system. Where telegraph instruments already existed for operating the permissive system these were retained and new regulations issued for absolute working. In 1871 a survey was carried out on the Liverpool to Manchester and Stalybridge to Leeds lines to determine what would need to be done to change to the absolute block system. In connection with this a meeting was held at Euston in December 1871 to consider the arrangements to be adopted. It was decided that where the absolute block was in use there would be no need to continue the use of the green light and the 45° position of the signal arm. The signals were to work simply to 'danger' and 'clear' (red and white lights). It was agreed that distant signals in both directions should be adopted in addition to the home signal at all train telegraph stations. With regard to the signals at stations it was decided that the station signals should be erected on separate posts for the up and down lines and these were to be placed on the ends of the respective platforms. Where the goods yard was in advance of the platform they recommended that separate starting signals should be provided to control the departure of goods trains after completion of shunting at such places. Arrangements were made to convert the two lines mentioned above to the absolute block system as soon as possible.

With the introduction of the absolute block system the normal position of the signals was altered from 'normally clear' to 'normally danger'. In practice the 45° or caution position was not abolished entirely but the signals at junctions and many large stations continued to show 'stop' and 'caution' only as a warning to drivers to proceed at reduced speed.

The system was found to work well and the task of converting the whole of the line was put in hand. By 1873, 571 miles out of 1119 miles of double track were worked on the absolute block system. By 1884 the whole of the passenger lines, with a few minor exceptions (**Figure** 1.7), were worked by the absolute block system. Block working was therefore installed on the LNWR well in advance of the passing of the Regulation of Railways Act 1889 which made its adoption compulsory.

Over the years the LNWR seems to have come in for a great deal of criticism, mainly on the grounds of safety, for its adoption of the permissive (time interval plus block) system of working. However it is important to consider the true reasons for its use. The permissive block system was devised as a means of overcoming the considerable congestion which occurred at the southern end of the LNW main line. The primary objective was to enable a greater traffic to be operated without recourse to expensive capital works. In the circumstances prevailing at the time the permissive system was extremely successful in achieving this. In 1873 Colonel Yolland conceded that there was no

Figure 1.7 SECTIONS OF LINE STILL WORKED BY THE PERMISSIVE AND TIME INTERVAL SYSTEMS IN 1884

Section of Line	*Distance* *miles*	*chains*	*Method of Working*
Bletchley to Swanbourne	5	0	Permissive Block*
Hartford to Greenbank	0	68	" "
Ardwick to London Road	0	38	" "
Dudley to Dudley Port (one additional line)	1	9	" "
Leighton to Dunstable	7	0	Time Interval
Wednesbury to James Bridge	1	60	" "

*Block plus time interval.
All remaining sections of passenger line were worked on the Absolute Block system.

proof that the LNW system contributed to or caused accidents. Indeed things would have been worse without it. However, what had been satisfactory in the 1850's did not suit the conditions of the late 1860's and the system degenerated somewhat towards the end — as Colonel Yolland found in 1869. By that time the need for change was somewhat overdue.

SAXBY AND FARMER

In 1862 John Saxby signed a contract with the LNWR for the supply of signalling equipment on a fixed scale of charges. Manufacture was undertaken at his new works in Kilburn which opened the same year. Things went well at first but by 1867 there was some dissatisfaction over the contract. Some of the LNW Officers felt that Saxbys were not entirely fulfilling the obligations of the contract while there were suggestions that the Company could probably do the work itself at less cost. Saxby and Farmer, following what seems to have been their standard business practice in such circumstances, wrote to remind the LNW that they held many signalling patents and any work undertaken would not be allowed to infringe these. Next, they submitted an offer to supply signalling equipment at a new fixed schedule of prices, which were generally less than under the 1862 contract. The offer was made on the condition that the LNW would obtain all of its signalling equipment from Saxby and Farmer during the period of the contract. After consideration, the LNW decided to accept Saxbys offer and a contract, to run from June 1867, was signed in November of that year (Appendix 4). In practice a number of items such as signal posts and signal cabin structures were provided by the LNW itself.

The LNWR was not the only company to be concerned about charges. In 1869 Saxby applied for extension of some of his Patents which were about to expire. The Great Western Railway was not keen on the idea of paying royalties for a further period and wrote to the LNW asking for support in opposing the matter. The LNW said that they would consider this. It just so happened that the LNW was in the middle of one of its periodic price disputes with Saxbys, this time over the cost of speaking telegraph instruments. In January 1870 the Directors were told that Saxbys had refused to reduce their prices, whereupon they immediately resolved to support the Great Western in opposing Saxby's application for extension of his patents!

1870, it seems, was one of the 'cold' periods in relations between Saxbys and the LNWR. Later in the year it was suggested that since Saxbys original patent had expired the LNWR should make its own signalling equipment or attempt to negotiate a lower price! In December a committee was set up consisting of Messrs Ramsbottom, Lee and Smith of the LNWR to advise the Board:—

> 'On the setting up of an establishment on a small scale at some central point with a view to the company doing their own work with respect to signals, points and crossings etc. instead of employing Saxby and Farmer and other manufacturers.'

Saxbys clearly got wind of what was afoot and in February, 1871 wrote to the LNWR offering to enter into an agreement to supply the LNWR with their signalling apparatus for a term of three years at a reduction of from 10 to 25% on their present prices. The General Manager was authorised to conclude an agreement on these terms. The scale of the reductions offered does perhaps suggest that the LNWR suspicions of overcharging had some foundation.

A period of relative tranquility followed, but in the summer of 1872 the question of the LNWR doing its own work was raised again and again a committee was set up to consider the question, the results of which are described in the next chapter.

The scale of the signalling work on the LNW and the part played in it by Saxby and Farmer can perhaps be judged by a few facts and figures. By 1873 approximately 60% of the points and signals on the line were fully interlocked and the Company had expended a total of £1,000,000 on signalling of which over £400,000 had been paid to Saxby and Farmer alone between 1864 and the end of 1872. The significance of this sort of expenditure to a firm like Saxby and Farmer can readily be imagined. As late as 1905, over 20 years after they had ceased to supply any significant amount of signalling equipment to the L&NWR, Saxbys still described them as 'Our greatest supporters and patrons in the past'.

When one considers the amount of money involved it becomes clear why the question of contract, or do it yourself, was raised so often. This was particularly so in signalling where the old feelings that it was not really necessary lingered under the surface. The concern over cost did not cease with the decision to do the work directly and the Signal Department's expenditure was questioned closely from time to time.

On the L&NWR the general practice in signalling matters had been to obtain new equipment from contractors who did the initial installation work and then handed the completed job over to the Company for operation and maintenance. The practice had grown up whereby the maintenance of the signals was carried out by the Permanent Way Department, while the Interlocking frames were maintained by the Traffic Department. These arrangements had been quite satisfactory when the quantity of signalling equipment in use was fairly small and of simple construction. By the early 1870's the increasing volume of work to be done and the greater complexity of the equipment was beginning to place a strain on the system.

The question of what to do to improve matters and to put things on a firm footing for the future was considered in 1872 and it was decided at the end of the year that responsibility for the whole of the maintenance work should be placed with the Permanent Way Department. This change came into effect in the early part of 1873, several of the Divisional Engineers taking on extra staff to deal with the work.

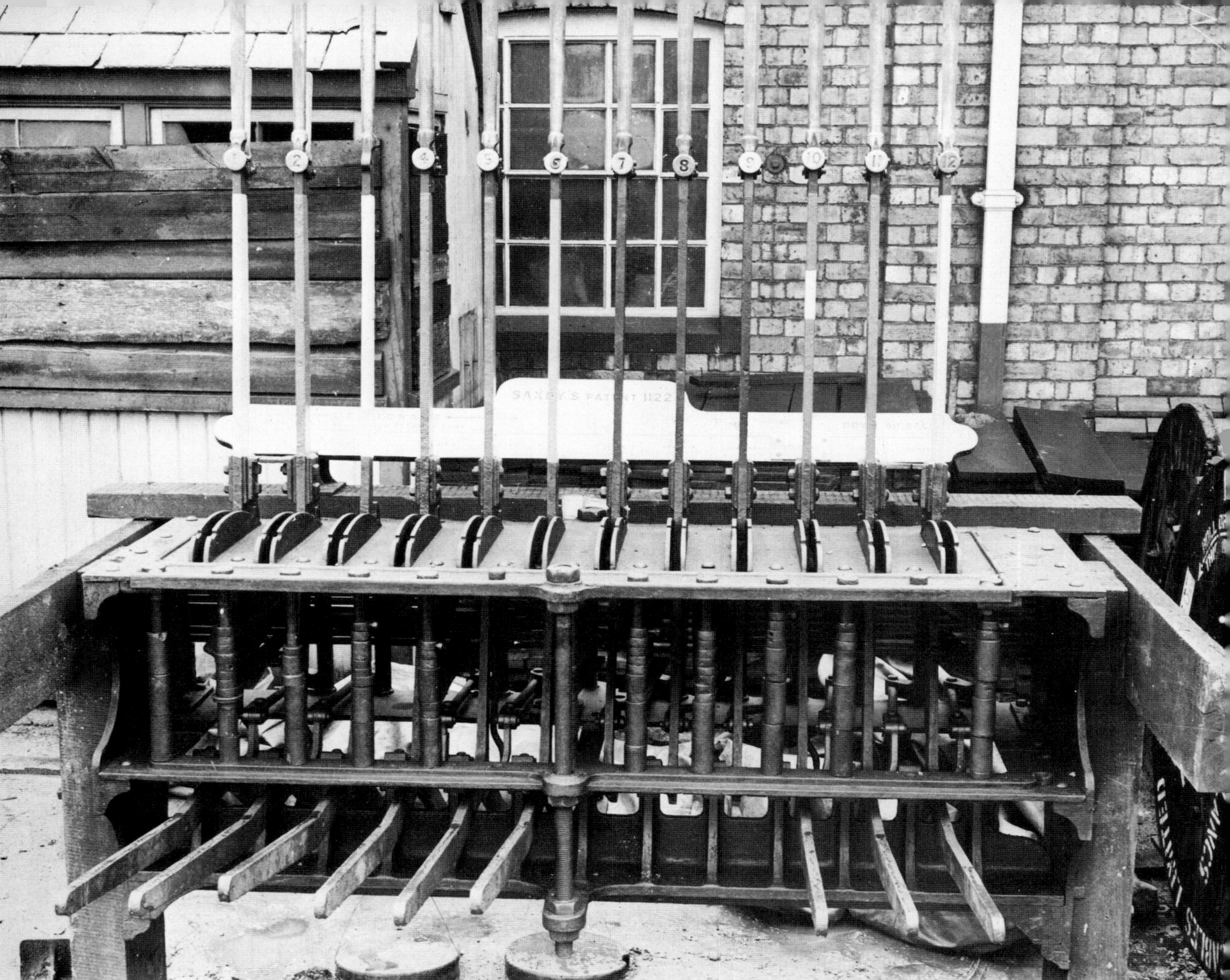

Plate 1.3 *The Saxby Spindle Frame from Penrhyn Sidings Cabin in the Signal Department Yard at Pedley Street, Crewe. This shows clearly the form of construction used in these frames and its working can be studied by comparing this photograph and* **Plate 1.4** *with* **Figure 1.8**. *The description board behind the levers was of brass with the lettering engraved on it. The inscription, in the raised portion at the centre, reads 'Saxby's Patent 1122' indicating that this was the one thousand one hundred and twenty second lever frame produced by Saxby and Farmer. This gives some idea of the vast quantity of signalling work done by this firm in the early days (the numbers were applied, of course, to all frames produced not just those installed on the L&NWR). The description 'Starting' for lever 10 is engraved on a separate piece of brass screwed on top of the main back board. This was due to the fact that the lever was spare when the frame was installed in 1870. The starting signal was provided in 1890 at a cost of £37.*

Photo: British Rail

Plate 1.4 *A rear view of the Penrhyn Siding frame. Attached to the catch blocks of levers 1 and 2 (No. 2 is shown reversed) are lugs which produce a simple form of 'lug locking' between the home and distant levers in order to prevent the distant signal lever being pulled with the home signal lever normal, or conversely, the home signal being put back with the distant 'off'.*

Photo: British Rail

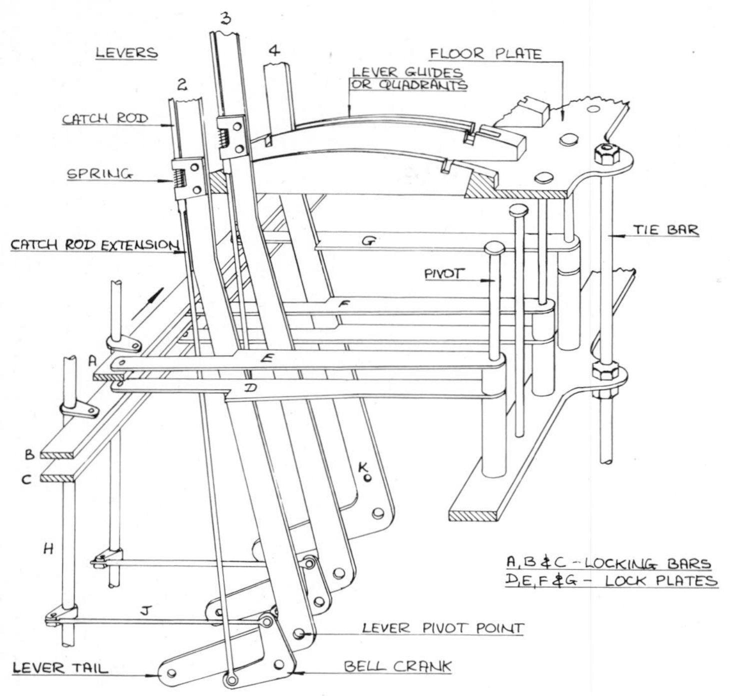

Figure 1.8 *A cutaway sketch of the 'Catch Handle' operated version of the Saxby Spindle frame as used on the LNWR. This should enable the operation of this rather simple form of interlocking to be understood. The interlocking is effected at the beginning and end of the lever stroke by the act of clasping and releasing the catch handle. This imparts a sideways movement in the appropriate locking bars (A, B and C on the drawing) via the catch rod extensions and the twist rods or spindles (H). This sideways movement of the locking bar moves the lock plates (D, E, F or G) attached to it sideways causing the projections or notches in them to lock or release the levers by gripping them like a hook. Thus the act of pulling lever 2 will move locking bar B to the right causing plate F to lock lever 4 in the normal position.*

Other simple locking combinations which can be studied in the drawing are:—

Pulling lever 3 locks lever 2 normal and releases lever 4.

Pulling lever 2 locks lever 4 normal and releases lever 1.

Lever 4 is locked normal by locking bar C.

The Great Western Railway 'Twist' locking is a development of the type of locking used in this Saxby frame. The similarity can readily be seen by comparing the drawing with Plates 150 and 151 in 'A Pictorial Record of Great Western Signalling'.

After the introduction of the well known Saxby 'Rocker' frame (patented in January 1874), frames of that type were supplied to the LNWR for new installations.

Chapter Two The Signal, Electrical and Telegraph Departments

THE SIGNAL DEPARTMENT 1873 TO 1903

Despite the reduced prices that had been obtained from Saxby and Farmer in 1871 the cost of the signalling work still gave some cause for concern and the feeling that the Company could probably do the work more cheaply itself lingered on. The question was raised again in the summer of 1872 and it was decided to set up a Committee to investigate the matter, their brief being:—

> 'Looking at the large amounts paid to Messrs. Saxby and Farmer for the supply of their signals and locking apparatus,' the Committee were to consider 'the most advisable and economical arrangements that can be made for the manufacture, by the Company, of the signals and apparatus and the points and crossings.'

The Committee met in November 1872 and was composed of Messrs Bancroft, Crossfield and Lyon, Directors, together with the General Manager, Mr Cawkwell. It was attended by Messrs Webb, Footner and Harley who explained the situation and the alternatives available.

The Committee were advised that Saxby and Farmer's main patent of 1856 involving the principle of locking had expired and that there would probably be no difficulty in arranging reasonable terms for the use of any of Saxby and Farmer's subsidiary patents should the Company be desirous of using them.

The Great Western and Midland Companies were reported also to be making their own signalling and locking apparatus at considerably less cost than the prices paid to Messrs Saxby and Farmer. Looking to the extent to which the locking apparatus had been adopted, and its probable further application as well as to the large amount of repairs that would always have to be attended to, it was resolved that:—

> 'It is expedient that the Company should undertake the manufacture of signal and locking apparatus as well as points and crossings. That Crewe will be the most suitable position for such an establishment. That it should be referred to Mr Webb to consider and report what provisions should be made in the way of workshops, machinery, tools etc., so that the Company may be in a position to undertake the business on expiry of Saxby and Farmer's contract at the end of 1873, and also as to what course should be adopted with regard to the use of any of the subsidiary patents of Saxby and Farmer.'

The recommendations were approved and in February 1873 Mr Cawkwell, the General Manager, was asked to secure the services of a competent and experienced Superintendent for this description of work at a salary not exceeding £700 per annum. In April he was able to report that he had secured the services of George Edwards at a salary of £650 and that he would take up his duties on 1st July, 1873. Edwards had previously worked for Saxbys and had been involved in a number of their installations on the LNW.

Francis William Webb, who had advised the Committee, had commenced his career as an apprentice in Crewe Works (where else!). He left the LNWR service in 1866 to take up a post as Manager of the Bolton Iron and Steel Company. In October 1870 he was appointed Locomotive Engineer of the L&NWR to succeed Mr Ramsbottom. His salary was to be £2,000 per annum rising to £3,000 after 12 months. With a salary of this sort his status in the L&NWR organisation can well be imagined. He took up his duties on 1st October, 1871. Webb was well aware of the economies to be gained from standardisation (not quite so easy in practice as in theory) mass production and simplicity. The opportunity to prove himself and increase the scope of Crewe Works by taking on the signal work and reducing its costs had come at just the right time and there can be no doubt what his recommendations had been! It is also clear that Webb was determined to bring the Signal Department under his control if at all possible. Officially, however, the Signal Superintendent was regarded as an independent departmental officer and Edwards reported to the Locomotive and Engineering Committee each month alongside Webb, Mr Bore of Wolverton, Mr Emmett of Earlestown and Captain Dent, the Marine Superintendent.

George Edwards too was a dynamic young man who wanted to get on in the world and saw his appointment as Signal Superintendent of one of the largest railway companies as a wonderful opportunity. Almost as soon as he took up his duties in July 1873 he realised that things were not going to be quite as he had expected. Webb had provided him with a set of offices, not at Crewe where the manufacturing was to be done, but at Heaton Norris! When questioned by the Board, Webb stated that it was merely a temporary arrangement until the permanent offices could be got ready in Crewe. Edwards finally moved to Crewe in 1876 by which time the majority of the equipment had been designed and was in production.

Edwards' first few weeks in office were somewhat eventful. He was called on to help investigate and determine the cause of the derailment of the Down 'Tourist' express at Wigan in August 1873. Later in the month he attended a meeting with Mr Cawkwell and Mr Webb to determine the scope of the Signal Department's activities and how they were to be arranged. It was agreed that Edwards would take over the maintenance of the existing signalling on 1st November, 1873, the staff for this work being handed over to him by the Permanent Way Department. He was also to organise sufficient staff to prepare the necessary drawings and information to enable Mr Webb to provide the machinery and make other arrangements for manufacturing the materials as soon as the Company commenced the construction for themselves. This Mr Webb expected to be possible on the 1st January, 1874 (Saxbys contract expired on 31st December, 1873).

Edwards' terms of reference were also modified to read:—

> 'That Mr Edwards report to the Locomotive Committee on matters affecting his Department but consulting Mr Webb on all questions relating to its mechanisation and machinery. He was to visit the signal establishments of the Midland and Great Western Companies comparing the quality of the work and the prices at which it was executed with similar work on the North Western line and the systems of locking to be adopted.'

The initial office staff appointments had been made at the beginning of August 1873 and in October he submitted his proposals for organising the maintenance of the existing signalling to the Locomotive Committee. It was proposed to

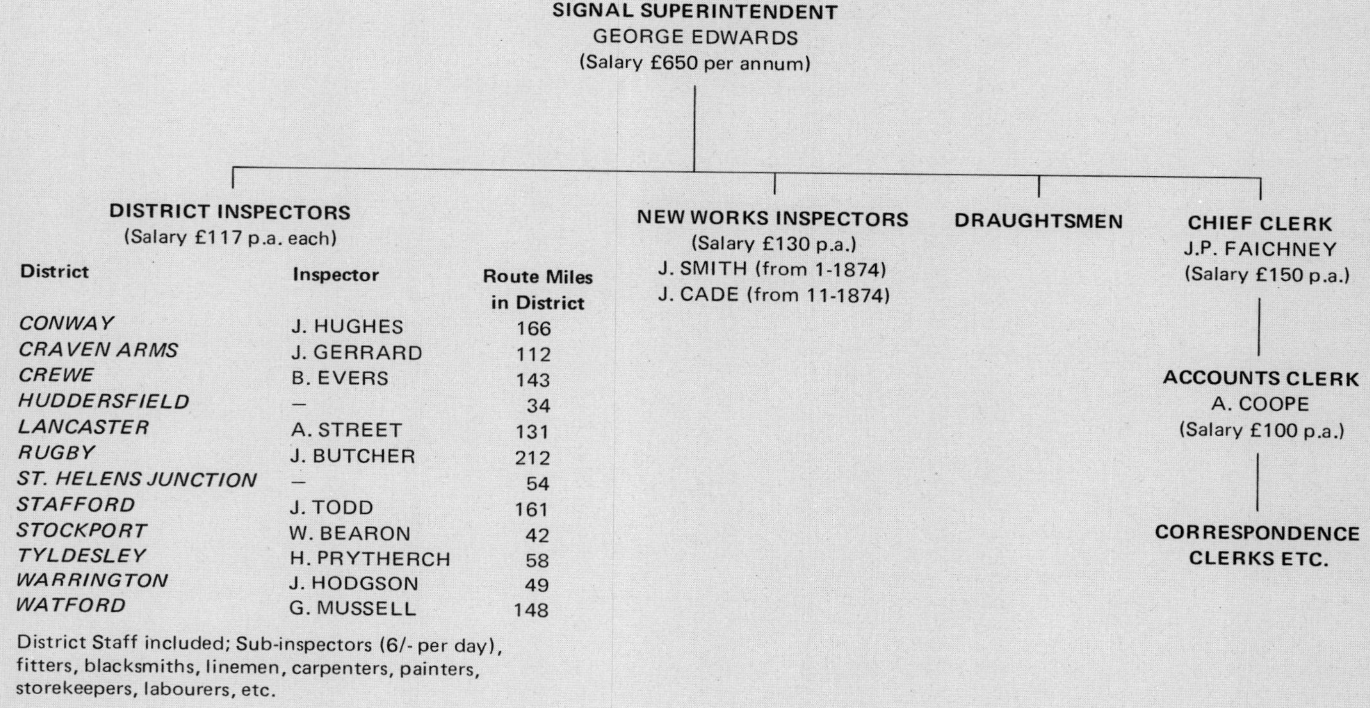

Figure 2.1 *Chart showing the organisational structure of the Signal Department as set up by George Edwards during 1873 and 1874. The initial salaries of the various posts are also given. Although the clerks were all salaried staff and were paid on recognised scales the draughtsmen were regarded as wages staff and received a weekly wage. The subsequent careers of the various members of the staff can be traced in Appendix 1.*

divide the line into 12 Districts each being under the charge of an Inspector. Each would have an appropriate staff of men and a store shed for the materials. Ten Inspectors were appointed the following month but the remaining two posts were never filled and those Districts (St Helens Junction and Huddersfield) were combined with the adjacent ones. In the event, it would seem that Edwards had got things about right for separate Districts were created in both these areas in later years. The basic structure of the Signal Department was completed in 1874 with the appointment of two Inspectors to superintend the new work. This initial organisational structure is set out in **Figure** 2.1 while Appendix 1 lists the senior staff of the Signal Department and their periods of office.

The scale of appointments in the Signal Department (a total of over 200) and the cost of the alterations at Crewe Works caused the Directors further concern, while Saxby and Farmer, not unnaturally, enquired about their own position in regard to the work they still had in hand and future royalty payments on patents. Yet more discussions were held in April 1874 and Edwards, not surprisingly in view of his exclusion from Crewe, recommended that new work should be carried out by contractors. He was over-ruled, however, and in June 1874 it was finally decided that the Signal Department was to do the work using materials from Crewe.

The majority of the drawings for the new equipment were done in the Locomotive Department Drawing Office at Crewe under the supervision of Charles Dick, the Head Draughtsman. Part of the works (including the old Tender Shop) was adapted for the production of signalling equipment at a cost of about £7,000. Crewe Works, then the largest engineering works in the world and largely self contained, were ideally suited for the work. Mr Webb provided fitting and erecting shops, carpenters shops and saw mills supplied with special machinery. Arrangements were made at the Company's steel works (which had been opened in 1869) for rolling the Bessemer steel point rods, locking bars and other steel work. Provision was made in the foundries and smithies for the large amount of cast and wrought iron work required.

Edwards was kept busy organising his District Inspectors and their staff. In a number of cases this involved building Company houses for key staff at places like Willesden and Craven Arms. He finally moved into his new offices on the Nantwich Road, Crewe in the summer of 1876. These were sited on the north side of the road in the area now occupied by the independent lines.

Naturally, the signal shops at Crewe were not able to produce all the new equipment required at the end of Saxby's contract. It took time to develop and try new designs and to build up production. This was particularly so in the case of locking frames, very few of which were made in the first couple of years. There is evidence that the LNW was very careful to ensure that, in introducing new items of signalling equipment, they did not get involved in litigation with Saxby and Farmer over possible Patent infringements. John Saxby had gained something of a reputation for going to law over alleged infringements of his patents and on several occasions during the 1870's threatening noises were made in the direction of the LNW. The Company's reaction was to offer Saxbys the opportunity of inspecting the work being carried out and to demand from any contractor supplying signalling equipment (for example on joint lines) a guarantee against all claims for infringement of patents. All this made the changeover process a little slower than it might have been. Saxby and Farmer, therefore, continued to supply new equipment although on a much reduced scale. Something of the progress made on the road to self sufficiency can be gauged from **Figure** 2.2 which lists the Signal Department expenditure for the four half years of 1874 and 1875. The signalling work carried out by Saxbys after 1873 took two forms, contracts for complete schemes and the supply of equipment for individual installations at times when the LNWR was unable to do all the work itself. In 1874 they were awarded a contract to carry out all the signalling work in connection with the widening of the line between Willesden and Bletchley. Saxbys standard equipment was used on this and the cabins erected were of the Saxby 'Type 2' design (See chapters 9 and 10). A contract for signalling work on the Stour Valley line was completed in 1878. In July 1876 a five year general contract for the supply and installation of signalling equipment was signed with Saxbys. Quite a number of installations were made under this contract, the apparatus was installed in cabins of LNW standard designs (Chapter 10) and signals of LNW standard design were also used. A little work was carried out by Saxby and Farmer after the expiry of the latter contract, although this was mainly confined to the completion of work commenced under it, the last payment not being made until 1884. Over the period from 1874 to 1884 inclusive the value of the new work done by Saxby and Farmer amounted to £178,666-8*s*-1*d*.

George Edwards obtained a position as Signal Engineer to the Gloucester Wagon Company and handed in his resignation on the 9th September, 1876, leaving to take up his new appointment on the 1st November. That Company allowed him more freedom and much of the signalling equipment they supplied, after this time, was of his own design. Like so many people whose early careers had been tied up with the LNWR, Edwards was to do well for himself and when the Railway Signal Company was set up in 1880 he became Managing Director. The works at Fazackerley were opened in July 1881 with a contract to supply signalling equipment to the Lancashire and Yorkshire Railway. In view of his later career his recommendation of April 1874 is again not so surprising and perhaps gives some further insight into the reasons why he moved on. At the Board Meeting of September 1876 he fired his parting shot by submitting a list of eleven signal cabins that he had completed but could not bring into use because Crewe Works had been unable to supply the interlocking apparatus, a further eight were nearly ready and also without apparatus.

With Edwards' departure the Signal Department was placed under the supervision of F W Webb, and Charles Dick was appointed Signal Superintendent at a salary of £400 per annum. He reported to Webb rather than the Locomotive Committee. G P Neele records that Dick had 'tramped to Crewe' in search of work. His excellent work in the night schools there attracted Webb's attention, and from 1st January, 1872 he succeeded Mr Kamp as head of the Locomotive Drawing Office at a salary of £160 per annum, this being advanced to £200 in March 1873.

Dick was an ingenious engineer and among other things developed a system for 'slotting' signals where one arm

Figure 2.2 SIGNAL DEPARTMENT ACCOUNTS – 1874 and 1875

Item	*Half Year to 30/6/1874*	*Half Year to 31/12/1874*	*Half Year to 30/6/1875*	*Half Year to 31/12/1875*
Maintenance of signals	£11,170 5s 2d	£14,308 12s 1d	£13,374 10s 11d	£16,672 14s 7d
New work ordered	43,278 12s 4d	42,005 8s 1d	28,137 10s 9d	25,084 1s 7d
New work for Wm. Baker (New lines)	2,051 1s 0d	8,589 13s 7d	6,160 6s 4d	17,626 14s 9d
Work for other departments	1,272 19s 10d	2,258 8s 4d	2,137 14s 4d	2,144 13s 3d
Work for other railways and charged to them	657 2s 0d	1,850 12s 8d	981 15s 10d	2,318 18s 1d
Work for private firms and charged to them	2,398 1s 3d	1,913 19s 0d	3,132 18s 3d	3,391 3s 5d
General	1,472 13s 9d	1,562 14s 10d	1,439 13s 0d	1,526 11s 2d
TOTALS	£62,300 15s 4d	£72,489 8s 7d	£55,364 9s 5d	£68,764 16s 10d
Value of new work	£49,023 3s 10d	£54,091 4s 9d	£39,652 6s 9d	£49,414 15s 8d
Proportion done by Saxby and Farmer	£45,895 15s 9d	£38,044 15s 11d	£10,752 9s 0d	£11,030 12s 3d

Figure 2.2 *These abstracts from the Signal Department accounts give some idea of the costs incurred by the LNWR in providing and maintaining the signalling system. Note how the proportion of work done by Saxby and Farmer rapidly declined to about a quarter of its previous level.*

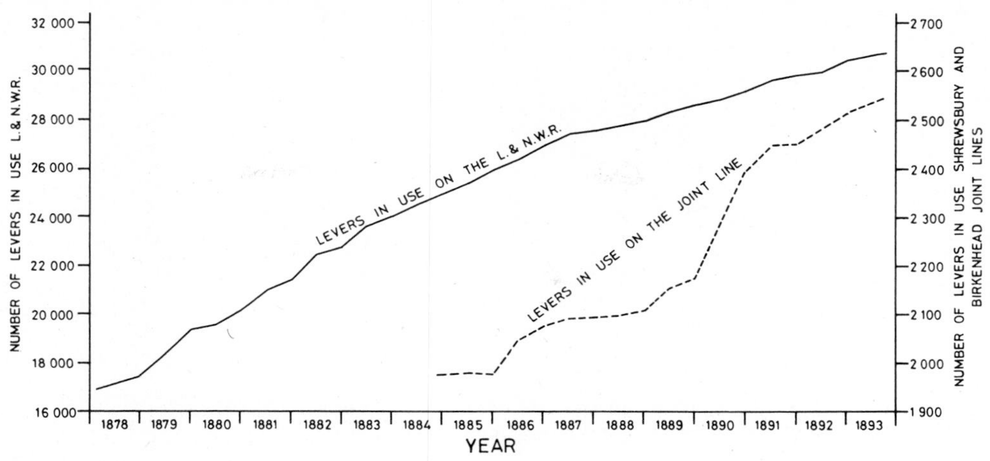

Figure 2.3 *Graph showing the number of levers in use on the LNWR for signalling purposes in the years between the late 1870's and the early 1890's. The phenomenal growth over the period demonstrates the enormous amount of work that was undertaken in order to introduce proper signalling and to interlock the railway. The bulk of the work was completed by the late 1880's (well in advance of the 1889 Regulation of Railways Act which made interlocking compulsory) and this is reflected in the change in the rate of increase which occurred around 1886/7. After this the bulk of the increase in the number of levers was due to the enlargement and extension of the existing system. By the end of 1902 the number of levers in use had risen to 38,000. The dotted line (and right hand scale) represents the number of levers in use on the LNW and GW Joint Shrewsbury and Birkenhead lines. The signalling on these lines was taken over by the LNWR in 1885. The large increase in the 1890/1 period was mainly accounted for by the enlargement and resignalling of Chester station.*

was worked by more than one cabin. This was extensively used on the line. Besides his work in the Locomotive and Signal Departments, he supervised the laying out of Queen's Park which was presented by the Directors of the Company to the inhabitants of Crewe. In January 1882 he succeeded Mr Worsdell in Crewe Works. After his death, which occurred on June 2nd, 1886, a shelter was erected in the park in his memory.

As a result of Dick's appointment, Edwards' Signal Offices and workshop at Crewe were handed over to the Gas Department and the Signal staff were moved into the Locomotive Department offices.

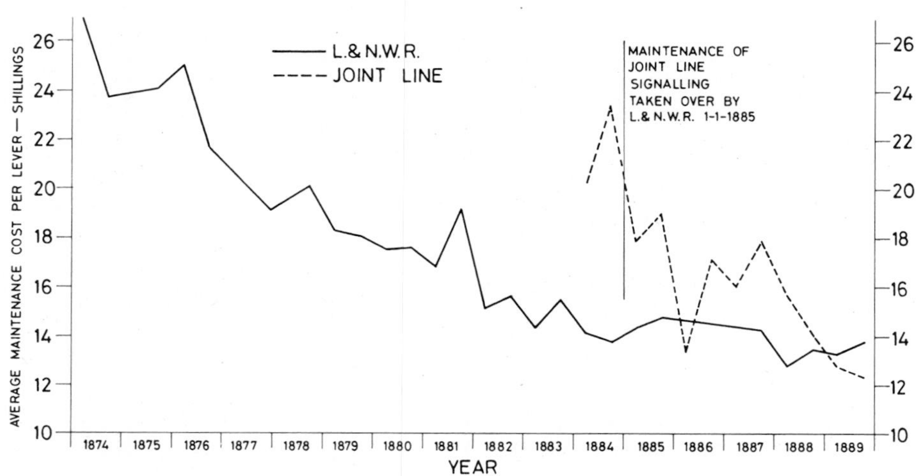

Figure 2.4 *Graphs showing the average cost of maintaining the existing signalling system (including new work costing £10 or less) expressed as a cost per lever in use, per half year. One of the main considerations in the LNW decision to manufacture and maintain its own signalling was that of cost and the belief that the Company could do the work more cheaply than could Contractors. As can be seen this object was actually achieved, the cost line showing a steady downward trend. The reductions obtained over the 16 year period can be seen to be quite significant. The cost of signalling on the Joint Shrewsbury and Birkenhead lines shows a similar decrease after it was taken over by the LNW. The cost line behaves more erratically because the cost of a major renewal was spread over a much smaller number of levers and could affect the total cost for one period significantly.*

Plate 2.1 *Crewe North Junction Cabin photographed in 1883. This cabin of 144 levers was constructed in 1878 and at the time this photograph was taken it was the largest on the LNWR. The cabin name 'North Junction No. 4' consists of small cast iron letters screwed directly to the woodwork, in accordance with normal practice. It was quite common to find that numbered cabins on the LNW were also referred to by names and in this case both the number and the name have been officially recognised by including both on the front of the cabin. The practice of numbering signal cabins at large places was introduced in the early 1870's and confirmed as the normal policy in 1875. The large embossed nameplate 'Crewe' mounted in the centre of the lower cabin structure was quite a common feature at large LNW stations and examples of cabins with similar boards existed at Stockport and Shrewsbury. Due to limitations of space at ground level the cabin is of relatively unusual construction. The brick base has had to be chamfered at the corners thus in order to accommodate it between the tracks and it extends to a height of about 16 feet to clear the loading gauge. A wider timber cabin structure (presumably to reduce the weight on the narrow foundation) is placed on top of this to bring operating floor level up to about 25 feet in order to give the signalmen a clear and unobstructed view of the layout under their control. An interesting feature is the provision of some standard 4′ 6″ cabin windows in the lower part of the timber structure, the cabin top being of standard size 'T'. On the end of the cabin are the Signal and Telegraph lineman's boards both showing 'all right' (See Chapter 15). Behind the cabin, part of the famous Spider Bridge structure can be seen. This cabin remained in use until 1906 when it was replaced by the Crewe system electric cabin (Chapter 14) of 266 levers.*

Photo: Courtesy National Railway Museum

Arthur Moore Thompson, the Signal Department Head Draughtsman, was appointed Signal Superintendent from 1st January, 1882. He was born in 1852 and entered LNWR service in 1872. He was to occupy the post for some thirty years and it was during his time that the majority of the standard equipment and practices came into use. Thompson's particular interests were in the electrical side and he patented a number of electrical devices. His most important works were the design and development of the electric train staff system and the 'Crewe' all-electric system of power signalling, both of which he patented jointly with Webb.

W Dandison became Head Draughtsman in Thompson's place, the post being redesignated Assistant Signal Superintendent in July 1883. He left in 1890 to take up the post of Signal Superintendent of the Great Southern and Western Railway of Ireland and was replaced by J T Roberts.

In the late 1880's the development of electric power for lighting had reached a stage where it could be considered as a reliable and economical alternative to gas. In addition, the light obtained was very much better. The LNW began to purchase generating plant and to install electric lighting at its major stations, goods depots, hotels and on its ships. Although J W Fletcher (see below) was originally designated the Company's Electrical Engineer, F W Webb was able to convince the Board that this 'heavy' electrical work should be done at Crewe under his supervision. The facilities available there would be able to handle the repair and maintenance of the equipment and even undertake the manufacture of some of it. Fletcher did not have any facilities of this nature under his own control.

Plate 2.2 *The Locomotive Offices at Crewe. These were constructed adjacent to the old Chester line. For the majority of the Webb era the Signal Department staff were also accommodated within this building.*

In 1892/3 J W Fletcher's electrical staff were ordered to be transferred to Crewe. In view of Thompson's interest in electrical matters it is perhaps not surprising that Webb placed the electrical work under his charge. J ('Johnny') S Bean, one of the Signal Department draughtsmen, was a competent electrical engineer and became Head Draughtsman of the Signal Department in 1891 at the age of 32. W W Gerald Webb, another of the draughtsmen, was appointed Thompson's outdoor assistant for the electrical work in January 1893, later being designated Electrical Assistant. He had originally joined the LNW service in 1886 at the age of 18.

Bean did a great deal of the detailed design work in connection with the Webb and Thompson Electric Train Staff system and the Crewe System of power signalling. He was appointed Assistant Electrical Engineer (Signal Department) on W W G Webb's resignation in 1902. The electric lighting schemes at Crewe and Manchester enabled power signalling to be installed at these places in later

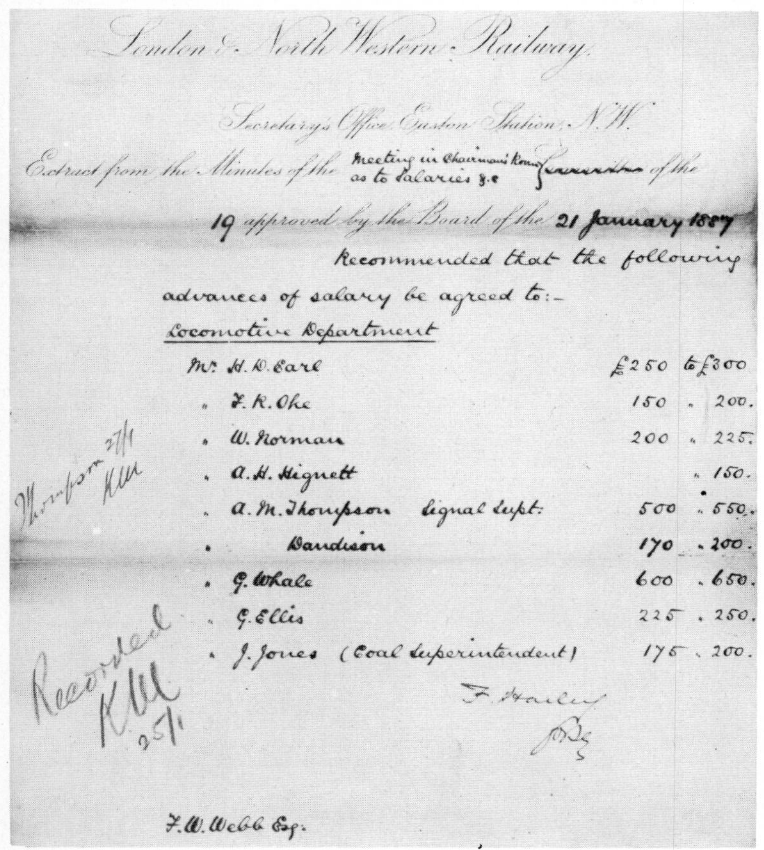

London & North Western Railway.

Secretary's Office Euston Station, N.W.

Extract from the Minutes of the Meeting in Chairman's Room as to salaries &c of the 19 approved by the Board of the 21 January 1887

Recommended that the following advances of salary be agreed to:-

Locomotive Department

Mr H. D. Earl		£250	to £300
" F. R. Ohe		150	" 200.
" W. Norman		200	" 225.
" A. H. Hignett			" 150.
" A. M. Thompson	Signal Dept.	500	" 550.
" Dandison		170	" 200.
" G. Whale		600	" 650.
" G. Ellis		225	" 250.
" J. Jones (Coal Superintendent)		175	" 200.

Thompson 27/1 KW

Recorded KW 25/1

F. Harley

F. W. Webb Esq.

Figure 2.5 *Copy of a letter sent to Mr Webb in 1887 to inform him that the salary increases he had recommended for members of his staff had been approved by the Board. These include A M Thompson, the Signal Superintendent, and his Chief Draughtsman Mr Dandison. One or two other well-known names can be found among those in the list.*

years. Bean was replaced by another electrical man, P G Wayne, who had previously been Foreman Electrician at the London Road Power Station, Manchester. Unfortunately Wayne suffered from ill health and had to resign in 1904.

Changes took place among the District Inspectors from time to time. First to go was Evers, the Crewe District Inspector, who was found to be incapable of carrying out his duties and was dismissed after about nine months service. It took rather longer to determine that J Gerrard suffered from the same problem as he was not dismissed until March, 1879. However, in view of his long service (he had been with the Company 33 years) he was told that he could apply for a subordinate position if he wished, one wonders if he did! The record for the shortest length of service was held by Thomas Stothert the third new Works Inspector who managed to hold his post for a mere three months! Dismissal could come for other reasons, Thomas Sear, the Lancaster Inspector, was accused of interfering with a lady passenger on a train from Lancaster to Preston and following suspension, while the matter was investigated, he was discharged at the end of November 1877. He had only been appointed to the post in June of that year. His predecessor, A Street had resigned his post in the same month as he was awarded a £30 p.a. pay rise!

Over the years some organisational changes were made in the Districts. The first of these occurred in the Craven Arms District in 1883. This area covered two distinct and separate groups of railways, the Central Wales line and the Merthyr Tredegar and Abergavenny lines. The bulk of the work was found to be on the M.T. and A section involving much travelling and inconvenience. A stores shed was, therefore, erected at Abergavenny (Brecon Road) at a cost of £360 and the Craven Arms stores closed. A portable hut was provided at Builth Road at a cost of £36 to house a Sub-Inspector who then took charge of the Central Wales and Swansea lines.

This arrangement was somewhat short lived for on 1st January, 1885 the LNW took over the maintenance of the signalling on the LNW and GW joint Shrewsbury and Birkenhead lines (Chapter 17). In order to cover the Shrewsbury and Hereford and Welshpool lines the stores at Craven Arms was reopened and Sub Inspector Greenwood at Builth Road was promoted to Inspector in charge of both the Joint and Central Wales lines and was transferred back to Craven Arms!

The vast increases in goods traffic in the 1880's and 1890's caused the workload of the Districts covering the industrial and mining areas to increase considerably. Tyldesley stores had to be extended at a cost of £340 in 1884, while in 1892 it became necessary to divide the Warrington and Stafford Districts. A new stores was established at Edge Hill to cover the western half of the Warrington District. The industrial Black Country and Cannock Coalfield lines were placed under the charge of an Inspector at Walsall. The necessary stores and other accommodation were provided at the two places at a cost of £600 each. Strangely enough the Stafford Inspector retained charge of the signalling on the Stour Valley line and at New Street Station, Birmingham.

The expansion of the LNW's interests in Yorkshire and the quadrupling of the main line considerably increased the work of the Heaton Norris District, necessitating the construction of a new Stores on the down side of the line at Heaton Norris at a cost of £800 in 1895. This was only a partial solution and it soon became apparent that the District would have to be divided. By the beginning of 1899 there were 3,820 working levers on the District compared with a mere 1,450 in 1879. It was decided to create a Yorkshire District to cover the lines east of Standedge Tunnel. Initially it was proposed to erect the stores at Mirfield but in the event ground was purchased at Ravensthorpe (between the LNW and L&Y lines) and the stores erected there at a total cost of £1,300. Sub Inspector James Punter of Heaton Norris took over as Inspector in December 1899. The Ravensthorpe District is of interest because it was used for a number of years as a training ground for new or relatively inexperienced Inspectors who were then moved on to take up more important positions elsewhere (Appendix 1).

The Lancaster District suffered similar problems to the original Craven Arms District in that it consisted of two physically separate groups of lines. In 1900 it was decided to administer them separately by setting up a small District stores at Workington to cover the West Cumberland lines. The new stores there was a more modest affair and cost £300.

THE TELEGRAPH DEPARTMENT 1870 TO 1903

In January 1870 the Company secured the services of Mr G G Newman, also of the Electric Telegraph Company, as the new Telegraph Superintendent at a salary of £500 per annum. Arrangements were put in hand to set up a suitable organisation to administer and maintain the existing Company telegraphs and to take on the installation of new circuits. The new organisational structure was basically of the same form as that set up in the Signal Department although the District boundaries were somewhat different and materials were bought-in rather than being manufactured by the Company. The first few years were beset by wranglings with the Post Office over the compensation to be paid for the telegraphs they had taken over and the rents for the use of the railway's land and poles. In November 1870 it was agreed that the Post Office would pay wayleaves on 6,345 miles of wire which they had taken over and that the LNWR would maintain 6,335 miles at an agreed charge (the remainder being underground cable which the Post Office would maintain themselves). Offices were provided for Newman and his headquarters staff at London Road Station, Manchester. The telegraph system was greatly extended over the years to cope with the enormous growth in the system and its traffic.

In 1876 two Assistant Telegraph Superintendents were appointed to assist Mr Newman. One, Mr W T Tonbridge, took charge of the Southern half of the line and was based at Stafford, while Mr J W Fletcher took the Northern half working from an office at London Road, Manchester.

The telegraphs in the Southern Division suffered damage between Blisworth and Birmingham during snow storms in January 1876, while storms in March 1878 brought down much of the wire between Willesden and Bushey. Naturally Newman was called in to explain these breakdowns and what could be done to prevent such occurrences in the future. He explained that they were now using stronger creosoted wooden poles (average cost 14/3d each) and proposed that in future the wires should be renewed more frequently and that the span between poles should be reduced from 88 to 70 yards. Following questions as to alternative methods he said that the cost of putting the wires underground or using iron poles would be prohibitive.

The winter of 1878/79 brought further snowstorm damage to the wires, this time between Watford and Tring and the Directors became somewhat alarmed at the continued failures and the increasing costs of repair and renewal. Newman's explanations and proposals were, apparently, not found satisfactory this time and in February 1879 it was resolved that he be given six months notice to determine his present contract. In the event the parting seems to have been quite amicable. It was agreed to pay Mr Newman an annual retaining fee of £100 so that he could be called upon to give any advice or assistance that might be required in the future.

Plate 2.3 *This interior photograph of Crewe North Junction Cabin was taken in June 1886. The lever frame is of the Webb tumbler type and when constructed, in 1878, it had a total of 144 levers mounted on 8 girders for 18 levers each. This was the first frame to be constructed with double locking racks divided by balancing rocking levers (Chapter 11), the two racks being of 38 bars each. The levers which appear white in the photograph are actually painted blue and were facing point lock levers. In order to work additional points and signals added later, special cut girders had to be added to the ends of the frame to accommodate the extra levers. Five levers were added at the left hand end of the frame in September 1885 (lettered A to E) and a further five at the right hand end in July 1887. Finally, a further lever 'X' was added at the left hand end of the frame in July 1888! Most frames erected in the 1870's and early 1880's seem to have incorporated very few spare spaces to allow for additional levers and this caused problems at a number of places in later years. Above the windows on the left are a set of four face discs (Chapter 15) in the normal or no indication position. Mounted on a fancy bracket, on the window pillar between them, is an electric signal arm repeater of the type used before the introduction of the Fletcher combined arm and light indicator (Chapter 12). The block shelves are suspended by single rods rather than the later and more usual double rods (see also* **Plate 12.12***). As was usual the block instruments were of the single needle type with separate bells in wooden cases. Those instruments with sloping fronts are tell tale block instruments of Tyers manufacture (see* **Plates 12.1** *and* **12.2***). The vertical fronted instruments on the first shelf all appear to be route indicating instruments, although the one at the left hand end is an electric fog gong switch and indicator. This was normally switched out of circuit but could be switched on in foggy weather in order to sound a gong as a warning to drivers of their position. The gong was usually sited a little in the rear of the signal and sounded only as the train passed and when the signal was standing at danger. The needle in the indicator normally pointed to 'Gong Silent', but when the gong was switched on and commenced to sound as a train passed it the needle moved to the 'Gong Sounding' position. The signalman had to depress the plunger on the front of the instrument to silence the gong and return the needle to the normal 'Gong Silent' position. These instruments seem to have fallen out of favour in later years and all had been removed by about 1900. Presumably it was thought cheaper to employ fogsignalmen, a system which also had the advantage of uniformity of practice. On the back wall of the cabin is a speaking tube instrument and bell. Illumination for the cabin at night was by the gas jets which can be seen suspended from the cabin roof.*

Photo: Courtesy National Railway Museum

It was decided to appoint John William Fletcher, the Superintendent of the Northern Division Telegraphs, as the new Telegraph Superintendent, at a salary of £400 p.a. (he had been receiving £300). Fletcher was born on 24th April, 1834 and in the early 1850's he joined the Electric and International Telegraph Company, where he learnt his trade. In due course he took charge of their Chester and Holyhead District. In about 1868, while engaged on work for the LNWR at Holyhead, he designed and fitted up a system of electrical communication between the passengers and guard in the carriages on the Trip Trains which ran between the main station and the pier. In later years this system was developed and installed on the LNWR Royal Train. When the telegraphs were taken over by the State, Fletcher joined the service of the LNWR where he was put in charge of the Chester and Holyhead District, effectively the same job as he had been doing before. As mentioned earlier, in 1876 he became Superintendent of the whole of the Northern Division. During 1878 and 1879 Fletcher's star was very much in the ascendant, the telegraphs under his charge having escaped any serious storm damage, while at the beginning of 1879 he had introduced the Tell-Tale block instrument which at last solved the problems of block working in busy station areas (Chapter 12). It is, therefore, not surprising that he should be chosen to succeed Newman. Mr Tonbridge retained his post at Stafford while Fletcher's old post was down-rated to Inspector and was filled by Mr Evelegh at a salary of £120. Fletcher devised and patented a number of electrical devices of which perhaps the best known was his combined signal arm and lamp repeater patented in 1884 (Chapter 12).

By 1890 Fletcher's outdoor maintenance staff consisted of nine Inspectors (largely based at main stations), three Sub Inspectors and 48 Linemen (there had been 34 when the LNW started its own maintenance work in 1870). In addition there were Assistant Electrical Engineers and New Works Inspectors based at his London Road offices.

Fletcher instructed that the first duty the Inspectors attended to each morning was to prepare a report on the state of the telegraphs on their districts. These were telegraphed to Manchester so that the reports would be on Fletcher's desk when he arrived for work. In this way he was kept fully in the picture and was able to deal, immediately, with any problems that may have arisen. The efficiency of the telegraph system on the LNWR was a tribute to his abilities and organisation.

Although the LNW had done its own installation and maintenance work since 1870 they continued to purchase new equipment from outside contractors. The Telegraph Department had the use of a large area of ground on the down side of the line opposite Stockport Station. This was used for the storage of telegraph materials, principally telegraph poles and wire, but there were also limited facilities for the repair and maintenance of the telegraph instruments. In the Summer of 1892, the old Stockport Workhouse situated in Daw Bank on the Western edge of the site became available and with the concurrence of the Company's General Manager, Fletcher took possession of it for use as telegraph workshops. This gave more suitable accommodation for the repair and maintenance of the equipment. More importantly, however, it allowed Fletcher to develop facilities for the manufacture of new equipment. It was agreed that he should gradually expand the manufacturing facilities at the new workshops so that he could take over the production of new equipment as the existing supply contracts expired. In addition to the advantage the Stockport site had in being adjacent to the existing telegraph depot there were other advantages. There had been a tradition of watch and clock making in the area and thus the skills required for the construction and maintenance of the instruments were readily available. In addition the site was near the Manchester headquarters of the Telegraph Department and Fletcher himself lived only a few minutes walk away.

The combined telegraph stores and workshop area at Stockport did not survive for long, for in October 1892 it was decided that much of the ground would form an ideal site for a new carriage shed and the Telegraph Department was asked to move the telegraph pole stacking ground elsewhere. An area of land was found for the purpose at Cheadle Village Junction a short distance away and an existing siding there was handed over for use by the Telegraph Department.

Fletcher's son, George Edwin Fletcher also joined the Telegraph Department and after a period as General Inspector he was appointed Assistant Telegraph Superintendent in the spring of 1893. He lived for many years with his father, first at Chester House, Chatham Street, Edgeley, and later at 'The Homestead' Cale Green. He too, devised and patented a number of electrical devices connected with railway signalling, including the Fletcher all-electric step by step train describer which was used extensively by the LNWR. He was also responsible for the design of the familiar LNWR combined block instrument.

J W Fletcher obtained authority in 1891 for the creation of three posts for 'Superior Apprentices' within his headquarters staff. These positions were intended for training youths of ability for posts within the Department in order to meet the demands of an expanding communications system and the increasing complexity of the work. Percy Douglas Michôd joined the Telegraph Department in 1893 as a lad and in the following year he was able to pass the necessary entrance examination and become one of the Superior Apprentices. In 1897 he became manager of the Telegraph Workshops but only occupied the post for a short while. He became Senior General Assistant to Fletcher in 1898 on the resignation of C W Neele and his salary was increased from £150 to £175 p.a. His place as works manager was taken by Oliver Hammond who had previously been Chief General Foreman there. As with the signal shops at Crewe, a standard range of telegraph and electrical equipment was designed and put into production.

The LNWR Board had passed a resolution in March 1875 whereby the normal retirement age of senior staff was fixed at 60. Special dispensation was generally required before employees were allowed to stay on after that age and these cases were reviewed periodically. J W Fletcher managed to evade the rule, however, presumably because of his length of service and experience, and it was not until 1903 when he had reached the age of 69 that his retirement was announced. This was to be effective from the end of June and rather than simply appoint a successor it was decided to make use of the opportunity to reorganise the Signal, Telegraph and Electrical Departments. By this time Fletcher's salary had reached £1,000 p.a. and in recognition of his very long and faithful service he was awarded a retirement gratuity of 500 guineas by the Directors.

Fletcher had been a member of the Society of Telegraph Engineers and of the Institution of Electrical Engineers, being one of the earliest contributors to their Journal. He was a member of the Conference of Railway Telegraph Superintendents and Engineers from its conception until his retirement and was President of the Conference in 1892. He died in July 1910.

THE SIGNAL, ELECTRICAL AND TELEGRAPH DEPARTMENTS 1903 TO 1923

As mentioned earlier, much of the 'heavy' electrical work had been dealt with by Thompson's Signal Department staff. This, coupled with the increasing use of electricity in signalling matters, made it a fairly natural decision to combine the Signal and Telegraph Departments together as the Signal and Electrical Department. A M Thompson became Signal and Electrical Engineer from the 1st July, 1903 and his salary was increased from £1,200 to £1,500. From the same date J T Roberts and G E Fletcher became Chief Assistant (Signal) and Chief Assistant (Electrical) respectively to Thompson, their salaries both being increased to £600 p.a. It was certainly a time of change for the Signal Department. F W Webb, under whose supervision the Signal Department had been since 1876, officially retired on 31st July, 1903 although George Whale, his successor, had actually taken up duties in May. Webb had also survived the age limit rule as he had by then reached the age of 67. Perhaps, with Webb and Fletcher retiring within weeks of each other, it might be said that the LNW was having one of its periodic clear-outs of over age officers! Webb moved to Bournemouth on his retirement and died there in June 1906.

In order to accommodate the combined Signal, Telegraph and Electrical Departments together under one roof approval was given in August 1903 for the construction of new offices, workshops and stores in Gresty Road, Crewe at a cost of £13,000. The new offices were first occupied in 1904 and over the next couple of years the telegraph staff were gradually transferred from Manchester and Stockport. The Stockport telegraph works were run down during 1905 and the work transferred to the new Crewe Workshops, Mr Hammond, the Works Manager, moving to Crewe at the beginning of 1906. The old workshops and some of the surrounding land were let for use by others, Mr Joseph Bibbington occupying them for many years. The telegraph pole store at Cheadle Village was also closed in 1906 and a new one opened at Crewe.

Over the next few years the amount of electrical work undertaken by Thompson's staff increased enormously. The electric lighting, power stations and electrical signalling installed between Euston and Camden in connection with the widening of that portion of the line between 1905 and 1907 together with lighting work at Willesden alone cost over £110,000. It was clear that this sort of work would increase rather than decrease in the future, particularly with the plan to construct the Watford 'New' line.

George Whale resigned due to ill health in 1909 and opportunity was taken for further reorganisation. The Signal and Electrical Departments were divided and F A Cortez-Leigh was appointed Electrical Engineer from 1st January, 1910 with offices at Euston. He took over some of Thompson's electrical staff. Thompson retained charge of the 'Crewe System' power signalling and of the work connected with the electric train staff system. The telegraph staff and workshops also remained at Crewe.

After nearly thirty years as Signal Superintendent A M Thompson retired on the 1st January, 1912 at the age of 60. Opportunity was, once again, taken for some reorganisation. The Signal Department was transferred from the Chief Mechanical to the Chief Civil Engineer (E F C Trench). John Troughton Roberts, Thompson's assistant, was appointed to replace him, the post being designated Signal Assistant to the Chief Engineer. Roberts was born in 1865 and entered LNW service as a pupil under F W Webb in October 1885. He became Foreman of Crewe steam shed in January 1890 and was transferred to the Signal Department as Assistant Signal Superintendent in January 1891. Although Thompson had always lived in Crewe at Holly Bank in Wellington Square (Delamere St.), Roberts did not move upon his appointment. He continued to live at Acton Cottage on the outskirts of Nantwich and was one of the first people in the area to own a motor car. Roberts was something of a gentleman and normally dressed in Harris Tweeds. He had connections in Scotland where he had a grouse shoot and would normally disappear North for the glorious 12th!

Alfred Oldham, the Head Draughtsman, was appointed as Roberts' assistant. He had joined the LNW in 1890 after an apprenticeship with a firm of builders and contractors. After a spell in Crewe works he transferred to the Signal Department as a draughtsman.

Cortez-Leigh is said to have been not very interested in the telegraph side of his Department and in 1913 Major J N C Kennedy was appointed Telegraph Assistant at Crewe. He had formerly worked for the Post Office and had been elected a member of the Institution of Electrical Engineers in 1899. His stay was to be very short and within a year he had disappeared from the scene. Kennedy's place was taken by Lawrence Webster ('Sammy') Swainson who was graded

Plate 2.4 *When the Signal and Electrical Departments were combined in 1903 it was realised that additional accommodation would be required for Fletchers' staff who were to be transferred from Manchester. Authority was, therefore, given for the construction of new offices for the combined departments in Gresty Road, Crewe. These offices, first occupied in 1904, are illustrated here; behind them was accommodation for the workshops and stores.*

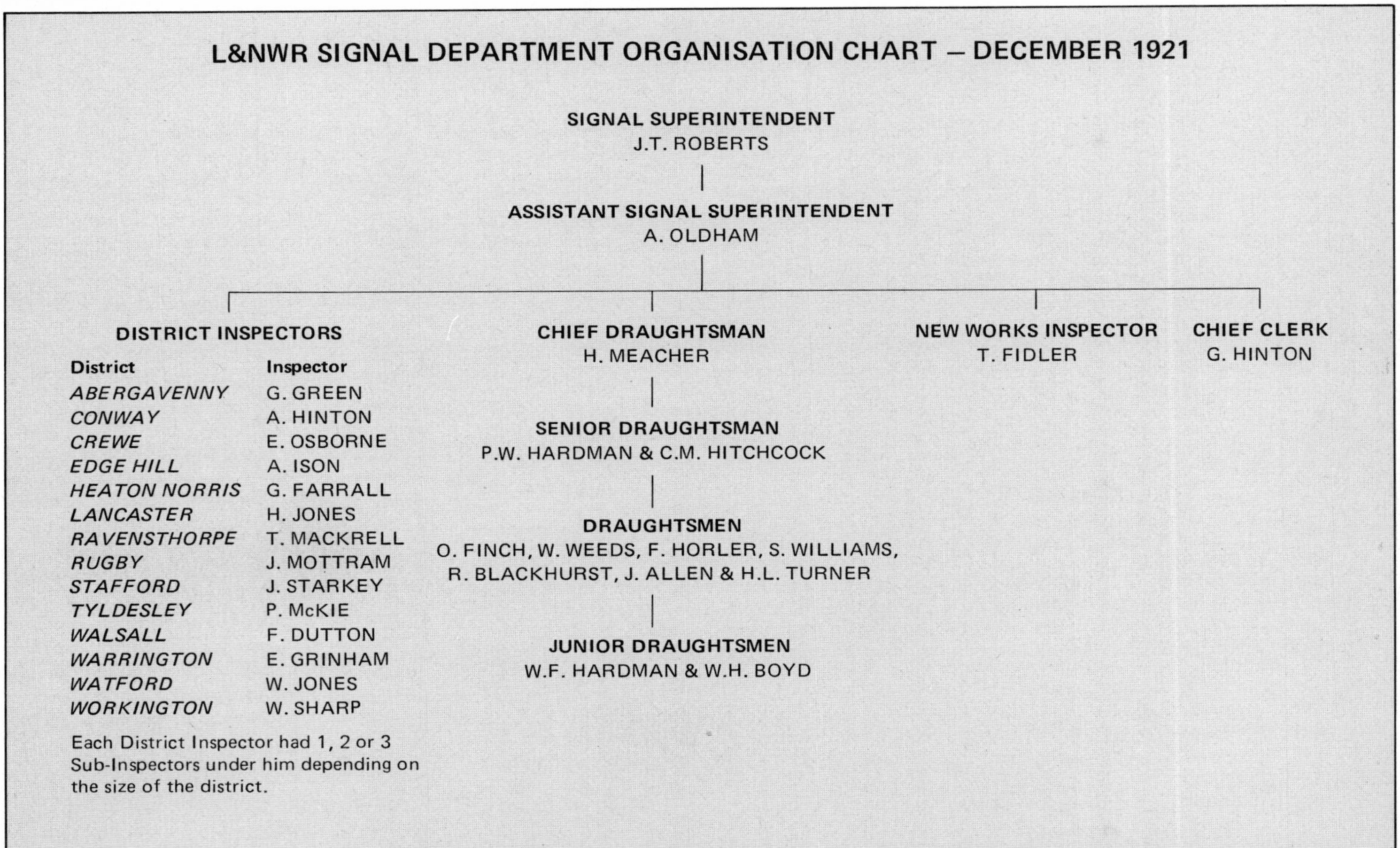

L&NWR SIGNAL DEPARTMENT ORGANISATION CHART – DECEMBER 1921

SIGNAL SUPERINTENDENT
J.T. ROBERTS

ASSISTANT SIGNAL SUPERINTENDENT
A. OLDHAM

DISTRICT INSPECTORS

District	Inspector
ABERGAVENNY	G. GREEN
CONWAY	A. HINTON
CREWE	E. OSBORNE
EDGE HILL	A. ISON
HEATON NORRIS	G. FARRALL
LANCASTER	H. JONES
RAVENSTHORPE	T. MACKRELL
RUGBY	J. MOTTRAM
STAFFORD	J. STARKEY
TYLDESLEY	P. McKIE
WALSALL	F. DUTTON
WARRINGTON	E. GRINHAM
WATFORD	W. JONES
WORKINGTON	W. SHARP

Each District Inspector had 1, 2 or 3 Sub-Inspectors under him depending on the size of the district.

CHIEF DRAUGHTSMAN
H. MEACHER

SENIOR DRAUGHTSMAN
P.W. HARDMAN & C.M. HITCHCOCK

DRAUGHTSMEN
O. FINCH, W. WEEDS, F. HORLER, S. WILLIAMS, R. BLACKHURST, J. ALLEN & H.L. TURNER

JUNIOR DRAUGHTSMEN
W.F. HARDMAN & W.H. BOYD

NEW WORKS INSPECTOR
T. FIDLER

CHIEF CLERK
G. HINTON

Figure 2.6 *Chart showing the final organisational structure of the LNW Signal Department as it existed at the end of 1921 before amalgamation with the Lancashire and Yorkshire Railway. J T Roberts the Signal Superintendent (also described as Signal Assistant) reported to the Chief Engineer E F C Trench and they both came under the jurisdiction of the Permanent Way Committee. Due to retirements a number of changes took place in the staff during 1922 and these are detailed in Appendix 1.*

Senior Assistant in the Electrical Department from the 1st of July 1913 at a salary of £400. Swainson was born in 1879 and following an apprenticeship in Crewe works he joined Thompson's Electrical Staff as a Draughtsman in 1902. He was appointed a Junior Assistant in July 1903 and was elected a Member of the Institution of Electrical Engineers in 1918. Sammy remained at Crewe in charge of the electrical and telegraph workshops and was redesignated Telegraph Assistant in 1923. He was promoted to the post of District Electrical Engineer, Crewe in November 1925 at a salary of £1,000 having responsibility for all electrical work including telegraphs on the Western Division outside London.

The New Works and District Inspectors in the Signal Department were generally appointed from among the ranks. The people concerned had to have suitable training and a wide experience of the work of the Signal Department, including if possible, new works experience. The early career of one of the Inspectors, Joe Harding, the last District Inspector at Edge Hill, is typical of many and serves to illustrate the promotion process. Joe came from Tarporley in Cheshire and received the nickname 'Tarporley Joe'. He commenced his career under indenture as an apprentice fitter in Crewe Works. On completing his training he joined the new works gang and was involved in the installation of new signalling equipment at such varied locations as Shrewsbury, Leeds, Manchester, Camden and in Ireland. He then spent a period as a lineman responsible for the maintenance of the power signalling on the 'Park' at Crewe (the goods lines and yards). In 1913 he was promoted to the post of Sub Inspector in the Edge Hill District. Because of his skills and the importance of the railway to the war effort his occupation was reserved and he remained at Edge Hill during the First World War. When Mr Ison the Edge Hill District Inspector retired in December, 1921, Joe who was then 41 years of age, was appointed Inspector in his place. At that time he was earning £5-11*s*-4*d* a week which was made up of a basic wage of 88/6*d* plus 8/4*d* per week bonus and an aggregation allowance of 14/6*d* a week. His new position was a staff post and his initial salary, as a Class 2 Inspector was fixed at £270 p.a. with an aggregation allowance of 15%. He was also given the opportunity of joining the superannuation scheme.

Turning briefly to some of the other Signal Department Staff, James William Punter, one of the New Works Inspectors commenced his career as an apprentice with Saxby and Farmer, assisting on a number of their contracts in various parts of Europe. He left Saxbys to join the Engineering Department of the Madras Railway, returning to join the LNW Signal Department as a Sub-Inspector at Heaton Norris. He was appointed Inspector of the new Ravensthorpe District in 1899 and became a New Works Inspector in 1901. James resigned in 1904 to take up the post of Signal Superintendent to the Egyptian State Railways. His work there was well thought of and he received several honours from the State including the Order of Osmanieh. He returned to England in 1909 to take up an appointment with Tyer and Company and was made General Manager in 1913. After a long period as Managing Director he resigned his full time position in 1945 remaining on the Board until shortly before his death in 1947 at the age of 81.

Jack Smith, after commencing service as a Draughtsman, where he had been involved in the work on the 'Crewe

System' power signalling, became a New Works Inspector in 1901. He returned to the Signal Office in 1905 as Head Draughtsman (Electrical), resigning in April 1907 in order to join Punter in Egypt, replacing him as Signal Superintendent. On his retirement in about 1930, he returned to live in Ruskin Road, Crewe where he, inevitably, became known as 'Egypt Smith'!

C W Neele, one of the District Telegraph Inspectors was promoted to the post of General Inspector at Fletchers headquarters in Manchester in January 1897. In 1898 he left the LNW service to become Electrical Engineer to the Great Central Railway, a post he retained until the Grouping.

Accidents were an ever present danger for the outdoor staff and over the years they claimed a number of victims from the Departments' staff. A number of men who lost legs in accidents applied for and received artificial limbs, which were made at Crewe or Wolverton, so that they could continue working. Indeed, in a number of cases the men subsequently applied for a second wooden leg to enable them to carry on working while the first was sent into the shops for repair. In some cases more suitable work was found for them. For example, W ('Billy') Weeds was knocked down by a light engine while working as a fitter on the installation of the Euston-Camden electric lighting in January 1906, his right leg having to be amputated above the knee. He was transferred to the signal office as a draughtsman when he returned to work. He was a competent draughtsman and invented a number of ingenious devices. These included a fluid drive for his car, the design of which was taken up by Rolls Royce and developed as a torque converter.

Peter McKie, the Tyldesley District Inspector was provided with an artificial foot after being knocked down by an engine there in 1912. Within the Traffic Department there were at least half a dozen signalmen who had been supplied with artificial legs following accidents while at work.

The 20th Century brought with it the beginnings of a movement among the men to organise themselves and agitate for better pay and conditions. Naturally it took a long time to achieve anything but some concessions were obtained. The First World War brought quite appreciable increases in wage rates although these were mainly 'cost of living' increases necessary to match the inflation which occurred during the war years.

In 1919 the normal working week for the wages staff was reduced from the 54 hours fixed way back in 1878 to 47 hours. As a result attempts were made to find ways by which the effects of the reduction could be minimised. An obvious way in which better use could be made of the men's time was by trying to reduce the time spent travelling from the Depots to their work and back. It was decided to create a number of new Sub-Depots at busy places where men could be stationed close to their work. In February 1919, authority was obtained for Sub-Depots at Willesden, Bletchley, Aston, Nuneaton, St. Helens, Carlisle and Nantybwch at a total cost of £750. No new men were taken on, some of the existing staff at the main Depots being transferred to the new ones. October saw approval for the expenditure of £750 on extending the existing small sub-depot at Chester and in March 1920 authority was given to spend £574 to provide proper facilities for the men stationed at Preston.

The amalgamation with the Lancashire and Yorkshire Railway in 1922 and the Grouping of 1923 made little real difference to the operations of the Signal Department other than some alterations to the titles of the jobs. Roberts was designated Signal Assistant 'A' Division (under the Chief Engineer) in 1922 and Signal Assistant Western Division LMSR in 1923. Cortez-Leigh became Divisional Electrical Engineer ('A' Division) and was promoted to the post of Chief Electrical Engineer LMSR in 1925. The telegraph section at Crewe was transferred to the Chief Engineer in 1922 and so once again there was a unified Signal and Telegraph organisation in the Gresty Road offices. Alterations were made to the office accommodation there to enable the two drawing offices to be amalgamated at a cost of £718. The situation did not last long however for in 1925 the telegraph section returned to the Electrical Engineer!

Perhaps the first significant effect of the amalgamations as far as the old LNW Signal Department was concerned was the transfer, in about 1923, of the Ravensthorpe District from Crewe to the old L&Y Signal Engineer's office ('B' or Central Division) at Manchester.

It soon became horribly apparent to the Directors of the LMSR that their new railway was being practically torn apart by the continuing rivalries between the various pre-grouping factions and the settling of old scores. It became clear that a good shake-up would have to take place among the senior staff if there was to be any hope of breaking down these barriers. Opportunity came as far as the Signal Department was concerned in 1927 when, by strange coincidence, J T Roberts retired on the 30th June and W C Acfield at Derby (formerly the Midland Railway Signal Superintendent) retired on the 25th August. Rather than appoint their respective assistants to the top posts an opportunity was taken to mix the staff. Alfred Oldham, Roberts' assistant, became Signal Assistant at Derby and H E Morgan from Derby came to Crewe as the Western Division Signal Assistant. The next and most important step in the reshaping of the LMSR Signal Department came in April 1929 with the appointment of A F Bound as Signal and Telegraph Engineer for the whole railway (See 'A Pictorial Record of LMS Signals'). The Telegraph Sections were transferred from the Chief Electrical Engineer to form a combined Signal and Telegraph Department, an arrangement which was to be permanent this time!

Mention might be made of the subsequent careers of one or two members of the LNW Signal Department staff. W R Jones, the Watford Inspector, moved to Crewe in 1928 as Assistant to Morgan, becoming Signal Assistant at Manchester in 1929 on the retirement of the old L&Y Signal Superintendent R G Berry. F J Dutton from Walsall replaced Alfred Oldham at Derby in 1935.

Percy Michôd became Thompson's Chief Telegraph Assistant in 1905 and in 1910 he moved to London to join Cortez-Leigh's staff as a Senior Assistant. He was released for war service between 1914 and 1919, joining the Royal Engineers as a Captain. After distinguished service in France during 1915/6, he served at Longmoor and was put in command of the Railway Operating Troops Depot in 1917 and received the OBE (Military) in 1919. He had been involved in the formation of the original Institution of Signal Engineers and was its Secretary for a time. A M Thompson, incidentally, had been offered the post of its first President but was unable to take it up owing to ill health. Roberts, Oldham and Michôd all served on the Council of the Institution of Railway Signal Engineers. In LMS days Michôd became Principal Assistant to A F Bound.

Sid Williams, one of the Draughtsmen, served with the territorial army between 1914 and 1919. In 1920 he was seconded to the Ministry of Transport, spending just over a year with them before returning to Crewe. He was involved with the Watford New Line resignalling scheme and served in a variety of posts within the LMS Signal Department. He became New Works Assistant to Bound at Euston in 1936 and was responsible for the Rugby, Wigan and Preston resignalling schemes and the class 'C' block scheme. He finally became Chief Signal and Telecommunications Engineer, London Midland Region soon after Nationalisation.

Chapter Three Signals—Pre 1883 Designs

Some of the signalling curiosities existing before the general introduction of the semaphore have been mentioned in Chapter 1. This chapter looks at the signals used on the LNWR before the advent of the well known and distinctive standard signals in 1883.

Many of the early semaphores were naturally supplied by Saxby and Farmer, although numbers were provided by other contractors such as Stevens (Plate 70 of 'LNWR Miscellany' Vol. 2). In addition, the LNW made signals itself, either at Crewe or in the Divisional Engineer's workshops. The railway was growing fast and inevitably many signals were taken down while still in good condition. Whenever possible these signals were re-used and many signals saw service at several locations during their lives. Where necessary, redundant signals were returned to the workshops for repair or modification before re-erection. Usually, the most vulnerable parts of the signals were the arms, through wear and storm damage, and the posts due to rot at ground level. Arms were easily replaced, while a rotting post could have its life extended by cutting off the offending portion and re-using the remainder in a location where a shorter post was required.

The majority of the signals were capable of showing three positions rather than two, this being required for the working of the time-interval system described in Chapter 1. The different signal colours for night signalling were achieved with a single lamp. A spectacle with two glasses (one red and one green) was attached to the signal arm push rod and passed in front of the white lamp to produce the appropriate coloured light. In the clear position the spectacle moved completely clear of the lamp exposing the white light (see **Figure 3.1**). A number of signals, such as distant signals, were only used in two positions and were fitted with a single spectacle with a red glass.

The progressive introduction of the block system triggered off some fundamental alterations in the way in which signals were operated. The absolute block rendered the third signal position 'caution train ahead' superfluous and it was gradually abandoned, except on the approaches to large stations and busy junctions. For some time it had been known that the 'clear' position of signals with the arm hidden in the post, effectively 'no signal', was not entirely satisfactory. A breakage of the wire or push rod could lead to the arm falling and showing a false clear, alternatively, the arm could have fallen off altogether! Another problem was that the arm could get stuck in the slot, as happened at Abbots Ripton in 1876. Apart from the fact that it would have been rather difficult to produce a satisfactory 'clear' signal with an externally mounted arm, the matter was probably never given much thought, the signals having always been like that.

The practice of working the signal arms to the 45° position (the old caution) gradually spread while some of the signals showed red and white lights and some red and green depending on the degree of caution required at that place. On those signals with double spectacles the white light was achieved by the simple expedient of knocking out the green glass. In due course all the signals on the absolute block lines were altered to show the horizontal and 45° positions, the vertical 'clear' indication persisting only on the 'time interval' lines.

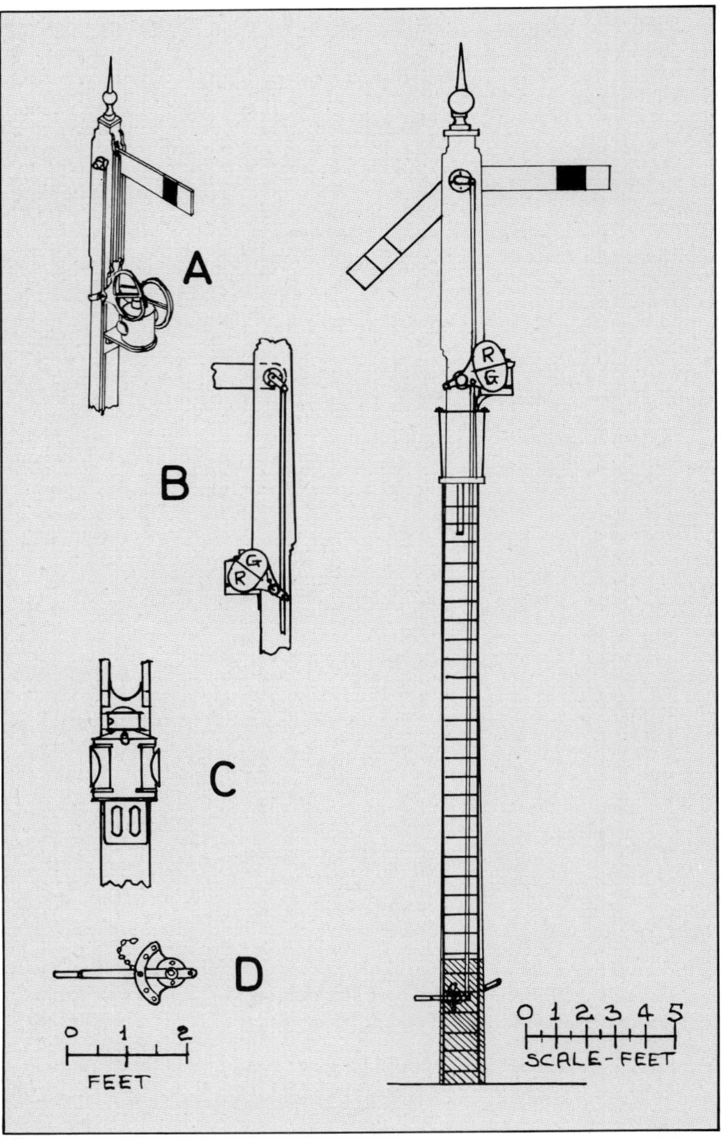

Figure 3.1 *Three Position Slotted Post Signal. An example of a 'station' signal with arms for both directions, operated from hand quadrants at the base of the post is shown here. The arm on the left (red arm and white stripe facing the traffic) is in the caution position. In this position the green glass (R = Red glass and G = Green glass) is in front of the spectacle to show a green light to the driver. The right hand arm (the back of the arm painted white with a black stripe is shown) is in the danger position. Detail 'A' shows the signal with the left hand arm in the clear position. Here the spectacle is raised above the lamp so that a white light is shown. Detail 'B' illustrates the arrangement of the spectacle (for the right hand arm) on the other side of the post. Note how the positions of the red and green glasses are reversed to enable the lamp colours to correspond to the position of the arm. Detail C is an enlargement of the signal lamp and bracket and detail D is of one of the hand quadrants which operate the arms. Where such a signal was operated from a signal cabin the quadrants would be replaced by balance levers and lead off wheels (See Chapter 4).*

Scale of reproduction: 4 and 8 mm to 1 foot (1:76 and 1.38).

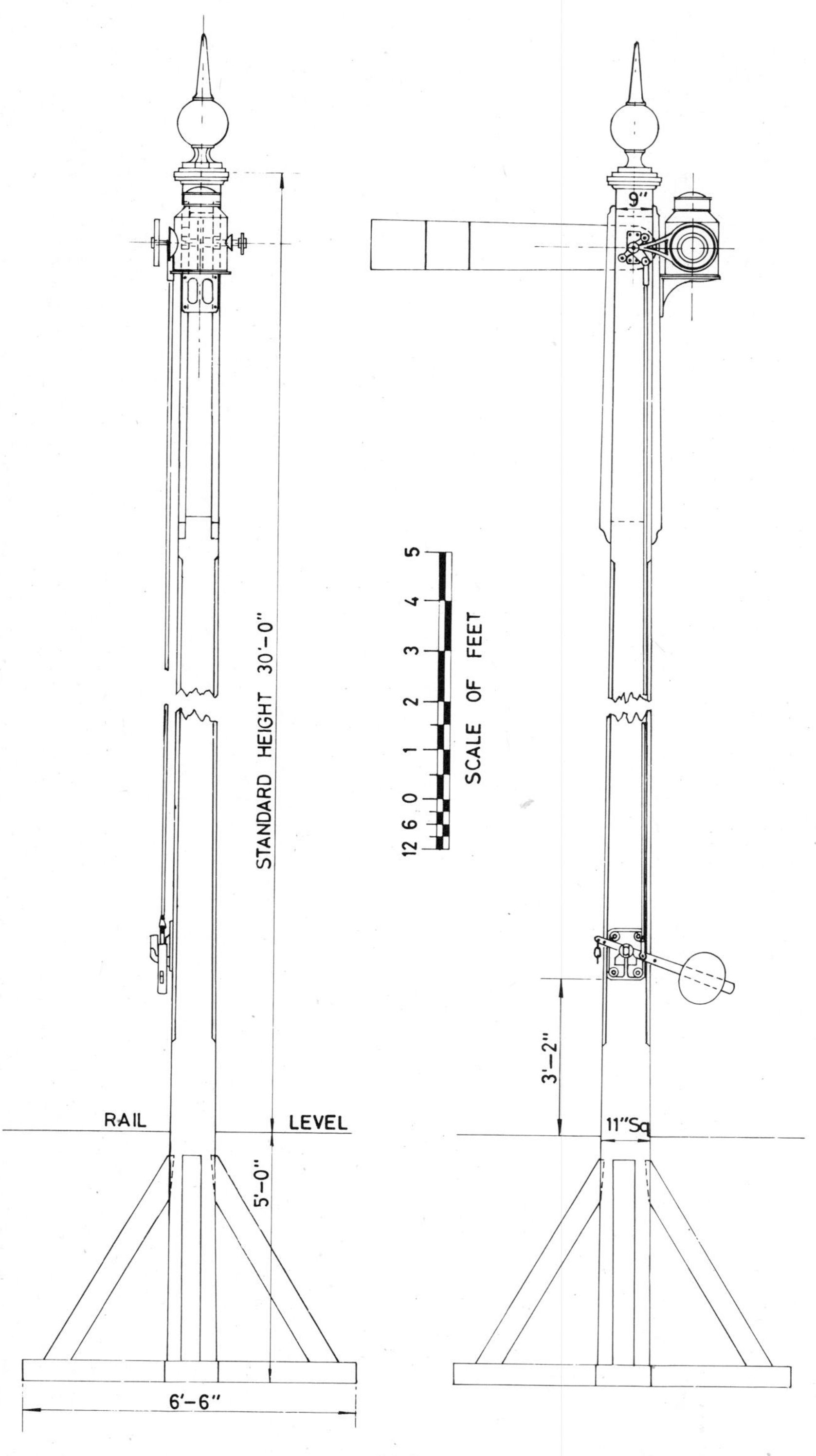

Figure 3.2 *Standard 1874 Straight Post Signal. This was the first type of signal manufactured at Crewe and was introduced at the beginning of 1874. The signal is of the 'slotted post' type and the ball and spike pinnacle will be noticed. This example has only a single spectacle with a red glass and in the danger position (arm horizontal as shown) a red light was displayed. When 'off' the arm worked to 45° (the 'caution' position) but the lamp then showed a white light. Strictly this was not correct but in practice it seems to have been a very common arrangement. Note the below-ground structure necessary to hold the post rigidly in place. By altering the arrangement of the push rod and balance lever the signal could be made to work to 90° – arm vertical – the true 'clear' position (see Figure 5 in 'Great Western Signalling'). Scale of reproduction: 7 mm to 1 foot) (1:43.5)*

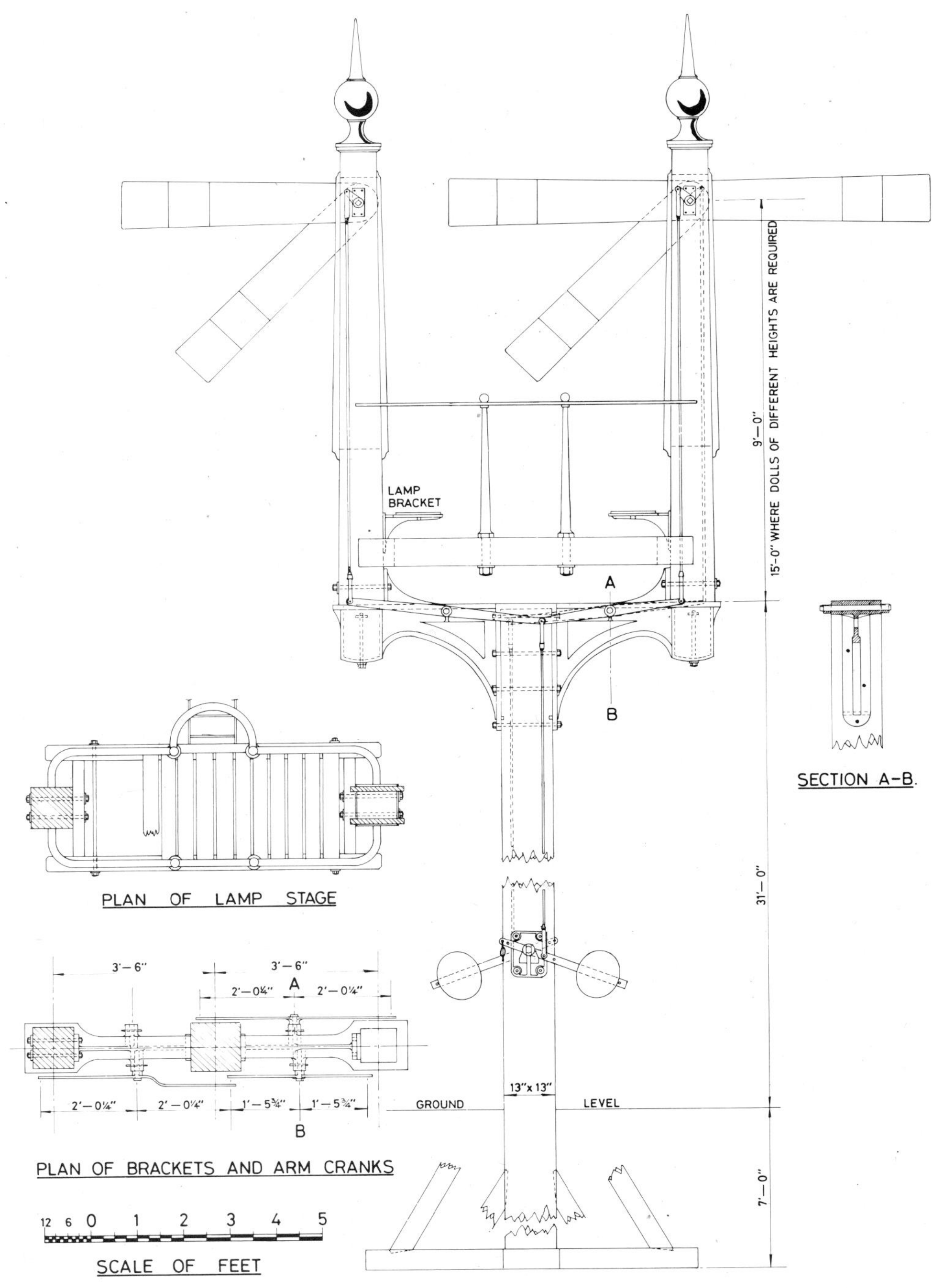

Figure 3.3 *Standard 1874 type Bracket Signal. The design of the cast iron brackets and separate lamp stage were inherited directly from Saxby practice. Single or double spectacles could be fitted to the push rods as required. The arrangement of rocking levers in the arm push rods should be noted. As can be seen, the practice of mounting two arms (for opposite directions) on the same post and spindle was retained in these signals. The junction signal arms have been drawn in both the danger and caution positions to illustrate the positions worked to. The use of a lower position for the signal lamps was very common in the 1874 and 1876 signals. It made lamping easier and by keeping it away from the slot in the post a stronger fixing for the lamp bracket was achieved. Scale of reproduction: ¼" to 1 foot (1:48).*

The practice of mounting the signal arms applying to different lines on the same post lingered on for many years after the adoption of the block system and was incorporated into the LNWR 1874 and 1876 standard signals (see **Figures** 3.3 and 3.5).

Slotted post signals survived the slow transition to more modern operating methods (concentration of levers in signal cabins and the introduction of the block system), and were developed to suit the new requirements. They were not without their problems, and in October 1874 an accident occurred at Farnley Junction through the spectacle slipping on the push rod and showing a false clear light at night. A check throughout the system revealed 2,326 such signals with the old fashioned 'loop pin' connection between spectacle and push rod (very simply, the spectacle drive pin was clamped to the push rod). Work started on altering these signals in February 1875 by drilling through the rod to give a positive fixing.

After the 1873 decision that the LNW would make its own signalling equipment in future, the design of a range of signals which could be mass produced, was put in hand. A portion of the works at Crewe was set aside for the production of signal parts. Design work for the new signals was undertaken in the Locomotive Works Drawing Office at Crewe under the direction of the Head Draughtsman, Charles Dick; a situation which was hardly calculated to please George Edwards.

The first drawings emerged in the early part of 1874. These 1874 signals were quite typical of the period, the arms working in slots in the posts which were fitted with ball and spike pinnacles. Two arms could be mounted in the same slot if required (**Figures** 3.1 and 3.3). It seems likely that the initial drawings were prepared in something of a hurry in order to get production started and it is probable that they were copied more or less directly from the signals then being provided by Saxby and Farmer. Hence the drawings give a good indication of the sort of outdoor equipment supplied to the LNWR in the last few years of the Saxby era. Certainly, the separate lamp stage provided on bracket and gantry signals (**Figure** 3.3) was characteristic of the Saxby signals provided on other railways at that time.

Once production had got underway and the new arrangements and management structure had had time to settle down there was an opportunity to re-appraise the designs. The original 1874 designs were tidied up and simplified in 1876 in order to reduce costs and aid mass production (**Figure** 3.5). As can be seen, the frills have gone and the whole thing is simple and workmanlike. The most distinctive feature of the 1874 design, the ball and spike pinnacle, has been replaced by a simple cast iron cap. These caps remained in use for the rest of the LNW days and were incorporated in the design of the 1883 signals. The cast iron brackets and separate lamp stage have gone too and been replaced by a simple arrangement of timber flitches resting on fabricated iron brackets, an arrangement perpetuated in the 1883 signals. The lamp stage rests on the flitches but retains the old style cross timbering.

This 1876 family of basic designs remained in use until the introduction of the 1883 signals although some detail changes were made from time to time. One such development was the substitution of angle cranks (**Figure** 3.6) for the lever arrangement of the push rods at bracket level shown in **Figure** 3.5.

Some problems seem to have been experienced with the old signals for in August 1878 the District Inspectors received a memo from the Signal Superintendent:—

> 'Caps for signal posts; I want all the pinnacles taken away from the signals and replaced by our galvanized iron caps. There are two sizes 8¾" square and 6¼" square. Order some now to cover the first few. You do not need to do all immediately, but do the worst ones first.'

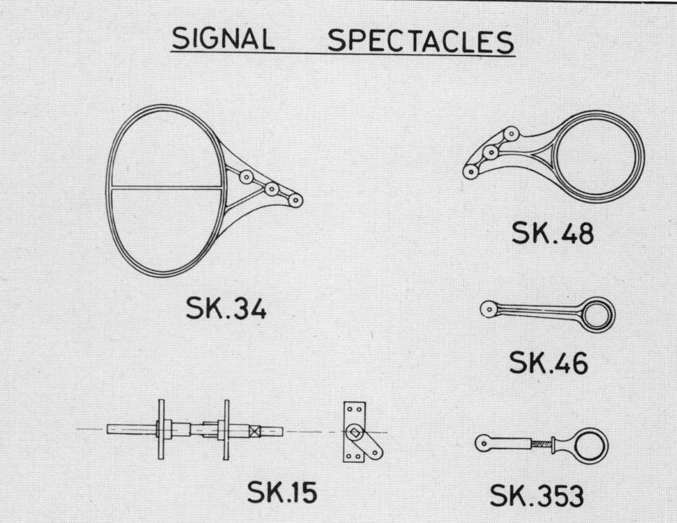

Figure 3.4 *Details of signal parts; SK34 is a standard red and green spectacle. This was pivoted on the centre fixing hole and the drive rod (arm push rod) attached to one of the other two to suit the installation (see* **Figure** 3.1*). SK48 is an 'All-right' spectacle with a single glass. The SK34 and SK48 spectacles could be used either way up to suit the particular situation (see* **Figure** 3.1*). Similarly the appropriate pair of holes were used for the push rod and pivot, the other being spare. SK15 is an arm centre with a long spindle, while SK46 is a back blinder for the signal lamp. This was fitted with a purple glass so that the back light of the signal showed purple with the signal arm 'On' and white with the arm in the 'Off' position (see also* **Figure** 3.7*). It was most important that a signalman should be sure that his signals had responded to the movements of the levers. On those signals which faced the cabin he could see this at night by the colour of the signal lamp. The back light was, therefore, provided for those signals which faced away from the cabin, hence the use of the back blinder to show him what position the arm was in. SK353 is an adjustable back blinder, introduced in March 1879 to enable the back light to show clearly the position of the arm when the signal was at an angle to the cabin.*

Presumably cases had occurred of pinnacles becoming loose and so becoming a safety hazard as well as not doing their job of keeping the weather out of the top of the post properly. It should be remembered that many signals would be quite old, dating back to the 1860's or even the 1850's and were probably not constructed of the best materials. The instruction explains why so few photographs exist which show signals with pinnacles on the LNW while they were quite common on other railways.

The rather uncertain origins of the distant signal have been touched on in Chapter 1. Despite its special purpose, the signal outwardly was identical to the stop signals, being painted red and with a plain end to the arm. The drivers were expected to know where they were and what the signal meant. The simple and distinctive 'fish-tail' shape to the end of a distant signal arm was introduced by the LBSCR in 1872, but did not appear on the LNWR until February 1877. However, once approval had been received to alter the signals the work was done rapidly and in May 1877 Mr Webb was able to report to the Board that the job had been completed. The cost conscious LNW Officers remarked that the alterations were simple and cheap to make! Despite the modifications to the signal arm to give a distinctive day signal, no alteration was made to the night signal and a red light continued to be shown at night to indicate caution. This situation was never changed

Plate 3.1 *This photograph of Crewe Station in April 1881, looking south from the North Junction Cabin, shows a fine pair of 1876 standard signals. The bracket signal on the right is of the SK61 type. The lamps and spectacles are mounted below the arms so that they can be fixed to the post clear of the slots. Note the small ladder provided on the right hand doll to give access to the lamp. Double spectacles, red and green, are provided and the arms work to danger and caution only. During the exposure of the photograph the centre arm has been 'pulled off' and the resultant double image gives an indication of the angle through which the arms usually worked. The arms on the outer dolls are operated via rocking levers similar to those shown in* **Figure 3.5**. *The straight post signal on the left has two stop arms mounted one above the other to save space and reduce costs. This time the lamps are at arm level but the pattern of the arms in relation to the bracket signal is preserved in the lamps since both are still lower than the lamps on the bracket signal. Immediately to the right of the bracket signal post, near the hut, can be seen a standard rotating disc signal. The point rodding runs are of interest. Webb standard channel rodding is used throughout and it will be noticed that much of it is boxed in with timber, particularly the cranks and the places where staff might walk. Timber ramps are provided over the facing point lock mechanisms – the very short locking bar on the points opposite the signals is worthy of note!*

Behind the signals is the Crewe Arms Hotel with the up side of the station to the right of it. The vehicles in the siding reading from left to right are:– 20 foot six-wheel Post Office, possibly No. 20 off the Crewe–Normanton service. 19' 6", four wheel Post Office possibly No. 31 or 32. Next is a 26 foot brake van with flat sides and overhanging roof. Behind the hut is a 14' 6" horsebox which is followed by a GWR van and another unidentified van.

Photo: courtesy the National Railway Museum, York. Information on vehicles by Philip A Millard

on the LNW and it was January 1929 before the LMS began to install yellow arms and lights for distant signals.

As mentioned in Chapter 1, good and early sighting of signals was an essential requirement and this resulted in many tall signals. At night things were different and the best sighting was often achieved by a light at a lower level. As a result the majority of the main line signals had the lamps and spectacles mounted lower down the post than the arms. Where the lamps were placed lower than the arms the spacing between lamps (e.g. for home and distant arms) had still to be the same as for the arms themselves. Not all signals were tall however, and the short signals would have the lamps at or near arm level. An LNWR instruction of September 1878 gives useful guidance on the installation of new signals:–

> 'Sighting signals; Home signals should be seen if possible from the distant. Distant signals should be visible far enough away to enable a train to stop at it or at the home, and should not be placed nearer

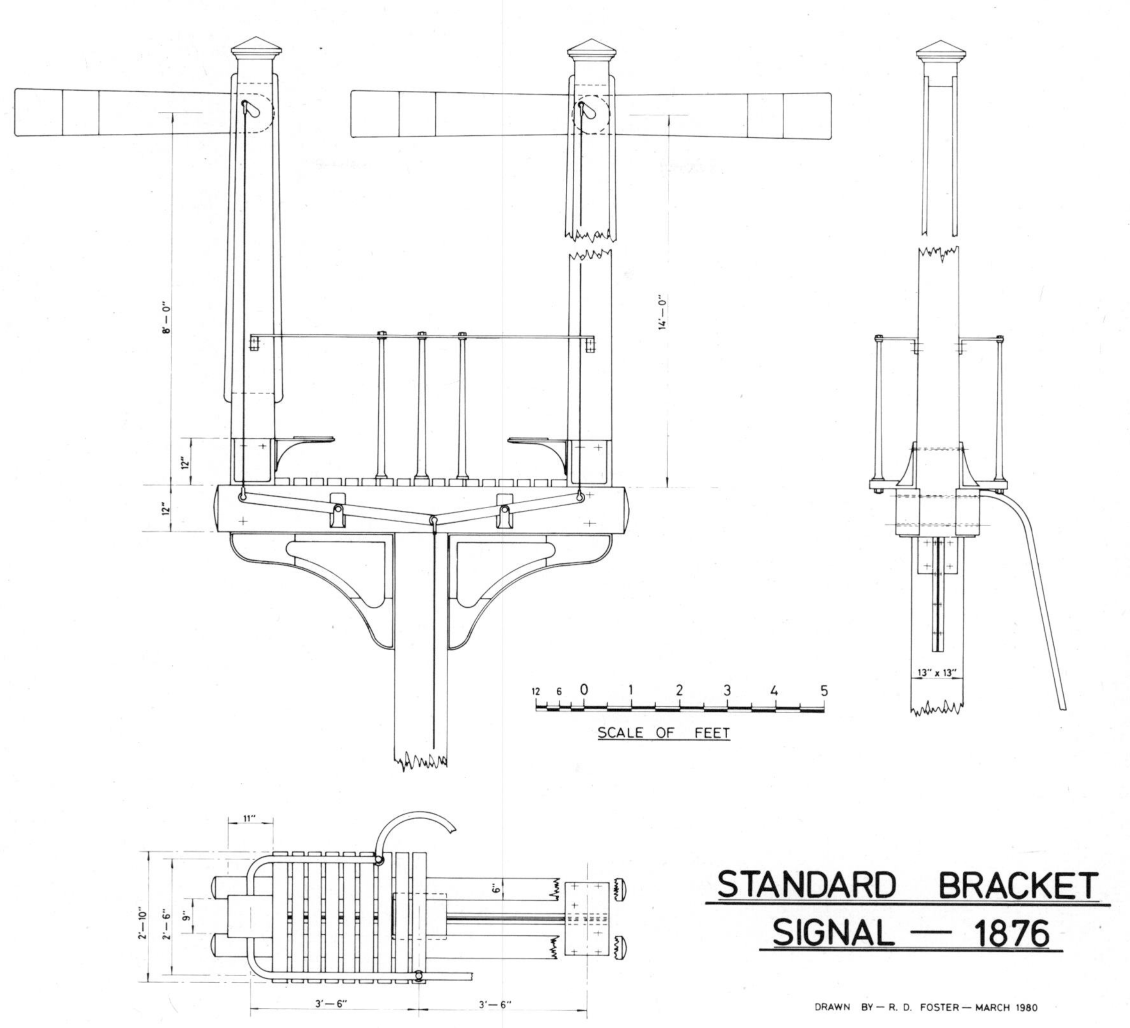

Figure 3.5 *The revised form of Standard Signal introduced in 1876. As can be seen, this was a much simpler product and brought the introduction of several features which were to remain standard until LMS days. These included the timber flitches (horizontal cantilever beams), the fabricated wrought iron brackets and the cast iron cap. Scale of reproduction: ¼" to 1 foot (1:48).*

to the home than 700 yards. Platform starting signals generally should be 16 feet high except in special circumstances. It should be seen on passing the home signal but this is not absolutely necessary. Advance starting signals should also be 16 feet high. They should not be more than 350 yards from the signal cabin and should be visible from it.'

Rules were provided for guidance of course, but circumstances often prevented them being adhered to completely and an indication of the heights of signals actually being erected in 1878 can be obtained from **Figure 3.13**.

Reference should now be made to the lighting of signals for night use. Originally, candles or oil lamps were used, but considerable problems were experienced in obtaining lamps which would give a good enough light to be seen and that would burn continuously without attention. The lights were very prone to being blown out by gusts of wind, they could also become very dim or go out altogether due to a build up of carbon deposits. An added problem was that most of the fuels available were very expensive. The normal practice was therefore to extinguish all the signal lamps as soon as it became light enough for the drivers to see the signal arms. The lamps were then removed for trimming and refilling. The LNW was very particular about avoiding the expense of the lamps burning any longer than absolutely necessary and during the 1870's practically every month saw at least one unfortunate Stationmaster or other responsible person being hauled before the Stores Committee to explain why some signal had been seen burning during daylight by a Director or Officer. In most cases the explanations were what one would expect, the man who carried out the work had been busy on other duties, or it was a dark and stormy morning and so the lamps had been left burning for safety.

It should not be assumed that signal lamps have always burned mineral oil. Many oils were expensive and did not give a good light while the lamps were rather prone to going out and required frequent attention. As mentioned above candles were used in some places while olive oil,

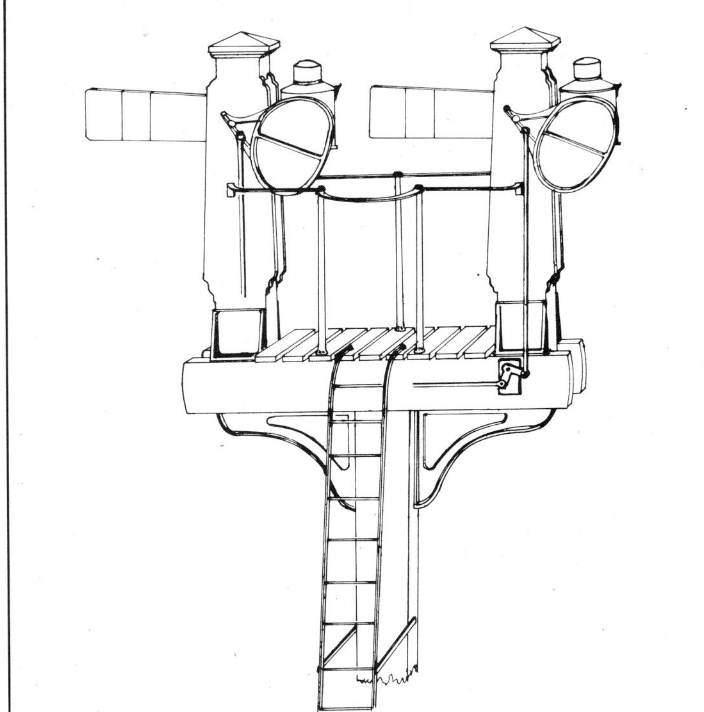

Figure 3.6 *Sketch of a small Bracket Signal of the 1876 type used for subsidiary lines, shunting, or where space was limited.*

Plate 3.2 *One of the last slotted post signals to remain in use was this one at Llanrwst, photographed in August 1933. The photograph gives a good appreciation of the appearance of this type of signal. The details of the slot for the arm and the shaped edging can be seen, while the arrangement of the ladder at the front of the post is of interest. Note that unlike the later '1883' standard signals the post is not increased in size at ground level.*

Photo: E R Whitworth

colza, rape oil, petroleum oil and gas were all used as fuels for lamps. When the LNW took over the maintenance of the signals on the Sirhowy line in May 1876, it was found that there were 60 signal lamps which burned Price's patent candles. These were replaced with standard LNW petroleum lamps at a cost of £90. Generally, the standard of the lamps available was poor. Perhaps the most reliable form of lighting was by gas. In the 1870's a large proportion of the signals on the LNW (and many other railways) were lit by gas. When one considers the cost of laying gas pipes out to signals, the majority of which were not near an existing supply, something of the lengths the signal engineer had to go to to obtain a reasonable light can well be imagined. In addition, the incandescent mantle familiar to many was a much later innovation so the light from the gas lamps was itself not that brilliant!

Efforts were made over the years 1874 to 1876 to develop a better, brighter, and more reliable signal lamp and one which could be made to burn a cheaper fuel. In December 1874 it was decided to fit up the signals between Crewe and Cheadle Hulme with a new type of lamp designed to burn petroleum. It was expected that if the lamps proved successful their adoption would effect considerable savings. In the summer of the following year it was reported that the experiment had been successful and it was decided that all new signal lamps, where gas was not available, should burn petroleum instead of olive oil. In February 1876 F W Webb introduced a new and improved form of signal lamp designed to burn petroleum oil. These were manufactured in the locomotive works and orders for 4,700 new or converted lamps were placed the same month. It was estimated that these alone would save the Company £16,000 per annum. In 1879 a start was made on converting the spare lamps, kept to cover any failures to the gas supply, from oil to petroleum. Although gas lit signals continued to be installed for some time, by the mid 1880's there were few gas lit signals still in use on the LNWR. At least that is what F W Webb claimed in public! In practice surviving evidence indicates that an appreciable number of signals (although perhaps a fairly small percentage of the total) in areas where a gas supply was available near at hand, continued to be lit by gas. Quite a number of '1883' signals were fitted up for gas burning, a situation which continued well into the twentieth century. Indeed designs were prepared in 1919 for adapting the new miniature (ground) signals (Chapter 7) for gas lighting.

The long burning oil lamp, which could burn unattended for periods of a week or more, was not introduced into Britain until 1903. This had obvious attractions in that lamping could be done once a week, instead of daily, leading to significant savings in staffing. As with most such things it took time to perfect a reliable form of lamp and to convince people that they would operate for long periods unattended with minimum risk of failure. It was not until 1912 that the LNW decided that the lamps were reliable enough for everyday service and that there was sufficient economic advantage to be gained from their introduction to justify the capital cost. In August of that year it was recommended that 18,096 inner lamp cases should be converted to the long burning type at an estimated cost of £9,300. It was estimated that the annual saving to be obtained from the use of these seven day lamps would be £3,350. Normally, lamping was done on a regular pattern every seven days, the lamp being replaced by a full one and the empty one removed for trimming and refilling ready for use the following week. The replacement of the old one day lamps took time of course but steady progress was maintained.

The April 1916 Appendix to the Working Timetables contained instructions for the operation and trimming of the signal lamps;

Cleaning of Oil Signal Lamps

1. Signal lamps, except the continous burning Lamps (for instructions in regard to these see Special Circular dated May 1913), must be taken from the signal posts each morning, unless otherwise authorised.

2. They must be cleaned and trimmed every day at the signal box or lamp room, unless otherwise authorised.

3. The wick must be sufficiently long to reach the bottom of the reservoir. The charred or burnt part of the wick must be cut off each time the Lamp is relighted. The wick in stock must be kept perfectly dry, and when a new piece is required it should be cut to a length of nine inches. It should be saturated with oil before it is used, and the insertion of the wick should be at the top of the burner; the burner must then be screwed on to the reservoir, and the wick finally lowered into it, otherwise in screwing on the burner the wick will become twisted. Care must also be taken to see that the wick is of the proper size.

4. The Lamps must be lighted a quarter of an hour before they are required, and they must be taken

Plate 3.3 *A photograph taken at Edge Hill in September, 1883, showing a portion of the new works carried out in connection with the construction of the gridiron marshalling yards. The low level lines in the foreground are the four tracks of the Liverpool and Manchester main line, behind and above these are the Wapping Goods lines which were still incomplete at the time the photograph was taken. Crossing them all at right angles are the Circular Goods lines. At the highest level are the lines and sidings at the top of the grid. The girders of the bridge, by which these lines cross the Circular Lines, bear the inscription 'Gridiron Bridge' and this is surrounded by a painted design.*

On the main lines are two signals of the 1876 standard design. The one on the left is fitted with a lower distant arm for Olive Mount Junction. The arms are fitted with distinguishing 'slow line' rings. That on the home arm is painted black and appears to be fixed to the back of the arm, while that on the distant arm is white and fixed to the front of the arm. Again the lamps are mounted at a lower level than the arms. Despite the instruction that the lamps should be placed the same distance apart as the arms, the lamps on the left hand signal are noticeably closer together than are the arms. Both signals are lit by gas and the gas pipes can be seen attached to the posts, while the supply main, mounted on short wooden stakes, runs along the foot of the cutting slope in the foreground. The open flat goods wagons, almost all with sheeted loads, deserve mention, covered vans being totally absent.

Photo: British Rail

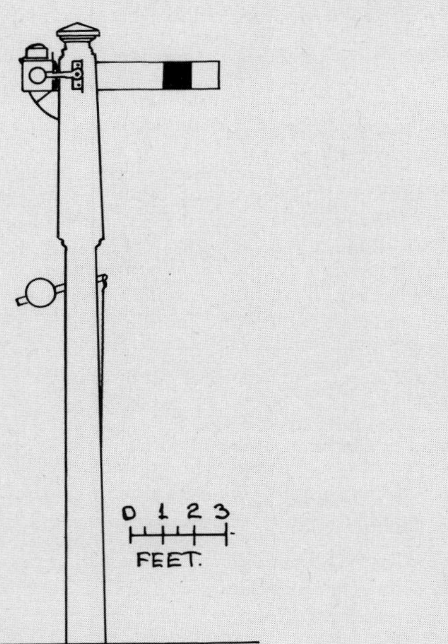

Figure 3.7 *Rear view of an 1876 signal to show the arrangement of the back blinder. This was over the back light of the lamp when the arm was 'on' (to give a coloured light) and moved clear when the arm was 'off', showing a white light to the signalman. The signal is fitted with an elevated balance lever and weight to avoid injury to personnel in a restricted location. The direction of the signal wire is changed by a pulley at the foot of the post. Scale of reproduction: 4 mm to 1 foot (1:76)*

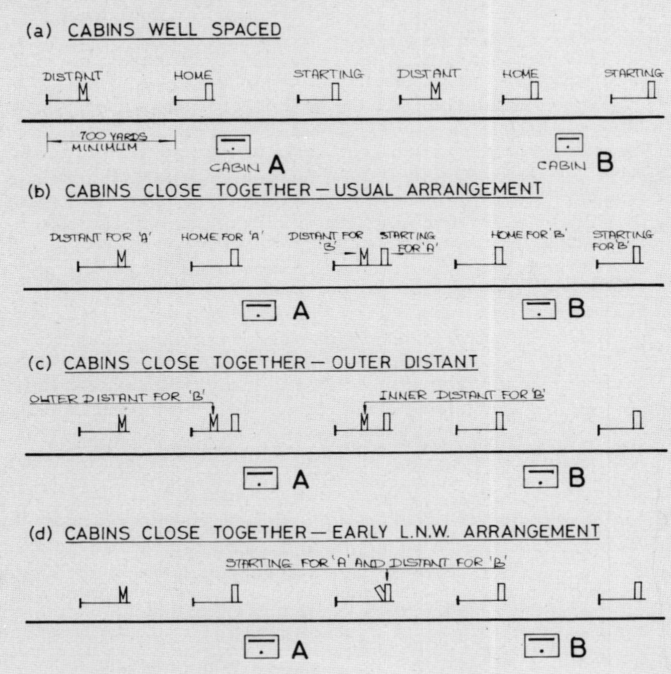

Figure 3.8 *Arrangements of Distant, and Slotted Signals. The diagrams show the most usual arrangements of home and distant signals. There were, of course, many variations to suit local circumstances. One that deserves mention is that when cabins were close together they would often only have one stop signal on each line rather than the two shown here. In the case of diagram (c), cabin B could, if necessary, have control over A's distant either directly by means of a slot, or indirectly by a local instruction to the effect that the signalman at A must not pull his distant lever until B has cleared all his signals for that route (later LNW Block Telegraph Regulation 34). A common variation on diagram (d) which can still occasionally be found today was where the starting signal for A is also the home for cabin B. In this case the signal would be slotted as shown. The distant for B would be provided under A's home and there would usually be control over A's distant. Another use of slotted home signals was to control entrance into a single line, between two cabins, which is worked in both directions (most commonly a platform line at a large station). The practice of slotted signals as in diagram (d) instead of a 'distant' arm was not confined to the LNWR, other railways indulging in the same practice.*

> to the signal posts already lighted. The wick, when first lighted, should be lowered down until the top of the flame becomes level with the top of the burner, and then gradually raised until it burns steadily without smoking.
>
> 5. Lamps requiring repair must be sent to the District Signal Inspector, with an advice showing the Station from which they have been despatched.
>
> The person lighting the Signal Lamps must on each occasion see that the spectacles and lenses of the Signals are perfectly clean, and have with him suitable waste and cloths for cleaning. This also applies to gas Signal Lamps. (See Instructions in Lamp Rooms.) (G.F., 2029)

By the time of the Grouping the LNWR was the largest user in Britain of the long-burning lamp, practically all the signal lamps on the line being of this type.

In conventional semaphore signalling practice it was usual to provide a distant signal on the approach side of (i.e. in rear of) the first stop signal at each signal cabin (**Figure** 3.8(a)). This was of course quite simple where the cabins were widely spaced. Where cabins were close together this raised problems, since in order to get the distant signal of the second cabin far enough back to give adequate braking distance it would often have to be placed close to the starting signal for the cabin in rear. It was undesirable for the signals to be separate because it could lead to a situation where the starter for one cabin is 'on' and the distant just beyond it in the 'off' position (perhaps for the previous train or because the second cabin was switched out). This situation could lead to a driver 'reading through' the stop signal to the distant and proceeding. Under these circumstances, the normal practice was to mount the distant arm below the starting signal arm (**Figure** 3.8(b)). The two arms were 'slotted' so that the distant would only come off when the arm above it was also off. In some cases, even this arrangement gave inadequate braking distance. The distant signal would then be reproduced under the home arm (**Figure** 3.8(c)). This arm would be slotted by both the home and starting signals of cabin A so that it would only show clear when they were both clear (and of course, the home, starting and inner distant at B were also clear).

In the early days the LNW often did not provide the distant arms in such circumstances. Instead, the cabin in advance slotted the starting signal arm of the rear cabin (**Figure** 3.8(d)). Slotting in this context means that the men in cabins A and B must both pull their signal levers before the arm will clear. The derivation of the word 'slot' is explained on page 30 of 'LMS Signals'. A mechanical device was fitted at or near the base of the post to make this happen automatically (**Figure** 3.9). If the man in cabin A pulled his signal lever the signal arm would remain at danger until signalman B also pulled his lever. Indicators were often provided in the cabins (usually a 'face disc' — see Chapter 15) to indicate to the signalman when the other man has pulled his lever. The use of slotted signals, rather than lower distants, probably developed as an extension of the LNW 'be prepared to stop at the distant signal' practice. The Board of Trade did not like the idea and complained to the LNW about it on a number of occasions. However it was well into the 1880's before the practice died out for new work. The LNW therefore, had many slotted signals (i.e. worked from two or more cabins) right from very early times and much effort was expended in devising suitable and reliable slotting mechanisms.

The slot itself was claimed to be an LNW idea. The first installation had been devised by Mr Gill, one of the Company's Assistant Engineers, at Shap in 1862, examples being installed at Carnforth and Carlisle shortly afterwards. Mr Saxby was apparently shown the apparatus and very soon after patented a slotting device of his own!

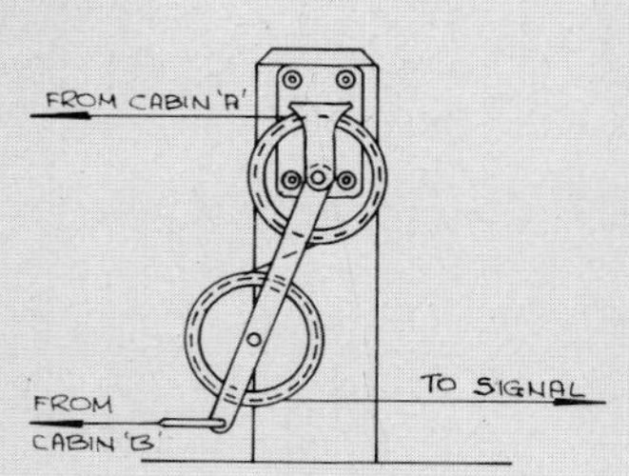

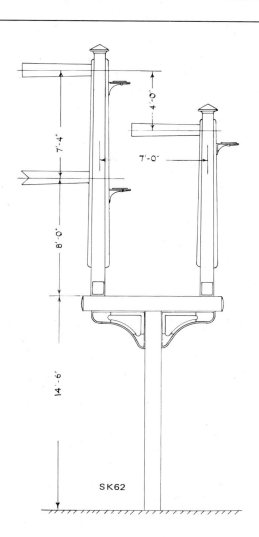

Figure 3.9 *Single Wire Slot. This was used where a signal arm was worked by two cabins, and could be used for the slotted signal shown in* **Figure 3.8(d)**. *Both cabins A and B have to pull their signal levers before the signal arm will be pulled into the off position. This design of wheel slot was introduced by A M Thompson in 1880. It could with extra parts be used to enable a single arm to be slotted by any number of cabins.*

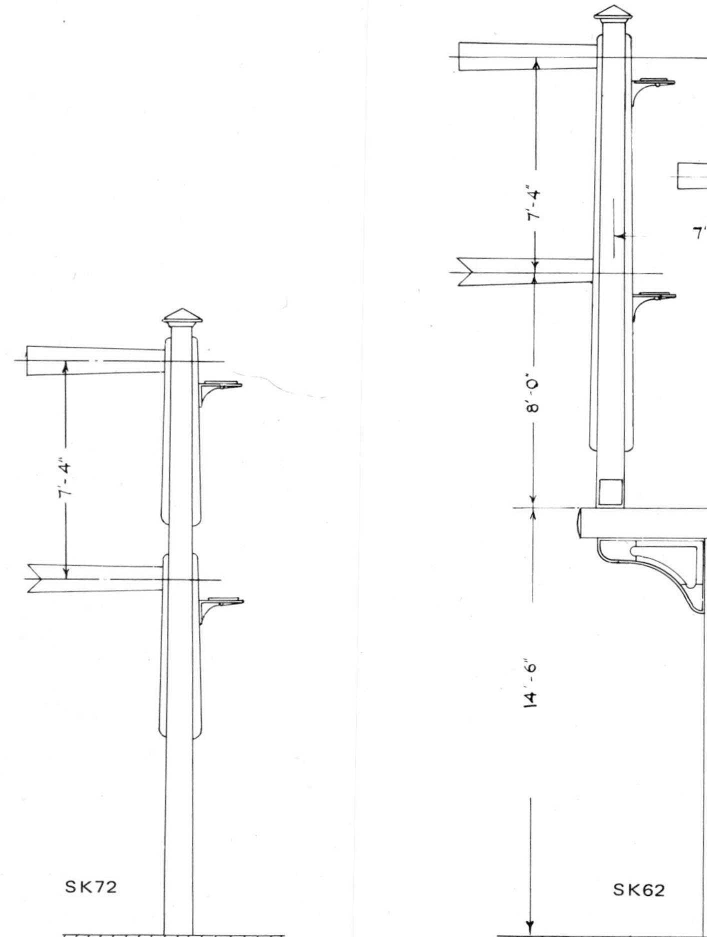

Figure 3.10 *Standard LNWR Slotted Post Signals. These are of the type introduced in 1876. SK72 is the standard straight post signal with (optional) lower distant arm and SK62 a standard bracket signal. These and the signals shown in* **Figure 3.12** *were standard signal profiles and the reference numbers were used to assist in ordering ready made signals from the works. Note the wide spacing of the home and distant arms to avoid confusion. Scale of reproduction: 4 mm to 1 foot (1:76).*

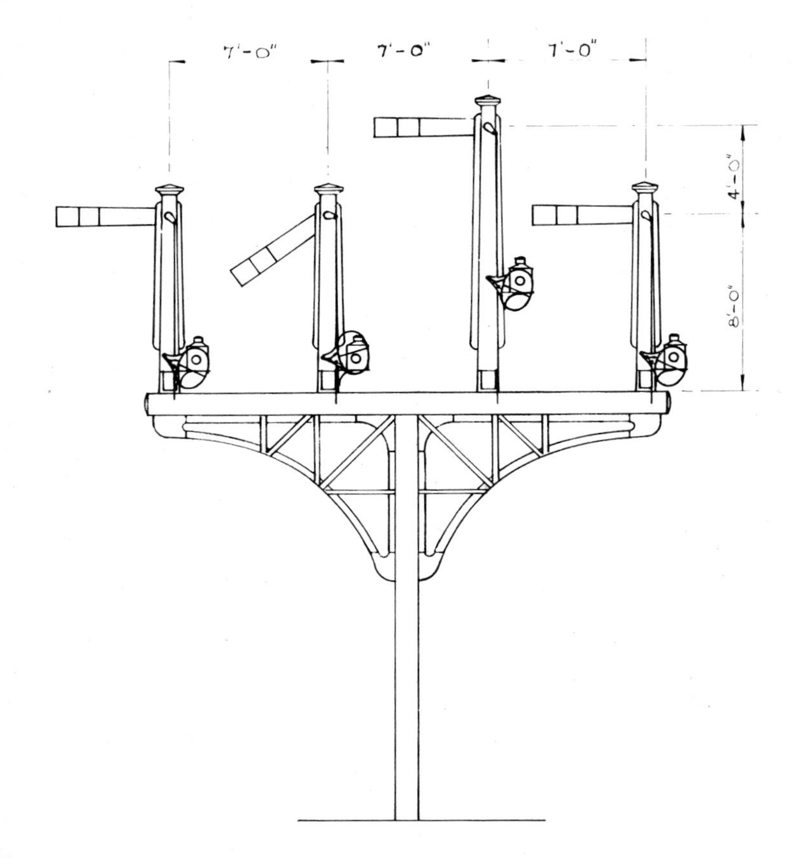

Figure 3.11 *Sketch of a 4 Doll Bracket Signal of the 1876 type. Note the large fabricated iron brackets and the arrangement of the low level lamps and spectacles. Scale of reproduction: 3 mm to 1 foot (1:102).*

Figure 3.12 *Standard Siding and Shunting Signals. SK52 was a wall mounted bracket signal. Where arms were mounted vertically above each other as shown here, the standard practice was that the top arm referred to the route on the furthest left (Top and Left Rule) the second arm to the next route on the left and the bottom arm to the route on the furthest right. In the beginning signals with the arms stacked like this were used on the main lines as well, but this was not liked by the Board of Trade. There was a risk that the driver would misinterpret the signal and not realise that his path curved sharply to the left or right and approach too fast. Scale of reproduction: 4 mm to 1 foot (1:76).*

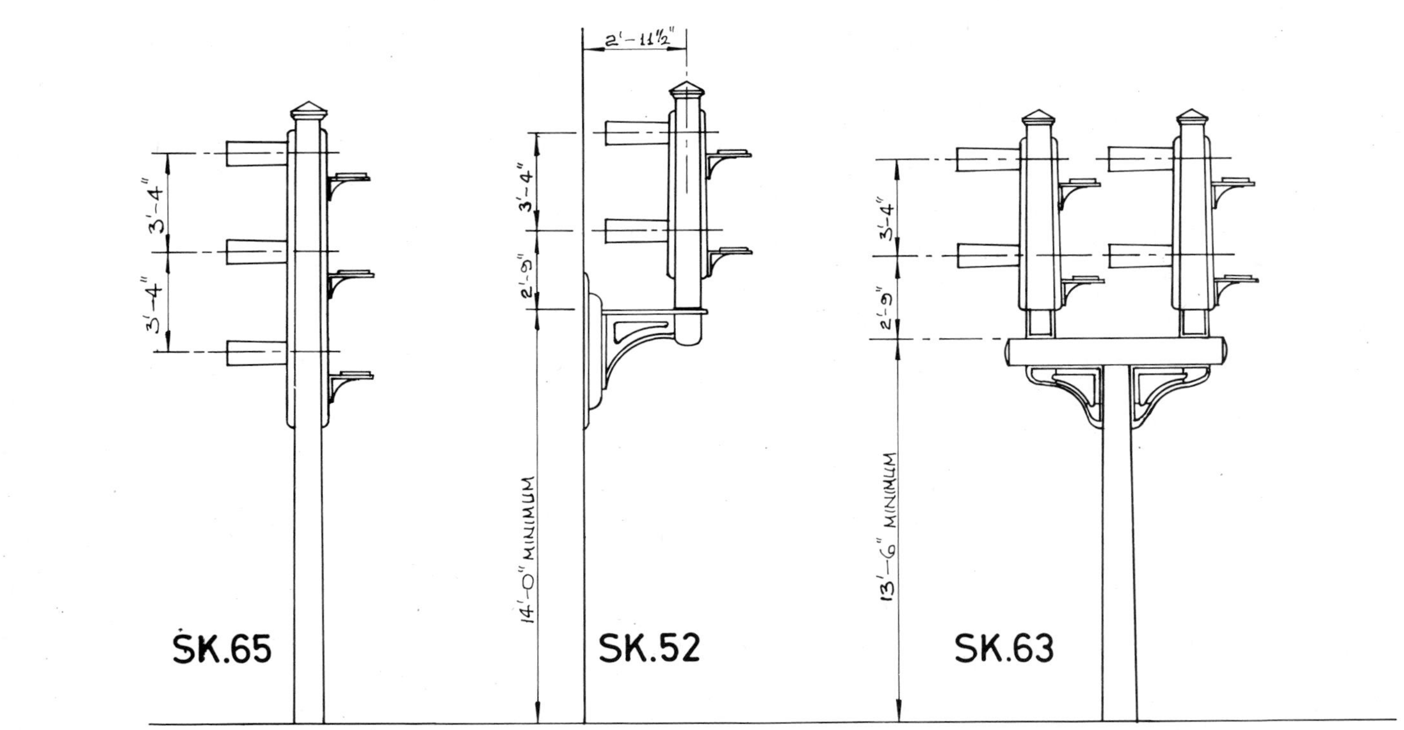

With the extension of the block system and the need to provide more signals to control the rapidly expanding traffic the LNW Officers became concerned about the number of occasions where it was necessary to allow trains to pass signals in the danger position for some purpose. This was of course against the principle that drivers should not pass signals in the danger position. Perhaps the most obvious instance of this was where the home signal was in the rear of the cabin. A signalman having stopped a train at his home signal often needed to give verbal (or even written) instructions to the driver.

The signalman therefore had to 'call-on' the driver to pass the home signal and stop him again (by hand signal) at the signal cabin to receive the instructions. This was done by the signalman either shouting or using a flag or lamp, or some other hand-held indication (even his duster!) but misunderstandings and confusion could clearly occur (for example where there were trains waiting on parallel roads).

During the late 1870's the LNW seems to have considered and tried out several arrangements for overcoming the problem. One such idea was the introduction, in about 1877, of a 'Draw Ahead' signal. This was placed below the home signal at a diverging junction and allowed a train, waiting acceptance from the next cabin, to draw forward onto the branch line in order to clear the main line for the passage of following traffic. The signals were only provided where there was a starting (section) signal ahead and the train was only allowed to proceed far enough to clear the junction (and not up to the starting signal).

In due course, probably as a result of pressure for standardisation, the various ideas were brought together and simplified to produce a distinctive signal described as a 'Calling-on' signal. As the name implies it was used to allow the signalman to call-on (without the need for hand signals) the train past the home signal and up to the cabin and they were installed where there was a regular need for this type of movement. The distinctive form of 'Calling-on' arm used on the LNWR (shown in **Figure 3.14**) was in use by 1880 and the use of the term 'draw ahead' signals for the purpose described above ceased in about 1882.

The LNW was one of the pioneers in the introduction of calling-on signals and even in 1889, when rules for their use were incorporated in the new edition of the Standard Rule Book, only five companies were using them. These were the Lancashire and Yorkshire, LNW, London, Brighton and South Coast, London, Chatham and Dover and the North London.

Rule 37a of the 1889 Rule Book described the use of the calling-on signals as follows:

> 'When a calling-on arm is lowered, the engine-driver must draw forward past the post of the signal on which the 'calling-on' arm is fixed, as far as the line is clear. If the signal box is ahead of the 'calling-on' arm, and the signalman in the box wants to communicate with the driver, he must show a hand danger signal from the box to stop him. The lowering of the 'calling-on' arm is not in any case, an authority for the starting signal to be passed at danger.'

The meaning of the Rule changed little over the years and with subsequent editions of the rule book (it was later remembered 43 and the difference between starting and advanced starting (section) signals was defined in the 1923 edition) until after the grouping.

Subsidiary signals were introduced in due course at two-cabin stations to enable a second train to proceed into the station behind a previous one, usually to do work. The second train was stopped at the home signal of the cabin at the entrance of the station, and was then brought up to that cabin if necessary to receive verbal instructions from the signalman. This was looked upon as part of Station Yard working, and not as contravening the normal principle of only one train at a time being allowed in what was, in essence, the block section between two signal cabins, one at each end of the station.

This principle of using a subsidiary signal beneath a running signal was sometimes extended to the provision of such a signal beneath a starting signal where there was an advanced starting signal, for the same general purpose but of course placed under a running signal normally ahead of the signal cabin (as was made clear in the 1923 edition of the Rule Book).

What was *not* done, was to provide such subsidiary signals under a running signal ahead of a signal cabin, where such signal itself marked the entrance to a 'normal' block

Figure 3.13 HEIGHTS OF NEW SIGNALS PROVIDED IN CONNECTION WITH THE WIDENING OF THE LINE BETWEEN RUGBY AND MARKET HARBOROUGH 1878

LOCATION	*Height of Arm Above Rail Level (Feet)*					
	Distant Signals		*Home Signals*		*Starting Signals etc.*	
	Up	*Down*	*Up*	*Down*	*Up*	*Down*
Clifton Mill	35	39	60+25*	46	25	18 35
Lilbourne	45	45	40	40	25	25
Cold Ashby Level Crossing	—	30	35	35	—	—
Yelvertoft	35	55+25*	35	40	30	35
South Kilworth Level Crossing	45	—	39	39	—	—
Welford & Kilworth	60+15*	40	40	44	39	20
Husband's Bosworth L.C.	45	45	40	40	—	—
Theddingworth	43	39	35	39	35	25
Lubenham	55+25*	53+25*	45	50+25*	35	25
AVERAGE HEIGHT (Excluding Co-acting signals)	40' 6"		39' 6"		28' 6"	

NOTES:

* Co-acting signals — Heights of top and bottom arms.

1. The top lamps on the Up Home at Clifton Mill and Up Distant at Welford were made to wind up into place to save the lampman from having to climb to the top of the post.
2. A single lamp 35 ft above rail level was provided for the Up Distant at Lubenham.
3. The lamp on the Up Home at Welford was set at 30 ft above rail level and that on the Down Home at 35 ft above rail level.

Figure 3.13 *This table lists the signals provided on the line between Rugby and Market Harborough when it was doubled in 1878, and serves as an example of actual signalling practice (as opposed to theory) in the 1870's. The signals would be of the 1876 pattern and were all straight posts. The use of quite high signal posts for the distant and home signals will be noted, an early and clear sight of these signals being fundamental to safe train working. The starting signals are somewhat lower, as might be expected, but still considerably higher than the recommended 16 feet! This line was fairly open and straight with few overbridges, while the stations were fairly small. The height of the signals was, therefore, more to do with obtaining a clear sky background than with bringing the arm clear of obstructions. At two of the intermediate level crossings distant signals were only provided in one direction although there were home signals in both directions protecting the crossings. Where there was no distant (e.g. on the up line at Cold Ashby level crossing) the line was straight and it was considered that the drivers would be able to see the home signal and crossing in sufficient time to stop if necessary (the old desire to save money by keeping signalling costs to a minimum died hard!).*

Plate 3.4 *One of the original standard ground disc signals similar to the SK53 type but with a larger base. This is a survival of the old point disc system, the disc is connected directly to the point rod and moved to 'clear' whenever the points were reversed, the lamp casing revolving through 90 degrees in order to show the clear face to a driver. Under this system, of course, the signal will show clear even if a move is actually being made into the siding. The points in this illustration are trap points protecting the outlet from a siding at Dolwyddelen and the photograph was taken in May, 1951.*

Photo: J Cooper

section (as distinct from the Station Yard working already explained).

If there was any necessity for a movement to be made, *for the purpose of shunting only*, into the block section, and not as 'right away', subsidiary arms known as 'shunting signals' (shunt for short) were provided. A train could not proceed into the section until the main arm was lowered (see Chapter 7).

In LMS days the naming of the signals was revised and the descriptions 'warning' and 'draw ahead' were introduced where necessary to define more accurately the purpose and use of the subsidiary signals.

On the LNW the call-on arms worked independently of the main arm and only one of the two could be 'off' at the same time (the principle in use today). In pre-grouping days this was not always so and a few companies worked the signals together. The call-on arm could be cleared and replaced on its own, but the main arm could only be lowered with the call-on arm in the off position.

The introduction of the standard signals described in the next Chapter did not, of course, mean the end of the old designs. These continued in use until they became life expired or were removed in connection with layout alterations and station enlargements. Quite a number of slotted post signals remained in use into this century, a handful surviving the 1930's.

Finally, mention might be made of a curious incident which occurred in about 1920 to one of the slotted post signals remaining in use on the Southern Division. As a result of a breakage in the signal arm push rod it was found that the arm fell to 'clear' instead of returning to danger under the action of the weight of the spectacle casting. This was against the fundamental 'fail safe' principle of signalling and naturally the offending arm was quickly removed and sent to Crewe for inspection. Examination revealed that in order to keep the arm clean and bright, in accordance with instructions, it had been diligently painted every few years. The resultant build up of lead based paint was found to weigh some seven pounds and this had been sufficient to 'overpower' the weight of the spectacle and to swing the arm to clear!

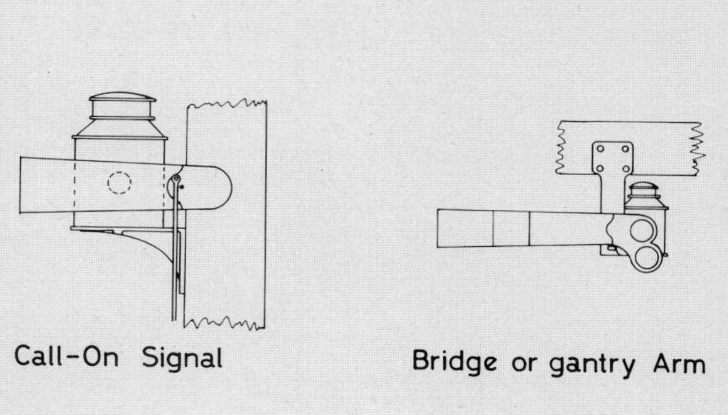

Figure 3.14 *Call-On Signal Arm. There was no spectacle with this arm and it showed 'no-light' when 'on', the arm obscuring the lamp completely. When pulled off the lamp was exposed, displaying a small white light to the driver. The bridge or gantry arm was used in restricted locations where an arm was needed near the drivers eye level. As its name implies it was designed for mounting under bridges, signal brackets and gantries or station roofs.*

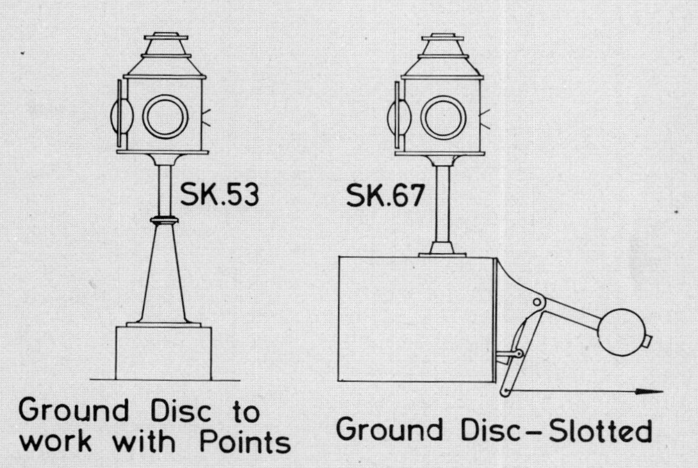

Figure 3.15 *Standard Ground Discs. SK53 is a 'point disc' and was simply attached to the point rod and operated with it on the same lever. (See* **Plate 3.4***). SK67 is a disc slotted by two cabins and would only show clear when both men had pulled their levers. The slotting mechanism was contained in the box under the signal itself. This type of disc could also be used as an ordinary disc worked by wire from one cabin.*

Chapter Four Standard Signals

In the early 1880's there was growing concern about the durability and maintenance costs of the signals then in use. A further concern was that of the fail-safe principle so important in signalling. While the balance lever and weight on a signal post would return the arm to danger in the event of breakage of the signal wire this was not the case if the push rod above them broke or became disconnected. In these circumstances the arm could swing to clear and give a false indication to an approaching train. The 1874 and 1876 signals had gone some way towards meeting these needs but there was still room for improvement. Each gale seemed to result in many signal arms being blown off or broken and, in some cases, complete signals were destroyed. Consideration was, therefore, given to a more modern design of signal which would benefit from the improvements in materials and methods which had occurred and which would be more durable, adaptable and easier and cheaper to construct. Things came to a head in January 1883 when it was reported that:

> 'The new signal cabin in course of erection at Springs Branch was blown down during the heavy gale on the morning of 26th January. The timber work was only partially finished and although much damaged it can be re-erected after repair. During the same gale 6 signal posts were blown down and about 55 signal arms blown off. As there are a large number of arms blown off during every gale, Mr Webb has arranged to make these for the new pattern posts of corrugated steel plates which should stand the heaviest gale without breakage.'

The new signals did not eliminate the incidence of storm damage entirely, of course. The severe gale of 22nd December 1894, for instance, destroyed 99 wooden signal arms and a further 53 steel arms were bent or otherwise damaged, while the following 23rd March saw a further 73 wooden arms blown off and 20 steel arms bent. The damaged steel arms could be easily and quickly replaced and spare ones were kept at exposed locations for this purpose.

The new signals (**Figure 4.1**) came into general use for new work in April 1883, and instructions were issued to the effect that the lamps were to be mounted at arm level unless it was absolutely necessary to do otherwise. The most distinctive feature of the signals was the pressed steel arm, with its two ribs or corrugations to give rigidity. Crewe Works was, of course, ideally suited for the mass production of arms of this type. Initially, the arms were painted but in later years enamelling was used. The arm was bolted directly to the spectacle casting to form a single unit which was in turn mounted on a pivot pin running in a casting bolted to the outside of the signal post. This avoided weakening the post and reduced considerably the work involved in manufacturing and repairing the signals as well as making alterations much simpler. The arm and spectacle casting were arranged so that if a breakage occurred in the push rod the arm would return automatically to danger under its own weight. (Similarly for a breakage in the operating wire from the cabin.) The signals were capable of showing two positions only, danger and clear, and double spectacles were provided in all cases. Needless to say someone raised the question of how to make the new arms work to three positions and in September 1883 a new instruction was issued:—

> 'The new signals must be ordered as usual to work red and green or red and white. In the latter case they will be sent out without the green glass but the arm in both cases will work to caution and the all-right position will be abandoned.'

This brought about the demise of three position signals and those working to the vertical (all-right) position on the LNWR.

The signal posts were solid pitch pine cut to a square section which tapered from 6 inches square at the top to anything up to 15 inches square at the bottom depending on the height and duty. The galvanised iron cap was retained for keeping the weather out of the top of the post. To prevent decay at ground level (always the most susceptible point due to the persistent damp) the section of the post was increased and the butt end charred in a special furnace provided for the purpose in the joiners shop. For additional protection a coating of gas tar was also applied. In order to assist in inspection work and assessment of the need for renewals, the date was normally burnt into the wide base of the post a little above ground level.

The lamp bracket was fixed to the posts with the same bolts as the arm spindle and also acted as a stop for the arm in its danger position. The back blinder for the lamp was made of a continuous strip of metal with a hole at one end. It showed a white light to the signalman with the arm in the 'on' position and no light with the arm 'off'. Back light blinders were, generally, only required on those signals which faced away from the cabin.

A little needs to be said about the colours of signal lights. As explained in Chapter 3, after the caution signal position was generally abandoned the majority of the signals showed a white light when at clear. Where a double spectacle was provided the white light was achieved by the simple expedient of leaving the bottom spectacle empty. The bottom spectacle was provided for those places where a green aspect was required. With the increasing numbers of signals at stations and in sidings the danger of confusion to drivers faced with large numbers of red lights at night increased. In an attempt to ease the problem it was suggested in October, 1873, that a purple light be adopted as the stop or danger signal in ground disc signals. The size of the light was also to be reduced as an additional aid. The idea was approved in April, 1874 and the work of changing the lights put in hand. The purple light was used in siding ground discs, signals for goods yards, shunting signals and bay starting signals. For instance, the small 'shunt out' arms provided below the platform starting signals at New Street Station, to allow engines and trains to be drawn forward for shunting purposes, showed a purple danger light. The system remained in use until the early years of this century.

After 1878 the LNW was therefore using four signal lamp colours, red, purple, green and white. As time went on stations and yards grew in size and the land adjoining the railway became built up. The numbers of white lights visible at night increased alarmingly and it became more and more difficult for the drivers to pick out which white light was their 'clear' signal. In places of great difficulty some signals had green glasses added to produce a green aspect at 'clear' or 'caution', these being in addition to those already showing caution. In 1884, approximately half of the LNWR's 11,542 running signal arms (on 7,785 posts) showed red and green aspects and the other half red and white.

At the Railway Clearing House Meeting of 27th July 1893, it was recommended:—

> (a) That the white light as a fixed signal be dispensed with, and that red and green lights only be used as Drivers Signals — Red being the 'Danger' and Green

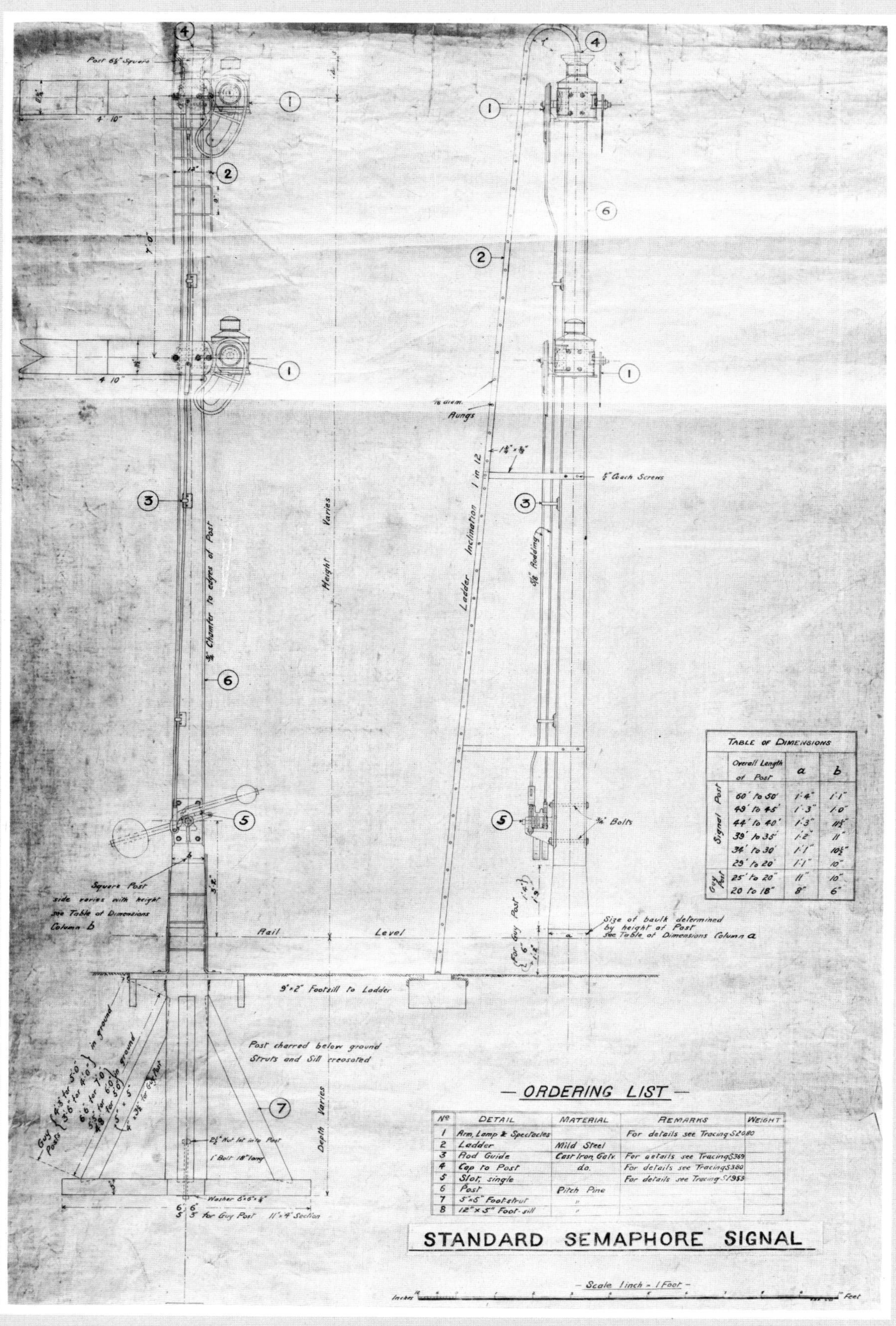
Post 6½" Square
4' 10"
4' 10"
Rungs
Ladder Inclination 1 in 12
¾" Chamfer to edges of Post
Height Varies
⅝" Coach Screws
⅝" Rodding
¾" Bolts
Square Post
side varies with height
see Table of Dimensions
Column b
Rail Level
Size of baulk determined
by height of Post
see Table of Dimensions Column a
9" × 2" Footsill to Ladder
Post charred below ground
Struts and Sill creosoted
Depth Varies
Washer 6" × 6" × ⅜"
11" × 4" Section
TABLE OF DIMENSIONS
Overall Length of Post
Signal Post
Guy Post
60' to 50' 1'4" 1'1"
49' to 45' 1'3" 1'0"
44' to 40' 1'3" 11½"
39' to 35' 1'2" 11"
34' to 30' 1'1" 10½"
29' to 20' 1'1" 10"
25' to 20" 11" 10"
20 to 18" 8" 6"
— ORDERING LIST —
Nº DETAIL MATERIAL REMARKS WEIGHT
1 Arm, Lamp & Spectacles For details see Tracing S2080
2 Ladder Mild Steel
3 Rod Guide Cast Iron, Galv. For details see Tracing S369
4 Cap to Post do. For details see Tracing S380
5 Slot, single For details see Tracing S1953
6 Post Pitch Pine
7 5" × 5" Foot-strut "
8 12" × 5" Foot-sill "
STANDARD SEMAPHORE SIGNAL
– Scale 1 inch = 1 Foot –
Feet

Plate 4.1 *A straight post signal of the '1883' standard design at Latchford, photographed in 1972. Many thousands of signals of this basic design (with detail differences, of course) existed all over the system. This example has the ladder placed in front of the post, a system introduced in 1901 (see text). The photograph also illustrates the balance lever, push rod and guying arrangements. Note how the post is increased in size at ground level in order to give additional resistance to decay.*

Plate 4.2 *A standard distant signal (the arm would, of course, be painted red with a vertical white stripe in LNW days) this time with the ladder at the back. A telegraph insulator fixing is attached to the post and carried the arm and lamp repeater wire. The guying arrangements of this between-tracks signal are worthy of note. The signal post has been 'godfathered' at ground level by the addition of a splint or flitch of timber on its left hand side. This has been done to strengthen the post which had begun to rot at ground level. Repairs of this type were quite common on wooden post signals and provided an economical means of extending the life of a signal and they can be seen in a number of the illustrations. This signal was erected in about 1902 and was the up distant signal for Bromborough.*

◁ **Figure 4.1 (Opposite)** *Standard Semaphore Signal. This LNW drawing shows the general arrangement of a standard LNW running signal with lower distant arm. This was the later pattern with the ladder placed in front of the post, a scheme adopted to encourage the men to keep the arm and spectacle glasses clean. The drawing clearly shows that erecting a signal was not simply a case of digging a hole and dropping in a post. A quite elaborate arrangement was necessary below ground to ensure that the post would be stable and remain in position in storms and allow men to climb it for lamping and maintenance. The drawing also gives the dimensions to be used in manufacturing guy posts (see* **Figure 4.6***). Scale of reproduction: ¼" to 1 foot (1.48).*

the 'All Right', and that when a White light is shown on a fixed post where a Red or Green light should be seen, it should be considered a Danger Signal, and treated accordingly.
(b) That the use of the Green back light, to indicate to the signalman that the signal obeys the lever, be discontinued, to prevent the posssibility of a Driver mistaking this back light as a Signal to proceed; and that all signals the position of which is danger, be arranged to show a White back light to the Signalman when 'at Danger', and either a purple light or a masked light, when at 'All Right'.

The General Managers put a rider clause on their approval, that the work was to be done as opportunity offered. The proposals were notified to the various Superintendents, who were responsible for putting them into effect, on 25th October 1893. On the LNWR, Thompson issued instructions for the change to his Inspectors on the 24th of November:

> 'It has been agreed that we should alter our white lights to green by degrees and station by station as alterations and renewals occur. As it is not very frequent that we do all the signals at a station together we will have to decide whether we renew all the other signals with green lights at the same time or not. Please advise me how much work is involved in each case. For the new type signals (i.e. those introduced in 1883) the work can be done simply by putting a green glass in the existing spectacles.'

Shortly afterwards it was resolved that expenditure on the changeover should not exceed £500 per annum. A couple of years later the order was put out to change all the remaining signals so that they too would show a green light. This work, of course, saw the end of the single spectacle signals.

As with all changes of this type, people got carried away with the idea, and since white was now a danger signal, it seemed to be logical to alter the white side lights in some lamps to green (despite recommendation (b) above!). An order to change the white side lights in level crossing gate lamps was issued in October 1897. The inevitable happened, of course, and the driver of a train standing in a station mistook the green side light in the gate lamp as his running signal and started into the section. Various attempts were made to get around the problem, such as by screening the side lamp. However, in December sense prevailed and the men were asked to restore the white lights. Conversion of disc signal back lights from green to white was ordered in April 1896, the work to be done concurrently with the alterations to the running signals.

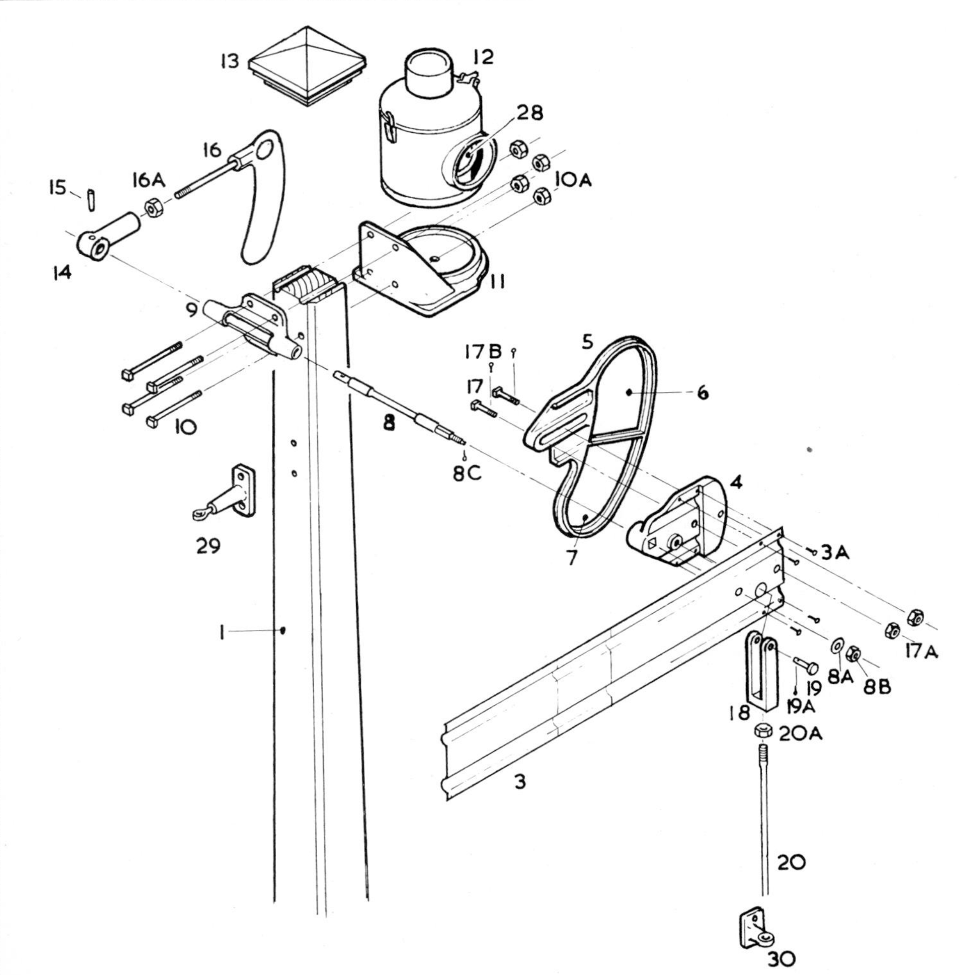

Figure 4.2 *Standard Semaphore Signal. This exploded view shows the various parts required to make up a single arm signal. The way in which they fit together can be seen in this drawing. The parts illustrated are:—*

1. *Post*
3. *Arm*
4. *Arm Cramp*
5. *Spectacle Casting*
6. *Ruby Screen (Glass)*
7. *Green Screen (Glass)*
8. *Arm spindle (with securing washer nut and split pin)*
9. *Arm Centre*
10. *Bolts for arm centre and lamp bracket (with securing nuts)*
11. *Lamp Bracket*
12. *Outer Lamp Case*
13. *Cap for Post*
14. *Back Spectacle Arm*
15. *Taper Pin*
16. *Back Spectacle (or Back Blinder or Blinker)*
17. *Spectacle Bolts (and securing nuts and split pins)*
18. *Jaw for Push Rod*
19. *Jaw Pin*
20. *Push Rod and securing nut (Rod is 5/8" dia. expanding to ¾" at screwed ends or ¾" dia. throughout).*
28. *Inner Lamp*
29. *Guy Wire attachment*
30. *Push Rod Guide*

Drawing by J K Nelson

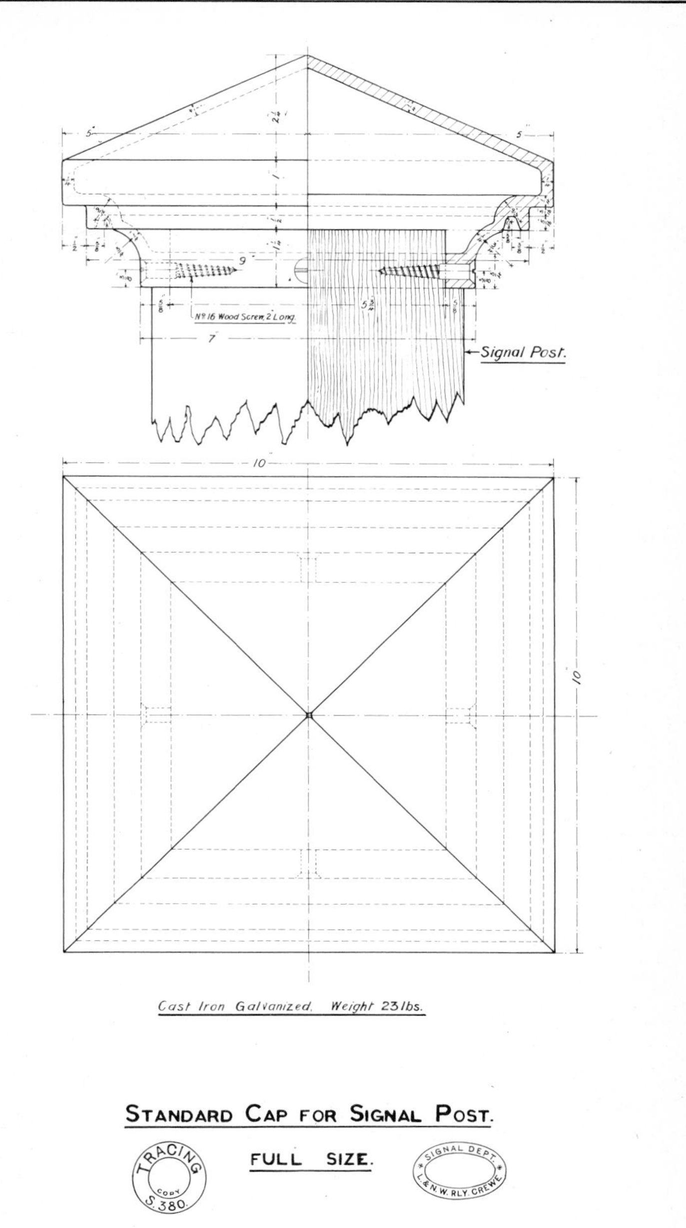

Figure 4.3 *Standard Signal Post Cap. This drawing shows the standard galvanised iron cap used on practically all LNWR signals. No frills here, just a simple, functional and cheap object. This was the standard size of cap for the 1883 signal posts and dolls. Scale of reproduction: ¼ full size.*

Plate 4.3 *This photograph of the back of a signal at Ellesmere Port shows the painting of the back of the arm and the arrangement of the signal lamp and back blinder. The lamp is of the LNWR large round case pattern, the lid of which has not been fastened down. When properly adjusted the back light of the lamp was supposed to show through the hole in the top of the back-blinder, in this position the light would only be seen when the arm was correctly in the horizontal or danger position. In practice, in later years at least, most back-blinders drooped like this one so that the back light showed over the top. In this position it was much easier to maintain as an absolutely accurate adjustment was not required. The blinder would, of course, still obscure the light when the arm was 'off'. The subsidiary arm on the right is a main to loop line subsidiary arm (see Chapter 7), the back-blinder for which is more or less correctly adjusted. The main arm is of a short pattern as the signal applies to a loop line and clearances are restricted between the tracks. This signal was erected in about 1926 and the photograph was taken in June 1975.*

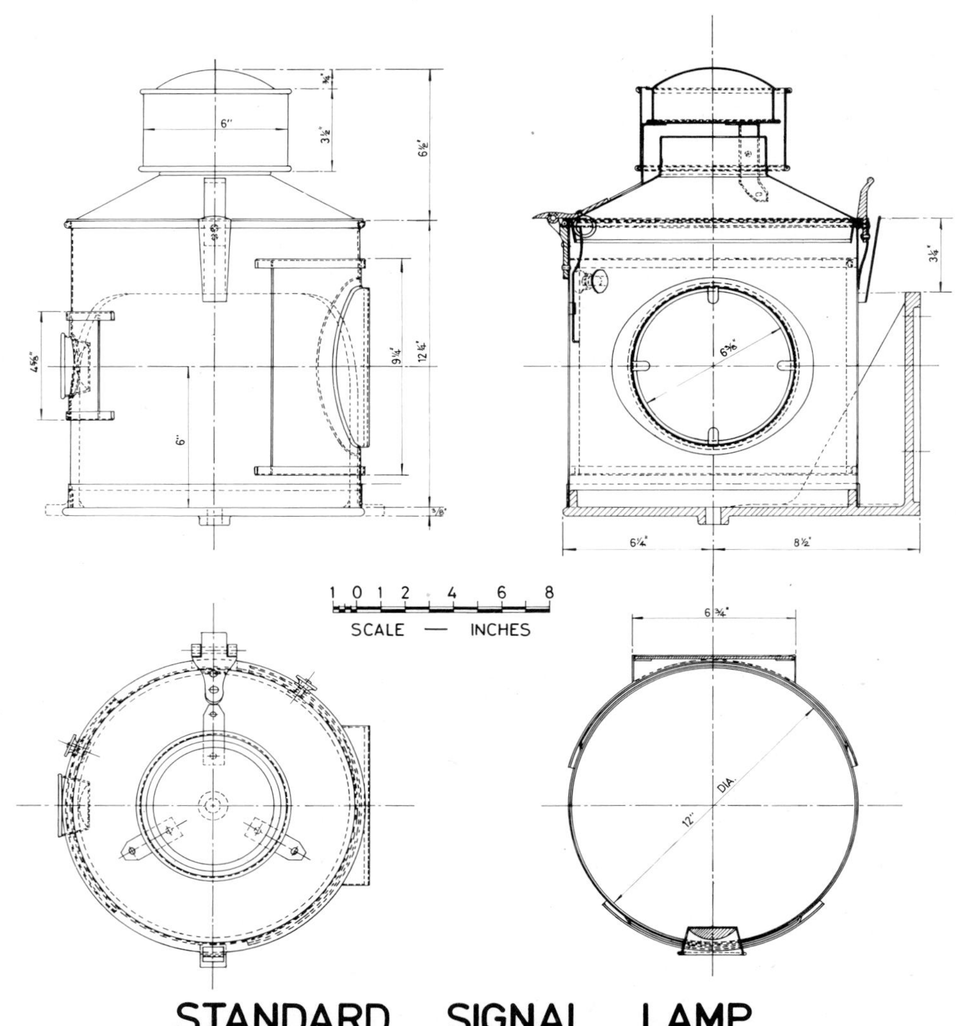

Figure 4.4 *Standard Signal Lamp (Outer Casing). The LNW used a large circular outer lamp case for its signal lamps. This drawing is of the S391 type used for the majority of signals. The lid is held by a spring clip and hinges back to allow access to the interior. The lamp assembly itself (burner, reservoir and case) was a separate unit and slotted inside the outer case. The cases were generally made from tinplate, but these were found to rot away quite quickly in the Widnes area due to pollution from the many chemical works. As a result a number of casings supplied for that area were made of copper. Scale of reproduction: 1/8th full size.*

After the security of the block system perhaps the most important consideration in signalling was the positioning and arrangement of the signals. It was essential that the drivers of trains should be able to see the signals clearly, interpret them correctly and at sufficient distance to enable them to act on their instructions. The LNW, therefore, laid down a set of standard rules to be worked to in positioning new signals. Because of the importance of Signal Sighting the rules as they stood in the early 1880's are reproduced in full in Appendix 3.

The recommended distance between distant signals and home signals had been increased from the 700 yards originally specified to 1000 yards in recognition of increased train speeds and weights. A good sight of the signals, particularly home and distant signals, was considered most important for safety and expeditious working of the traffic. In practice things were not perfect, the line curved and sight was restricted by bridges, buildings and other obstructions. In some cases this necessitated tall signals to enable the arms to be seen above the obstructions. The LNW seems to have become associated with tall signals, but as can be seen from the sighting rules they were not provided everywhere nor were they provided without reason. In the early days a consideration in the provision of tall signals was the fact that before the advent of continuous brakes the train brakes were under the control of the guard(s). An early sight of the signals by the guard and the brakesmen under his charge, who were located along the train, was therefore desirable as a back up to the whistle signals from the engine. This often necessitated tall signals to enable them to be seen above the train. After the general introduction of continuous brakes the guard still had a duty to observe the signals and take action if he considered the train was out of control or had run past signals. A further consideration was that of obtaining a good and clear sight of the arm. While the arm might be visible from a satisfactory distance, if the driver saw it against a confusing background of, say, trees or buildings it could be difficult to interpret its position. The best possible background was the sky and a number of signals were made tall to obtain it. In a few other cases white patches were painted on bridges, or a white sight board was provided fixed to the signal post behind the arms. The requirement that the signals should be visible from the cabin and that electrical repeaters should be avoided where possible resulted in a number of tall signals in positions where the drivers sight of a lower signal would otherwise be satisfactory.

Where signals were over 45 feet high lower duplicate

Plate 4.4 *A detail view of the foot of the post illustrated in* **Plate 4.3** *showing the arrangement of the balance levers and operating wire. The wire from the cabin is attached to a chain before it passes around the pulley wheel. This is because a wire would soon wear and snap with the continued flexing and rubbing around a wheel, and a chain is more durable in these circumstances. The chain wheels themselves are bracketed out from the post, a very common arrangement. Since the two arms do not need to be slotted together ordinary balance levers are used, one being mounted on each side of the post for simplicity. The balance weights are not mounted directly on the levers but hang from them. This was done in order to keep the width of the apparatus to a minimum and so reduce the risk of accidents to staff working in busy or congested areas.*

or fog arms were generally provided. These arms worked (or co-acted) with the top arm on the same push rod (**Figure 4.8**, page 51). They were provided to assist the men in seeing the position of the signal when their train was standing at it or where the top arm was obscured by a bridge or the station roof when the engine was close to it. As the name implies, the arms were of especial use in fog when the top arm was obscured. Both the driver and the fog-signalman would then find the bottom arm of considerable assistance. In addition, at night the need for tall signals was not as great, and the light at the lower arm would often be of more assistance to the driver than the top light.

Not all co-acting signals were simply straight posts with home or distant arms, or both. Junction signals often required top or sky arms. Where all the routes were important all the arms would be reproduced at the top and bottom while in other cases the subordinate arms would only be found at the bottom of the post. The arrangement of the arms could also be different at top and bottom if site conditions made this necessary. Another variation sometimes found in co-acting signals was that small arms were used for the lower or fog arms. This saved space and reduced costs and was not detrimental to sighting since they were only used for sighting over short distances. The figures and plates illustrate some variations that could be found.

As with the 1874 and 1876 signals it was not always possible in practice to install the signals in exact accordance with the rules. In order to indicate the heights of the signals actually provided on the line details of over 1,000 straight post signals have been collected and the information assembled into the charts contained in **Figure 4.5**. Since the sighting requirements of distant, home and starting signals were somewhat different, separate charts have been prepared for the three types of signals. As can

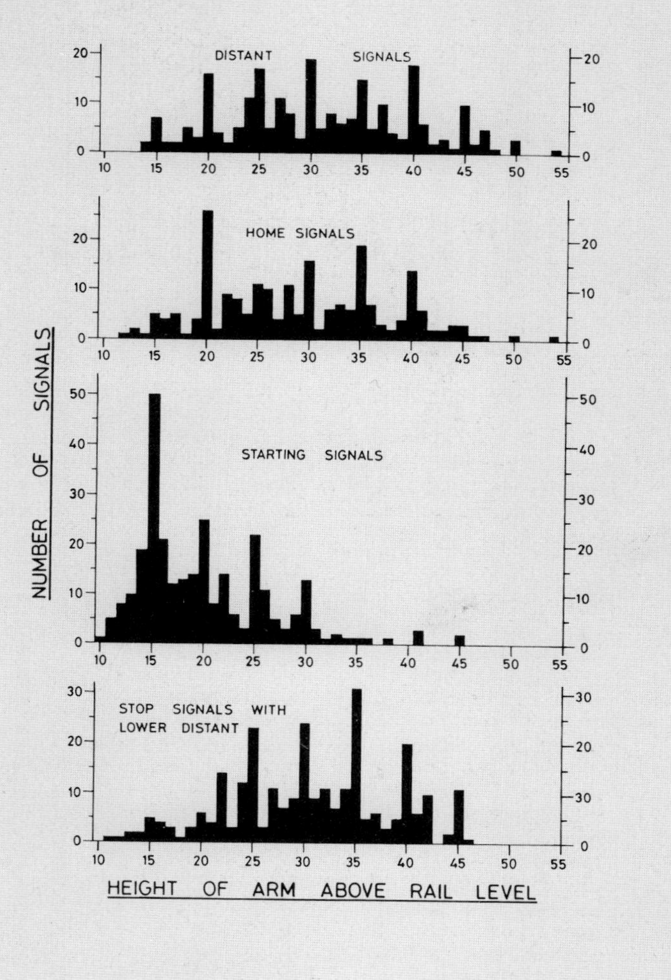

Figure 4.5 *Diagrams showing the distribution of the heights of approximately 1,000 actual LNW straight post signals. Separate charts have been prepared for each main type of signal to show how their heights varied with their duty.*

Plate 4.5 *This photograph, taken in 1905, shows the Down Slow Starting Signal at Prestatyn Station. It carries the distinctive ring provided to distinguish between signals applying to slow, loop or subsidiary lines and those applying to main or most important running lines. The ring was painted black and placed symmetrically about the stripe on the arm. This signal carried an 'elevated' balance lever, placed about half way up the post so that it was out of the way of passengers moving to and from the ground level 'platform' provided for the Dyserth Branch train. The signal, which was 16′ 6″ high, was moved some distance forward in 1920 to allow the station platforms to be extended. The 'train' is one of the new LNWR motor cars (No. 1) constructed in 1905 for branch line services. The photograph was taken shortly after the opening of the Dyserth Branch for passenger services, which were worked by this type of car. The cars were fitted with a set of folding steps for use by passengers boarding or alighting at the ground level halts. The coach was powered by a small steam locomotive at the near end and in order to produce a neat and tidy design this was enclosed and disguised in the bodywork of the coach. The boiler can just be seen through the windows in the end of the vehicle while the chimney is visible poking through the roof.*

Photo: Courtesy Clwyd Record Office

be seen, the heights of distant signals were spread fairly evenly over a range of from 15 to 50 feet. As with all the other signals an attempt had been made to standardise heights to multiples of 5 feet (total heights of 15, 20, 25, 30 etc. feet). One cause of the scatter around these standard heights was the relative positioning of the signal arms on multiple track lines. It was common (but not universal) practice to place the signal arms for slow or subsidiary lines 3 feet 6 inches lower than the equivalent arms on the main or fast lines. (The signal heights in the charts have all been rounded off to the nearest whole number of feet).

The charts clearly indicate that distant and home signals were generally taller than starting signals and that the standard height of 15 feet for starting signals was adhered to in a good proportion of cases, (approximately 20% of starting signals being of this height). Although the general rule was that signals above 45 feet were to be fitted with duplicate or co-acting arms, in practice a few single-arm signals existed with heights of up to 55 feet. No signals with two arms, a stop (home or starting) arm with lower distant, were found above 46 feet in height however.

Co-acting signals (**Figure 4.9**, Page 51) consisting of pairs of home or distant arms or both (making a total of four arms) ranged in height from 25 to 66 feet, the majority occurring in the 40 to 55 feet range. The number of examples used in each chart gives a guide to the relative

Plate 4.6 *A straight post signal with home and lower distant arms, photographed at Hednesford No. 3 in 1972. The signal was erected in 1923, in connection with the opening of No. 3 cabin to control new colliery sidings and was 35 feet high. The wide (7 foot) spacing of the arms will be noticed and between them is a small telegraph spar and insulators for the distant arm and lamp indicator provided in the next (No. 2) cabin.*

Plate 4.7 *A very short two-arm signal at Latchford. The distant arm is of the fixed or unworkable type introduced in order to reduce the cost of installations. The arm has been fixed directly to the post and no spectacle casting or glasses provided. The lamp is fitted with a yellow (red in LNW days) lens to provide the correct night signal. The distant lamp casing is a replacement and is much smaller than the LNWR pattern which is still in use for the top arm. The chain and pulley arrangement for altering the direction of the signal wire at the bottom of the post can be seen. This signal survived until 1973 and on the resignalling of the West Coast line, in connection with electrification, it had the curious distinction of acting as an outer distant for the new Warrington Power signal box!*

proportions of the different types of straight post signals to be found in use on the line. The total sample represents approximately 10% of such signals in use on the LNWR at any one time.

In order to assist the drivers in distinguishing the signals which applied to them on multiple track sections, the signal arms on slow and goods lines were fitted with rings. At some places where there were several adjoining lines of equal status (for example the platform lines at Euston and New Street) the signals were provided alternately with rings on one line and without on the next (see also **Figure 6.3**). For the 1883 standard signals the rings were painted black on both sides (prior to 1883 practice varied, see **Plate 3.3**). The circular metal rings were 30 inches in external diameter and 3 inches wide for full size arms and correspondingly smaller for short or small arms. On the North London Railway the rings were applied to the No. 1 line signals and were painted white on the front and black on the rear. A vertical bar, similarly painted, denoted goods or siding lines (see also the section on painting below).

The rules required that signals were placed on the left hand side of the line and this was reinforced by an instruction in December 1892:—

> 'It will be necessary in future that every signal be fixed on the left hand side of the driver and although there will be cases where the sight will not admit, still in every case you must do your best even at the

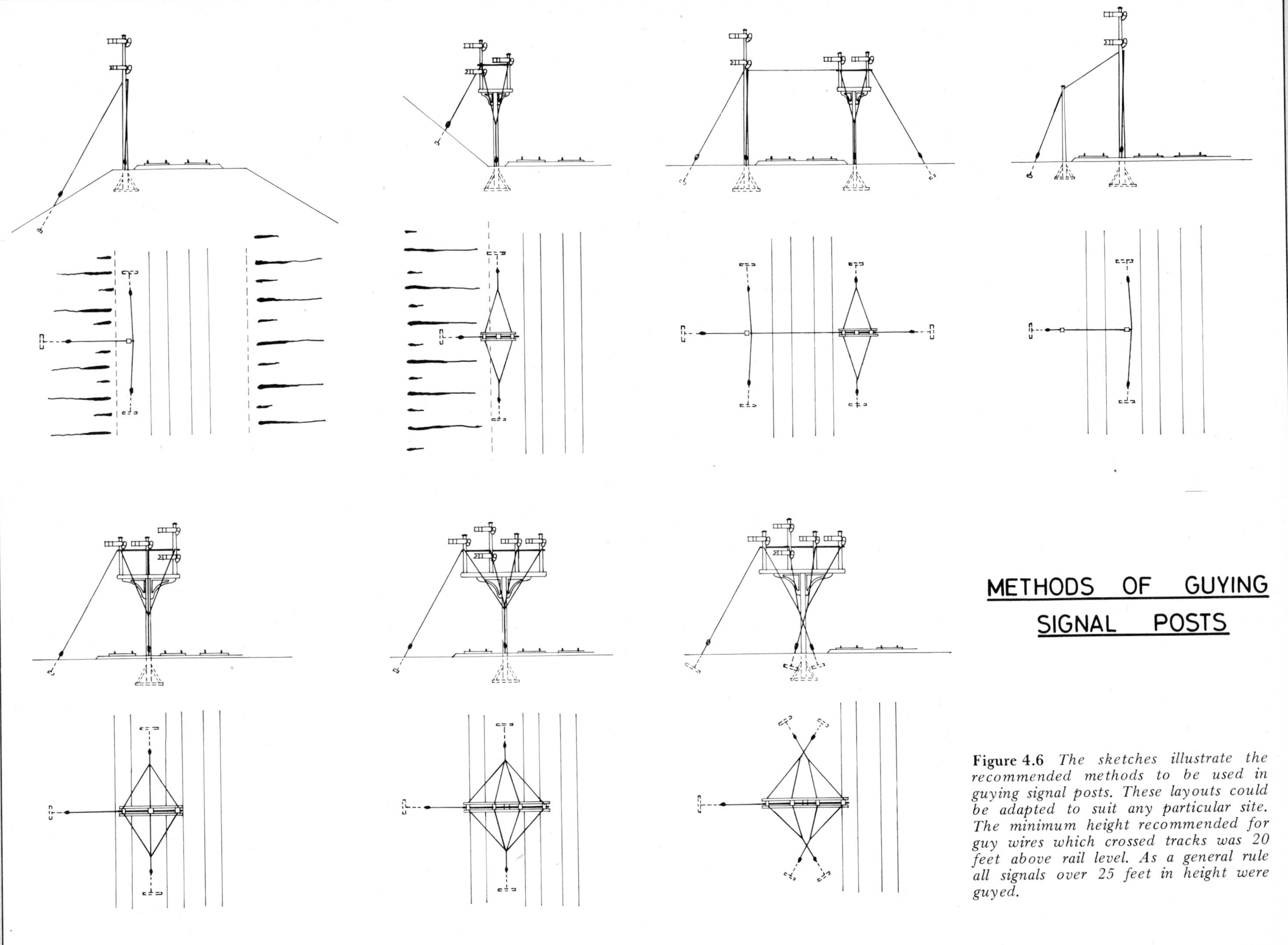

Figure 4.6 *The sketches illustrate the recommended methods to be used in guying signal posts. These layouts could be adapted to suit any particular site. The minimum height recommended for guy wires which crossed tracks was 20 feet above rail level. As a general rule all signals over 25 feet in height were guyed.*

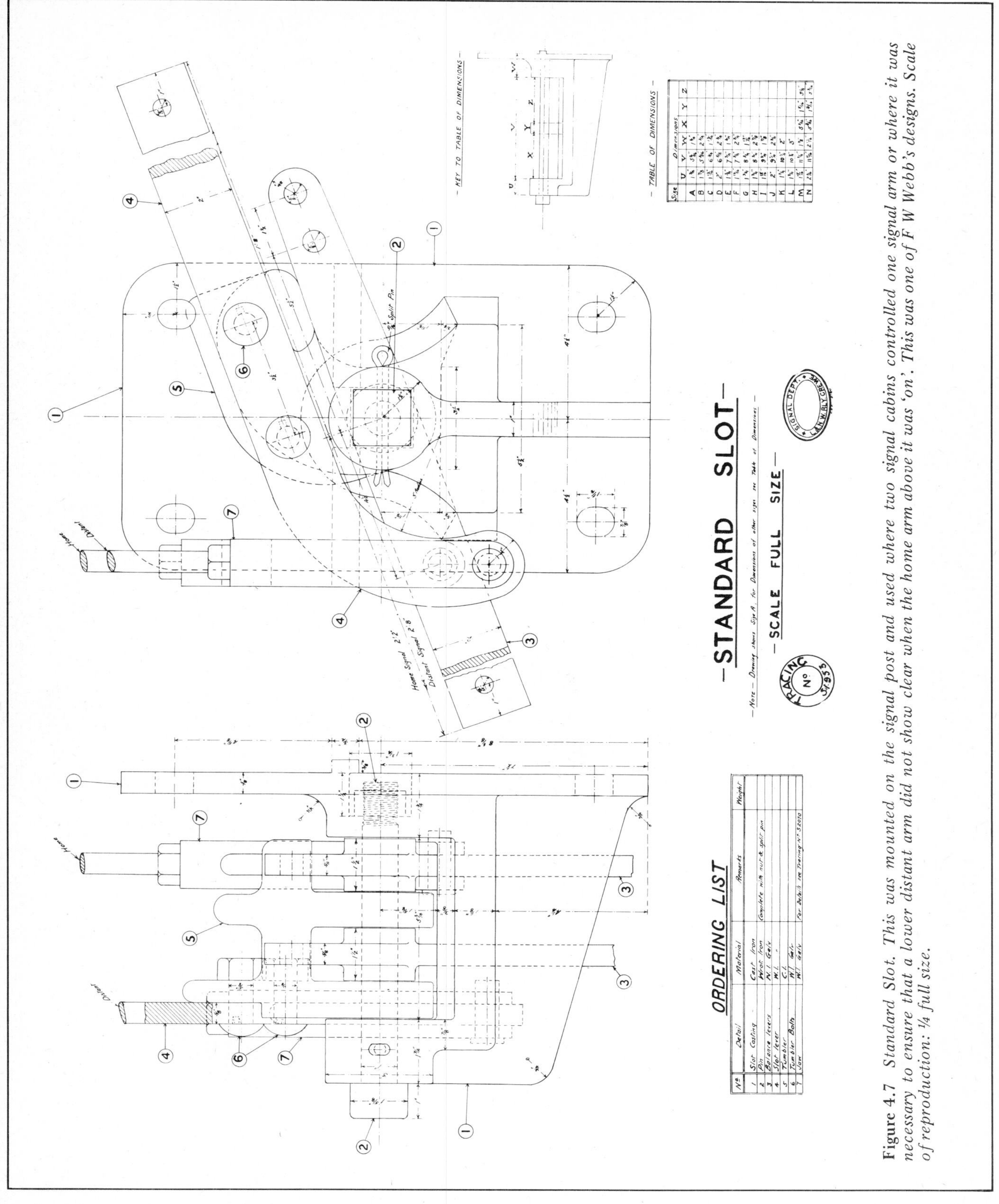

Figure 4.7 *Standard Slot. This was mounted on the signal post and used where two signal cabins controlled one signal arm or where it was necessary to ensure that a lower distant arm did not show clear when the home arm above it was 'on'. This was one of F W Webb's designs. Scale of reproduction: ¼ full size.*

expense of a little loss of sight to get them uniformly on the left hand side of the road to which they apply. In every case where there is difficulty give full details on the sighting form.'

As indicated by the instruction there were problems in applying the rule in practice. In addition to obstructions, the view forward from the cab of a steam locomotive was considerably restricted, particularly on right hand bends, adding to the problem of good signal sighting, while on left hand bends lineside features could restrict the sight of signals. Here improvement could sometimes be obtained by placing the signal on the right hand side of the line so that it could be seen by the driver as the locomotive

Plate 4.8 *This photograph, taken from inside Canada Dock Tunnel in the 1930's, shows a neat solution of the problem of lack of space in the deep cuttings at Atlantic Dock Junction, Liverpool, the signal arms for both lines being mounted on the same post. The arm facing the camera was placed low down on the post so that it could be seen from inside the tunnel. The junction signals, visible in the background, have had to be suspended from a gantry in order to get them as low as possible so that they could be seen by the driver of a train approaching through the tunnel.*

Photo: D Ibbotson

rounded the curve. When an engine approached close to such a signal it would, of course, be obscured from the driver's sight but if it was necessary to stop at it the fireman could watch it if required. A number of signals were, therefore, to be found positioned on the wrong side of the line because of site conditions, but they were exceptions. Another reason for siting signals on the wrong side of the line was to economise on signal posts. By placing the signal arms for both directions on the same post savings in cost could be made. This practice was common all over the line in early times but largely died out on the main lines with renewals and the increasing complexity of layouts. The practice continued on the branch lines where the economies were sensible and with limited traffic there was little chance of misunderstanding. Examples of this practice were still to be found in BR days.

On double track lines it is well known that the inner rails were placed a nominal six feet apart (the six foot way). With the construction of additional running lines, particularly the third, and later fourth, lines at the south end of the main line it was natural to place these at a similar distance from the existing tracks. This saved on formation width but caused problems in that signals, water columns and other objects could not be placed between the tracks. The arrangement was also a source of danger to staff examining and dealing with freight trains standing in sidings and loop lines adjacent to running lines. The signal department strongly advocated the provision of a ten foot space between additional running lines and the main lines to enable the signal posts to be placed in the spaces. The space between loop and other subsidiary lines was soon increased to allow for these factors wherever possible. In due course the Board of Trade incorporated a requirement that additional lines were to be spaced further from existing tracks in their requirements for passenger lines. On the sections of main line, particularly Euston to Bletchley, which were widened before these rules came into force the tracks remained close together. Of course, they could not be easily altered and much of the line is still like this today. It presented a problem for the signal engineers in that the signal posts could not be placed adjacent to the inner running lines. Rather than resort to the use of many expensive gantries the distinctive arrangements of placing both fast and slow line signals together on one side of the line, illustrated in **Figure 4.10** was resorted to. Not all signals were laid out in this manner, however, and **Figures 4.10** and **5.10** show some alternative arrangements.

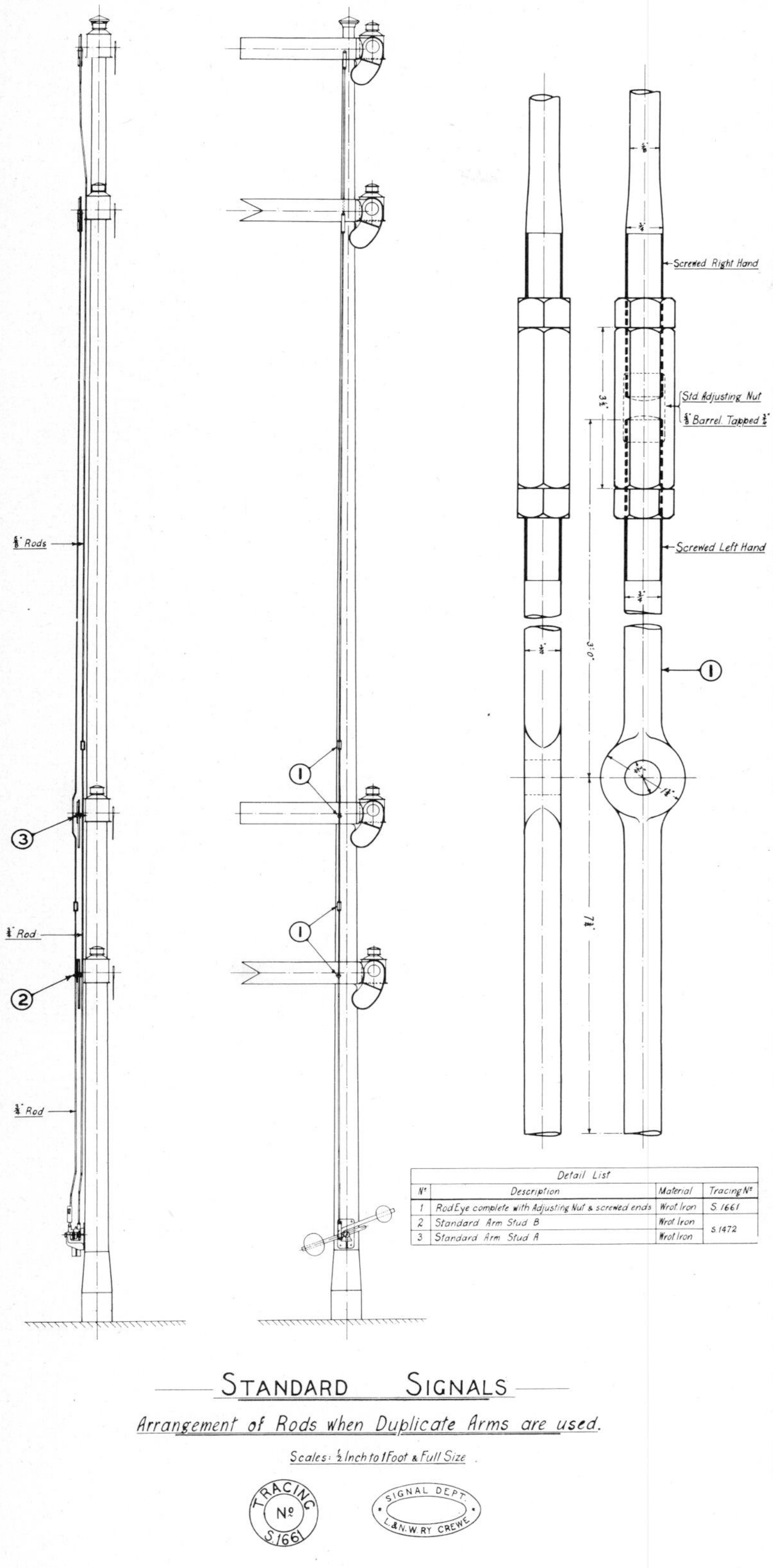

While bracket signals with several arms usually denoted diverging routes ahead, the presence of two straight post signals side by side, as shown in **Figure 4.10**, did not always apply to two parallel lines. Two straight post signals could also be used in place of a bracket at a junction where they would both apply to the same line (**Figure 4.11**). In some cases the arm applying to the less important, or low speed route would be placed lower than the arm for the main route (Chapter 5). The use of straight post junction signals was quite common in LNW days.

As can be seen from the illustrations the position of the signal ladder varied somewhat from signal to signal. This was caused partly by changes in practice from time to time and partly by conditions imposed by the location of the particular signal. A memo from Mr Thompson to his Inspectors dated 3rd September 1883, shortly after the introduction of the standard signals stated:—

> 'I have arranged for the ladder of all single signal posts to be fixed at the back of the post directly under the lamp bracket. Have you any suggestions on this?'

A memo dated 2nd October, 1901 marks the introduction of the familiar and distinctive arrangement of the ladder extending over the top of the post:—

> 'You will notice that in the signals we are sending out the ladder goes over the cap and before we finally decide on this form of ladder, I should like to know what the men who light the lamps think of them, or is the old pattern better?'

Two ladders were provided on some signals to give access to lower or subsidiary arms, elevated balance weights

Detail List

Nº	Description	Material	Tracing Nº
1	Rod Eye complete with Adjusting Nut & screwed ends	Wrot. Iron	S. 1661
2	Standard Arm Stud B	Wrot. Iron	S. 1472
3	Standard Arm Stud A	Wrot. Iron	

STANDARD SIGNALS

Arrangement of Rods when Duplicate Arms are used.

Scales: ½ Inch to 1 Foot & Full Size

TRACING Nº S.1661

SIGNAL DEPT. L.&N.W.RY CREWE

Figure 4.8 *This drawing shows how the push rods were arranged on a signal fitted with co-acting or duplicate arms. An adjuster screw was provided to ensure that both arms would operate correctly together. Scale of reproduction: 1/8″ to 1 foot and ¼ full size (1:96 and 1:4).*

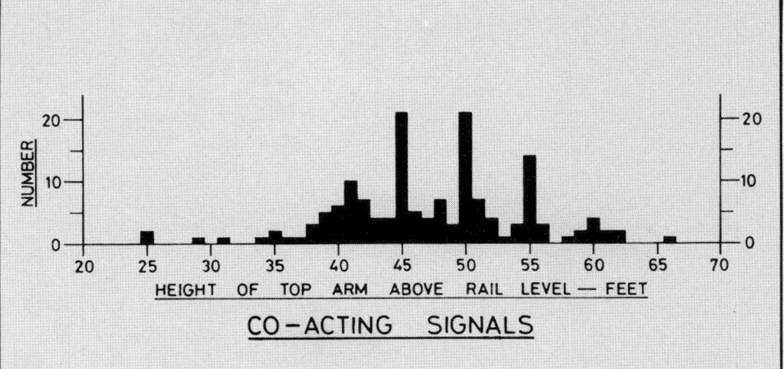

Figure 4.9 *Chart showing the heights of some co-acting signals on the LNWR. This includes stop and distant signals and combined stop signals with lower distants. The height was measured from rail level to the topmost arm. The tallest signal found was one of 66 feet at Kilsby and Crick, although it is said that they could, occasionally, be found at up to 80 feet in height.*

Plate 4.9 *A pair of co-acting distant signals in Tring Cutting, photographed in December 1936. This illustrates the practice adopted on the old sections of multiple track line of placing the fast and slow line signals together on one side of the formation (see* **Figure 4.10***) and the taller signal applied to the fast line. Note how the two posts are braced together with horizontal bars to give additional rigidity. Just in front of the left hand post is a fogman's hut, this also 'fogged' the slow line by means of a 'Woodhead' fog machine. The timber covering to the track for this can be seen between the running lines.*

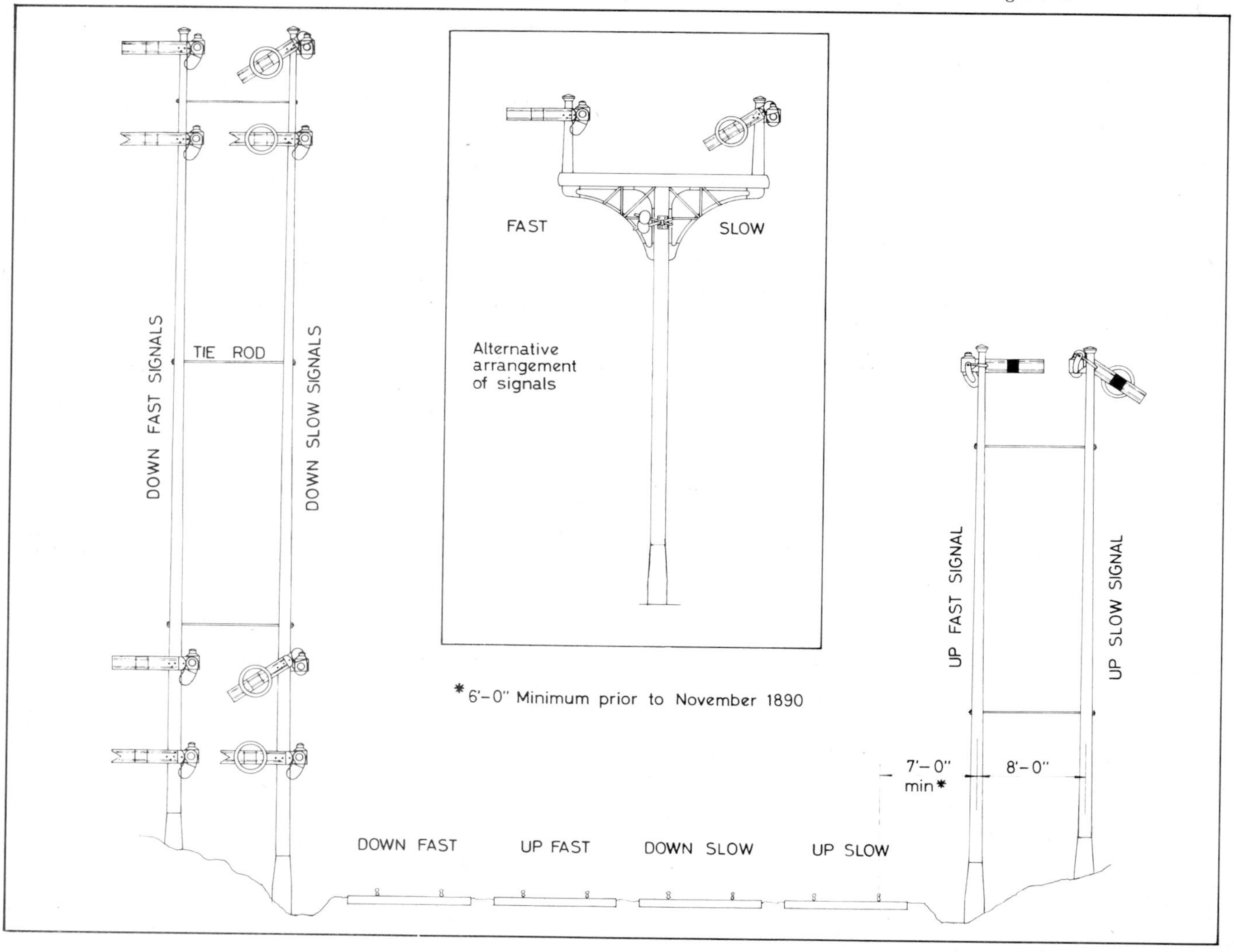

DOWN FAST SIGNALS
TIE ROD
DOWN SLOW SIGNALS
FAST
SLOW
Alternative arrangement of signals
UP FAST SIGNAL
UP SLOW SIGNAL
* 6'–0" Minimum prior to November 1890
7'–0" min*
8'–0"
DOWN FAST
UP FAST
DOWN SLOW
UP SLOW

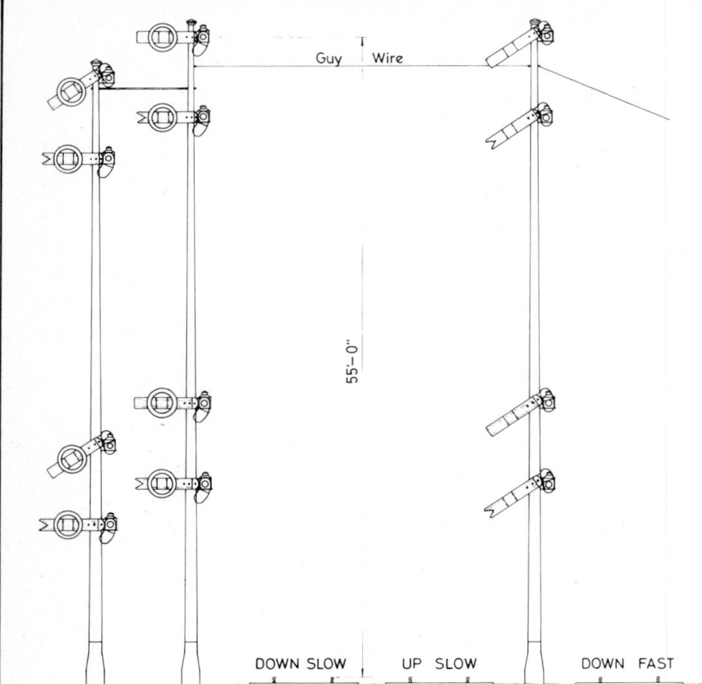

Figure 4.11 *Sketch showing the down home signals at Skew Bridge signal cabin, near Preston. This shows an alternative arrangement of signals on a quadruple track section where there was space for a signal between the running lines. The sketch also illustrates the use of separate posts for diverging junction signals. The signal on the left applied to moves from the Down Slow to Down Loop Line, while that next to it applied to moves along the Down Slow. Note that the Slow and Fast line signals were of the same height. Scale of reproduction: 1.5 mm to 1 foot (1:203).*

Figure 4.10 *On some quadruple sections of line there was insufficient room between the tracks for the posts. This sketch shows some typical arrangements adopted for the signals. Layouts of this type were used in preference to gantry signals, although such an approach would have allowed the signal arms to be placed near to the tracks they referred to. Gantries were only used where absolutely necessary. The signals on the left apply to the up lines and are of the co-acting type with combined home and distant arms. Rings are affixed to the Slow Line arms to assist the drivers in recognising the signals which apply to them. Advantage was usually taken of the fact that the signal posts were side by side to tie them together with steel rods to give additional stability. On the right, the Down Line signals are not so tall and have top arms only. In some instances there was insufficient space at the side of the line for two signal posts to be placed side by side, and a bracket signal would sometimes be used (as shown inset). This situation arose in a number of places when the 'New' line to Watford was constructed. Several signals of the type shown in the main drawing had to be replaced with brackets. The use of bracket signals with arms applying to parallel lines was not common practice, and the presence of a bracket signal with several arms normally signified the existance of a junction ahead. Bracket signals could occasionally be found as starting signals from adjacent platforms at a station. The seven feet minimum distance required between signal posts and the nearest rail was worked to as far as possible but could not be maintained in all cases (particularly where signal posts were between the tracks). Scale of reproduction: 2 mm to 1 foot (1:152).*

Plate 4.10 *Surrounded on all sides by coal wagons, where else could this signal be but in South Wales? The home signal for Blaenavon Furnace Sidings cabin has been combined with the fixed distant signal for the next cabin, on a short post sited part way up the cutting slope. The distant still has its large LNW circular lamp housing although the lamp for the home arm has a more modern small size case. Corrosion seems to have well and truly set in on the home arm by the time this photograph was taken in 1961! Amongst the weeds at the foot of the post is a rotating disc shunting signal with LMS circular enamel faces. This signal gave advance warning that the train was being diverted to the down and up loop and illustrates the practice of providing disc signals for this type of move rather than a full size or subsidiary arm (see Chapter 7).*

Photo: G H Platt

and other fittings. They were also necessary to give access to both the front and back of route indicating and banner signals.

In addition to the standard size signal arms miniature or shortened arms could also be provided. These were used on main lines where clearances were limited, short arms placed closer together often being necessary to obtain the best sight. Small arms were also used for subordinate lines and routes.

Comments have been published on a number of occasions over the years about the shallow angle many LNW signal arms seemed to work to in the 'Off' position and it has even been suggested that it was a fault with the design of the signals and apparatus. In fact the signals were designed so that adjustments for everyday use would not need to be too

Plate 4.11 *It was not always possible to fit the standard five foot arms onto the signals due to space restrictions. This photograph shows a signal at Warrington (Bank Quay) Low Level in 1962 which has been cramped into the narrow space between the tracks and the boundary wall, the short wooden arm just clearing the coping stones! The clip secured to the left hand end of the arm is provided to prevent the thin timber from splitting. This signal is obviously something of a lash-up since it is mounted on the bottom of what had been a much taller post (possibly from elsewhere) which is thus too large for the cast iron cap! The use of a wide post has caused the spectacle plate to have to be mounted further over than normal (to line up with the lamp). Since the arms were not always at the top of the post, the fixing between arm and spectacle was made adjustable for this purpose and the adjustment slot is visible here between the arm and top spectacle glass (see* **Figure 4.2**). *The signal is controlled by two cabins (the two wires can be seen below the balance levers) and is worked via a 'slot' so that the arm will only come 'off' when both cabins have pulled their signal levers. When the photograph was taken one of the signalmen had reversed his signal lever to clear the signal but the lever in the second cabin is still normal maintaining the arm in the 'on' position. Reversing the latter lever would allow the balance lever connected to the signal arm to fall and so lower the signal. The chain fastened to the weight on the right was provided to prevent it falling if it became detached from the lever. These retaining chains will be seen in a number of the illustrations and were normally provided where there was a risk of injury or damage in the event of their falling. Below the balance levers are a couple of electric contact boxes provided to detect the positions of the various levers. Mounted on top of the lamp casing is the expander contact box for the lamp repeater. The object in the 'V' between the lower spectacle and arm is the arm stop and is provided to prevent the arm moving above the horizontal position.*

Photo: G H Platt

critical and consequently a wide range of angles of the arms in the 'Off' position were permitted. A signal was regarded as showing an adequate 'Off' indication when it was 29 or more degrees below the horizontal, the lamp then being completely behind the green glass. At the other extreme the angle of the arm could be as great as 70 degrees. Most other companies required their signals to fall to at least 35 degrees before they were considered to be showing an adequate 'Off' indication. As far as practicable, LNW signals would be adjusted to work to an angle of between 35 and 50 degrees. It may be worth mentioning that many railway photographs were taken on warm sunny days when the wires could well have become slack.

To compensate for the fairly shallow angle allowed for the 'Off' position of the arm, the tolerances at the 'On' position were fairly stringent and the arm had to be within 3½ degrees of horizontal. The LNW signal arm contact box used in conjunction with the Fletcher arm and light repeater was adjusted to give an 'On' indication between horizontal and a 3½ degree drop and 'Off' at 29 degrees and beyond. The repeater showed 'Wrong' for angles between 3½ and 29 degrees.

DISTANT SIGNALS

Originally, working distant signals were provided for practically all routes from main lines. This included routes leading to terminal platforms or bays and goods lines. A Board Minute of March 1876 records approval of a recommendation of the Company's Officers:—

> 'Stations having facing points leading to passenger bays and goods loops to be provided with separate distant signals to indicate to the drivers of approaching trains whether the points are set for the main line or loop.'

Indeed this practice was required by the Board of Trade. In later years it was recognised that where the signals applied to low speed routes there was a risk of drivers taking the clear distant too literally and proceeding too fast.

The fixed distant signal was introduced for use on low speed routes and, as its name implies, was only capable of showing a danger (caution) aspect. It was realised that there was little point in having several 'splitting' distants of the fixed type in rear of diverging routes so a single distant arm was often provided. This could be working or fixed: if it worked it could usually be cleared for the main or highest speed route only. When the road was set for another direction it would remain at caution. In this case the driver, of course, would not know whether the signals ahead were at danger or if the signal was clear for a diverging route. He thus had to bring his train speed down to allow him to stop at the home signals if necessary. If the signal was clear it ensured that the train was travelling slowly enough to negotiate the junction safely.

The idea of only providing a distant signal for the main route was later incorporated in revised Board of Trade rules. About 1905 the LNW began removing distant signals applying to low speed divergences, a process which was accelerated after an accident at Ditton Junction in September 1912, and by the beginning of the first World War few remained. A number of photographs taken after this time show bracket signals in use with 'empty' dolls where the splitting distant arm had been removed. Not all 'splitting' distants were removed however. This applied particularly where the junction layout allowed reasonable speeds over more than one route. They were retained in some instances where a slow or running loop line commenced. The provision of a working distant applying from the main line to the subsidiary line enabled the driver of a train to approach the junction at a higher or more steady speed knowing the line ahead was clear. This allowed the train to clear the main line for following traffic much more quickly and it could reduce the margins between trains by several minutes. In some cases the distant signals were fixed at danger and the policy of stepping the arms of signals at junctions to distinguish more clearly between main and subsidiary routes was extended.

At large stations it had been common practice, at least for the main routes, to provide working distant signals throughout. It was realised that this was an unnecessary complication and expense, in many places, since train speeds had, of necessity, to be low. It therefore became normal practice for new work not to provide working distant signals in these circumstances. The existing working distant signals were gradually altered to the fixed form. In late LMS and early BR days the practice was taken a stage further and many of the fixed distant arms were removed altogether. Preston and Chester Stations are examples of places where both these practices were carried out.

PAINTING OF SIGNALS

The signal arms were painted (later enamelled) bright red (two parts red lead plus one part vermilion) on the front face with a vertical white stripe. The back of the arms were white with a vertical black stripe. This treatment was applied to both home and distant arms.

Signal posts were generally painted white. Experiments were made from time to time in an attempt to find a more durable and cheaper material as this memo of December 1883 shows:—

> 'For the future paint all posts on your district white. I want you to use white lead for some of the posts and zinc silicate for others and assess the qualities of each.'

The experiments were terminated in May 1884 and the men instructed to use white lead in all future work. The foot of the post and the metal work (including balance weights and the signal spectacle and lamp casing) were painted brown, although red oxide seems to have been used in places, particularly in the earlier years. Guy posts were generally painted the same as for the signal posts, an instruction dated September 1886 stating:

> 'Painting guy posts; for the future paint these as for signal posts; with white tops and brown bottoms.'

The wrought iron brackets on bracket and gantry signals were painted a stone colour. From the late 1880's new brackets were sent out from the works galvanised and were not painted. Once the galvanizing began to break down

Plate 4.12 *Where short arms were provided on signals with more than one arm these were placed much closer together than they were on full sized signals. An example of this arrangement is shown here, photographed at Oxford Road in 1956. The distant arm here has been made 'fixed' at danger by the simple expedient of not providing a push rod and balance lever! Note that the green glass is still provided in the spectacle. This type of fixed distant was preferred in later practice since the arm is indistinguishable from a working one and so encouraged the driver to take notice of it. They could become familiar with fixed signals and become complacent about their meaning. The weight on the balance lever bears the manufacturer's name, Railway Signal Company, Liverpool. This firm of signalling contractors supplied a good deal of their standard signalling equipment to the Manchester South Junction and Altrincham Railway in pre-grouping days (see Chapter 17).*
Photo: T Horn

Plate 4.13 *This photograph shows a short signal post, at Denton, practically filled with short signal arms. The fixing holes for the 'Slow line' rings can just be seen in the arms. The lower two arms do not have back blinders for the lamps since they face the cabin; the distant signal lamp has a detector (pyrometer), however, and the insulator for the wire is just above the arm. This arm was worked by Denton Junction and applied to the signal shown in* **Plate 5.3.** *Angle cranks, rather than pulley wheels, are provided here to transmit the drive from the signal wires to the balance levers. The godfathering of the post is a noticeable feature.*
Photo: G K Fox

Plate 4.14 *This signal probably represents the ultimate in short arms. It is cramped between the tracks at Holyhead and acts as the starting signal from platforms 2 and 3 (the track on its right). If the arm was any longer it would foul the loading gauge for the left hand track and if it was any higher it would not be visible under the road bridge!*

and rusting started the brackets were painted as before. The iron gantries were treated in a similar way to bracket signals.

A few variations occurred with time: in some cases black was substituted for the brown. The iron brackets varied somewhat in colouring some being turned out in black and others brown, while in later years some were found painted white like the signal post itself. The iron gantries were, occasionally, painted black or grey. A few signals received special finishes, for example, at the request of the Earl of Lichfield several signal posts in the vicinity of Shugborough Park (between Colwich and Milford & Brocton) were painted green.

Rotating disc signals had a red 'stop' face, the remainder of the ironwork was normally painted brown. One of the remaining faces of the disc was often painted white to assist the signalman in seeing the position of the disc, this being arranged so that it could be seen with the signal 'Off'. An instruction dated September 1883 stated:

> 'New pattern ground discs; please paint one side white so that when the signal is pulled off the white face can be seen by the signalman.'

In LMS and BR days the colouring of the signals remained much the same except that black was generally substituted for the old brown. Commencing in January 1929 distant signal arms began to be painted yellow with a black chevron on the front face and white with a black chevron on the back, with a yellow glass substituted for the red in the spectacle. This change was carried out gradually and took some years to complete.

Plate 4.15 *In sidings and loop lines the old practice of stacking the arms for diverging routes on one post continued and this photograph shows a set of four arms on one post applying to the Down Slow line at Edgeley Junction No. 1. Speeds were generally low on such lines and this arrangement was acceptable; it was also a useful space saver in crowded areas and reduced installation costs into the bargain! Where arms were 'stacked' like this a standard 'top and left' rule applied. The top arm referred to the route on the furthest left, the next arm to the next furthest route and so on, the bottom arm reading to the route on the furthest right. The number of arms provided would, of course, vary with the number of routes available. This signal is the slow line equivalent of that shown in* **Plate 5.14** *and clearly demonstrates the advantage of this type of arrangement to the Signal Engineer! The photograph was taken in 1953 while preparations were being made to replace the signal with a new structure.*

Photo: G H Platt

Plate 4.16 *The problems of traffic working in war time are quite well known. What is perhaps not generally appreciated was the effect of war on the activities of the Engineer's Departments. The first world war (as did the second) cut off supplies of imported timber, particularly that from the Baltic, which was used extensively by the railways. This caused a general shortage and since many Companies used timber for their signal posts there were problems when signals needed renewal or new work had to be carried out. A number of Companies, therefore, experimented with alternative materials at about this time. An obvious choice was steel, already used extensively on some lines and several Companies, including the LNW, tried reinforced concrete.*

This very nice example of an LNW concrete post signal stood at Gwyddelwern and was photographed in 1961. The arms for both directions are mounted on the same post, a sensible economy measure at such a small station. At a crossing station on a single line, however, the fouling points for up and down lines are in different positions. Placing both arms on the same post means that only one can be sited at its fouling point. A train for the other direction had to stop at the fouling point rather than at the signal, a continuance of a very old practice. Signals could also be placed in advance of the fouling point (usually points and lift bars) because of the limitations of the site and the need to allow trains to draw up as far as possible in short platforms. The points at Gwyddelwern were worked by the key system described in Chapter 11 and the levers with their key lock can be seen near the foot of the signal post. Since the points are worked locally no lift bar is provided with the facing point lock bolt.

Photo: G H Platt

Chapter Five Bracket Signals

Plate 5.1 *This close up photograph, taken about 1935, shows a balanced two doll bracket signal which stood on the platform at Buxton. The arrangement of the push rods can be seen clearly.*

Photo: G H Platt

Where a line split into two or more diverging routes or parallel lines, separate signal arms were provided for each route in order to give the driver advance information as to which way the points were set. The driver was expected to have sufficient route knowledge to know what speed limit (if any) applied to the line over which he was to travel. The clearest way of displaying the information to the driver was by placing the signal arms for each route side by side, the left hand signal arm applying to the route on the left and so on. While several posts side by side could be used to support the arms, a better solution was to use a bracket signal. This had the advantage of using less space on the ground, which was very important in many places due to restrictions in the width of land available. The bracket signal usually (but not always) had a single leg and so used little space at ground level. The structure was generally more economical in the use of timber and it brought the signal arms together in a distinctive group which aided recognition. There were, however, structural problems with large or unbalanced bracket signals and for this reason separate posts were sometimes provided.

The L&NWR philosophy of standardisation was put to work in the design of bracket signals and as a result there were just two standard designs of '1883' bracket signal, one for two dolls (S62) and one for three dolls (S61), both of which were developed directly from the 1876 standard designs. A larger form of the S61 signal bracket was made, if required, for large four doll brackets where the full seven foot spacing was provided between the dolls (**Figure 3.11** shows the 1876 version).

In the vast majority of cases LNW bracket signals were balanced. That is, the dolls were arranged more or less symmetrically about the centre line (although individually they were often of different heights), while the support post was positioned more or less on the centre line. Structurally a balanced bracket was a better proposition, being subject to less stress, and therefore tended to be more durable. They were also easier to construct, fix and maintain.

Unbalanced or handed brackets were relatively unusual and were only used in special cases. They were provided where sighting or space restrictions precluded the use of a straight post or standard bracket. The majority of such signals were found in large station and yard areas. Wherever possible the parts (brackets, flitches etc.) of the standard S61 and S62 signals were utilised in making up the signals. Suspended dolls could be produced by turning the appropriate parts upside down.

An obvious and distinctive feature of the bracket signals was the metal brackets used to give added support to the bracket timbers or flitches. These were not cast, as they were on the signals of most other companies, but were fabricated. This had two advantages, the fabrications were lighter than a casting, and so reduced the weight of the structure, making erection easier. They also presented less surface area than would be the case with castings of equivalent strength, and so reduced the effects of wind loading on the structure. The two types of metal brackets were used for practically all types of signal and

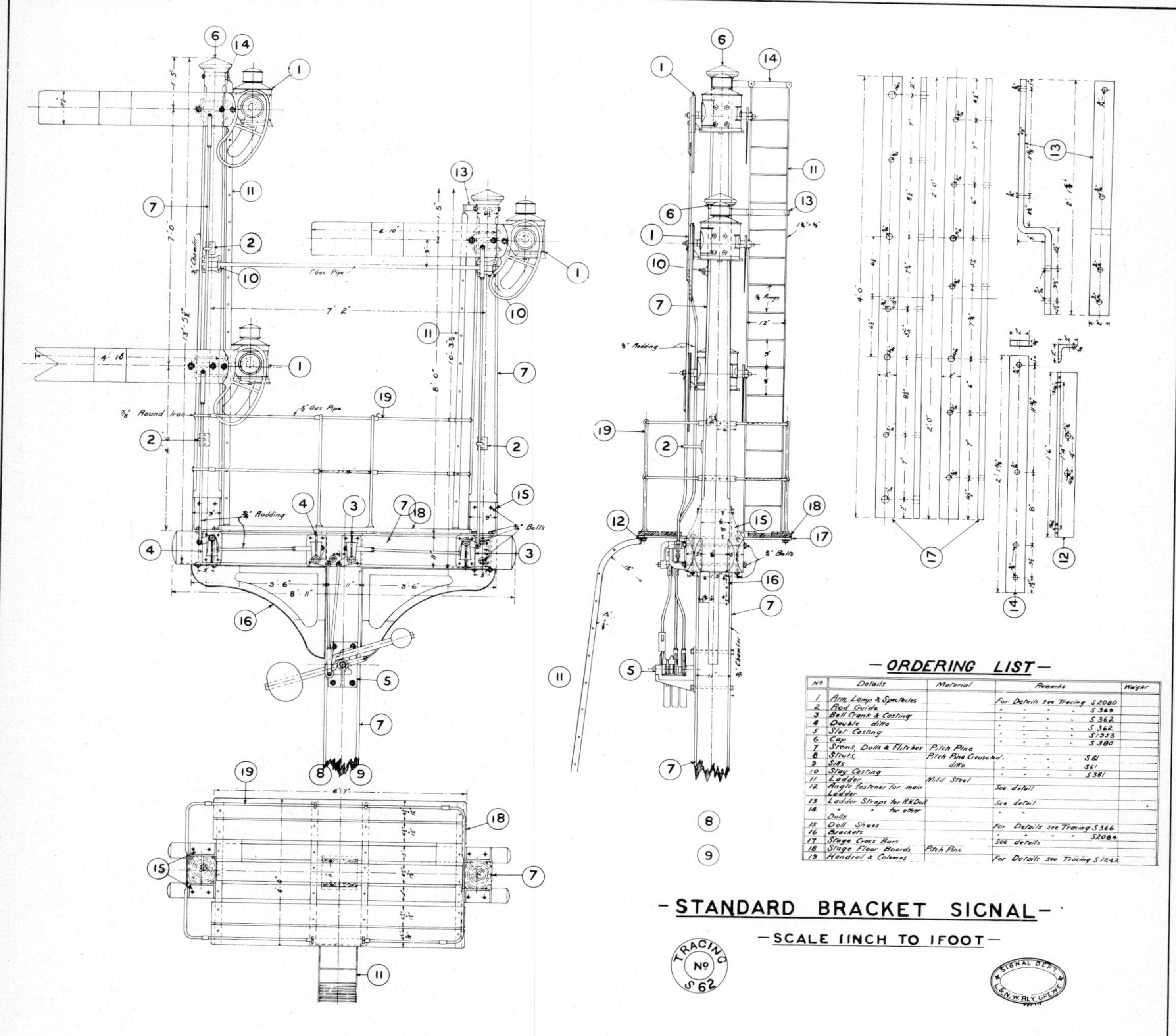

Figure 5.1 *Standard S62 Two-Doll Bracket Signal. The arrangement of the dolls and arms would, of course, vary to suit the location. This signal is a direct descendant of the old SK62 slotted post bracket, illustrated in* **Figures 3.5** *and* **3.10**. *This drawing shows the signal with the later style of handrailing, which was introduced in February 1913. Two horizontal rails of smaller diameter were used instead of one large one and the handrail columns altered. This type of handrailing would, normally, only be provided on new signals and few of the existing signals were altered. The old type of handrailing is shown in* **Figure 5.3**. *Scale of reproduction: ¼" to 1 foot (1:48).*

they even found use in stiffening the main beams or girders in the gantry signals.

ARRANGEMENT OF SIGNAL ARMS

In deciding on the arrangement of the signal arms to be adopted at a place where a number of arms were required together, a number of considerations had to be taken into account. First and foremost, the driver of a train should be able to get a good and clear sight, at an adequate distance, of all the arms (or lights) that applied to him. One stop arm was generally provided for each diverging route ahead (although ground discs or special forms of arm could be provided as described in Chapter 7), the arms being arranged in the same left to right sequence as the divergences. The heights of the arms relative to each other were varied to give an indication to the driver of the purpose and importance (or speed) of each route, the arms for the most important (or highest speed) routes being the highest. The basic LNW policy was to place all the arms for through passenger routes at the same height (see **Figures 5.8** and **6.3** and **Plate 7.10**) although the exact arrangement adopted depended on site and traffic consider-

(continued on page 62)

Plate 5.2 *A nice example of the S61 type of balanced bracket signal at Willesden No. 1. The tallest doll on the right denotes the most important route. Fixed distant signals are provided on the centre and right hand dolls while a call-on arm, of the later type, is mounted low down on the left hand one. The balance weights are placed high up on the main post to avoid injury to shunters and other staff. Note the arrangement of the guy wires at this restricted site, and the use of tie rods to give added rigidity between the dolls.*
Photo: British Rail

Figure 5.3 *Standard Three Doll Bracket Signal. It is a direct descendant of the original SK61 type. This drawing is dated November 1896 and shows the arrangement of single handrails used on bracket and gantry signals prior to 1913. Scale of reproduction: ¼" to 1 foot (1:48).* ▷

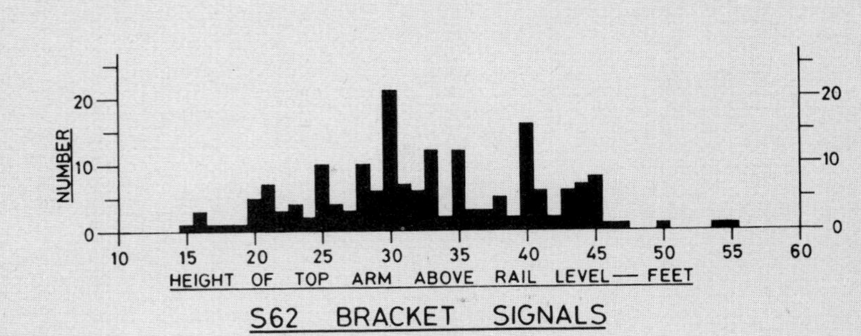

Figure 5.2 *Chart showing the heights of a selection of bracket signals of the S62 type. As can be seen, they were normally to be found with heights in a range of 20 to 45 feet. The information is taken from the same sample as used in the charts in Chapter 4, and gives an idea of the proportions of S62 brackets and straight post signals on the line.*

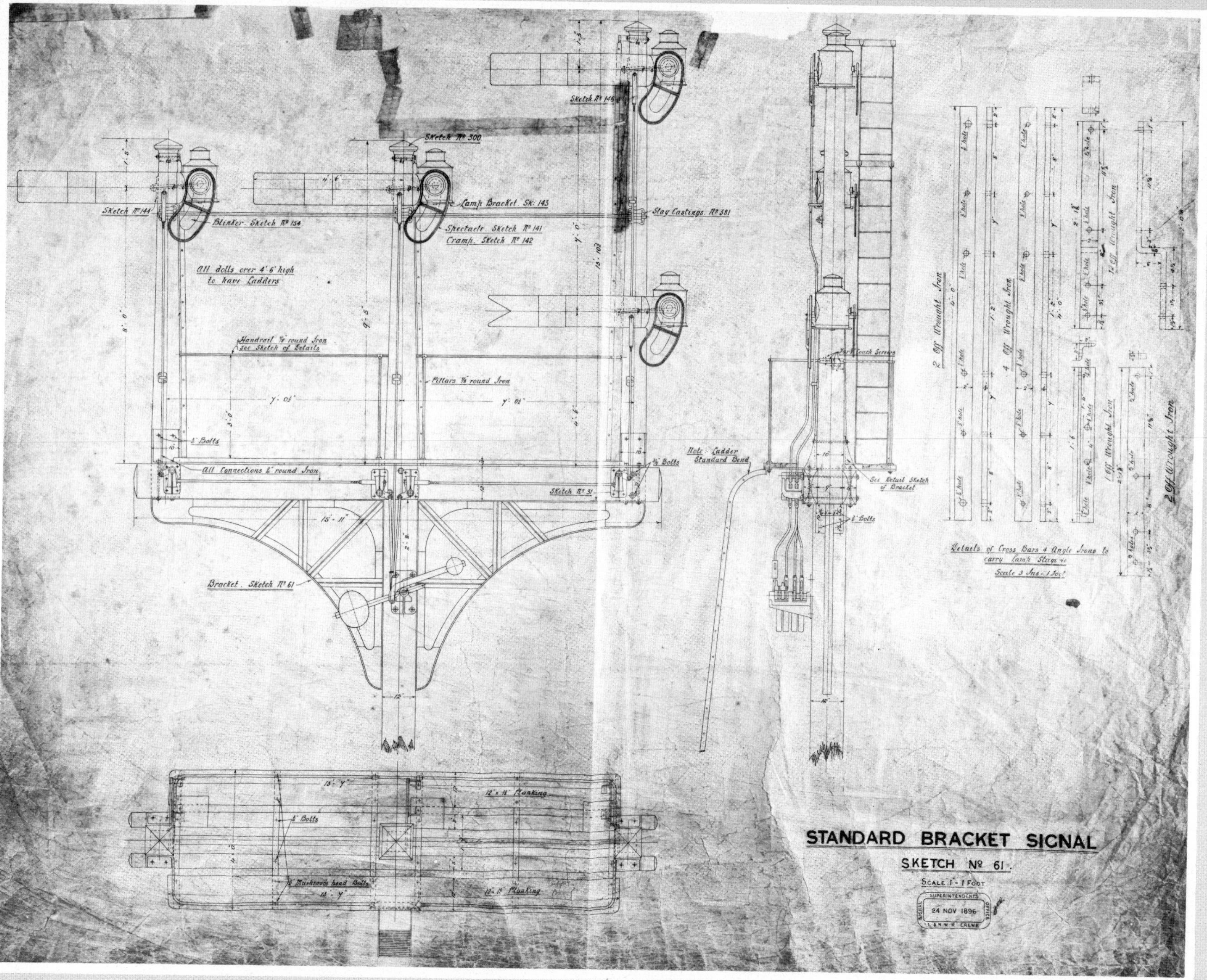
STANDARD BRACKET SIGNAL
SKETCH No 61.
SCALE 1" - 1 FOOT
SIGNAL SUPERINTENDENT'S OFFICE
24 NOV 1896
L. & N. W. R. CREWE
Sketch No 144
Blinker. Sketch No 154
Sketch No 300
Lamp Bracket. Sk: 143
Spectacle Sketch No 141
Cramp. Sketch No 142
Sketch No 145
Stay Castings. No 581
All dolls over 4' 6" high
to have Ladders
Handrail ¾" round Iron
see Sketch of Details
Pillars ¾" round Iron
All Connections 1" round Iron
Sketch No 31
Bracket. Sketch No 61
Note. Ladder
Standard Bend
See Detail Sketch
of Bracket
12" x 4" Planking
Mushroom head Bolts
2 Off Wrought Iron
4 Off Wrought Iron
1 Off Wrought Iron
Details of Cross Bars & Angle Irons to
carry Lamp Stage &c
Scale 3 Ins - 1 Foot

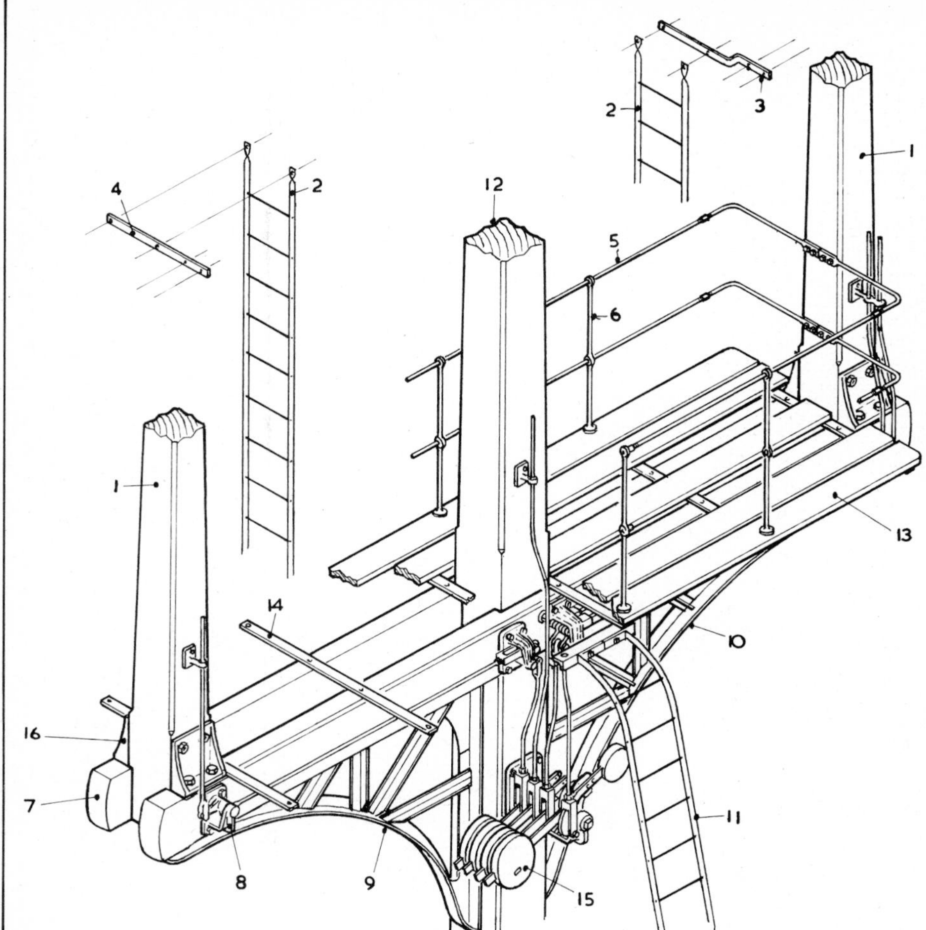

Figure 5.4 *Isometric view of a S61 Bracket Signal showing construction of the Brackets, Flitches and Platform. Also shown are the arrangements of the push rods and cranks used to transmit the drive for the arm from the main post to the dolls. Elevated balance levers are shown, these were used where clearances at ground level were restricted, or where low level levers could be a danger to staff or members of the public. There are push rods for two arms on the right hand doll, as seen here, and single push rods on the other two dolls.*

List of the Parts shown

1. *Doll*
2. *Doll ladder*
3. *Ladder strap (with ladder to the left of the post)*
4. *Ladder strap (with ladder to the right of the post)*
5. *Handrail*
6. *Handrail column*
7. *Flitch*
8. *Bell crank casting and pin*
9. *Left hand bracket*
10. *Right hand bracket*
11. *Standard ladder*
12. *Main post or stem*
13. *Stage floor boards*
14. *Stage cross support bars*
15. *Balance levers and slot mechanism*
16. *Doll shoe*

Drawing by J K Nelson

ations. Following the Ditton Junction accident in 1912 it was decided to 'step' (place at different heights) the arms of junction signals in order to further assist the drivers in distinguishing them. This policy was applied for new work and some of the existing signals were altered where this was thought to be desirable. For instance the slow line signals in **Figure 5.10** were stepped in 1914.

The second consideration was to create a clear and unmistakable pattern of arms (or lights) for the driver so that he could instantly pick out the signals which applied to him and the route he was to take. On occasions this resulted in the arms not being to the left of, or over, the line to which they applied.

The site of the signal would dictate the exact form it would take, space had to be found for the post(s), while the signal had to be in a position where the arms could be adequately seen as mentioned above, this consideration also determining the heights of the arms above rail level. While the signal would usually be placed just to the left of the running line it could be positioned elsewhere if space was restricted, or if a different position gave an appreciably better sight. As far as possible standard bracket signals would be used or, if necessary, (due to a particularly difficult site or a large number of arms to be accommodated) a gantry signal.

In some cases there was insufficient room for a satisfactory signal with full size arms and the full seven foot spacing between dolls. The sizes would then be reduced as necessary, the spacing of the dolls could be reduced to about 6′ 6″ without altering the arms, beyond this the length of the arm was reduced (standard sizes of 4′, 3′ 6″ and 3′ generally being used). Where shorter arms were used the vertical distance between stop and distant arms was reduced to a similar degree in order to preserve the proportions or look of the whole signal as will be seen in some of the photographs.

Plate 5.3 *Denton Junction in February, 1970. This three doll bracket has arms of equal height and controlled movements from the goods lines to the three diverging routes ahead. At the time the picture was taken the line to the right (the Hooley Hill Line) had been closed and the signal arm removed. The signal is placed on the 'wrong' side of the line and has been godfathered on both sides in order to extend its life. A wooden platform is provided to allow access to the balance weights.*

Plate 5.4 *A bracket signal with short arms at Preston photographed in 1946. This was sited at the north end of platform 2 and the left hand doll applied to movements to the Down Through line and the right hand doll to the Down Slow line. A disc signal for shunt moves is sited low down at the base of the post. Above it, the white object is an illuminated indicator reading 'Call-on to Cabin only' and refers to the call-on arm mounted on the left hand doll. It indicated that when the call-on arm showed a proceed aspect, drivers could draw forward as far as the signal cabin which can be seen in the background. Further instructions could then be given to the driver there. Both distant arms were fixed since train speeds in the area were low. Lamp indicator expander boxes can be seen on the lamps to the top arms.*

Plate 5.5 *Bracket signals were not always provided to accommodate multiple arms. They were sometimes used to improve sighting. The example in this photograph stood on Platform 8 at Carlisle. Here, the post was placed at the back of the platform so that it did not obstruct access to the trains. The arm has been mounted on a left hand bracket to bring it nearer to the line and enable it to be seen under the Victoria Viaduct. The signal was unusual in that the arm applied to movements to the down main via two different routes. One was forward along the Bay 8 line to a further signal which allowed long trains to use the Bay. Alternatively, the signal could apply to a move over a crossover just beyond the signal leading to the Bay 7 line and thence directly to the down main. Separate levers were provided for the two routes to simplify the interlocking and detection arrangements. Just in front of the signal can be seen a new colour light signal erected in preparation for the Carlisle Power Box. The signal has a hood and cross over the lenses to signify that it is not in use.*

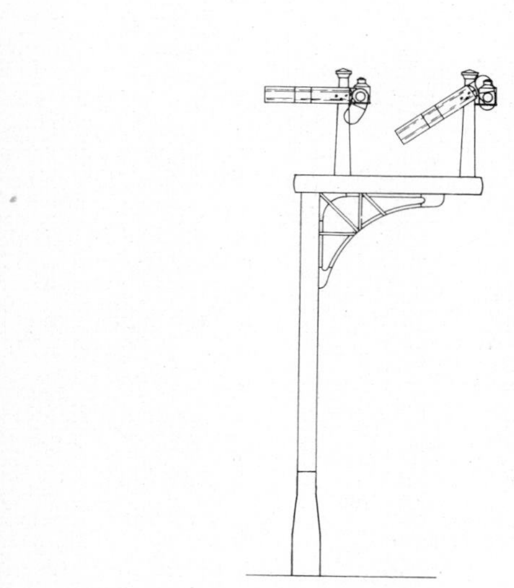

Figure 5.5 *The majority of LNW bracket signals were of the 'balanced' type with the dolls placed more or less symmetrically about the central main post. Unbalanced or handed brackets were only used where circumstances (usually difficult sighting) made this necessary. This sketch shows how a right hand two doll bracket could be produced by adapting the S61 type bracket. Scale of reproduction: 2 mm to 1 foot (1:152).*

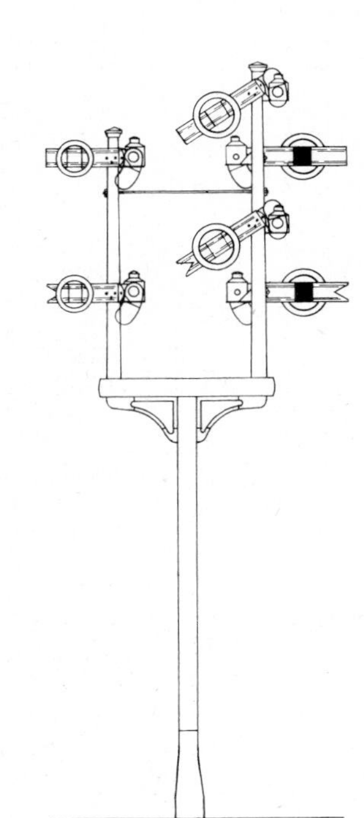

Figure 5.6 *The Up Slow home signal at Kings Langley No. 1, erected in 1906, had something of a Christmas tree air about it with arms bristling in all directions! The main arms (shown 'off') applied to the Up Slow line while the left hand, short, arms applied to trains from the Up Slow line to the Up Loop line, which extended to Watford Tunnel North End. The lower distant arms on these two signals were for that cabin. The arms on the far right were for the Down Slow line, the lower distant being for Kings Langley No. 2. Since all the arms applied to the Slow lines, they are all fitted with rings. Scale of reproduction: 2 mm to 1 foot (1:152).*

Plate 5.6 *A bracket signal on the Down Slow line at Hooton South photographed in 1972. The arrangement of the signal arms, brackets, handrails, ladder and guy wires can be seen. When this signal was erected, in connection with the widening of the line in 1902, a short doll with splitting distant arm was provided on the right hand side of the bracket. This applied to moves from the Slow to Fast lines at Hooton North cabin. In line with the policy of not providing distant signals for low speed movements, this arm was later removed. The home signal arm on the left hand doll was 36 feet 6 inches above rail level.*

Plate 5.7 *The LNW philosophy of laying out stations with very long platforms incorporating central crossovers to facilitate remarshalling of trains resulted in signals being required under the station roof at a number of places. This three doll bracket signal stood at the centre of Platform 6 at Preston. Again, short arms have been used to save space – there was no detriment to sighting since train speeds were very low – and fixed distant signals have been used for similar reasons. Call-on arms were included to assist in the work of joining and splitting trains and changing engines. The signals were worked from Preston No. 3 cabin and the left hand doll applied to moves to the East Lancs Loop. The middle doll signalled moves to the Platform 7 line and the right hand one to those straight along the Platform 6 line. The trolley loaded with pigeon baskets, the gas lights and LNW station signs give a period flavour to this 1950's photograph.*

Photo: British Rail

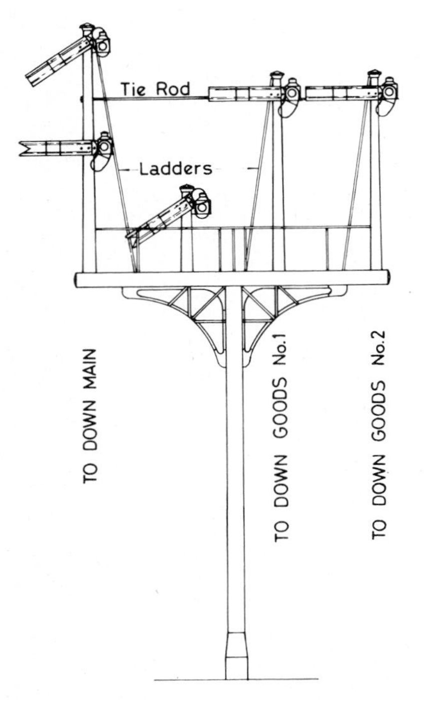

Figure 5.7 *The S61 three doll bracket could be adapted to produce a four doll signal by extending the flitches: to limit the loading and length the spacing of the dolls has been reduced slightly. Note how the dolls are arranged symmetrically to balance the structure and the arrangement of the doll ladders. This particular example was the down home signal at Old Oak Junction where the two additional goods lines diverged from the main line. The drawing illustrates the use of splitting distant signals. At the next cabin, Acton Wells Junction, there was a further divergence and the two distant arms apply to the junction signal there. The distant arm on the left hand doll applied to the main (N&SWJR) line to Acton. With the main line arm and the right hand distant off, as shown, the signal indicated that the signals were off at Acton Wells for a train to proceed onto the curve to the GW main line. Where a larger four doll bracket, with the full seven foot spacing between the dolls, was required larger brackets were used as shown in* **Figure 3.11**. *Scale of reproduction: 2 mm to 1 foot (1:152).*

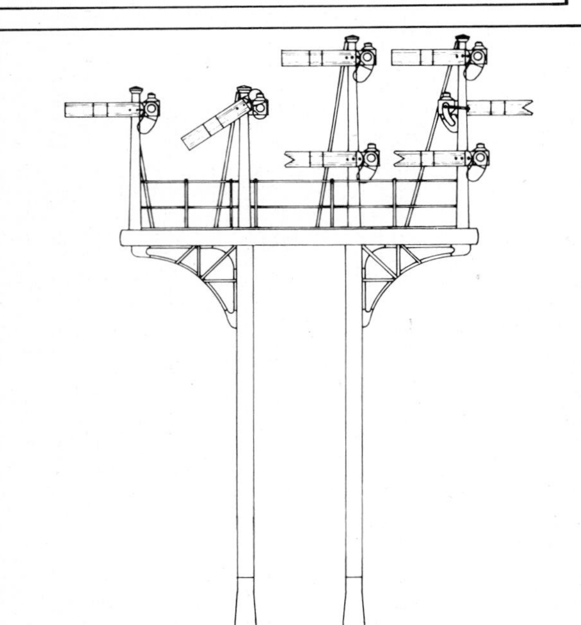

Figure 5.8 *Where space was available or a more substantial structure was required two main posts were provided as shown here. Once again the standard S61 brackets are used. This particular signal stood at Stafford No. 5 signal cabin as the Up Shropshire Union line home signals. The dolls applied (from left to right) to Bay Platform, to Up Platform, to Up Fast Line and to Up Slow Line. The separate distant arm on the right hand doll was the Down Distant signal for Stafford No. 7 cabin.* **Figure 6.8** *shows the matching up main line home signals protecting the same junction. Scale of reproduction: 2 mm to 1 Foot (1:152).*

Plate 5.8 *The signal in this view controlled exit for down trains from Platforms 3 and 4 at Preston. The bracket is supported on two posts which are extended upwards as the centre two dolls. The right hand doll has been extended downwards to accommodate the calling-on arm. By the use of small arms it has just been possible to squeeze the signal in between the tracks, a low signal being required for sight under the station roof. Two arms are provided for each platform to control movements to Down Slow (left) and Down Fast lines. Just behind the signal is the steel structure of the colour light signal which was to replace it. The view was taken in September 1959 and the signal illustrated in* **Plate 5.4** *can be seen in the background.*

Photo: M N Bland

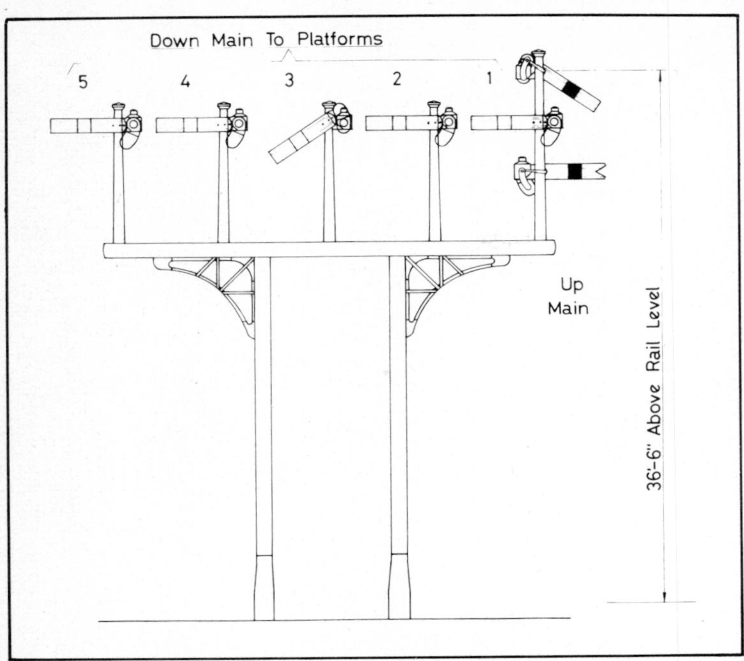

Figure 5.9 *A Five Doll Bracket Signal mounted on two posts. The S61 brackets are used and again the structure is 'balanced' to avoid undue loads or stresses. This example formed the down home signals at Llandudno (station) No. 2 cabin, and was known locally as 'Big Dobbin'. The five arms controlled entry into the station platforms, while the stop arm with lower distant on the right hand doll formed the Up Main Starter and No. 1 cabin Up Distant. Scale of reproduction: 2 mm to 1 foot (1:152).*

Plate 5.9 *An underslung or gallows bracket signal at Bangor No. 1 in September 1953. This arrangement, and the use of short arms, had been adopted in order to enable the arms to be placed as low as possible for sighting under the station canopies and footbridge. The signal is mounted on two posts, one of which has been continued above the flitches (horizontal cantilever beams) to support the tie rods. The fast line signals have been placed at a higher level to distinguish them from the platform line signals. Since the signals are suspended a separate access landing has been provided, to the arms and lamps, at low level. To the right of the photograph is Bangor No. 1 cabin, erected in 1924 (as were the signals) when the station was enlarged and altered. The signal in front of it, also fitted with short arms, controlled departure from the Bethesda Bay platform, which was added at that time.*

Photo: G H Platt

Plate 5.10 *This three doll bracket signal stood in the carriage sidings on the approach to Euston Station. It was worked by the 'Crewe' electric system, the solenoid motors for which can be seen on the dolls. The photograph, taken during cleaning and maintenance operations, illustrates clearly just how dirty signal arms could become in busy and polluted areas and how this could reduce the clarity of the signals, making the drivers job even more difficult than it was already.*
Photo: British Rail

Plate 5.11 *Naturally, some special signals were provided on occasion to suit circumstances. A particularly nice example was this small bracket attached to the front of the signal cabin at Dolau. The signal was erected in 1921 and a small access platform and ladder arrangement, from the cabin window, has been provided to give access to the signal lamp. Note the chain attached to the end of the balance lever, again provided for safety reasons.*
Photo: M Christensen

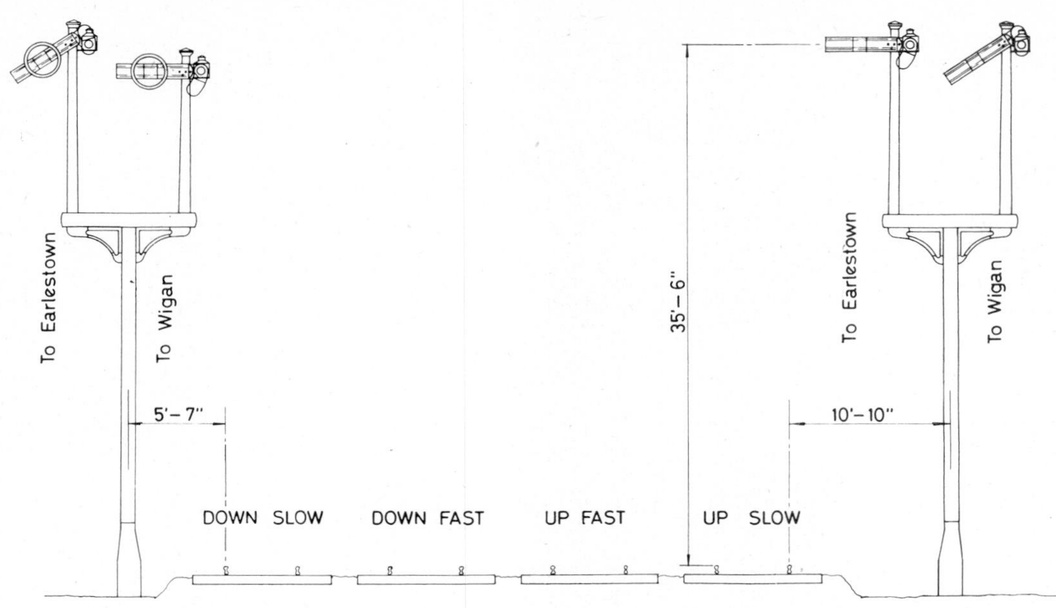

Figure 5.10 *This sketch shows two S62 signals controlling a junction on a four track main line. This example was the Down home signals for Winwick Junction where the quadruple line diverged into two double track lines. The drawing illustrates a different solution to the problem of where to put the signal posts when there were a number of parallel lines (see also* **Figures 4.10** *and* **4.11***). This arrangement was quite common on the multiple track sections of line in the Wigan and Warrington areas. The sketch also shows an alternative way of setting out the tracks, these are paired by direction while those in* **Figure 4.10** *are paired by use. It should be noted, however, that the arrangement of the signals was interchangeable and the layouts shown in both figures could be found on lines arranged in the other way. It will be seen that the arms on the Fast Line bracket are placed at the same height, and the Slow Line arms are fitted with rings. Scale of reproduction: 2 mm to 1 foot (1:152).*

Plate 5.12 *Restricted clearances were always a problem for the Signal Engineer. The deep rock cuttings and tunnels necessary to reach the Liverpool Docks were especially difficult. This view, in the cutting leading from Alexandra Dock Station, shows a bracket signal at the entrance to the No. 2 tunnel and is taken from the portal of No. 1 tunnel. The problems of signal sighting can readily be appreciated here. Not only do the arms become dirty and merge into the background, but they have to be seen by the driver in the short distance available after emerging in a swirl of smoke and steam from the first tunnel. A fogman's hut and brazier can be seen a few yards in advance of the signal. To obtain sufficient clearance the rock has been cut away to accommodate it, even so, the hut is diminutive in size and the spartan facilities available to the fogman can be appreciated.*

Photo: D Ibbotson

Plate 5.13 *A S61 type bracket signal fitted with arms applying to both the up and down lines. The stop signal facing the camera is the Up Starting signal at Pontllanfraith with lower distant arm for Blackwood No. 2. The arms with their backs to the camera are the Down Outer Home signals for Pontllanfraith and provided drivers with advance information of their route at the junction ahead (which was protected by the next signal). As seen in this view the left hand arm reads to Bird-in-Hand West GWR, the middle arm to the branch siding and the right hand arm to the LNW line to Tredegar Junction Lower. The centre doll seems to have been altered at some time. The photograph was taken in August 1954.*

Photo: G H Platt

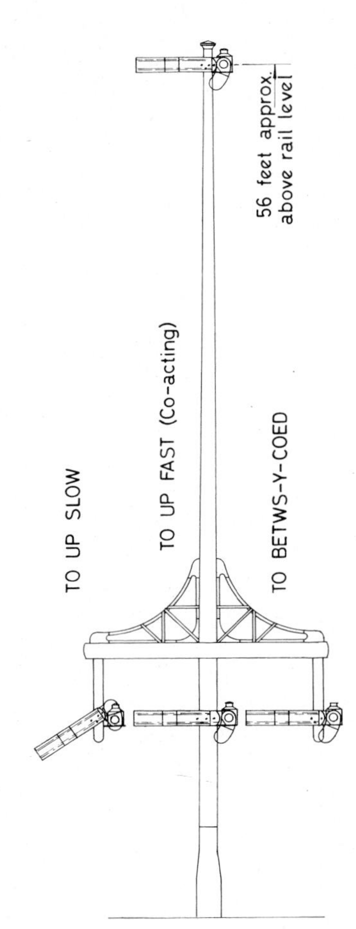

Figure 5.11 *An alternative form of Tall Junction Signal. This one stood at the end of the Up Fast platform at Llandudno Junction and was controlled from No. 1 cabin. It was the up fast home signal and a distant sight was required of the main arm (reading along the up fast) above the station buildings and footbridge, and a high arm was provided with a lower co-acting arm for close sighting. The other two routes were low speed divergences and thus an early sight was not necessary and low level arms only were provided. In order to give a good sight under the station canopy the three low level arms were placed as low as possible and suspended from an 'upside down' S61 type bracket. The drawing shows the routes the arms applied to. This signal was erected in 1897 in connection with the enlargement of the station. Scale of reproduction: 2 mm to 1 foot (1:152).*

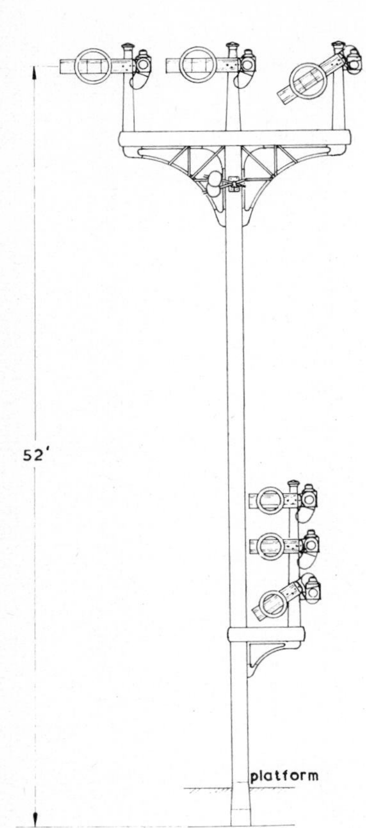

Figure 5.12 *Junction Signals at Ditton Junction No. 1. Here high arms were required to give the drivers a distant sight over the station buildings and road overbridge. For close sighting lower arms were necessary, and because of the restricted space and sight, they were mounted one above the other on a bracket. The 'top and left' rule applied to these arms as is illustrated by the pair shown 'off'. Note the use of short arms at the lower position where space was limited and a distant sight was not required. Scale of reproduction: 2 mm to 1 foot (1:152).*

Plate 5.14 *A co-acting bracket signal at Edgeley Junction No. 1 is illustrated here. The large top arms, which were about 50 feet above rail level, were duplicated by low level short arms on suspended dolls. A subsidiary post has been provided behind the main one to give the structure stiffness and strength. As can be imagined, the overturning moment of a large signal like this could be considerable. The arrangements of the access ladders and platforms are worthy of study. The local staff often had affectionate names for the big signals. This one was known as 'Long Tom', while the co-acting up fast home signal at Lancaster No. 3 was known locally as 'Big Bertha'. The co-acting bracket at Edgeley was the Down Fast Home Signal, the nearest arm applying to trains continuing along the Fast Line. The middle arms referred to movements to the Down Slow and the other arm to moves to the No. 1 Down Through Siding. A co-acting signal was required to give an early sight above some overbridges and the lower arms for nearer sight under them. The signal was placed between the Up Slow and Fast lines to assist in sighting. When this photograph was taken in August 1953, preparations were being made to replace it and parts of the new signal gantry can be seen in the background. The new signal was provided with banner repeaters in rear of it to assist in sighting.*

Photo: G H Platt

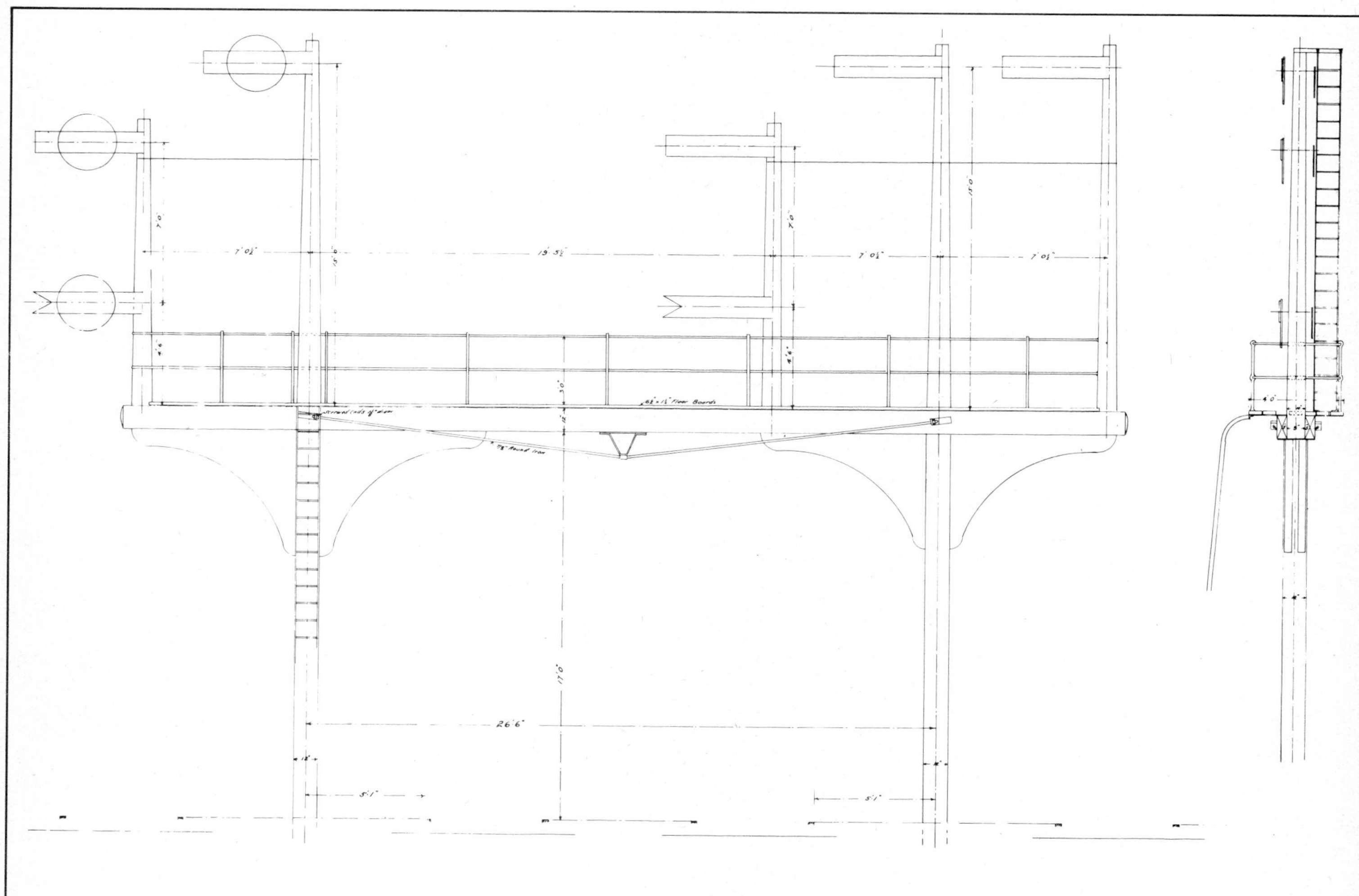

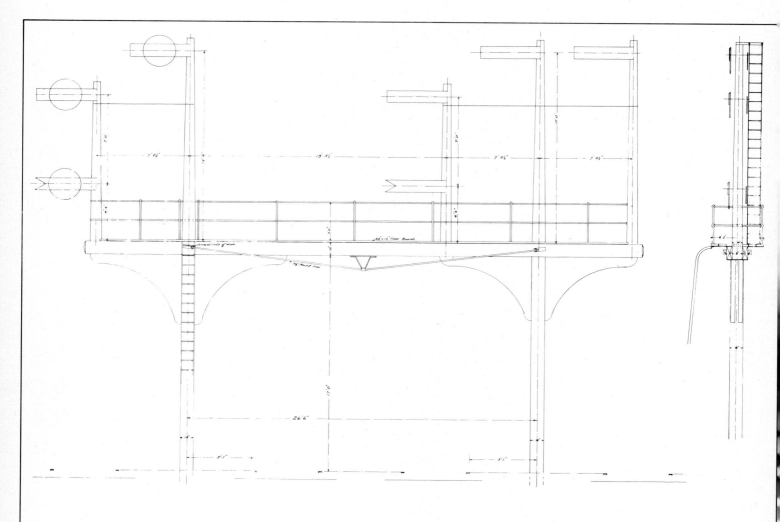

Figure 6.1 *Standard Timber Gantry Signal. The standardisation policy of the Signal Department can be seen here in that the standard wooden gantry was produced simply by joining together two S61 bracket signals. Again the actual arrangement of dolls would be made to suit the location for which the signal was required. This gantry is arranged to span two tracks, but they could be arranged to span more or less tracks or to accommodate more dolls as necessary by altering the dimensions. Scale of reproduction: 3.5 mm to 1 foot (1:87).*

Plate 6.1 *A rear view of Edgeley Junction No. 1 Up Home Signals. This timber gantry is of the* **Figure 6.1** *type and spans a single track, the Up Slow line. The arms read from left to right (as seen here) as follows:– (1) Along Up Fast; (2) Up Fast to Up Buxton Branch (with lower distant for Davenport Junction); (3) Up Slow to Up Fast; (4) Along Up Slow (with calling-on arm); (5) Up Slow to Buxton Branch (with lower distant for Davenport Junction). Elevated balance weights were used in this confined location. Immediately in front of the signal can be seen a lift bar in the Up Slow line working in conjunction with the branch line facing point lock.*

Photo: G H Platt

In some cases the number of arms required for a signal, or site restrictions, meant that it was not possible to mount them on a bracket structure and a gantry signal had to be used. The majority of the gantries were of timber construction and where possible they were of standard designs (**Figure 6.1**). The arrangement of the truss rods which strengthen the cross timbers should be noticed. The gantries however, had to be made to fit the location they were intended for and this criterion had to come before that of standardisation. However, it was usually possible to use standard components and standardised construction to achieve the required form as can be seen from the drawings and photographs.

Gantry signals were also used where a signal was needed immediately outside a tunnel mouth. This usually required the use of arms suspended below the gantry in order to bring them down as near as possible to the loading gauge so as to give the best sight through the tunnel.

As the complexity of yards and stations increased some of the timber gantries required became quite enormous (**Figure 6.3**). These signals were extremely heavy and were difficult to erect and maintain, while the quantity of timber required in their construction made them somewhat expensive. In the early 1890's a new standard iron gantry was designed and introduced for use where large spans were required or where a large number of dolls had to be accommodated. Quite a number of these iron gantries were erected over the next 30 years, particularly in the vicinity of large stations and yards. After the introduction of the iron gantry the wood gantries were generally only used for spans of up to two tracks. If more lines had to be spanned without intermediate supports, an iron gantry was usually used. The iron gantries were of standard layouts, the dimensions of the components being adjusted to meet the requirements of each particular installation. As a general rule, the larger the span and weight the greater were the cross sectional dimensions of the lattice box structure.

Plate 6.2 *Another gantry of the basic S61 type but this time with a much greater span and only small end overhangs. This attractive signal, photographed in 1938, was at Carnarvon No. 2 and controlled entry to the station from the south. The two lines passing under the gantry were not, as one might expect, a conventional double line. In fact they were two parallel single lines, the left hand one from Afon Wen and the right hand from Llanberis. The left hand four dolls referred to the Afon Wen line and the remainder to the Llanberis line. The dolls read from left to right as follows:– (1) To Up Goods; (2) To Up Platform; (3) To Up Local Platform; (4) To Up and Down Platform; (5) To Up Goods; (6) To Up Platform; (7) To Up Local Platform; (8) To Up and Down Platform; (9) To Bay. The BR signal which replaced this one had one stop arm for each line with route indicators.*

Photo: G H Platt

Plate 6.3 *By no means all timber gantries overhung at the ends. An example at Willesden High Level, looking towards Acton, is illustrated here. Two of the arms refer to the Goods Loop and the two on the right to the Down Main, the pairs of arms applying to the diverging junction ahead. In LNW days the arms on the two left hand dolls were fitted with rings. The bridge between the signal and High Level Junction cabin carries the line over the London and Birmingham main line. Note the stay rods attached to the ends of the gantry in order to give the structure the necessary rigidity and the lamp indicator contact boxes on the lamps for the distant signals applying to the right hand route (to Old Oak Junction). The photograph was taken in November 1953.*

Photo: British Rail

Plate 6.4 *Where several tracks had to be crossed and a number of arms accommodated, a more substantial structure was necessary. This example at Chester No. 1 has four horizontal timber beams, each 12" by 6", to support the dolls and walkways, each having its own truss rods. The end posts are each made from two 12 inch square posts cross braced together to give the structure adequate stiffness. Note how all four legs have been 'godfathered' in order to restore the strength lost through rot at ground level. In this way the life of the structure, which would be expensive to replace, was extended appreciably. The dolls are supported by brackets of the simple S62 type mounted upside down on the top of the beams. The underside of the beams were 21' 6" above rail level and the centres of the tallest arms were 32 feet above rail level. The structure had a span of 53 feet and the legs were sunk 7 feet into the ground to give adequate stability. When it was erected there were no calling-on arms, but distant arms were fixed under the 3rd and 6th dolls from the left. The signal was erected in 1890 in connection with the enlargement of the station. Gantries of similar construction were also provided at Huddersfield No. 2 and Walsall at about the same time.*

Photo: R A Mills

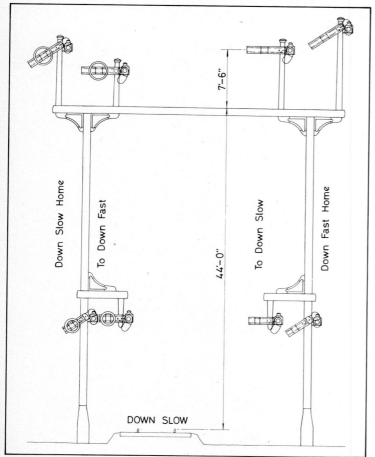

Figure 6.2 *Co-acting signals could occasionally be found in gantry form as this example shows. The signal is clearly made up of two S62 bracket signals joined together for rigidity. The short bottom arms are mounted on S62 type brackets set upside down to bring the arms down near to the loading gauge. This signal was erected in 1907 as the down home signals for Colwyn Bay No. 2 Cabin and stood at the western end of the down platforms. The top arms gave a distant sight above the station roof and footbridge while the bottom arms allowed close sighting under the canopies for trains standing in the platforms. The down fast line was just to the right of the right hand post of the gantry. Scale of reproduction: 2 mm to 1 foot (1:152).*

Plate 6.5 *This suspended gantry junction signal at Pighue Lane Junction has had to be placed in advance of the facing point lift bar because of the position of the points right at the tunnel mouth. A walkway to the arms has been provided from one end only. The home and distant arms were mounted close together so that they could be seen through the tunnel. A similar signal existed at Atlantic Dock Junction, but there the beam was trimmed into the brick retaining walls and the support legs not provided. Note also the siting of the home signal for Olive Mount Junction, at the other end of the tunnel, on a short post placed on the wrong side of the line so that it could be seen clearly through the tunnel. A couple of LNW type point detectors are just visible in front of the right hand post of the gantry.*

Photo: D Ibbotson

Figure 6.3 *Before the advent of the iron gantry some of the timber gantries became quite large as this example which used to stand at Chester, demonstrates. This enormous structure formed the combined up home signals for Chester No. 3A and starting signals for No. 4 signal cabins. The arrangement of tracks at Chester No. 4 was such that the fast lines from North Wales became the main lines on passing the cabin, while the up and down Birkenhead lines became the Fast lines. To avoid confusion to drivers approaching from North Wales on the fast lines there were no rings on the up main line signals. In accordance with the normal LNW practice of adding distinguishing rings to the arms applying to one line they were, in this instance, attached to the fast line arms. Elevated balance levers and slotting gear were used and these were mounted in groups at the positions marked 'X' on the drawing. Note how double raking main posts were used to give the structure rigidity. The signals applied as follows:— Doll A — To Goods Yard, B — To Up Slow, C — To Up Fast, D — To Up and Down Platform, E — To Up Platform, F — To Up Main. Scale of reproduction: 2 mm to 1 foot (1:152).*

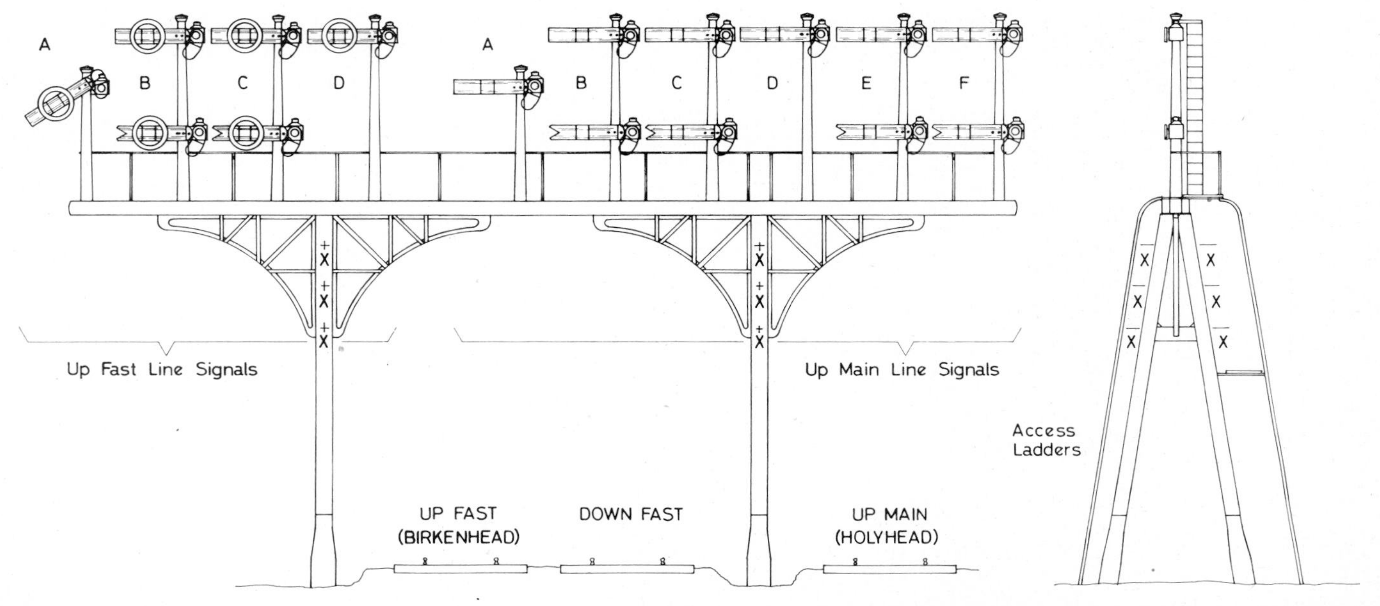

Plate 6.6 *This photograph taken in the 1930's shows the entrance to Canada Dock Tunnel, Liverpool and was taken from the Dock end near Bootle No. 1 cabin looking towards Atlantic Dock Junction which was at the other end of the tunnel. Because of the congested site the pointwork extended into the tunnel and in addition to that visible in the photograph there was a trailing crossover within the tunnel to allow trains departing on the right hand tracks to gain their correct up line. The signals facing the camera control movements into the tunnel, the large top arms applying to moves through to Atlantic Dock Junction while the shorter lower arms apply to shunt out moves. These allowed trains to shunt into the tunnel to clear the points and so enable them to set back onto another line. Two shunt arms are placed on the right hand doll to apply to shunts made wholly on the down line and those made across onto the up line. Crammed in just under the gantry beam can be seen two more arms signalling moves out of the tunnel, these have been placed as low as possible to give sight in the tunnel. The arms are well in advance of the points in the tunnel and would be repeated by disc signals placed at the fouling point inside the tunnel, (see also* **Plate 9.6***). Note the very simple form of water column provided on the end of the dock on the left – just a pipe from the water tower!*

Photo: D Ibbotson

Plate 6.7 *Stockport Edgeley No. 1 Down Home signals were sited in between the bridges and tunnels on the approach to the station. The arms were, therefore, suspended from the gantry for sighting, the left hand four dolls applying to the Down Slow and the remainder to the Down Fast. Calling-on arms are placed below each of the main arms. Note the smoke deflector plates placed over each of the tracks to protect the signals and the truss-rod arrangements used to support the structure.*

Photo: G H Platt

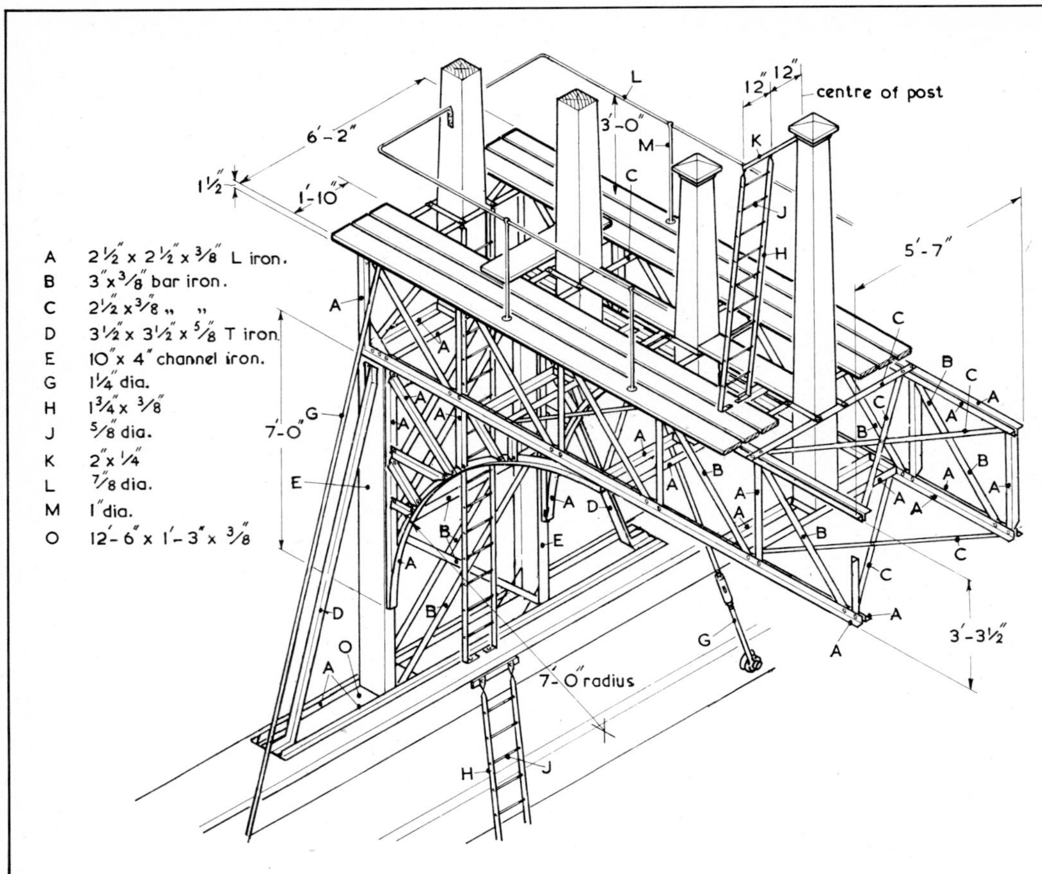

Figure 6.4 *Isometric Sketch of a LNW Iron Gantry. This shows the method of construction and the components used. This particular gantry stands on top of a wall, such as a parapet wall of a viaduct. The overall dimensions (width and depth) of the gantry varied to suit the site.*

Drawing: J K Nelson

Plate 6.8 *An iron Gantry Signal at the North end of Longsight Station, photographed in 1958. The left hand three dolls refer to the down slow line, and the remainder, separated a little to give a clear pattern of arms, to the Down Fast. The brackets at the top of the support posts are simply enlarged versions of those fitted to the S61 signals. Note the smoke deflector plates on the underside of the gantry. The lattice beam is of the Pratt or 'N' truss type and was the normal form of beam used for the LNW iron gantry signals. This basic form of gantry was adopted by the LMS as its standard.*

Photo: T Horn

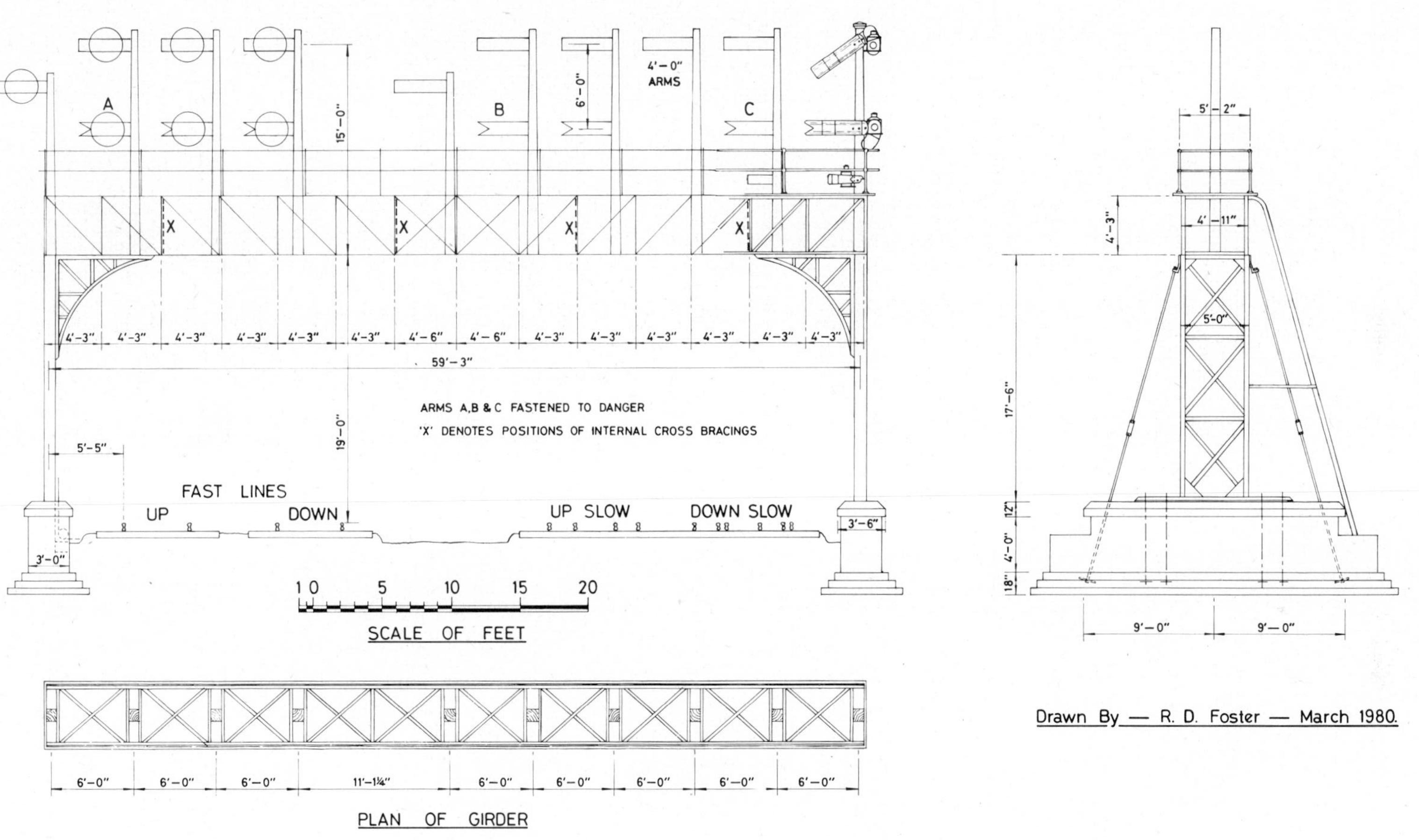

Figure 6.5 *In 1912 the timber gantry shown in* **Figure 6.3** *was removed and replaced with one of iron construction as shown here. The signal arms read to the same routes, and again the rings were mounted on the fast line arms. The distant signal arms marked A, B and C were fixed at danger. In BR days all the distant arms were removed completely. Note how the dolls are placed at 6 foot rather than 7 foot centres in order to save space and how the arms are shortened and the distance between the arms reduced to maintain the proportions of the signals. Scale of reproduction: 2 mm to 1 foot (1:152).*

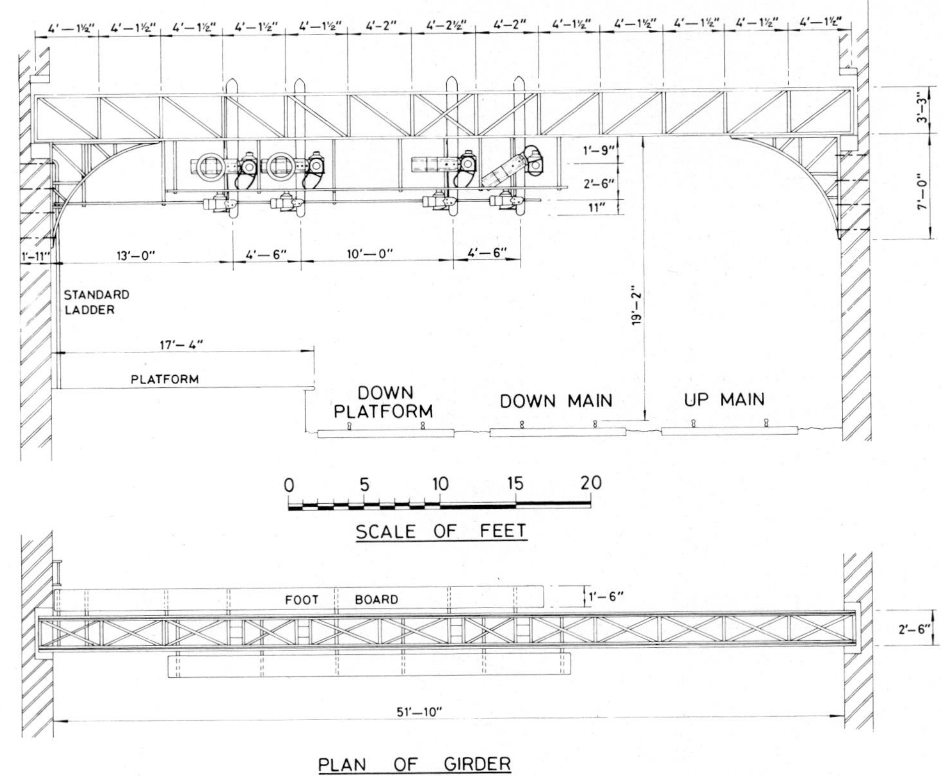

Figure 6.6 *The Down Home Signals at Chester No. 3 Cabin. This signal was sited near the centre of the main down platform to protect the scissors crossover near the footbridge. It was erected in 1908 at a cost of £250 to replace a timber bracket signal. Short arms are used due to the restricted space available and in order to give a good sight under the station roof these are suspended below the gantry structure. Note also the suspended footboards to give access to the arms for lamping and maintenance. Scale of reproduction: 2 mm to 1 foot (1:152).*

Figure 6.7 *The drawing shows the main dimensions of the Rugby Gantry and gives some idea of its true size. The lettered section lines illustrate how the gantry was cut up by the LMS in 1940 to form a number of smaller structures elsewhere. The proposed sites for the new signals were:—*

Section A for Rochdale West
Section B for Beeston South
Section C for Newbold
Section D for Brewery Sidings

Scale of reproduction: 1 mm to 1 foot (1:304).

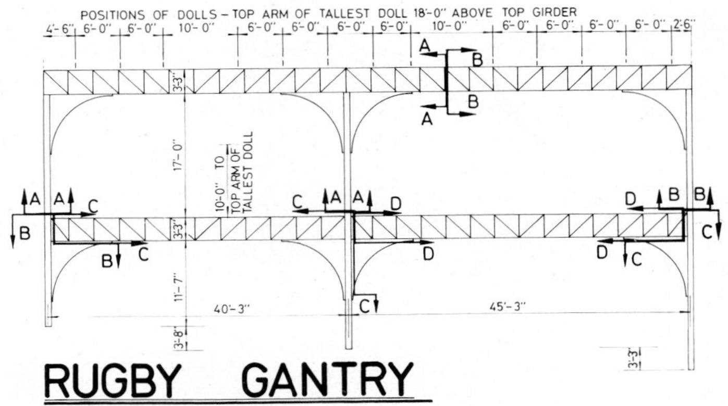

Plate 6.9 *One is a little reluctant to present a picture of the Rugby bedstead, since pictures have been published before, and the signal is not really representative of LNW practice in general. Indeed, it would seem probable that it would not have been constructed in this form if the LNW had been faced with the whole cost itself. The photograph demonstrates a few points which perhaps justify its inclusion. The construction of the Manchester, Sheffield and Lincolnshire Railway's London Extension line necessitated resignalling work at Rugby station on the LNW line and the cost of the work, estimated at £3,325 13s 9d plus £216 towards the operating cost of the new Locomotive cabin, was charged to the MS&LR. Further south the MS&L were charged an additional £449 10s for resignalling work at Loudoun Road. The bridge over the south end of Rugby station caused problems in sighting the down line signals and the gantry shown here was erected in 1895 to overcome these. Tall signals were regarded as necessary in order to give clear and early sight, while lower arms were provided for close sighting and for use during fogs. With three lines to signal and multiple junctions ahead the result was this huge double gantry signal.*

The photograph illustrates quite well the problems of sighting semaphore signals, the lower arms being quite difficult to make out clearly against the background of the bridge girders, while the top arms are perfectly clear.

The way in which the signals applying to each line are grouped together to assist the driver in recognising his signal can be seen (the purpose of each signal is listed below). Since the lower arms were intended only for close up sighting an economy has been made by fitting them with short arms. The application of different sizes of rings to full sized and short arms is also illustrated. The gantry structure actually consists of two standard iron gantries placed one above the other.

Working from left to right the arms applied as follows:—

Left hand Group: Applying to Down Main line from Blisworth
- *To Goods*
- *To Down Through*
- *To Platform*

Centre Group: Applying to Down line from Northampton
- *To Goods*
- *To Down Through*
- *To Platform*
- *To Bay*
- *To Bay*

Right hand Group: Applying to up trains from Market Harborough
- *To Goods*
- *To Down Through*
- *To Platform*
- *To Bay*
- *To Bay*

When the LMS resignalled the Rugby area in 1939 by replacing the existing semaphores with colour lights, the gantry became redundant. The structure itself was still in good condition and so the LMS made use of the standardised construction by cutting it up in such a way that the majority of the parts could be re-used elsewhere. **Figure 6.7** *shows the way in which this was done and where the various parts were intended for.*

Photo: British Rail

Plate 6.10 *This photograph was taken in December 1959 at Manchester Mayfield during stagework for the London Road Power box. The signals are of the 'Crewe system' power operated type and are hung from the girders formerly supporting the station roof. An access walkway is suspended from the same girder. Between the tracks is a power operated rotating disc signal. Newly erected gantries for the 25KV electrification are visible in the background.*

Photo: G H Platt

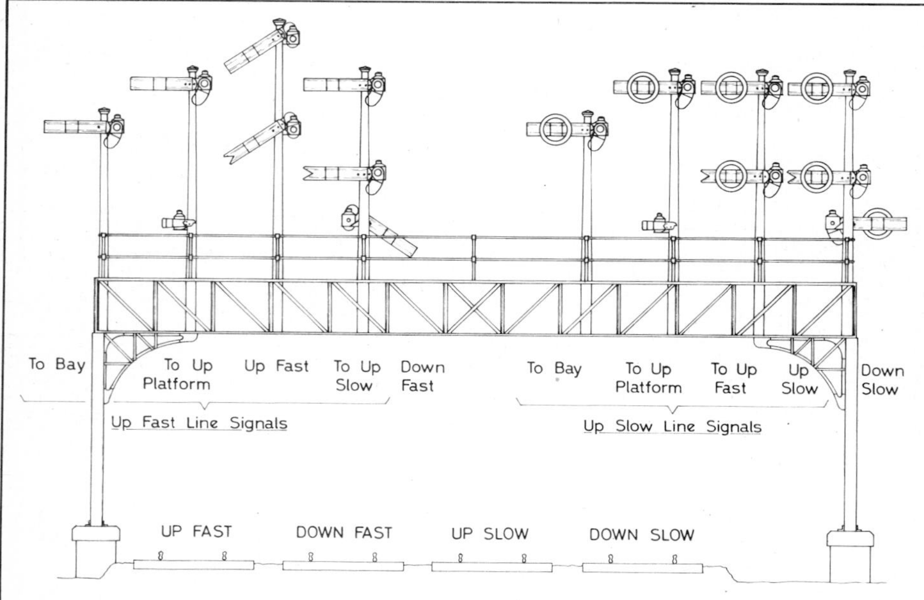

Figure 6.8 *An Iron Gantry Signal at Stafford No. 5 Cabin. This was the main line equivalent of the signal shown in* **Figure 5.8.** *The drawing illustrates some of the principles used by the LNW in laying out signals. The most important consideration was to present a clear and unmistakable arrangement or pattern of arms to the driver. The signals are thus arranged in two distinct groups, one for the fast line and one for the slow. The top arms are of different heights to indicate the relative importance of the routes ahead. This has resulted in the up slow line arms being offset considerably to the right of the line. However the consideration of presenting a clear and unmistakable pattern of arms (or lights) to the driver was considered the most important criterion.*

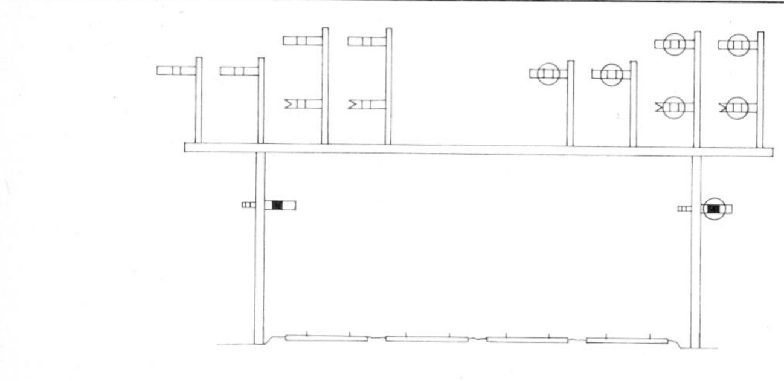

Figure 6.9 *The iron gantry shown in* **Figure 6.8** *replaced an earlier timber gantry and this is sketched here for comparison. Note the position of the calling-on arms (added to the existing gantry in 1881) and the down line signals. The relative heights of the arms differed slightly from those on the later signals. Scale of reproduction: 1 mm to 1 foot (1:304).*

Figure 6.10 (Opposite) *This drawing illustrates the down line signal gantry provided at Crewe South Junction when the new all-electric signal cabin was opened in 1906. A photograph of this signal appears as the frontispiece to this volume. The use of shortened arms at reduced centres in order to preserve the proportions and patterns of the signals is clearly illustrated. The positioning of the signal motors is also shown. It will be noticed that the end stiffening brackets are an enlarged form of the basic S61 bracket. This gantry structure was larger than usual in order to support the weight of the large number of dolls. Iron gantries, although more expensive than steel, had the advantage that they did not suffer from corrosion to the same degree and could therefore have quite long service lives. Indeed the gantry structure illustrated here was still in use at the time of writing to support colour light signals and cables. Note the use of the term 'down home 2' signal rather than 'inner home'. This practice of numbering rather than naming signals at large places was later adopted as standard practice on the LMS and the London Midland Region of British Railways. Scale of reproduction: 2 mm to 1 foot (1:152).* ▷

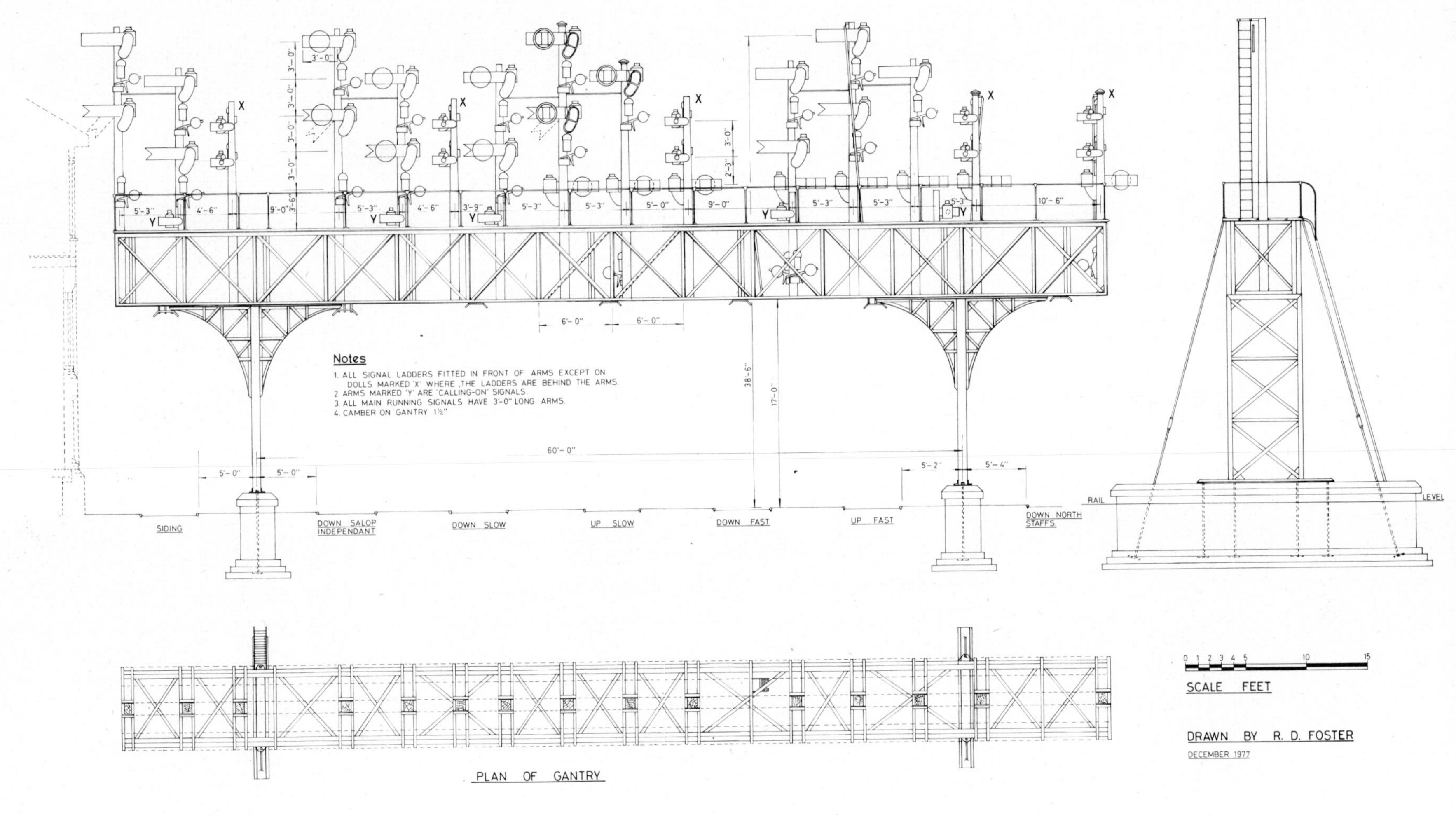
X
Y
5'-3"
4'-6"
9'-0"
5'-3"
4'-6"
3'-9"
5'-0"
9'-0"
10'-6"
3'-0"
2'-3"
6'-0"
38'-6"
17'-0"
60'-0"
5'-0"
5'-2"
5'-4"
RAIL
LEVEL
SIDING
DOWN SALOP INDEPENDANT
DOWN SLOW
UP SLOW
DOWN FAST
UP FAST
DOWN NORTH STAFFS.
Notes
1. ALL SIGNAL LADDERS FITTED IN FRONT OF ARMS EXCEPT ON DOLLS MARKED 'X' WHERE THE LADDERS ARE BEHIND THE ARMS.
2. ARMS MARKED 'Y' ARE 'CALLING-ON' SIGNALS
3. ALL MAIN RUNNING SIGNALS HAVE 3'-0" LONG ARMS.
4. CAMBER ON GANTRY 1½"
PLAN OF GANTRY
0 1 2 3 4 5 10 15
SCALE FEET
DRAWN BY R. D. FOSTER
DECEMBER 1977

CREWE SOUTH JUNCTION DOWN HOME 2 GANTRY SIGNAL

Plate 6.11 *Gantry Signals, if that is the correct term, were not always independent structures and, where possible, opportunity was taken of the existence of any structures which could be used to accommodate the signals and thus save the cost of a separate structure. The next two illustrations show some examples of the practice.*

This photograph, taken in 1962, shows the Up Loop Starting Signal at Stechford which was attached to the road overbridge. An access walkway has been provided and attached to the bridge also. No. 1 signal cabin is visible beyond the bridge.

Photo: G H Platt

Plate 6.12 *At Chester No. 3 the signals for the Up Main (and Up Main to Up Platform 10) line were mounted on the footbridge structure. They have an independent walkway for access from the cabin. On the left is the No. 3 cabin, a somewhat curious structure of 1890, placed on a wall and sandwiched between the loading gauge (it overhangs the line on both sides of the wall) and the station roof. In fact a roof beam passes through the centre of the cabin making headroom inside rather limited. Note the special 6 pane tall windows (with two horizontal glazing bars) provided in the cabin wall to give the signalman the best possible sight. A similar type of special window was provided in Euston No. 2 cabin in 1891. Special large plate glass window panes have been provided in the end windows to improve the signalman's view even further. Note also the arrangement of signal wires and rods on the station wall. The corrugated iron roof was a temporary affair as a result of the removal of the main overall roof covering.*

Photo: G H Platt

Chapter Seven Ground, Subsidiary and Special Signals

This chapter looks at the other types of signals and arms used on the LNWR.

DISC SIGNALS

Disc signals placed at ground level were used to control shunting moves to, from, and in sidings. On most railways they were of the rotating type. That is, when they changed from the danger to the clear position the body of the signal rotated through 90° to show a separate face. One face was painted as a danger face while the one normally obscured from the driver was the 'clear' face. This type of signal dates back to the time when they had usually worked with the points as point discs. Then it was a simple matter to make the signal turn by connecting it to the point stretcher. The rotating arrangement also made the signals fairly simple since the lamp could be made to have a green lens on one side and a red one on another.

The disc signals were also worked directly from the signal cabins by separate levers. This had the advantage that the signal would only come 'off' when required, instead of whenever the points were reversed. After the mid 1870's few 'point discs' were installed and new discs were made to operate independently and the existing point discs were gradually converted to independent operation. By 1900 very few point discs remained in use on the line.

The LNW like most companies was somewhat parsimonious with the provision of disc signals and many points did not have them. They were generally only fitted to points some distance from the cabin and particularly where control of movements to running lines was required. They would also be provided where the connections were very frequently used. At other places hand signals from the cabin were regarded as sufficient. Inevitably as time went on more and more discs were provided.

Where several disc signals were required at the same place (to cover several diverging routes) these were placed side by side. Where there was insufficient space for this to be done the discs were placed behind each other, the ones at the back were made taller so that they could be seen. An alternative arrangement was to make the same signal apply to several routes. A different lever for each

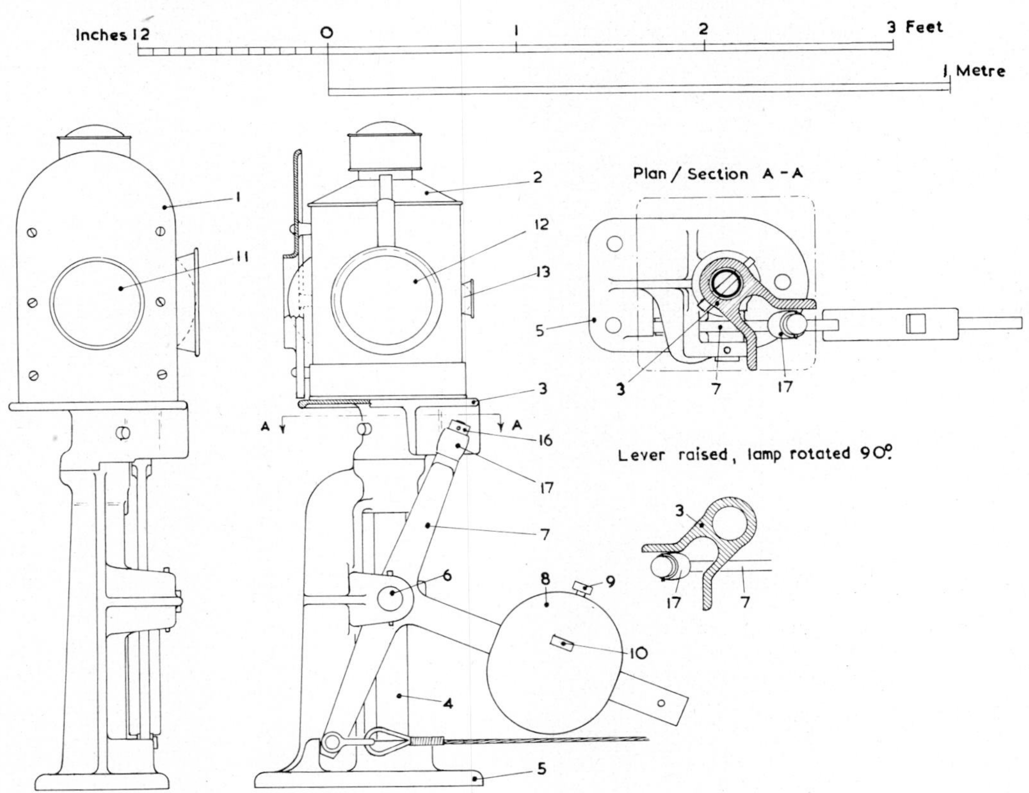

Figure 7.1 *Standard Ground Signal. This drawing is of the standard rotating ground disc signal used by the LNW. This pattern was introduced in 1881 and was used right through to the introduction of the standard miniature signal about 1915. Scale of reproduction: 1 inch to 1 foot (1:12).* Drawing by J K Nelson

List of parts shown in **Figures** 7.1 and 7.2
1. Red Face; 1A. Securing bolt; 2. Outer lamp case; 3. Lamp support; 4. Spindle tube; 4A. Securing pin; 5. Support casting; 6. Lever pin; 6A. Securing pin; 7. Balance weight lever; 8. Balance weight; 9. Balance weight fastening screw; 10. Balance weight pad nut; 11. Red lens; 12. Green* lens; 13. Back light lens; 14. and 15. Lens retaining rings; 16. Collar; 16A. Securing pin; 17. Roller.*
**See text with regard to lamp colours.*

Plate 7.1 *The front face of a rotating disc signal at Stockport, photographed in 1953. The red 'danger' face is bolted on and surrounds the red lens. The 'clear' face, with its green lamp, is on the right hand side. Note the spring clip which secures the lid closed, the lid opened on hinges to allow access to the lamp itself which sits inside the outer case.*
Photo: G H Platt

Plate 7.2 *The rear face of the rotating disc signal shown in* **Plate 7.1**. *This shows the small white light displayed to the signalman when the disc was standing in the 'on' position. This indicated to the signalman at night that the lamp was burning and the signal was correctly showing danger. For daytime use the rear face was painted white so that it could be easily picked out by the signalman. When the signal was turned to clear the case revolved through 90° so obscuring the back face and light from the signalman.*
Photo: G H Platt

route was usually used to work the signal (this simplified the interlocking) and so the one signal could be worked by several levers. The signal could only be cleared by pulling the lever applying to the route which was set up. One disc signal at Ordsall Lane No. 1 cabin for instance was worked by five levers (for five forward routes into sidings) and for good measure it was also slotted by No. 2 cabin!

For the Crewe power signalling schemes the standard rotating disc signals were used and equipped with solenoid motors. Because of the difficulties of fitting up LMS signals to work on this system some of these discs survived well into BR days.

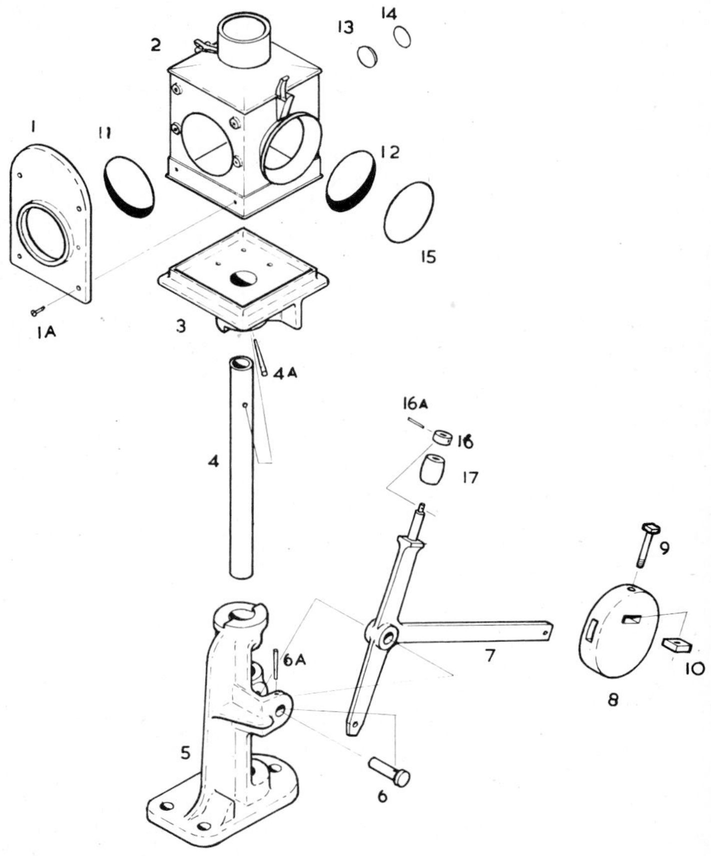

Figure 7.2 *Exploded view of ground disc signal which shows the method of construction.*
Drawing by J K Nelson

Plate 7.3 *Where two discs were required at the same location and there was insufficient space to have them side by side they were placed one behind the other, the one at the back being mounted on a long stem to enable it to be seen. An example at Carnforth is illustrated here.*

Photo: J P Richards

Just before the First World War it was felt that the time had come for something more in keeping with modern requirements. A new miniature signal was, therefore, designed. In accordance with the LNW policy of standardisation and avoiding anything different which was likely to cause confusion to the staff, the new signal was given a miniature semaphore arm (**Figure** 7.3). The limitations of the rotating discs were taken into account and the new signal was arranged so that several arms could be placed one above the other (**Figure 7.5**). Different bases were used with the multiple armed signals in order to accommodate the additional balance levers. A white painted bar was included on the back of the signal to assist the signalman in distinguishing the position of the arm when it faced away from the signal cabin. This was set normally vertical to reduce the risk of injury to shunters. As with the disc signals, in a number of cases where clearances were limited, single miniature arm signals were provided which could apply to several routes.

Disc signals normally displayed red or purple and green lights (red or purple and white before the change of 1893). There was some concern about the number of red lights to be seen at night in large stations and yards, so in a number of cases a white light was used in ground signals as the danger aspect. This reduced the number of red lights and assisted the drivers to distinguish their signals. As a general rule white lights were not used in signals applying to movement from sidings and loops to main running lines. The arrangements do not seem to have been entirely satisfactory, nor consistently applied, as the notices of 1912, reproduced in **Figure** 7.4, indicates.

At the same time as these notices appeared, the Midland Railway was announcing, in its notices, that the lights of all signals applying to main lines or for setting back movements had been changed to white on its lines.

In 1914, the Railway Companies agreed with the Board of Trade that the lights in disc signals which referred to the exits from sidings to running lines should be red. On the LNW it was anticipated that to change those discs which showed white lights would cost £400. The white danger light remained in use for other functions in many places,

Plate 7.4 *In LMS days a standard design of ground disc signal, having a white circular face with a horizontal red bar, was introduced for new work. The face moved through 45° to produce a diagonal red bar corresponding to the position of a signal arm at clear. In an attempt to effect some standardisation a new design of enamel iron face was designed for fixing to the LNW rotating disc signals. Since the disc itself rotated on these, two enamel discs or faces were provided — one with a horizontal bar for the stop face and one with a diagonal bar for the clear face. They were intended as replacements for the LNW faces and a number of signals were fitted up. This photograph illustrates a nice set of three such signals at Camden. These signals are also of interest in that they are fitted with 'Crewe System' solenoid motors for electric operation.*

Photo: British Rail

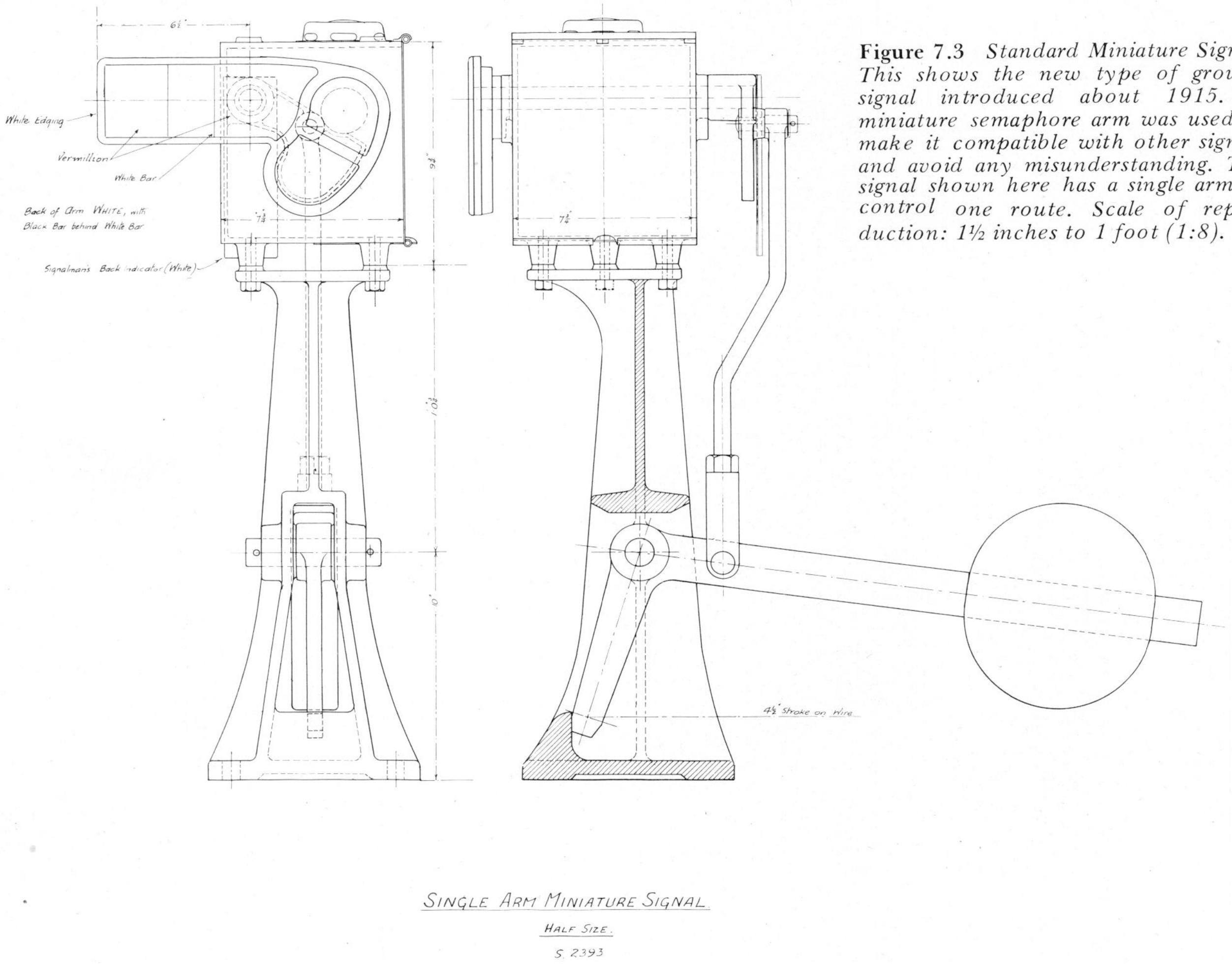

SINGLE ARM MINIATURE SIGNAL

HALF SIZE

S. 2393

Figure 7.3 *Standard Miniature Signal. This shows the new type of ground signal introduced about 1915. A miniature semaphore arm was used to make it compatible with other signals and avoid any misunderstanding. The signal shown here has a single arm to control one route. Scale of reproduction: 1½ inches to 1 foot (1:8).*

those at Ellesmere Port No. 3 Cabin, for instance, were converted to red in January 1929.

The idea of using yellow arms and lights in ground signals to signify that the signal could be passed during shunting was introduced in July 1929. This situation occurred where the move was made past the signal along a route to which it did not read. An example would be a ground signal controlling movement from a siding to the main line but where shunting could continue safely into a headshunt. This system was widely applied in LMS times. Prior to 1929, drivers were expected to know to which routes the signals applied and under what circumstances they could be passed.

Plate 7.5 *An example of the LNW standard miniature signal. This one was photographed at Carlisle in 1971. The enamel arrow, an LMS addition, was provided to assist drivers and pointed to the line to which the signal referred.*

Plate 7.6 *A double (two arm) version of the standard miniature signal at Workington. The detector slides, which ensure that the points are correctly set before the signal will clear, can just be seen behind the lower arm. Note the arrangement of the base which has to accommodate both balance levers. Where more arms were required or slotting devices had to be accommodated a wider base was necessary.*

Plate 7.7 *A rear view of the signal in* **Plate 7.6**. *This illustrates the arrangement of the backlight blinder which doubles as the drive crank for the arm. The white bar, provided to enable the signalman to check the position of the arm during daylight, is also attached to an extension of the crank. These bars worked entirely within the width of the lamp case in order to reduce the risk of injury to shunters and other staff.*

Figure 7.4 CHANGING OF LIGHTS IN GROUND DISC SIGNALS

The white light as the danger signal has been changed to red, in the following cases, on the dates shown:

Date		Place	Particulars
Monday	26-2-1912	Lancaster No. 2	Disc from up loop to shunting neck
Tuesday	27-2-1912	Carnforth No. 2	Four discs for Furness Bay line Disc from down loop to down main
Thursday	29-2-1912	Tebay No. 1	Disc from up N.E. Bay to siding
Friday	1-3-1912	Penrith No. 1	Disc from Keswick line to sidings
"	"	Penrith No. 2	Disc from down line to Eden Valley line
"	"	Penrith No. 3	Disc from goods loop to main line
Monday	4-3-1912	Carlisle No. 4	Disc from up line to road 1 and sidings
"	"	Carlisle No. 4A	Disc from road 3
"	"	Carlisle No. 5	Discs from down LNW and down North Eastern lines to road 4 Discs from road 1 to High Wapping Sidings
"	"	Carlisle No. 12	Discs from up goods yard to shunting line and up through goods

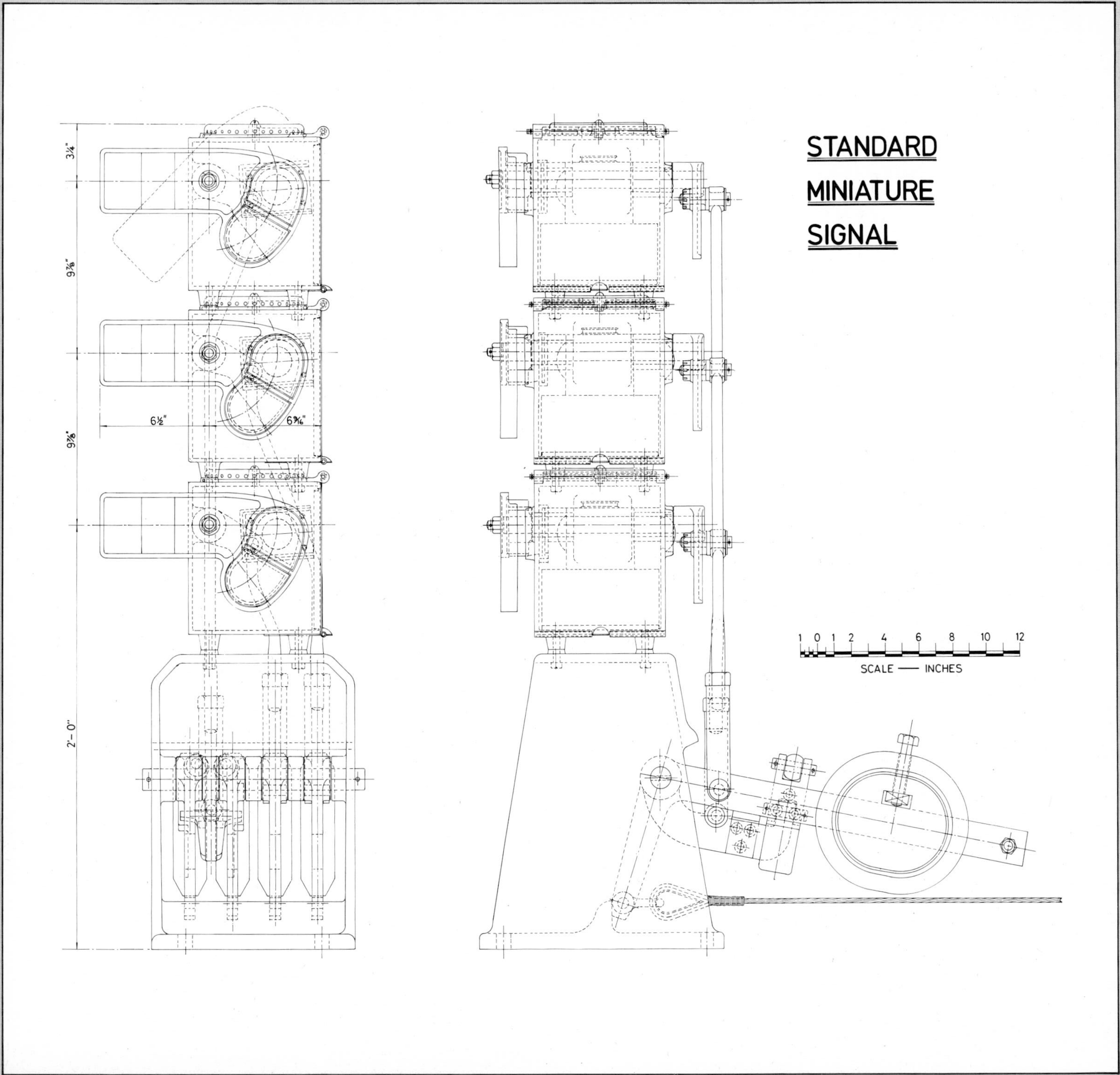

STANDARD
MINIATURE
SIGNAL

3¼"
9⅜"
9⅜"
2'–0"
6½"
6⁹⁄₁₆"

1 0 1 2 4 6 8 10 12
SCALE — INCHES

Figure 7.5 *Standard Miniature Signal. An advantage of the new signals was that they were designed so that several arms could be stacked one above the other to control a number of routes. This took up considerably less space than the old discs which had to be mounted side by side or one behind the other (see Plates). Any number of arms could be stacked together but a different base was required to accommodate the different arrangements of cranks and balance weights. It was however quite rare to find more than four arms in a stack. In the example shown the top arm is slotted by two levers. Scale of reproduction: 1/8 full size.*

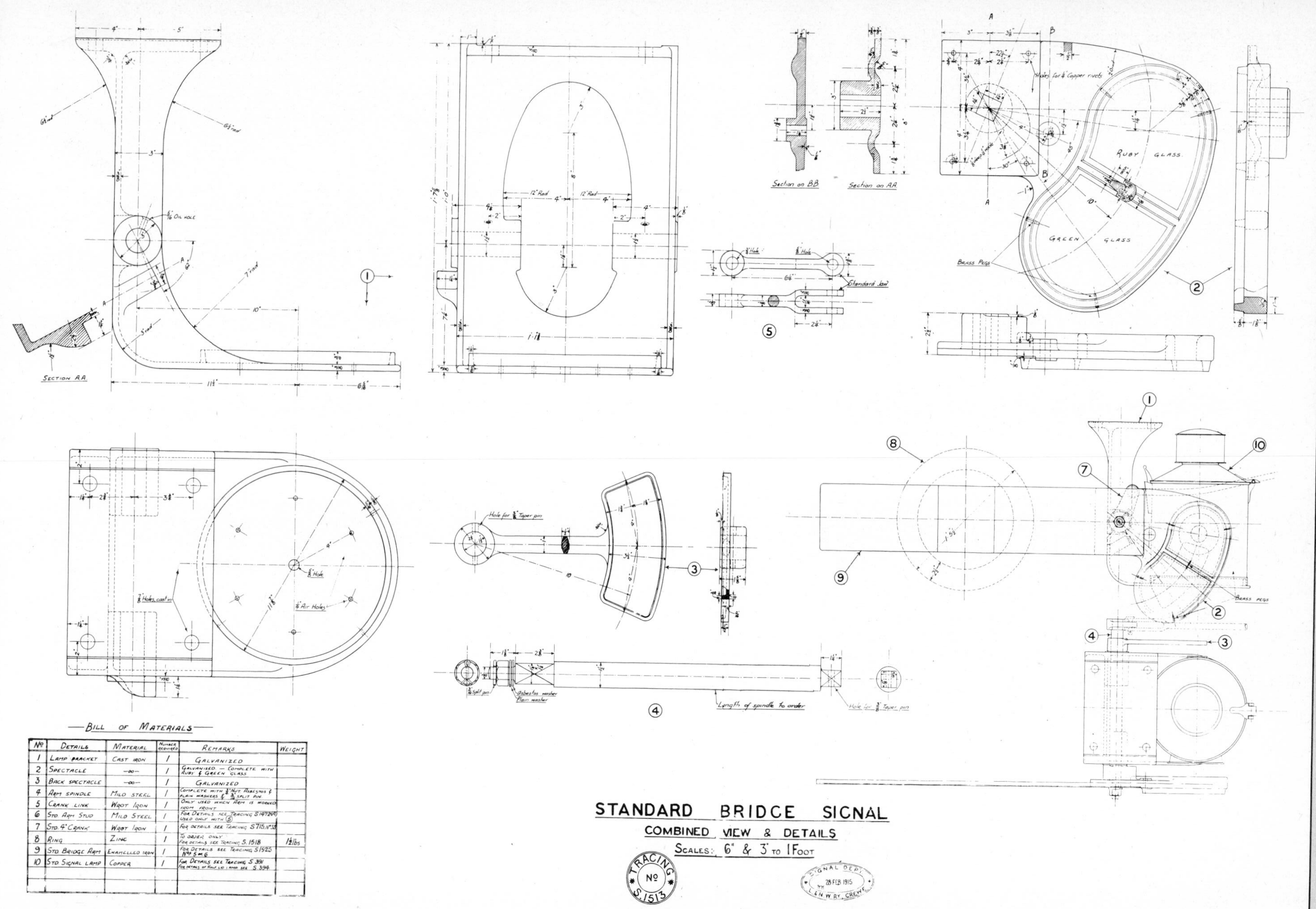

№	DETAILS	MATERIAL	NUMBER REQUIRED	REMARKS	WEIGHT
1	LAMP BRACKET	CAST IRON	1	GALVANIZED	
2	SPECTACLE	—DO—	1	GALVANISED — COMPLETE WITH RUBY & GREEN GLASS	
3	BACK SPECTACLE	—DO—	1	GALVANIZED	
4	ARM SPINDLE	MILD STEEL	1	COMPLETE WITH ⅜" NUT ASBESTOS & PLAIN WASHERS & 3/16" SPLIT PIN	
5	CRANK LINK	WROT IRON	1	ONLY USED WHEN ARM IS WORKED FROM FRONT	
6	STD. ARM STUD	MILD STEEL	1	FOR DETAILS SEE TRACING S1472(A) USED ONLY WITH (5)	
7	STD. 4" CRANK	WROT IRON	1	FOR DETAILS SEE TRACING S715 Nº 33	
8	RING	ZINC	1	TO ORDER ONLY FOR DETAILS SEE TRACING S.1518	1½ lbs
9	STD. BRIDGE ARM	ENAMELLED IRON	1	FOR DETAILS SEE TRACING S1523 Nºs 5 & 6	
10	STD. SIGNAL LAMP	COPPER	1	FOR DETAILS SEE TRACING S.391 FOR DETAILS OF HALF LID LAMP SEE S.394	

Figure 7.6 *The later form of Bridge Signal. The drawing includes the bracket used to support the arm and lamp. As can be seen this signal was normally fixed to the underside of a bridge or other structure. Some signals of this type are illustrated in* **Plate 14.12**. *Where the arms were used on wooden bracket or gantry signals a slightly different form of lamp bracket was used. The top of the bracket was fixed to the front of the flitches. Scale of reproduction: 1½ inches and ¾ inch to 1 foot (1:8 and 1:16).*

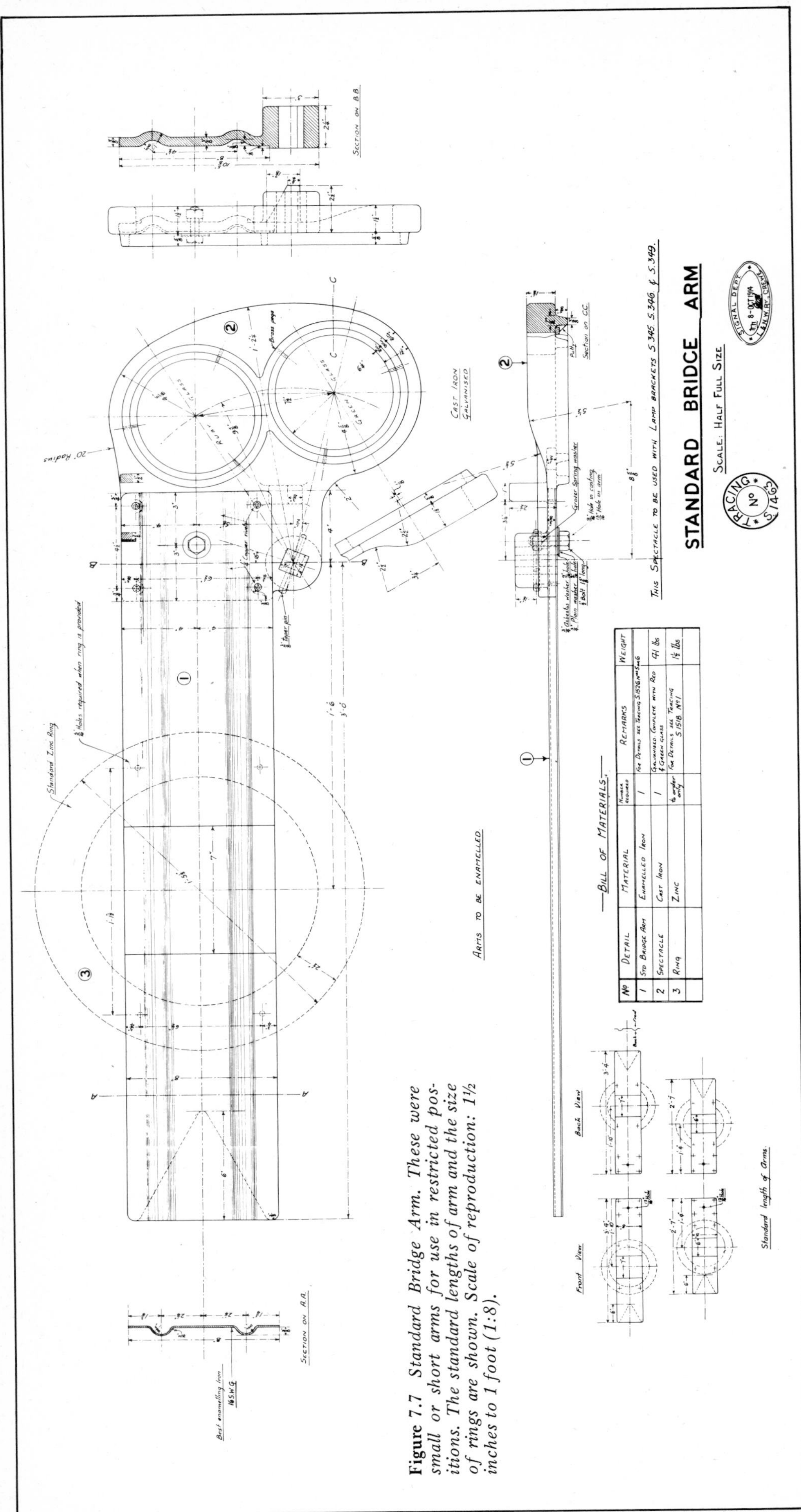

Figure 7.7 *Standard Bridge Arm. These were small or short arms for use in restricted positions. The standard lengths of arm and the size of rings are shown. Scale of reproduction: 1½ inches to 1 foot (1:8).*

BRIDGE SIGNALS

Two special types of arms were produced for use in places where signal arms had to be sited above the tracks but where clearances were very limited. As their name implies, the most usual situation in which these arms were used was suspended off the underside of a bridge. They were also used where the signals needed to be sited near to drivers eye level but limitations existed on how high or low they could be mounted. Examples of the places in which they were used included under station canopies and suspended from signal gantries, brackets or bridges, in order to give sight under station roofs and bridges.

The S1463 (**Figure 7.7**) type of arm was a direct descendant of the original form of bridge arm (**Figure 3.14**) and enabled the old arms to be replaced if necessary by new ones while retaining the original fittings. The S1513 type (**Figure 7.6**) was a later design intended to produce an arm of similar appearance to the standard '1883' arms.

Plate 7.8 *A pair of bridge arms of the S1463 type (***Figure 7.7***) at the centre of the old No. 6 platform at Stafford. These controlled movements through the central crossover (left hand arm) and straight along the platform. Just beyond the platform clock are a similar pair of signals protecting the crossover in the reverse direction. The crossovers and signals were worked by No. 6 cabin which can be seen in the background. Beyond this is Stafford steam shed.* ▷
Photo: British Rail

Plate 7.9 *A photograph taken at Macclesfield in LNW days. On the left is a home signal with lower distant and calling-on arms. The calling-on arm is of the S1542 type (***Figure 7.8***); it and the distant arm are painted the standard LNW colours of red with a vertical white stripe. In order to give drivers the best possible view of the arms, the distant arm is much closer to the home arm than the normal seven feet. The signal on the right has been positioned so that it could be seen through the curved tunnel. Both signals are gas lit and the gas pipes can just be seen below the lamp casings. Note the position of the correctly adjusted back blinder to the lamp of the right hand signal and the 'slack' signal wires, the normal practice at the time.* ▷

REFRESHMENTS
SUTTON'S SEEDS

Plate 7.10 *This photograph was taken on the 3rd July 1916 and shows the up home signals at Cheadle Hulme. These were junction signals and illustrate the practice used at a number of locations of providing separate posts rather than a bracket for the arms. The photograph shows clearly the arrangement of the tie rod between the posts, the guy wires and the thickening of the two posts at ground level. The right hand arm referred to the Crewe line and the left hand to the Macclesfield line, below which is a calling-on arm. This allowed trains to draw forward onto the branch and so clear the main line for other traffic. It is set low down on the post to avoid its being confused with the main arm. The arm itself is of the traditional LNW calling-on pattern (***Figure 7.8***) where the arm obscures the lamp completely in the 'on' position and is painted to the standard LNW pattern for such signals. The form of painting shown in most of the other illustrations of calling-on arms, with a distinctive horizontal white stripe, was not introduced until LMS days. A wooden access platform has been provided off the main ladder for the lamp. The black box on the left hand post just above the balance levers is an electric signal reverser (automatic home signal release). It was designed to enable the signal to be 'approach released' by trains so as to prevent a driver approaching a diverging junction too fast as had happened at Ditton Junction in 1912. The signalman 'pulled off' for the train in the normal way but the signal arm remained at danger until the train reached a track circuit a couple of hundred yards from it. This ensured that the driver had his train properly under control before the signal was lowered. The cost of this experimental installation was £37. Approach releasing is of course a standard feature of modern colour light signalling on British Railways. These signals were erected in 1896 and the signal reverser installation was authorised in November 1914.*

Photo: Courtesy National Railway Museum

CALLING-ON SIGNALS

The original form of calling-on signal arm, introduced on the LNWR in the late 1870's survived the introduction of the 1883 standard signal arms and remained in use almost unchanged until about 1920 (compare **Figures 3.14** and **7.8**). The arms were always painted red with a vertical white stripe and showed no light when on and a small white light in the off position. The function of calling-on arms is explained briefly in Chapter 3.

SHUNT AHEAD SIGNALS

At a number of places it was frequently necessary for engines, during shunting, to move a short distance past a signal controlling the exit from one line before setting back onto another line. Perhaps the most common instance of this would be at a station where movements from one platform to another or to a siding occurred regularly, in connection with the marshalling of trains. In these cases it was not desirable to lower the main arm since this could be misinterpreted by the driver, who might proceed too far or too fast. Indeed, in some cases, the line might not be clear for the full distance controlled by the signal. The use of hand signals from the signal cabin was not desirable since these could be misunderstood. A separate 'shunt' or 'shunt out' arm was therefore provided at places where such moves occurred regularly. These were fixed below the main arm and although the full size spectacle was normally used a shorter arm was fitted (**Plate 6.6**). They were painted the same as the main arm, with a vertical white stripe. When this arm was lowered (the main arm remained at danger) the driver knew he could move forward to a specified point for shunting purposes or that the road was set for him to proceed into a siding. The function of these shunt signals should not be confused with that of a 'call-on' signal. Unlike calling-on signals the shunt signals could be mounted below starting or advance starting (section) signals in which case their use was covered by the Rule Book:

> 'Where these signals are fixed as lower arms upon the starting or advanced starting signal posts the lowering of the shunting arm authorises a driver to pass, for shunting purposes only, the starting or advanced starting signal when at danger, but no train must go forward on its journey until the starting or advanced starting signal as the case may be is lowered.'
>
> *(Rule 46 in the 1916 and 1923 LNWR Rule Books).*

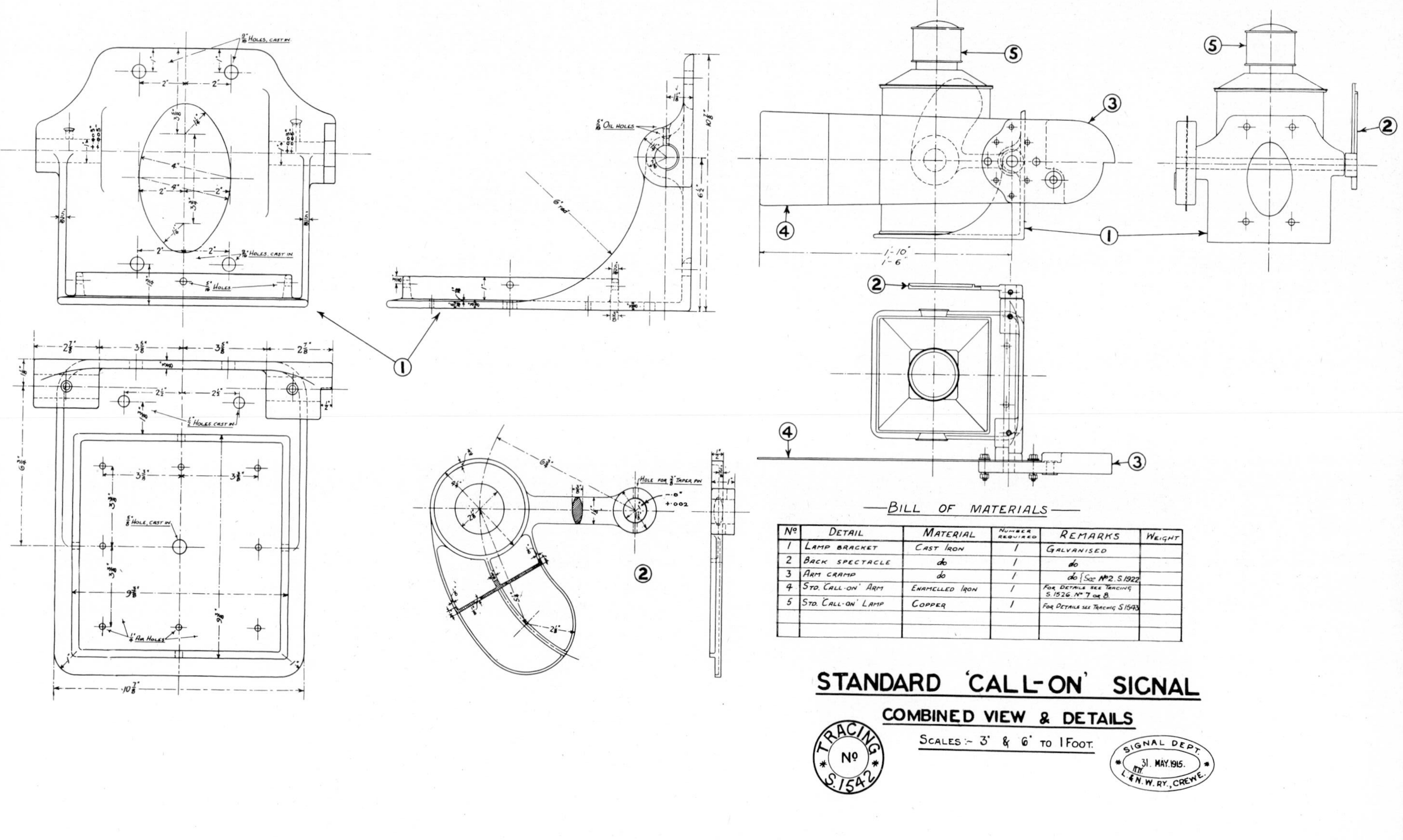

Nº	DETAIL	MATERIAL	NUMBER REQUIRED	REMARKS	WEIGHT
1	LAMP BRACKET	CAST IRON	1	GALVANISED	
2	BACK SPECTACLE	do	1	do	
3	ARM CRAMP	do	1	do (See Nº 2. S.1922	
4	STD. 'CALL-ON' ARM	ENAMELLED IRON	1	FOR DETAILS SEE TRACING S.1526 Nº 7 OR 8	
5	STD. 'CALL-ON' LAMP	COPPER	1	FOR DETAILS SEE TRACING S.1543	

Figure 7.8 *Standard Call-on Signal. This was the type of arm in use on the LNW from the introduction of the call-on signal in 1877 right through to the early 1920's. It showed a light only when the arm was in the 'off' position. The light was obscured behind the arm when this was in the 'on' position. In the 1920's a two spectacle arm similar to that shown in* **Figure 7.10** *was introduced. Scale of reproduction: 1 inch and 2 inches to 1 foot (1:12 and 1:6).*

Plate 7.11 *This photograph shows a stack of the distinctive form of shunt signal arms introduced in the early 1910's, these examples having wooden arms. The photograph was taken in 1952 at Heaton Norris and the signal is on the 'up' side looking north. The view can be compared with* **Plate 4.15** *which shows a stack of full sized arms. Signals of that type were used for tall shunting signal functions in the days before the introduction of the special shunting signal arms illustrated here and, of course, they continued in service until renewal or alterations were necessary.*

Photo: G H Platt

Plate 7.12 *A tall siding signal at Camden, this time with pressed steel arms. This illustrates the appearance of one of the arms when in the 'off' position. The circular objects on the post between the arms are contact boxes to detect the position of the arms. The arms are actuated by 'Crewe' system solenoid motors mounted on the back of the post, which had ladders at the front and back. On the right, beyond the bridge, are the LMS enginemen's lodgings, which were opened in 1928.*

Photo: British Rail

Plate 7.13 *A three doll short arm bracket signal of the S61 type at the south end of Stockport Station in August 1953. Shunt ahead signals are provided below the centre and right hand dolls for shunt moves from the platform. The shunt function is denoted by the letter 'S' attached to the arm, this was an LMS addition (as was the use of this type of arm for the shunt function) again introduced as an aid to drivers. The 'S' on the left hand arm has practically corroded away however! Note the separate distant arms by the tunnel mouths only a few yards ahead of the platform signals.*

Photo: G H Platt

Plate 7.14 *A rear view of a signal at Abersychan and Talywain. Bracketed off the main post at a much lower level than the main arm (so that there was no risk of confusion with the main arm or lights) is a main to loop line arm. These were usually mounted on metal brackets attached to the side of the main post in order to produce an arm which was off-set from the main arm in the same direction as was the divergence ahead. This is a right hand type and a rear view of a left hand (the most common) type can be found in* **Plate 4.3**. *This photograph also illustrates the details of the guy wires, ladders and other fittings.*

Photo: G H Platt

NEW PATTERN CALL-ON AND SHUNT SIGNALS

Early in the 1910's a distinctive form of shunt signal arm (**Figure 7.10** and **Plate 7.11**) was introduced for new work. This enabled the driver to recognise the function of the signal with no risk of confusion with a 'main' arm. These new shunt arms were painted red with a vertical white stripe. At first they seem to have been confined to sidings and yards but their use was gradually extended and in about 1915 the arm was applied to the shunt ahead function described above. In about 1920 this form of arm was adopted for the call-on signal, which up to that time had shown no light when 'on' and a small white light when 'off'. This new form of call-on signal showed lights in both positions. This type of arm was substituted for the existing ones and within a few years all the call-on arms in use were of this type. The arms continued to be painted red with a vertical white stripe well into LMS days, when the form of painting still in use today (red with horizontal white stripe) was introduced. In order to distinguish the function of the new arms a box containing cut out letters, 'C', 'W' or 'S' (call-on, warning or shunt ahead) as necessary, was attached to the side of the signal lamp behind the arm. This could be seen by the driver with the arm in the 'off' position and was illuminated at night. This device was not universally applied however.

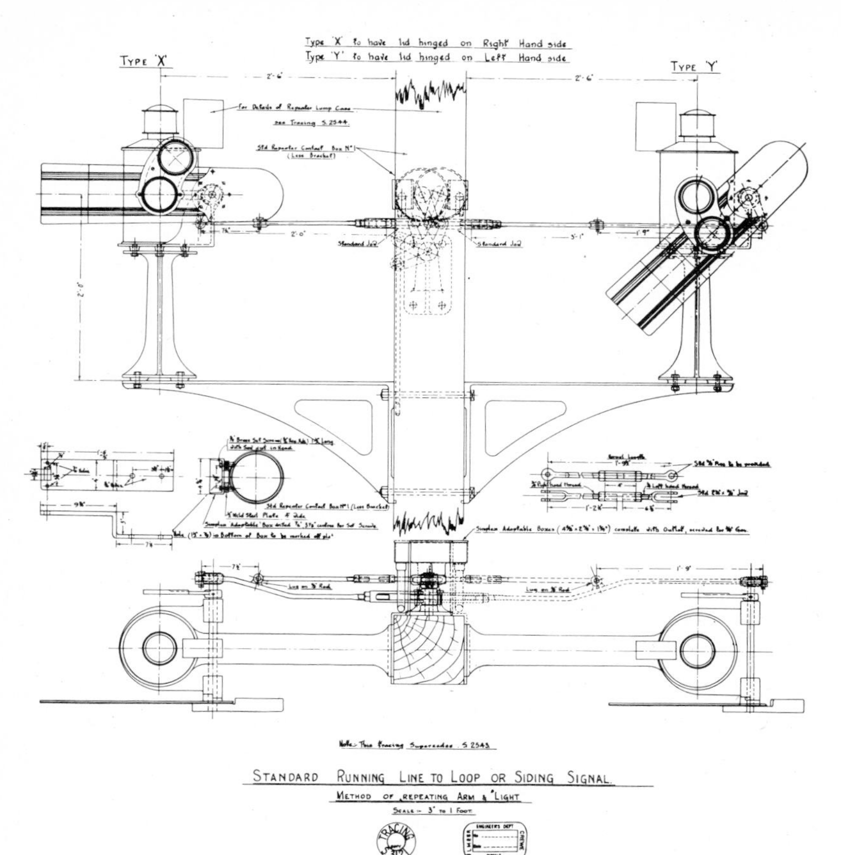

Figure 7.9 *Standard Running Line to Loop Signal. These signals are technically not LNW signals at all, having been introduced in 1923/4. They are very much in the LNW tradition, however, and were designed by the LNW Signal Department staff. Many examples were installed by the LMS over the years until the advent of the upper quadrant signals in the early 1930's. This drawing shows the fittings necessary for electrically repeating the position of the arms and the state of the lamp in the cabin. If these fittings were not required they were not provided and the drive rods omitted. The contact boxes could be found on many signals not visible from the cabin. The lamp expander box deserves mention. This contained the expanding contact used to detect the state of the signal lamp and work the Fletcher arm and lamp indicator (Chapter 12). Many signals, particularly distants, were fitted with these boxes. Scale of reproduction: ½ inch to 1 foot (1:24).*

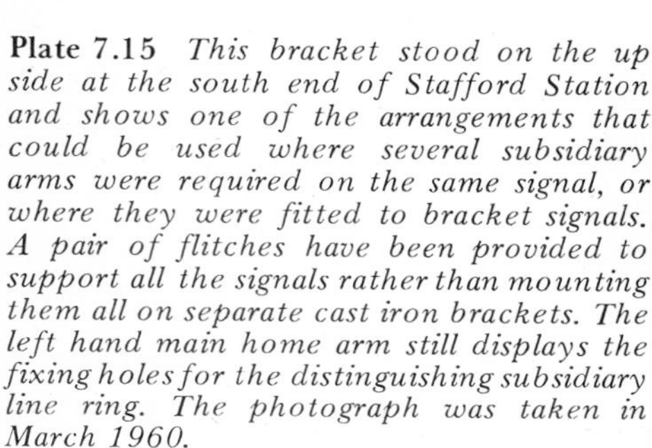

Plate 7.15 *This bracket stood on the up side at the south end of Stafford Station and shows one of the arrangements that could be used where several subsidiary arms were required on the same signal, or where they were fitted to bracket signals. A pair of flitches have been provided to support all the signals rather than mounting them all on separate cast iron brackets. The left hand main home arm still displays the fixing holes for the distinguishing subsidiary line ring. The photograph was taken in March 1960.*

Photo: British Rail

LOOP LINE SIGNALS

The distinctive main line to loop or siding signals introduced in 1923/4 are illustrated in **Figure 7.9** and **Plate 7.14**. Prior to this LNW policy on the subject had varied somewhat. At the beginning it was usual to provide a full size arm reading from the main line to the loop. Indeed, if the exit from the loop was controlled by another cabin a lower distant arm would often be provided. It was recognized later that for short storage loops and sidings the provision of a full size arm could lead to a driver mistaking the nature of the line he was to enter and proceeding too fast.

From about 1910 it became the custom not to provide full size signal arms for access to short loop lines. Instead a ground disc signal was provided, sited at the foot of the main line signal post (see **Figure 7.11**). When renewals or alterations were carried out, the existing signals were altered to conform with this arrangement. As an example, the signalling for the down loop line at Heyford was altered in the summer of 1914.

Signals controlling the entrance to goods running loops and slow lines continued to have full size arms since speeds could usually be higher as the trains would, normally, be continuing along that line (see also **Figure 5.6**). After the introduction of the main line to loop signal these were substituted for many of the disc signals and some full size signals. (See **Figure 7.11**).

ROUTE INDICATING SIGNALS

These were introduced about 1915 and were principally intended for use on goods lines and sidings to save the cost and space required for a bracket signal. A single siding signal arm was provided at the top of the post. When the signal was required to be pulled off for a particular route, the appropriate lever was pulled. This operated the indicator and caused the appropriate cut out metal letter or number to rise and be displayed. The signal arm was also pushed into the clear position. Examples could be found at Chester, Rhyl and Llandudno Junction.

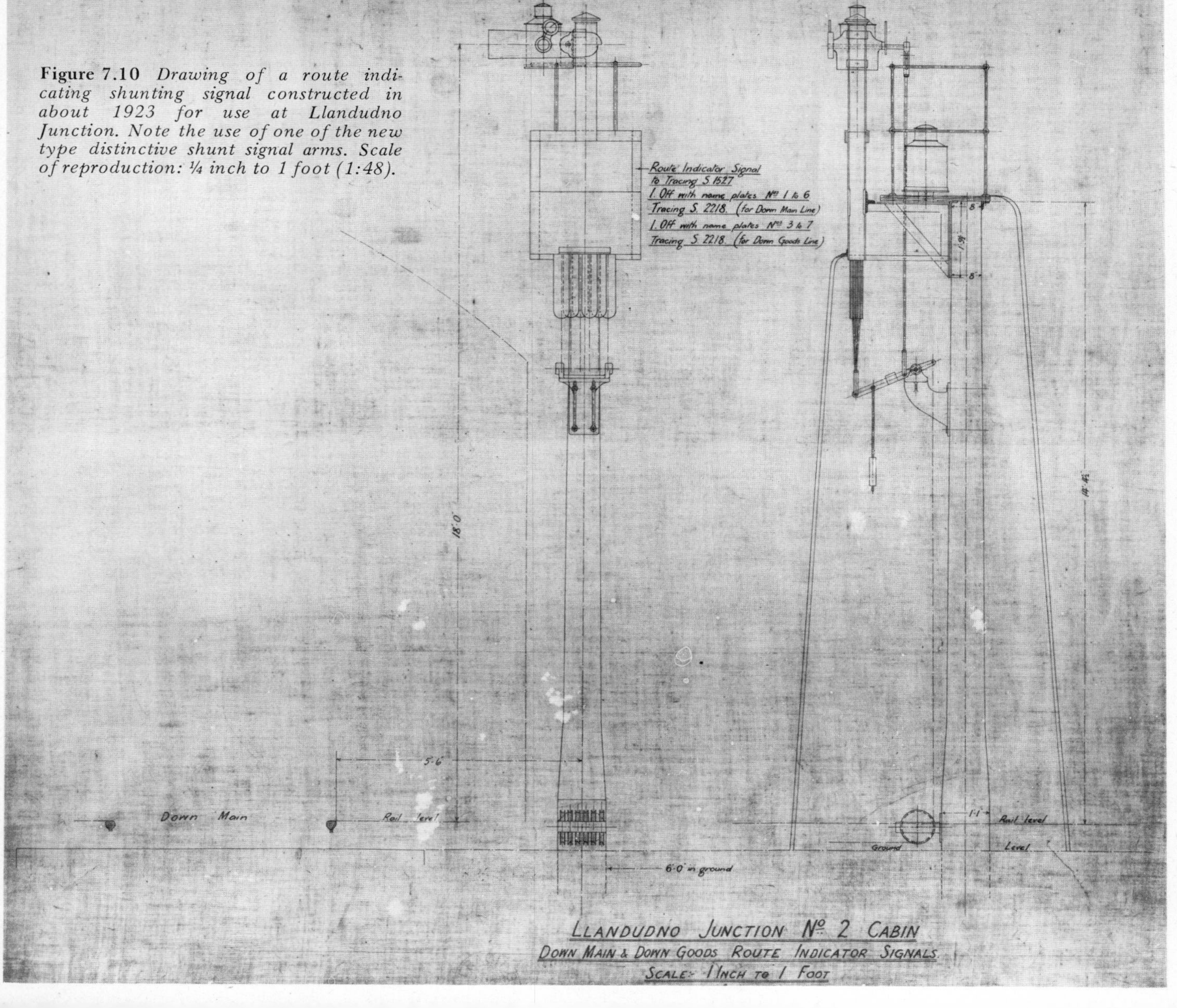

Figure 7.10 *Drawing of a route indicating shunting signal constructed in about 1923 for use at Llandudno Junction. Note the use of one of the new type distinctive shunt signal arms. Scale of reproduction: ¼ inch to 1 foot (1:48).*

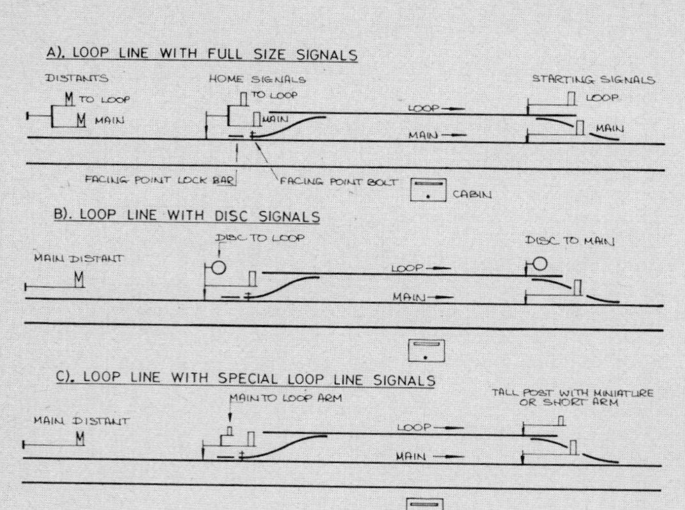

FIGURE 7.11 – LOOP LINE SIGNALLING

Figure 7.11 *The diagrams show three alternative methods of signalling a loop line. The layout in diagram 'A' was common in the early days and was used throughout LNW times for signalling entrance to long loops and additional running lines. In later years the loop line distant signal (particularly for entry to goods lines) would not be provided.*

Diagram 'B' shows the system normally used on the LNW after about 1910 for signalling loop lines. A disc signal only was provided for the movement to the loop. Since the disc would only be visible when the train was close to it, the driver had to approach slowly in case he had to stop. This ensured that the train would be able to take the points and stop safely within the loop. Generally, but not universally, this system of signalling was used for short loops worked entirely by one cabin. In a few cases where a stop signal was provided in the rear of the signal controlling access to the loop the disc signal was repeated at that signal forming, in effect, an outer home for the loop line. This gave the driver of a goods train advance warning of the route he was to take ahead and allowed him to proceed faster than would otherwise be possible and so clear the main line more quickly. Examples of this practice were to be found at Hawkesbury Lane and Foleshill Station where there were level crossings which needed to be kept clear.

Diagram 'C' shows the arrangement used after the introduction of the special main to loop line signals. This arrangement superceded many installations of type 'B' and some of type 'A'.

Where the exit from the loop was controlled by a separate cabin, lower distant arms would be provided under the home signals for the first cabin. This would usually apply to both main and loop arms in diagram 'A' (See **Figure 5.6***) but the main line home signals only in diagrams B and C.*

Plate 7.16 *A route indicating signal at Windermere photographed in March 1968. The signal acted as the down home signal and controlled access into the four platforms ahead. The use of a route indicating signal on a main running signal like this was fairly unusual, normally their use was confined to signals in sidings and on subsidiary lines or for shunting movements. In this photograph the indicator should be displaying the figure '2' to indicate to the driver that his train was being routed into platform 2. Unfortunately the signal does not seem to have come off far enough to display it properly! The subsidiary signal on the left hand side of the post signalled movements into the sidings on the down side.*

COLOUR LIGHT SIGNALS

In the last few years of the LNW's independent existence some thought was given to the use of colour light signals. Several such signals were designed and installed on the new tube lines in the Camden area in 1922 (Chapter 14). In the same year a daylight colour light signal was also developed and two were installed on the Midland side of New Street Station, Birmingham (the LNW were responsible for all of the signalling in the station area) early in 1923. The latter signals consisted basically of a metal tube of about the same diameter as the standard signal lamp case (**Figure 4.4**) in which two electric light bulbs were placed (one above the other). A red lens was fitted in front of one and a green lens in front of the other. The signals were developed by Sid Williams and Bill Hardman and remained in use for many years.

Chapter Eight Level Crossings

Level crossings fall into three main categories, those where public roads cross the railway, occupation and accommodation crossings. The latter two give access along private roads and to land on either side of the railway. They are generally operated by the owner or user and the hand gates are hinged to open away from the railway. This chapter is concerned with the majority of the crossings which fall into the first category, the attended level crossings.

Initially, most level crossing gates were hand worked on the ground by a crossing keeper. Evidence exists of this practice today in the presence of a keeper's cottage adjacent to many crossings, even where they have been worked from a signal cabin for close on 100 years. This arrangement was perfectly satisfactory in those far off days when road traffic outside the towns was very sparse and rail traffic on many lines much the same. It was a requirement of the Law (Railway Clauses Consolidation Act 1845 and others) that the gates were kept closed to road traffic and only opened to allow a vehicle across. This requirement was later incorporated in the standard Rule Book as Rule 99. The requirement was not normally relaxed until an Act of 1933 made it possible to obtain exemption for individual crossings. Today, the majority of crossings have this exemption.

The great problem in the early days was for the crossing keeper to know when a train would come along. The timetable was a useful (and often the only) guide but did not cover late running and specials. Hence it was quite common for accidents to occur through trains arriving unexpectedly. Many of the busier crossings were provided with signals for protection. These could be either worked by levers (or winches) on the ground or from a raised cabin. At that time the signals and gates would rarely be interlocked with each other.

With the construction of signal cabins or policeman's huts in connection with the introduction of the 'permissive' (time interval) block system it became obvious that these could be located, where appropriate, at the level crossings. This enabled the policeman (or signalman) to be used to operate the crossing therefore saving on wages. The signals could also be used to protect the crossing, an important safety consideration.

Even with the advent of the raised cabin the gates continued to be worked by hand on the ground. This was quite adequate at some crossings where traffic was sparse and in a number of cases this arrangement continued into recent times. It did mean that the signalman had to leave the cabin to work the gates and at busy places the time taken could lead to delays both to road and rail. There was also the problem, particularly where there were pedestrians, of users opening the gates themselves with obvious dangers, since the gates were not usually locked from the cabin either. However progress made improvements possible at the busier crossings. Sympathetic gates, where the act of pushing one gate causes all the other gates to move in 'sympathy' had been introduced in 1853. Mr Lea of Stafford devised a method of working the gates from the cabin by levers in 1863. Anyone who has seen how difficult it was at many crossings to swing the gates by wheel can imagine what sort of effort would be required to pull some of these gate levers.

Mr Lea supplied his patent gate operating gear to the LNW for use at a number of places. For example, the crossing at Garston was fitted up for £120 at the beginning of 1864, while in June of the same year £100 was expended on Lea's apparatus for the Queensville crossing (plus £50 for a new set of gates). This type of treatment was the exception rather than the rule however, and only very busy or difficult crossings were fitted up.

In 1868, for example, the new Liverpool line through Runcorn was under construction and the new junction at Ditton was connected to the existing signal cabin. The Board of Trade Inspector was most concerned about the arrangements at this cabin where not only was the locking not as close as it should be (a quite common complaint at that time) but the gates of the adjacent level crossing were neither worked or controlled from the cabin. In view of the additional traffic the new line would bring, he considered the arrangement to be unsatisfactory. The LNW pointed out that they already had a Bill before Parliament for enlarging the station and abolishing the level crossing and hence did not want to incur the expense of the new cabin and interlocking frame that would be required to comply with the Inspector's wishes. The Inspector was not satisfied however and refused permission to open the line.

The LNW made a number of suggestions to get over the problem including offering to introduce an extra man whose sole duty would be to work the gates. The Inspector was still not satisfied but conceded that a cheap form of interlocking would be satisfactory in view of the temporary nature of the installation. The signalling contractors, Saxby and Farmer, came up with a simple form of interlocking (an underbolt arrangement) which met the Inspector's requirements and which could be installed at the existing cabin for about £20 or £30. All this illustrates how unusual controlled and worked gates were at this time.

By 1872 controlled and worked gates had become more common. The report on the inspection of the newly doubled line from Craven Arms to Knighton, in March of that year, gives a useful insight into the practice at level crossings at that time. In connection with the widening a new signal cabin was provided adjacent to the level crossing at Bucknell and arrangements were made for the crossing gates to be controlled and worked from it, the existing gate keeper and his lodge being dispensed with. The Inspecting Officer said that this was a good idea but thought that a flat chain around the gate post would answer better, as a means of working the gates, than the rack and pinion machinery proposed. He also asked that lamps be provided for the gates and crossbars (painted red) be fixed to them three feet above the centre line as a warning.

The introduction of interlocking on a large scale during the 1870's brought many installations of Saxby and Farmer's system of patent level crossing gates. In many cases gates were locked open or shut (controlled) from the signal cabin but continued to be operated by hand on the ground. Gates operated by wheel had been introduced by 1880 and this quickly superceded operation by lever for obvious reasons.

From these beginnings developed the normal arrangements adopted for working, protecting and controlling level crossings. The Board of Trade set out minimum standards for new work and this abstract from the 1905 edition of their 'Requirements' indicates what was expected:—

> 'At all level crossings of public roads the gates to be so constructed that they may be closed either across the railway or across the road at each side of the crossing, and a lodge, or, in the case of a station, a gate-keepers box, to be provided, unless the gates are worked from a signal box. The gates must not be capable of being opened at the same time for the

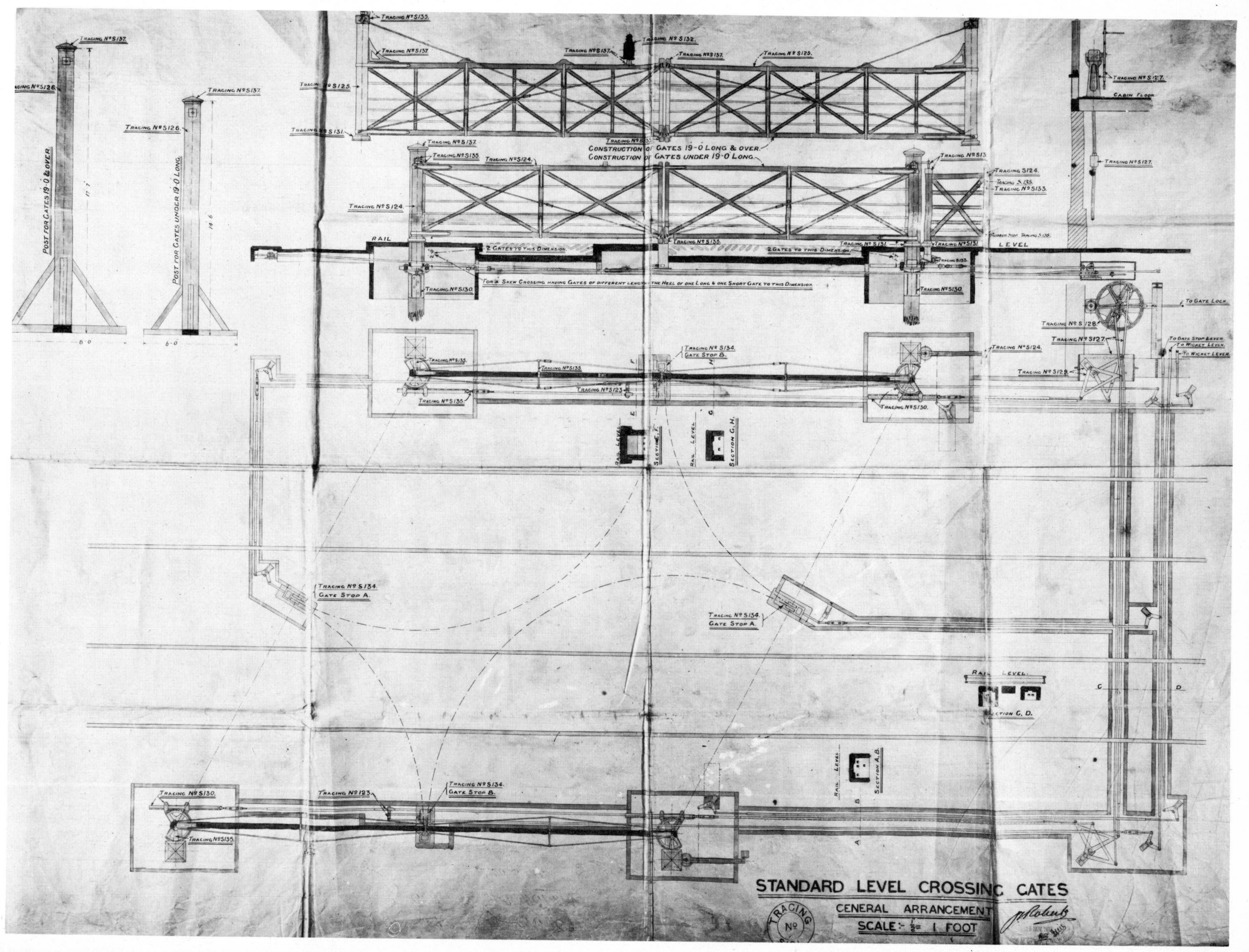
STANDARD LEVEL CROSSING GATES
GENERAL ARRANGEMENT
SCALE:- ½" = 1 FOOT
TRACING Nº
POST FOR GATES 19-0 & OVER
POST FOR GATES UNDER 19-0 LONG
CONSTRUCTION OF GATES 19-0 LONG & OVER.
CONSTRUCTION OF GATES UNDER 19-0 LONG.
2 GATES TO THIS DIMENSION.
FOR A SKEW CROSSING HAVING GATES OF DIFFERENT LENGTH THE HEEL OF ONE LONG & ONE SHORT GATE TO THIS DIMENSION.
RAIL
LEVEL
CABIN FLOOR
TO GATE LOCK
TO GATE STOP LEVER
TO WICKET LEVER
TRACING Nº S135.
TRACING Nº S137.
TRACING Nº S132.
TRACING Nº S125.
TRACING Nº S126.
TRACING Nº S131.
TRACING Nº S124.
TRACING Nº S133.
TRACING Nº S130.
TRACING Nº S134.
GATE STOP A.
GATE STOP B.
TRACING Nº S123.
TRACING Nº S128.
TRACING Nº S127.
TRACING Nº S129.
RAIL LEVEL
SECTION A.B.
SECTION C.D.
SECTION E.F.
SECTION G.H.

Plate 8.1 *A square crossing with the standard arrangement of gates and wickets at Watery Lane. Note the use of the red warning lamp for road and rail and the circular target in the centre of the gates as an additional warning for road users. Two gas lamps are provided by the wicket gates for the benefit of pedestrians and to assist the signalman in ascertaining that the foot crossing is completely clear before he operates the wicket lock levers.*

road and railway, and must be so hung as not to admit of being opened outwards towards the road. Stops to be provided to keep the gates in position across the road or railway. Wooden gates are considered preferable to iron gates, and single gates on each side to double gates. Red discs or targets must be fixed on the gates, with lamps for night use, or semaphore signals in one or both directions interlocked with the gates may be required. At all level crossings of public roads or footpaths a footbridge or a subway may be required.'

Despite the statement about single gates, the majority of crossings on double lines were provided with two gates each side (a total of four). This kept the length of the gates to a minimum and provided a stronger and more practical job. With the use of sympathetically worked gates there was no detriment in the provision of four gates as opposed to two.

Turning now to look at the equipment used by the LNW, the first equipment manufactured at Crewe was based on Saxby's designs. Operation of some gates by wheel was achieved by chain gear while they were locked in position by bolts acting on the gate heels.

In the late 1870's and early 1880's the gates and operating equipment were redesigned and the designs which were to remain in use for the rest of the LNW era were brought into use. This equipment is illustrated in the drawings and photographs.

◁ **Figure 8.1** *LNW drawing showing the general arrangement of a level crossing controlled and worked from a signal cabin. The arrangement and working of the drive rods for the gates and the gate stops can be understood by studying the drawing. The rods ran in ducts under the road. The angle and width of the crossing was altered to suit the site. This particular print was issued to one of the District Inspectors in 1913 and is signed by J T Roberts. Scale of reproduction: 1/8" to 1 foot (1:96).*

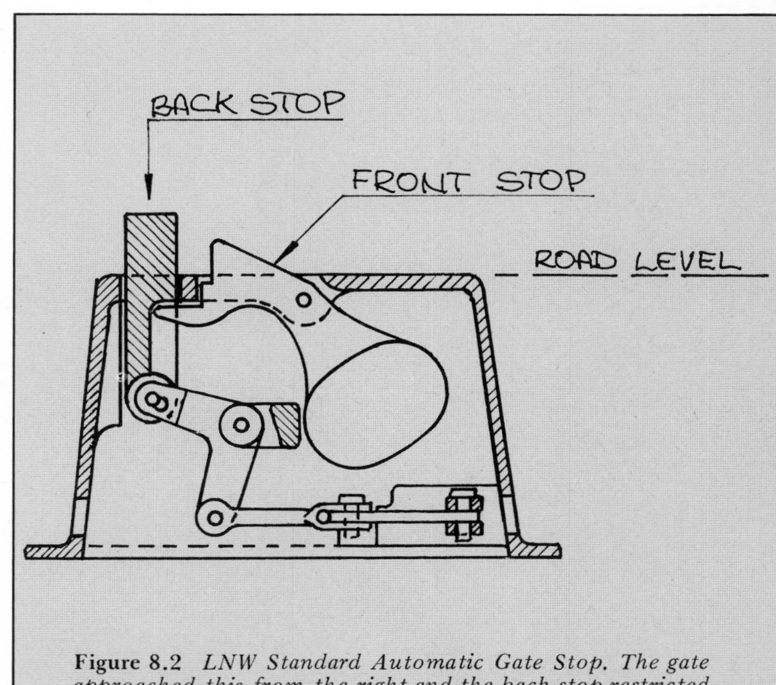

Figure 8.2 *LNW Standard Automatic Gate Stop. The gate approached this from the right and the back stop restricted its travel.*

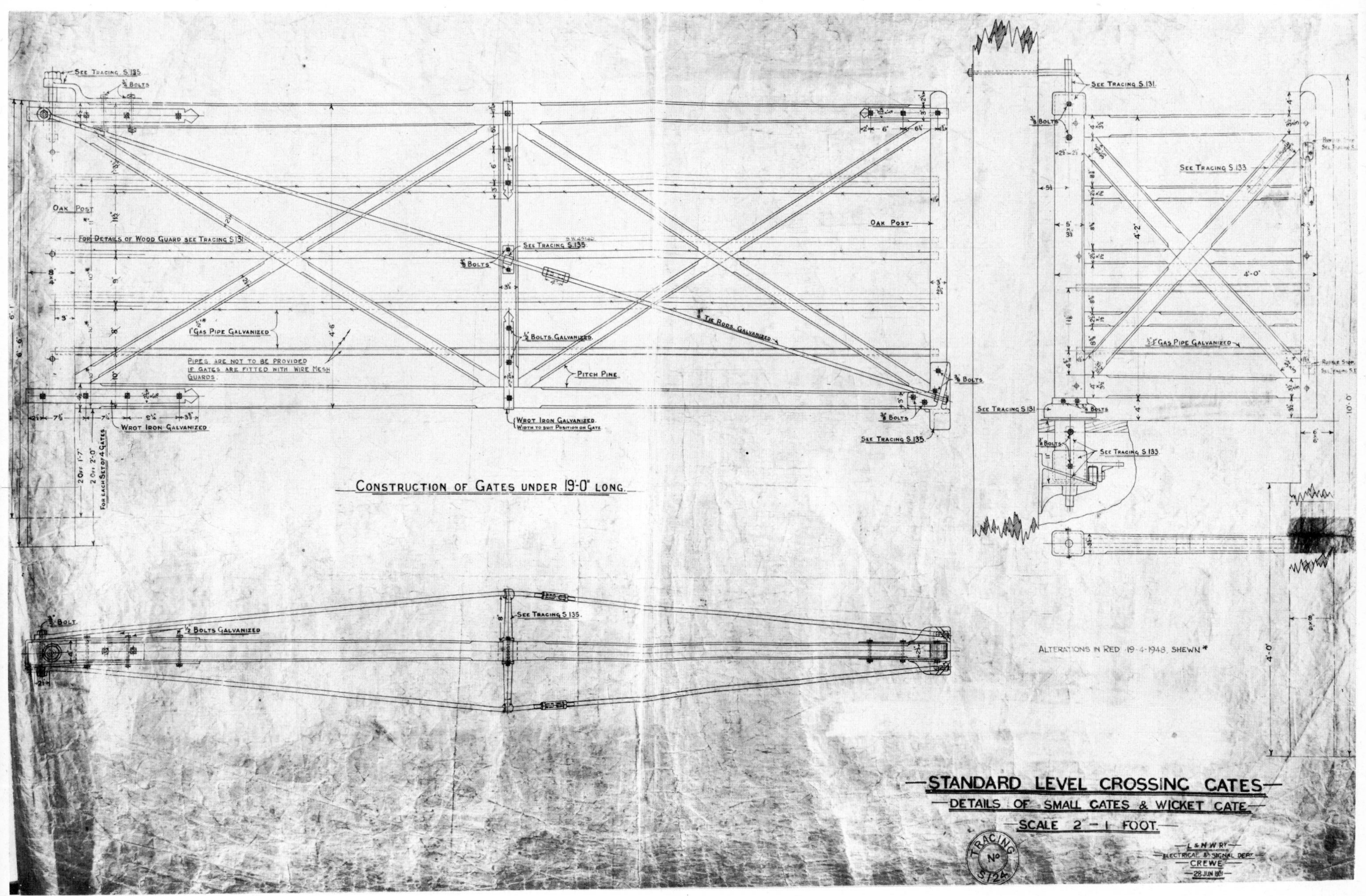

See Tracing S.135
Oak Post
For Details of Wood Guard see Tracing S.131
1" Gas Pipe Galvanized
Pipes are not to be provided if gates are fitted with wire mesh guards
Wrot Iron Galvanized
See Tracing S.135
½" Bolts Galvanized
Pitch Pine
Tie Rods Galvanized
Wrot Iron Galvanized. Width to suit position on gate
Oak Post
See Tracing S.135
For each set of 4 Gates
Construction of Gates under 19'-0" long.
½" Bolts Galvanized
See Tracing S.135.
See Tracing S.131
See Tracing S.133
Gas Pipe Galvanized
See Tracing S.131
See Tracing S.133
Alterations in red 19-4-1948. Shewn *
—Standard Level Crossing Gates—
—Details of Small Gates & Wicket Gate—
—Scale 2" - 1 Foot.—
Tracing No S.124
L & N W Ry
Electrical & Signal Dept
Crewe
28 Jun 10

Plate 8.2 *A large type LNW level crossing gate at Newton Road. This one seems to have got into rather poor condition by the time this photograph was taken. It will be noted that the gate lamp is mounted square on top of the gate, despite the fact that due to the skew nature of the crossing it would not show directly along the line of the railway or road when the gate was closed across them. This seems to have been quite a common feature of LNW skew crossings.*

A gate wheel was provided in the cabin to operate the gates and this was normally placed at the end of the cabin adjacent to the crossing so that the signalman could keep an eye on the road while the gates were on the move and so be able to stop them if a vehicle or person moved onto the crossing. This was particularly important with children while today's impatient motorists are seemingly oblivious of the damage all that swinging timber could do! The wheel was normally set parallel to the end of the cabin to save space and to enable the signalman to face the crossing while working it. By means of a set of bevel gears a vertical rod and a large gear wheel at ground level were rotated. This imparted a to and fro motion to the drive rods for the gates which passed in ducts under the crossing to the gates (**Figure 8.1**).

When level crossing gates were worked from the cabin it was obviously necessary to provide some means of stopping them when they had travelled their proper distance. Otherwise the gates' own momentum would carry them on, with the possibility of damage to the fittings or waiting traffic. A gate over-running could also ride up on the road surface and become grounded. The simplest means of stopping the gate was to provide a projection in the road and railway surface high enough to catch the bottom of the gate at its outer end and so prevent it moving further. However, a fixed stop in the middle of the roadway would constitute a hazard to road traffic and pedestrians and could cause damage or injury. Lever operated stops were therefore used in the roadway which could be raised or lowered flush with the road surface by the signalman as required.

Because of the arrangement of the drive for all level crossing gates there was always some play in the mechanism. A positive method was required to hold the gate in position against the back stop to counteract this and prevent the gate moving due to wind action or pedestrians pushing on them. A second or front stop was therefore used (**Figure 8.2**). This consisted effectively of a weighted lever with a

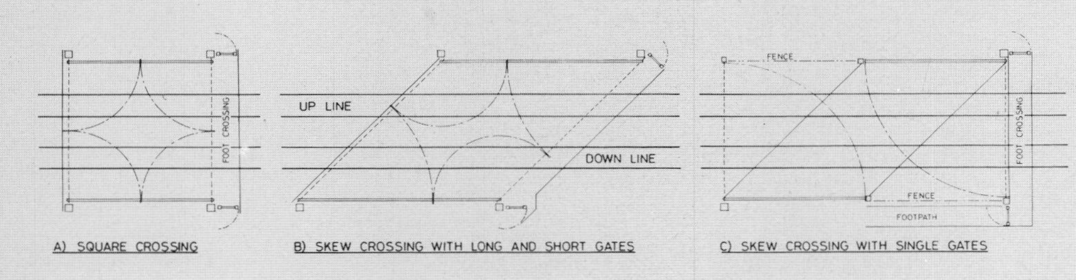

Figure 8.4 *Sketches showing arrangements of gates on square and skew crossings. Sketch A shows an ordinary crossing of the type shown in* **Figure 8.1**. *If the angle between the road and railway became too great it was necessary to provide gates of different lengths (one short and one long each side), as shown in Sketch B, in order to prevent the gates on the short diagonal colliding with each other when they were swung. Sketch C shows an arrangement adopted by the LNW at a number of skew crossings on minor roads. The Board of Trade rules required the road and railway to be completely fenced off from each other, hence the gates move back to stops clear of the track when across the line and the spaces are fenced in. In practice few of the crossings of this type had separate wickets since the roads were usually fairly minor and in many cases the gates were worked by hand.*

Figure 8.3 *LNW Standard Small (for lengths of up to 19 feet) Level Crossing Gates and Wicket Gates. This was a standard drawing and the gates could be constructed of any length to suit the intended location, the dimensions of the members being adjusted accordingly. This drawing also shows the way in which the design was modified in 1948, horizontal bars or pipes of smaller diameter being used and the spacing altered to more or less equal centres. The LNW design had the bars placed closer together near the bottom to prevent children and animals climbing through between them. As an additional precaution some crossing gates in towns had wire mesh secured across them. Scale of reproduction: ½" to 1 foot (1:24).*

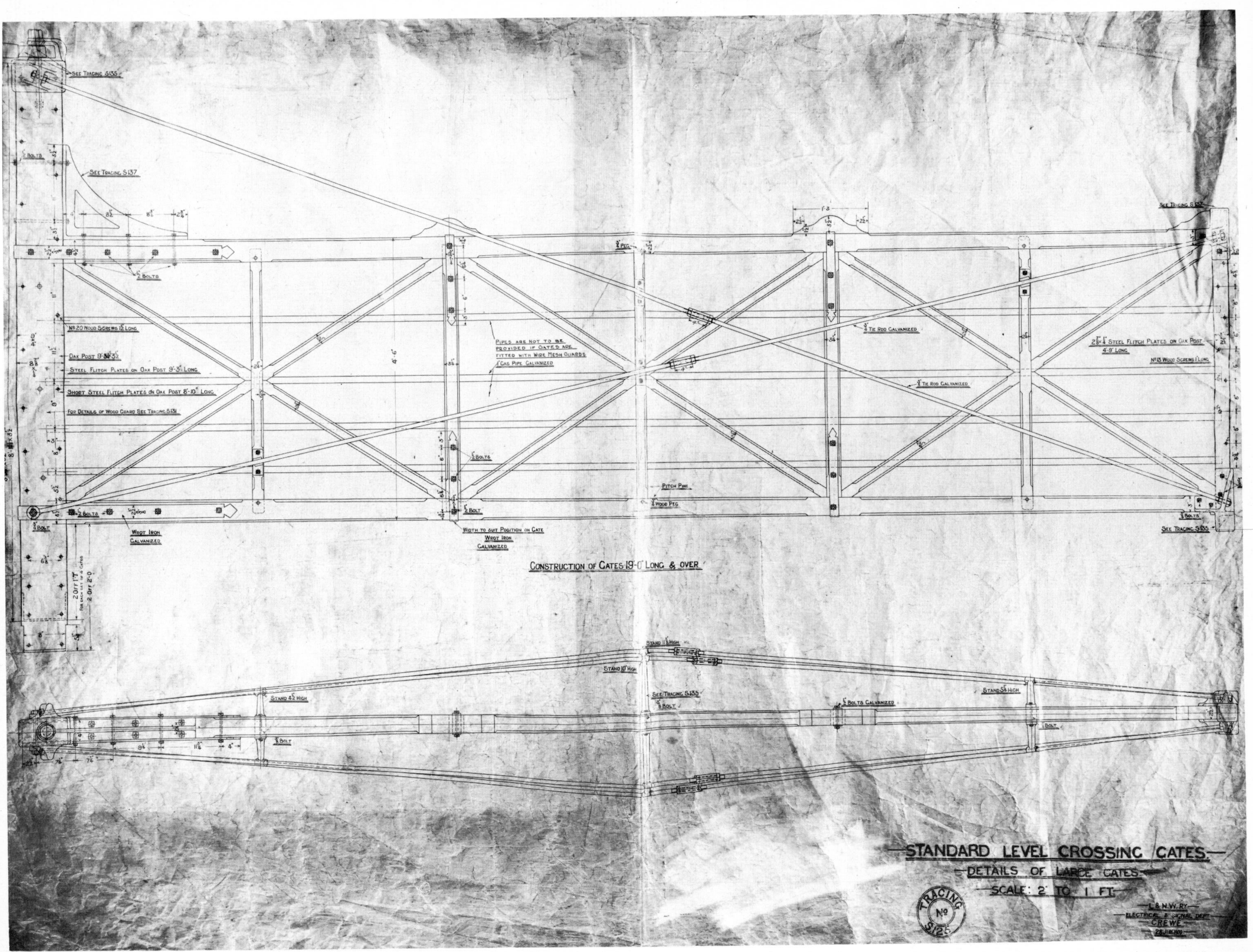

STANDARD LEVEL CROSSING GATES.
DETAILS OF LARGE GATES.
SCALE: 2" TO 1 FT.
L&N.W.RY.
ELECTRICAL & SIGNAL DEPT.
CREWE.
TRACING
No
S125
CONSTRUCTION OF GATES 19'-0" LONG & OVER
SEE TRACING S135
SEE TRACING S137
PIPES ARE NOT TO BE PROVIDED IF GATES ARE FITTED WITH WIRE MESH GUARDS
TIE ROD GALVANIZED
STEEL FLITCH PLATES ON OAK POST 9'-3" LONG
SHORT STEEL FLITCH PLATES ON OAK POST 8'-10" LONG
FOR DETAILS OF WOOD GUARD SEE TRACING S131
WROT IRON GALVANIZED
WIDTH TO SUIT POSITION ON GATE
PITCH PINE
WOOD PEG
BOLTS GALVANIZED

◁ **Figure 8.5** *Standard design of Crossing Gates over 19 feet long. The additional bracing and tie bars provided to give adequate stiffness and strength will be noticed. Scale of reproduction: ½" to 1 foot (1:24).*

triangular piece of metal exposed above the road surface. The gate rode across the sloping section of the lever depressing it. As the gate reached the back stop it ran off the lever, allowing it to rise again: the vertical edge then came up behind the gate and held it in position. This arrangement automatically held the gates in position and prevented them bouncing back as they hit the back stop. The front stop could be lowered by the gate stop lever in the cabin (which also worked the backstop in the case of the stops in the roadway) to allow the gates to be moved again.

The stop system described above still had the disadvantage that the roadway stops were raised as soon as the gate stop lever was operated to release the gates when they were across the railway. Road traffic could still be passing at this time. The LNW therefore used an automatic gate stop in the roadway. Instead of operating the stops directly, the stop lever operated a lever arrangement in the rodding trunking near the stops. As the gates approached the end of their travel a pin on the gate drive rod came into contact with the lever and pushed the stops into the raised position just before the gates reached them. This arrangement minimised any hazard to road users. **Figure 8.2** illustrates the LNW automatic gate stop.

A problem with level crossings was to ensure that non-stop trains were not delayed by passing the distant signal at danger. Since the gates were interlocked with the signals these had to be locked across the road and the signals cleared before the time when the train might be expected to reach the distant, which itself could be nearly a mile from the crossing. It could therefore be an appreciable time (particularly in the case of a slow goods train) before the train passed. Such a delay was obviously unnecessary for pedestrians and separate wicket gates were normally provided for them (unless there was a separate footbridge or subway). The wickets also provided a safe footpath away from the road traffic. They could be locked shut but were not interlocked with the signals. Use of the wickets could

Plate 8.3 *An LNW cabin gate wheel and pedestal. The former is of the 'Ship's Wheel' type with handles around the perimeter. However a handle at right angles to the wheel could be fixed in one of the holes in the spoke at the top right if this made operating easier. The gearing for the vertical drive rod is enclosed in the circular metal case at the top of the pedestal.*

Plate 8.4 *An LNW horizontal gate driving wheel. These were situated under the signal cabin at ground level. The vertical drive shaft with its small gear wheel leading down from the gate wheel is on the right. The horizontal drive rods for the gates are in the centre and disappear out of the top of the picture. The gate lock did not operate directly on the gates, but bolted the driving wheel in position. The bolt is visible below the wheel just to the left of the centre pin. The connection to the gate lock lever can be seen disappearing off the left hand end of the photograph.*

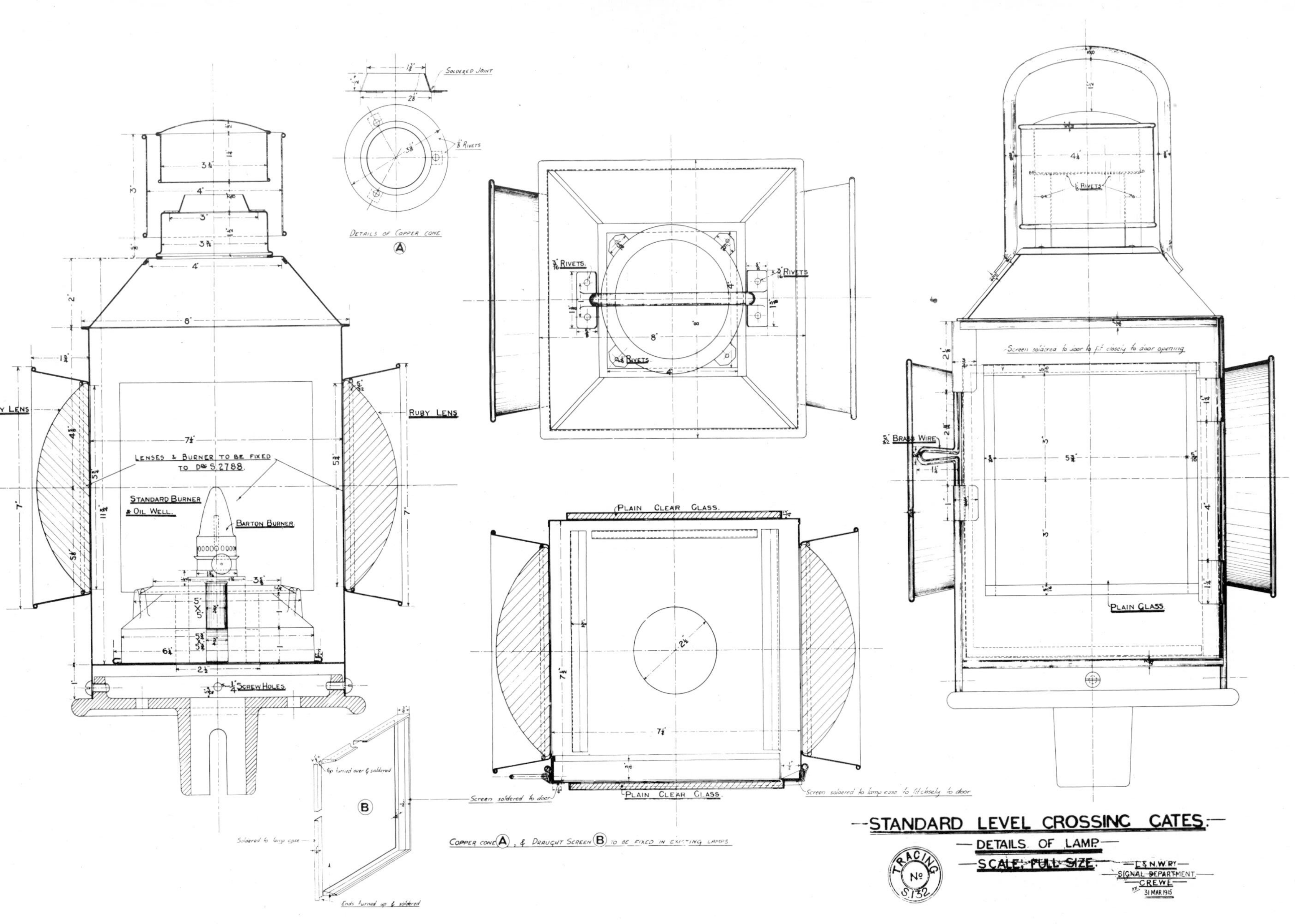

Figure 8.6 *Detail drawing of an LNW Level Crossing Gate Lamp. This had a spigot base and slotted into a square socket on the top of the gate so that it could easily be removed for trimming and filling. The socket used on the gate was a standard LNW locomotive lamp socket. These sockets continued to be used on the gates after they were discontinued for locomotive work and many remained in use until recent times. Scale of reproduction: ¼ full size.*

Plate 8.5 *This skew crossing at Woburn Sands illustrates the use of long and short gates (see* **Figure 8.4 (B)***). The main gates are of the modified '1948' type, with half inch gas pipes at altered spacing instead of the one inch ones originally provided (see* **Figure 8.3***). The foot crossing has been partially straightened, the wicket gate being adjacent to the main gates at the left hand end but separated from them by a section of fence at the right hand end. Note the stay bar giving additional support to the left hand gate post.*

therefore continue after the main gates had been closed and the signals cleared. When the train was approaching the signalman could lock the wickets shut to prevent further use. For this reason the wickets on each side of the line were locked by separate levers. This allowed one gate to be locked to prevent any further pedestrians from entering the crossing, while the other gate could be left free until everyone was clear, otherwise there was the possibility of trapping someone inside the crossing. Although the gates were worked by the pedestrians they were fitted with a lock from the cabin working on the foot of the gate. The bearing at that point ran in a sloping track so that the whole gate rose slightly when opened, the weight of the gate then caused it to close automatically after use. In this way the gate did not have to be operated from the cabin but the wicket lever would lock it shut. The arrangement of the standard level crossing with its four main gates and two wickets on one side is shown in **Figures 8.1** and **8.4**.

Now that some of the basic elements making up the level crossing system have been mentioned a description of the operation of the gates may be of assistance. The gate wheel drove a vertical spindle with a small gear wheel at the bottom. This worked on a horizontal driving wheel placed at ground level in the locking room of the cabin (**Plate 8.4**). The gate wheel was turned until the slack in the system was taken up, the gates moved and all of them had gone properly home. Adjustments did not need to be too critical therefore and the gearing of the system made operating relatively easy. An LNW gate wheel required about 2½ turns (or 900° of movement) to give the 90° of movement necessary in a normal crossing. The LNW ratio of movement of 10 to 1 was quite low and the majority of companies had ratios in the region of between 40 and 80 to 1, although the Great Western used a 6 to 1 ratio.

The ground level driving wheel had a cross bar representing its three foot diameter. This gave a radius of operation adjustable up to nine inches for each of two drive rods which were connected to adjustable sleeves, one on each side of the centre of the wheel giving a pull on one rod and a push on the other. The four gates were coupled in diagonally opposite pairs through the medium of four 24 by 24 inch cranks and from each of these cranks a rod

Plate 8.6 *A set of very long single gates (of different sizes!) on a skew crossing at Deganwy. Note how only the roadway portion of the area between the gates is boarded out. The nearest gate has two sets of stay bars, while the stay rods necessary to assist the gate post in supporting the weight of the gate will be noted. The gates are of the '1948' type and have a more modern design of gate lamp. A footbridge, interestingly crossing diagonally over the roadway in order to shorten the span, is provided instead of a footway and wickets.*

was connected to a rack and pinion at the heel of each gate (see **Figure 8.1**). The main adjustment for a pair of gates was therefore given at the horizontal driving wheel and further slight adjustment could be made at the adjustable coupling.

An advantage of this method of operation was that the transmission rods ran parallel and were easily accommodated in the trunking under the road. It was also suitable for gates working through obtuse angles. The rodding ran alongside the roadway stop rod in order to operate the automatic stop raising gear. Standard LNW channel point rodding was used for the gate drive rods. Despite their substantial nature it was sometimes possible for them to become bent when large gates were operated in high winds, a problem common to most types of crossing.

In addition to the gate wheel, four levers were normally provided in the cabin to control a level crossing. These consisted of two wicket gate lock levers (where wickets were provided), plus a gate stop lever and a gate lock lever. The stop lever worked all four sets of stops, these consisted of two (one each side) to hold the gates across the road and two to hold them across the railway (see **Figure 8.1**). The gate lock lever operated a bolt in the horizontal drive wheel which prevented it turning. The bolt locked the driving wheel in position when the gates were across the road. This method of locking the gates had the advantage that the bolting gear did not need to pass outside the cabin.

As a general rule the two wicket gate levers were placed at the end of the lever frame nearest the crossing. This enabled the signalman to observe the crossing when operating them. In some cabins the main gate stop and lock levers were positioned with the wicket levers. More commonly, the stop and lock levers were placed together near the centre of the frame, more or less mid way between the up and down line signals. Cabins with hand gates locked by Black's locks or some similar device would only need one lever unless separate wickets were also provided.

Naturally, not all level crossings were square or had more or less equal widths of road and railway. Here special arrangements had to be made, sometimes by providing single long gates, pairs of long gates or one long and one short gate in each pair. Skew and large crossings presented two problems, the longer gates could strike each other as they opened and shut and it was possible for the railway stops to come in an awkward position. To get over these problems it was common practice to provide one long and one short gate on each side (**Figure 8.4**). Where more than two tracks had to be spanned by the main crossing (many siding lines were protected by a separate hand worked crossing) the length of the gates could be considerably greater than the width of the road. In these circumstances the large gates were used to make a square crossing and only one half of the square boarded out for the roadway. As an example, four 24′ 7″ gates were provided in 1921 (replacing a similar crossing) at Carterhouse Junction to span four lines. The roadway was only about 20 feet wide and was placed down one side of the gate layout. Indeed one of the other gates simply butted up against a building when closed across the road.

At stations where there was a level crossing, the station cabin would usually be placed next to the crossing to enable the signalman to supervise it. This often meant that the cabin was some distance away from the goods yard points producing an awkward layout with long rodding runs. In many cases the cabin was too far away, especially in the early days when the distances over which points could be worked was strictly limited, and a separate ground frame had to be provided to work the points. This could be controlled from the cabin by means of a bolt lock or midway release (see Chapter 15). Alternatively, the frame could slot the necessary running signals to protect its points or it could be controlled by Annett's key (see Chapter 11).

In some cases the layout at the other end of the station from the level crossing was felt to be more important than the crossing. An example would be a junction between two lines. The cabin was therefore placed near to that rather than at the crossing. Here the gates would be worked by a porter or crossing keeper and some means of interlocking provided between cabin and gates, or gates and signals. Examples of this practice occurred at Hest Bank and Bare Lane (both later replaced by cabins near the crossings) and Seaton Junction.

The first gates built at Crewe were probably, like much of the other outdoor equipment, based on Saxby practice. They were usually constructed completely in timber and were of the five bar field type design. The standard LNW design of road gates illustrated in this chapter seems to have been introduced at the beginning of 1879. The design then remained in use practically unchanged for the remainder of the life of the LNW. Following a fatal accident on the level crossing at Smethwick, it was decided in February 1885 that lattice work (mesh guards) should be fitted to gates in built up areas in order to prevent children climbing between the bars and getting onto the line. The guards were generally provided in addition to the bars and the note on the drawings stating that bars were not to be provided was a later addition (**Figures 8.3** and **8.5**). In practice the number of gates fitted with mesh guards seems to have been fairly small. The LNW designs of gate were adopted for use on the Central and Western Divisions of the LMSR. In 1948 the arrangement of the horizontal tubes was altered (**Figure 8.3**) but otherwise the gates became the standard for the Western and Central sections of the London

Plate 8.7 *A pair of gates locked by Annett's Keys at Lidlington, showing the standard arrangement of bolts, locks and keys.*

Midland Region. The standard design of wicket gate was introduced in March, 1882. Many gates, mostly of the post 1948 arrangement, are still in use today, although the majority will be replaced by lifting barriers as renewals become necessary. In some cases the former Lancashire and Yorkshire Railway design of gate wheel has been used in preference to the LNW design when renewals have been required. The L&Y wheel was broadly similar to the LNW pattern, but had exposed bevel gears and was not fitted with the ship's wheel type handles. It had a greater reduction ratio than the LNW wheel and had the advantage that it made the operation of the gates at large or awkward crossings somewhat easier.

As already mentioned, not all crossings were worked from signal cabins (if indeed a cabin was provided at all). There were many crossings which were not at block posts and were worked by hand by keepers and a number at the 'key interlocking' stations. The gates themselves were usually of standard design although in some cases no separate wicket gates were provided. In a few instances a

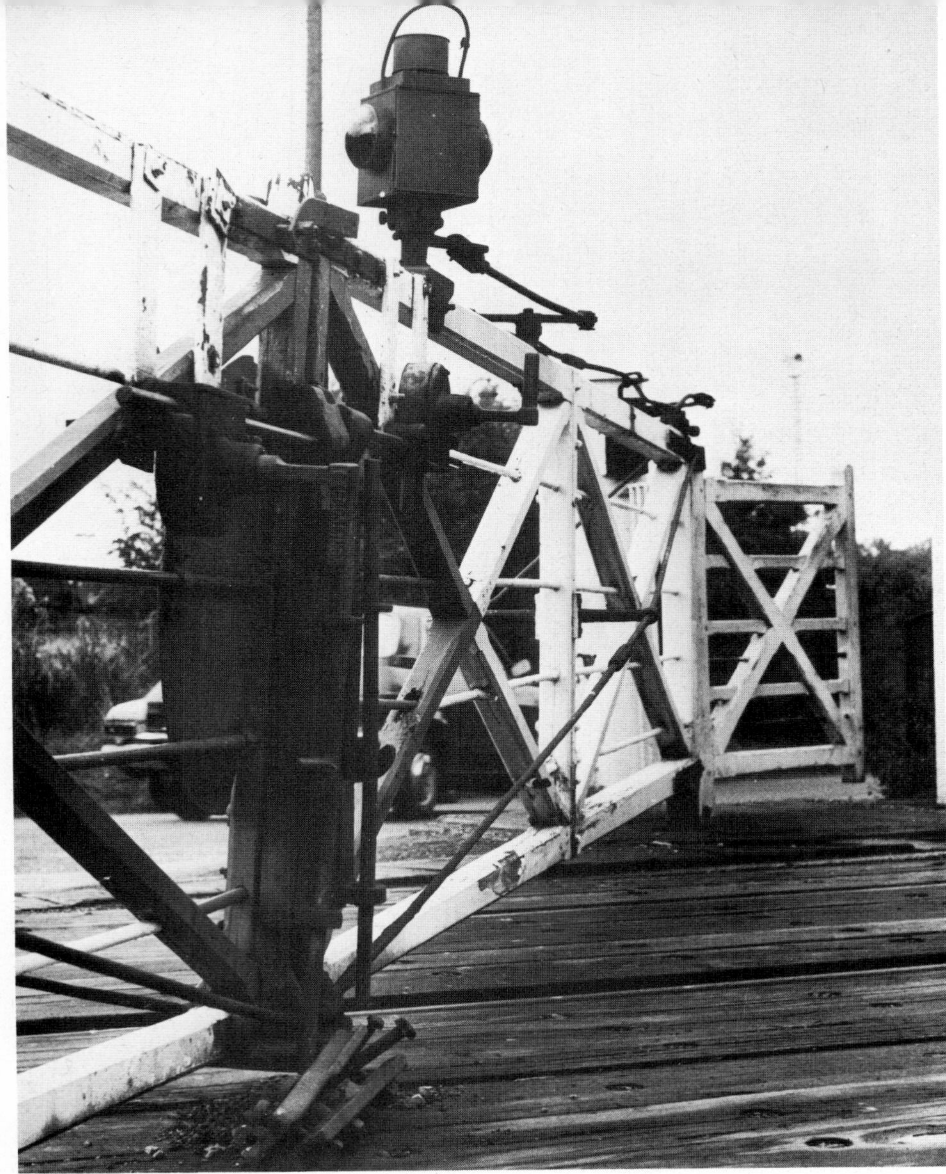

Plate 8.8 *An alternative form of Annett's Key gate locking at Bedlam Gates. Here the keys lock the two gates together by bolts rather than locking the ground bolts. This is a skew crossing and the lamp is mounted on a pivot so that it can swivel to face directly along the road or railway. A drive rod (to the right of the lamp) is attached to the lamp and gate post and arranged so that it automatically turns the lamp through the required angle as the gate swings from one position to the other. The disadvantage of using a fixed lamp can be seen in* **Plates 8.2** *and* **8.6**.

degree of mechanisation was adopted by providing sympathetic working gear.

At the hand worked crossings some form of interlocking was obviously desirable to prevent the gates being open to the road with the signals clear for a train, or to prevent an enterprising member of the public from opening the gates as soon as the operator had gone away (the Law and Board of Trade requirements still applied of course). In some cases conventional gate stop and lock levers were provided in a cabin or in a ground frame. More commonly a 'Black's Lock' was used. This device, invented by Mr P Black in 1877 was simplicity itself, and consisted of a rod running from a lever in the cabin to the gate post against which the gate closed when across the road. The rod ran up the post via a crank to a lock with a bolt hole in it. The gate had an ordinary bolt, and when the gate was across the road the bolt fitted into the lock on the post to secure the gate closed. When the lock lever was pulled the rod moved and held the bolt in position (**Plate 9.3**).

The simplicity of the 'Annett's Key' system is described in Chapter 11 and it was also used to lock crossing gates. Here two or four keys were provided, one for each gate. Where the gates worked sympathetically together two keys only were sometimes provided, one for each pair of gates. The Annett's keys used were of configuration 'C' 'Crossing' (see **Plates 8.7** and **8.8**). An Annett's lock was mounted on the gate working with a ground bolt. When the gates were closed across the railway the keys were locked in the locks on the gates, since the bolt holes in the ground in this position did not permit the bolt to move far enough to release the keys. With the gates across the roadway the ground bolts on the gates were able to pass further into the bolt holes in the ground and release the keys. The act of removing the key locked the bolt in the lowered position and so prevented the gate being moved. The keys fitted into locks in the lever frame working the signals (which could be of the key interlocking or large type), and it was necessary to have all the keys in the frame before the signals were released. Complete interlocking was achieved by the fact that, with the signals 'off', the keys were locked in the frame.

In LNW days the level crossing gates were generally painted white, the ironwork and fittings being standard brown. Some of the men thought that black looked better, and a few crossings could be found with black fittings. 'Head Office' was not impressed however, and a memo was sent out on the 24th October, 1887:—

> 'I have noticed that some men are painting the ironwork on level crossings etc. black. Standard brown must be used for all work.'

In LMS and BR days the gates were usually white with black metalwork.

Chapter Nine

Signal Cabins – Pre 1874 Designs

Plate 9.1 *This delightful cabin at Horseley Fields Junction, near Great Bridge, was probably constructed in 1866 to control the junction with the Great Western spur from Swan Village opened in September of that year. It, therefore, represents one of the earliest types of cabin erected by Saxby and Farmer. Even in those early days Saxbys were using 'standard' designs for their signal cabins and cabins of similar basic design were erected on a number of railways at about this time. It was similar, for instance, to cabins found on the Brighton Line (see Plate 131 of 'Southern Signals'). The vertical planking of the timber top is characteristic of much early work. The need for a tall cabin to give the signalman adequate sight of the layout was solved in this instance by placing the cabin near the top of the cutting slope. A disadvantage of this method was that the rods and wires had to run down the cutting slope. These sloping runs were difficult to install and maintain, and so this type of construction was not very common. Another example occurred at Platt Bridge Junction near Wigan, where the cabin controlled two lines at different levels. (See also* **Plate 10.5***). A characteristic of many small early cabins was that they often tended to be square or even to be wider than they were long. This one had a 'length' (parallel to the tracks) of 12 feet and a 'width' of 14′ 6″. A cabin of similar design, but mounted on a tall wooden base to give sight over a bridge, existed in the early days at Eden Valley Junction near Penrith and this too was wider than it was long. The Saxby lever frame at Horseley Fields was replaced by an LNW Tumbler frame of 18 levers, mounted on wooden uprights, in 1886, and the cabin remained in use until closure of the junction in December 1970.*

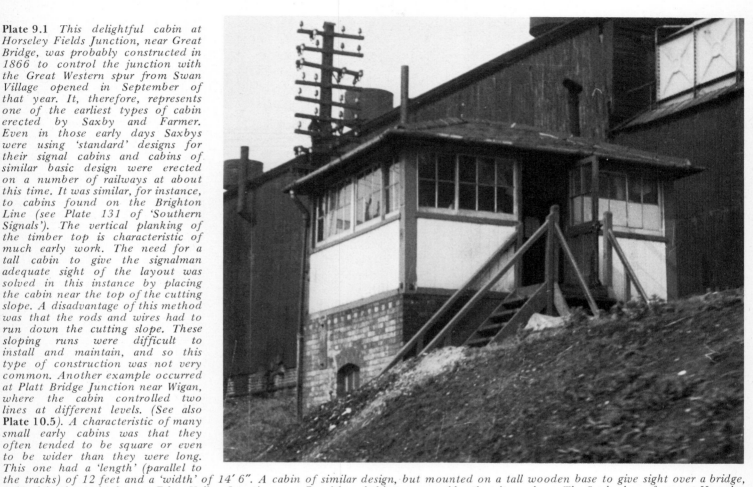

Photo: G H Platt

In this Chapter and Chapter 10, as well as elsewhere in the book, a series of type designations have been used to describe the most common designs of signal cabin used on the LNWR. The first two types were provided by contractors (Saxby and Farmer) and are described in this chapter. The remaining types (three to five) were the successive designs of cabin adopted and constructed by the LNWR for its own signalling work between 1874 and 1923.

These type designations have been used for convenience and as a clear, but brief, means of referring to the different designs of cabin. It should be noted, however, that these descriptions were never used by the LNWR itself to whom they were simply standard signal cabins.

As outlined in Chapter 1, change was very rapid in the early days as ideas and practices developed and evolved. The signal cabins developed by stages from the 'sentry boxes' provided as a shelter for the policemen who were at first responsible for regulating the traffic. These were simply shelters and the policeman had to leave them to work the point and signal levers which were dotted about the layout. The movement towards the concentration of levers brought more of them together near the cabin, while the introduction of proper interlocking frames heralded a considerable step forward. The interlocking mechanisms then available were fairly delicate and to protect and keep them in good condition it became the practice to place them in the huts. It was quickly recognised that this was

Plate 9.2 *Illustrates the standard design of cabin used on the Chester and Holyhead section, around 1870, when the block system was put in. This example is at Llanfair. The cabin was placed away from the station in order to supervise the level crossing over a minor road a short distance to the east. A ground frame was provided to work the station goods yard. The level crossing was initially protected by hand worked gates but in 1893 the station was resignalled and a new set of gates and wickets were provided and connected to the cabin. A new 18 lever LNW Tumbler frame and a gate wheel were installed in the existing cabin to control the new layout, this work costing £289. However, as can be seen the cabin is rather small, the external dimensions being 14′ 10″ x 10′, having been built to suit a much smaller frame without gate controls. In order to get the frame and gate wheel in the cabin, the door and staircase were removed from the left hand end to the rear of the cabin. Even so things were very cramped and there was little room to move about when any levers were pulled over. Today things have almost turned full circle, the cabin remains only to supervise the crossing and has a mere four levers. The gate wheel too has gone and the gates are again worked by hand. At the left hand end of the roof is the bracket for the signal cabin bell, a common feature of LNWR cabins (Chapter 15). Quite a number of cabins of this type existed until recent years and were characterized by the six pane windows.*

advantageous from all considerations and so the signal cabin, as we know it, was born. The original huts had been largely provided at ground or rail level for cheapness and convenience, although a few were placed at the top of cutting slopes or other features. An example of this practice existed at Wolverton Blue Bridge, where in October 1855 it was instructed that:—

> 'On the engine of a down goods train passing the auxiliary signal, the policeman on duty at the Blue Bridge is to turn the auxiliary signal on red before descending to the points to turn the train into the siding.'

With the new signal cabins it became the practice to raise them a few feet above rail level. This had the advantage of giving the policeman or signalman a better view of the lines under his control as well as providing space to accommodate the interlocking and other apparatus below floor level.

With the spread of the train telegraph system (initially in the permissive, time interval form) in the 1850's recognisable signal cabins began to appear. Since these now had to house the instruments and interlocking apparatus they became somewhat more substantial and durable than the small huts and shacks previously provided. Inevitably, in most cases only the tiny wayside cabins remained long enough to give us an idea of what was done. The basic theme of a small brick or timber (or a timber top on a brick base) structure with a hipped roof and a reasonable area of glass in the front, to give a good

Plate 9.3 *This shows, perhaps, one of the best known of all LNW signal cabins. Scout Green was situated midway up the notorious 1 in 75 climb from Tebay to Shap Summit and generations of railway photographers have stood on the fells around this cabin waiting for the stumpy down home signal to be lowered and herald the approach of a train working hard against the grade.*

This was a Lancaster and Carlisle section cabin, erected in 1871 in connection with the introduction of block working on the line. The tiny cabin remained in use until power signalling came along in 1972 and shows how some of the oldest equipment could survive even on the main lines. It supervised a tiny level crossing which did not warrant gates worked from the cabin and single hand gates (one of which can be seen in the photograph) were provided. A Black's lock, to secure the gate across the road, was provided in 1942 and one can be seen on the left hand end of the gate in the photograph. Like the standard type Saxby cabins, the windows had only a single horizontal glazing bar. The LNW signal cabin nameboard, fitted to all signal cabins where the cast iron letters could not be screwed directly to the woodwork, was retained to the end. The shape of the board with its pointed ends is worthy of note. LNW nameboards were always placed on the front of the cabin (as were those of most Companies). The board on the end is of LMS origin.

Photo: M J Borrowdale

view for the signalman, was adopted for the work. The signalling contractors themselves probably led the way towards some measure of standardisation by providing suitable buildings as part of their contracts. In other cases the Divisional Engineers would knock up something suitable. The use of cabins raised high above the line on stilts, characteristic of Saxby's work on the Brighton line, was introduced onto the North Western but does not seem to have found much favour. The quality of timber available in the early days and the rudimentary knowledge of preservation techniques, meant that timber structures could have fairly limited lives and hence did not appeal to the LNW who liked something a little more permanent. Thus began the LNW tradition of brick structures (or at least structures with brick bases in order to lift the wooden portion out of the wet). The first recognisable standard design of cabin was produced by Saxby and Farmer and first made its appearance in about 1863 (**Plate 9.1**).

The introduction of proper signalling and interlocked cabins did not really get under way until 1865/6 and then the installations were scattered around to meet local needs and in connection with new stations and junctions. The introduction of the block telegraph began in earnest in 1870 (Chapter 1) and in connection with the work many hundreds of new cabins were constructed over the next few years. Because of the amount of work to be done and the speed with which it was required, some of the Divisional Engineers assisted during the first year or so by building some of the cabins. This resulted in Divisional designs of cabin, such as those on the Chester and Holyhead and

LAMBRIGG XING.

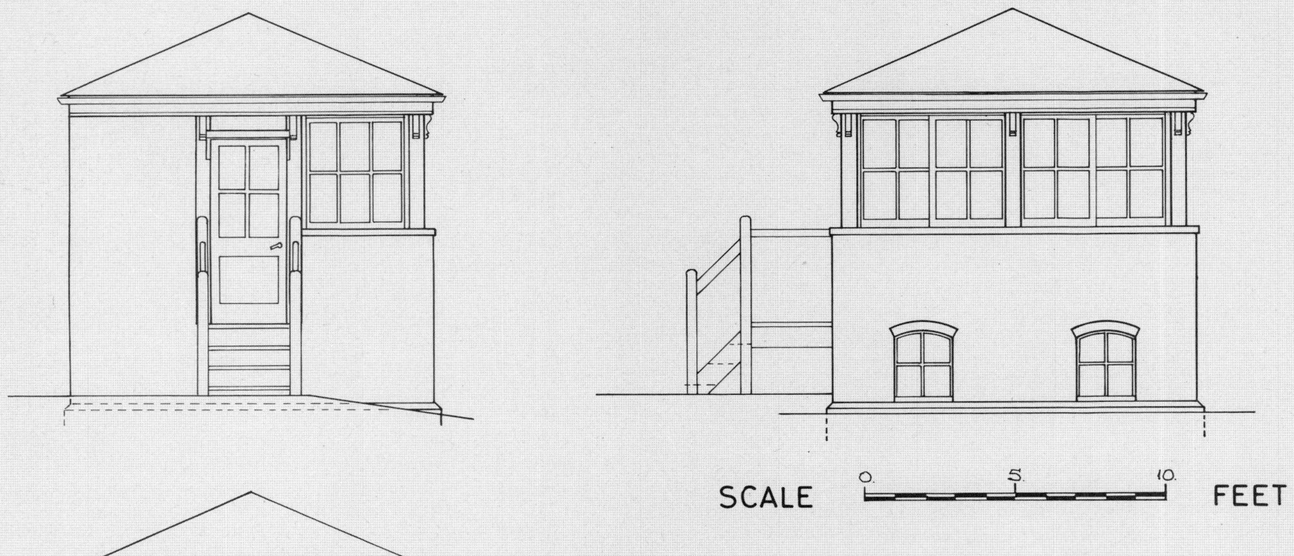

SCALE 0. 5. 10. FEET

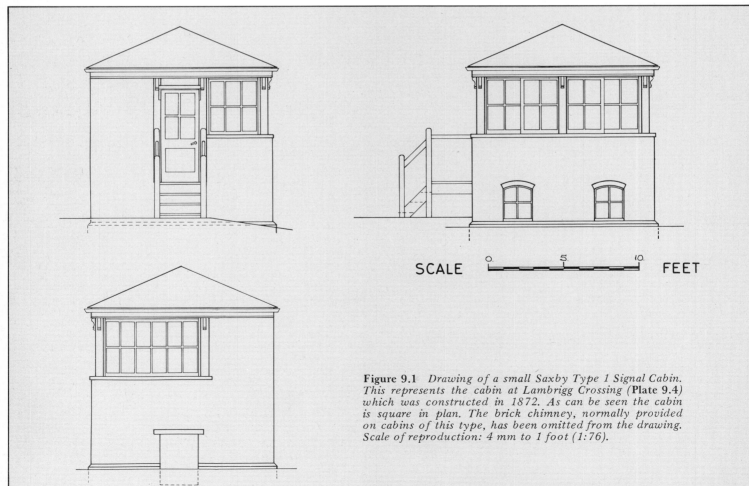

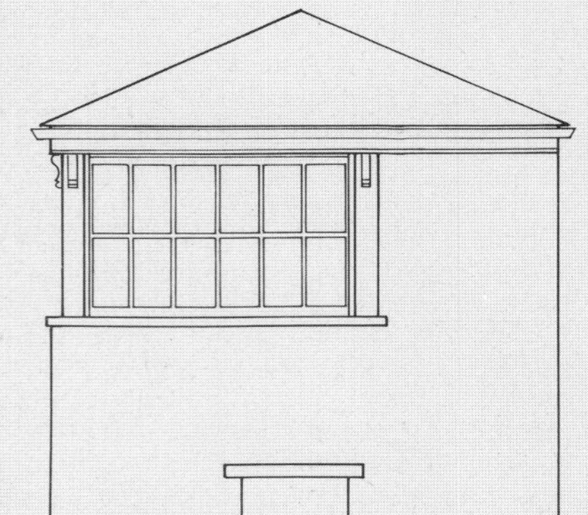

Figure 9.1 *Drawing of a small Saxby Type 1 Signal Cabin. This represents the cabin at Lambrigg Crossing (***Plate 9.4***) which was constructed in 1872. As can be seen the cabin is square in plan. The brick chimney, normally provided on cabins of this type, has been omitted from the drawing. Scale of reproduction: 4 mm to 1 foot (1:76).*

◁ **Plate 9.4** *This diminutive cabin is a good example of the Standard 'Type 1' design of cabin described in the text. The cabin at Lambrigg Crossing was a gate and intermediate block cabin situated on the climb from Oxenholme to Grayrigg. The small ornamental mouldings, at the top of the window pillars, can be seen clearly in this illustration. A feature of most early cabins was the brick chimney and this too is visible. A drawing of this cabin appears in* **Figure 9.1**. *It will be noted that the plinth of this cabin is practically buried in ballast. It seems unlikely that it was constructed like this and the photograph shows the effects 100 years of relaying and reballasting could have in raising general track levels and in altering the appearance and gradients of railways. The cabin was photographed in June 1968.*

Lancaster and Carlisle sections illustrated in **Plates 9.2** and **9.3**. Saxby and Farmer's new contract of 1867 included for the provision of brick signal cabins (Appendix 4). Two standard designs of cabin were introduced for this work.

On the northern sections of the LNW an all brick design was adopted (**Plate 9.4** and **Figure 9.1**). Distinctive features were the small ornamental wooden brackets on the corner and middle window posts under the eaves and the cast iron locking room windows, which were to appear throughout the history of LNWR signal cabins. For convenience this can be referred to as the LNW 'type 1' or Northern type signal cabin. As can be seen, the Divisional types illustrated in **Plates 9.2** and **9.3** have much in common with the type 1 with which they were contemporary. This was particularly so in the case of the Lancaster and Carlisle type. The type 1 design was also adopted by Saxbys for other work in the north of England and many examples appeared during the same period on the Lancashire and Yorkshire Railway while odd examples were to be found on other lines such as the Manchester, Sheffield and Lincolnshire.

On the southern sections of the LNW a different design of cabin was adopted. This was a design used by Saxbys for work all over the south of England. Once again, the cabins had a hipped roof like their type 1 counterparts in the north but this time the brick structure extended only up to floor level, the structure above being entirely of wood, except for the chimney. As can be seen from **Plate 9.7** the most distinctive features were the timber upper structure and the long narrow (about 8 inches deep) window panes between the main windows and the roof. For convenience this type of cabin may be referred to as the 'type 2' or Southern design. Large numbers of cabins of this design were erected by Saxbys on the Brighton line (see Plates 130 and 134 of 'Southern Signals') while examples also appeared on other railways south of Crewe such as the Great Western. The cabins on the LNW differed in one important respect from the equivalent structures erected on other lines in that the majority were constructed with brick bases. On most other lines in the south during this period the cabins were provided in all timber form.

For convenience the dividing line between the 'Northern' and 'Southern' designs may be taken as Crewe. This division was not absolute and a few cabins spilled over it. The Chester and Holyhead line was of interest in that both the Type 1 and Type 2 cabins appeared as well as the Divisional design.

A few general comments might be made about the signal cabins on the LNW in the years between 1865 and 1875. As already explained these were usually of brick construction although all-timber versions were also built, particularly where foundation conditions were poor. The all-timber cabins were, of course, rather less durable than their brick counterparts and hence the vast majority disappeared many years ago. Generally the cabins were small, layouts at most stations were usually very simple (the great expansion of freight traffic did not really get under way until the 1870's) and the signalling itself was very simple. Most layouts only consisted of two or three signals each way plus a few points and the lever frames were fairly small. The majority of stations on the North Western were reconstructed after 1874, in some cases several times, and this swept away many of the early cabins.

In most cases the Saxby cabins were constructed to dimensions which made up to whole numbers of feet (for example lengths or widths of 10, 12 or 14 feet and so on). Where site conditions allowed it they tended to be quite

Plate 9.5 *Another example of the 'Type 1' cabin, this time at Penrith and photographed in 1971. This cabin was made tall in order to give sight over an adjacent overbridge. An interesting feature is the way it has been perched on top of an existing wall, perhaps an early example of doing things on the cheap! Just above the stone plinth and below the windows are the LNW nameboards. These read 'Penrith No. 3 North' and illustrate the common LNW practice of giving cabins both numbers and names (although only one of the two usually appeared on the cabin itself). Penrith No. 1 cabin incidentally was 'C K and P Junction' and No. 2 was 'Station'. A comparison of this photograph and* **Plate 9.4** *serves to illustrate an important difference between the design of windows used in the Saxby cabins and those used in the LNW standard cabins (types 3, 4 and 5). In the case of the LNW cabins the windows were made to standard fixed sizes and the cabins effectively constructed around them. In the Saxby cabins the windows were made to fit the size of cabin required, this being done by altering the width of the window panes so that some arrangement of windows would fit the space required, the height of the windows remaining the same. In the case of Penrith No. 3 the window panes have the effect of making the windows look narrower than those at Lambrigg. The cabin at Penrith has had its chimney replaced by a stove pipe, a modification carried out to many old cabins in later years.*

Plate 9.6 *This is the final illustration of one of the early standard northern Saxby cabins. The type 1 cabin at Whitehaven Bransty No. 1 controlled the station throat and the entry to the single track Furness Railway tunnel to Corkickle and Barrow. It was brought into use in 1874 and rather embarrassingly for Saxbys, an accident occurred here through a signalling error on the day the station cabins were brought into use! A problem at Bransty was always the limited space between the tunnel mouth and the platform and as can be seen the pointwork extends into the tunnel. This presented a signalling problem as there was insufficient space in the tunnel for a signal. The best that could be done was to erect the gantry seen at the far end of the cabin. This has 'bridge signal' arms of the S1463 type (***Figure 7.7***) to enable them to be placed as low as possible so that the drivers could see them in the tunnel. They were, of course, well in advance of the points in this position. The arms were, therefore, repeated in the tunnel by ground disc signals at the points. This practice also occurred at Euston No. 4 on the Up Engine line, on the Up Slow line at Primrose Hill Tunnel, and in the tunnels at Huddersfield No. 1. At Bangor No. 1 the junction bracket signal, immediately outside the tunnel, was just in rear of the points, but in order to protect a crossover road in the tunnel two ground discs had to be provided as home signals in the middle of the tunnel. Returning to the photograph, note also the fixed distant signal for Corkickle No. 2 cabin by the tunnel mouth, only a few yards in advance of the platform starting signals.*

Photo: M N Bland

wide, often being appreciably wider than the 12 feet which was adopted as standard in the LNW cabins (see **Figures 9.2** and 9.3). Indeed in the case of some small cabins it was by no means uncommon to find that the width of the cabin was greater than its length (**Plate 9.1**).

As was common practice at the time for small buildings many of the early signal cabins did not have slate roofs, the timber roof boarding being covered with a layer of zinc sheeting to keep out the weather. No doubt this sort of treatment was cheaper due to the relatively high cost of slates in those days. This form of treatment was applied originally to the majority of the type 2 cabins. No evidence has yet come to light on the original form of roofing applied to the type 1 cabins but it is possible that some had zinc coverings. In July 1877 Dick reported that the zinc roofs of about 80 old cabins were in need of repair

Plate 9.8 *This photograph of Bulkington Station in about 1880 epitomizes the English country station, with the small station buildings incorporating the Station Master's house, short low platforms and a small signal cabin nearby. An interesting feature of this station is its name on the gable end of the building. This apparently consists of individual white painted letters attached directly to the brickwork. (Although in later years the lettering was painted onto the brickwork). The clutter of enamelled iron advertising signs was a disease of Victorian times.* ▷

Turning to the signal cabin, this was one of the standard 'Type 2' cabins and was erected in 1873. It will be noted that even by 1880 the top windows had been painted over. Most early cabins originally had a zinc covering to the roof rather than slates, as became the norm later, and the zinc roof can be seen in this photograph. On the front of the cabin are the diamond shaped signal lineman's board and oval telegraph lineman's board. Both are happily in the 'all right' position (see Chapter 15). The cabin nameboard is between the signal and telegraph boards, in its usual position on the front of the cabin. This is one of the 'round ended' type illustrated in **Plate 10.20**. *Note the tall brick chimney provided in an attempt to lift the smoke above the eddies created by the overbridge behind the cabin. The telegraph poles behind the cabin are worthy of note and show the old system of mounting two wires only on each spar or cross arm (rather than the four that are common today). The arms are alternately long and short, possibly to help prevent a broken wire falling onto the one below, and most of them are not straight!*

Plate 9.7 *A standard Saxby 'Type 2' cabin as used on the southern half of the LNWR. The narrow top windows are characteristic of these cabins. Those in this example have been painted over at some time. Many cabins received this treatment during the second world war as a blackout measure and, of course, the paint was never removed. In other cases it was possibly the result of complaints about glare from bright sunlight passing through these windows and causing irritation to the signalmen. The plate attached to the front of the cabin in the centre of the woodwork is a Saxby and Farmer makers plate. This cabin opened in 1874 and remained in use until September 1964.*

Photo: M Billington

Plate 9.9 *The cabin at Banbury Lane on the main line south of Rugby. This is basically one of the Saxby 'Type 2' cabins but with a gable type roof. The cabin here was moved diagonally across the crossing from the up to the down side in 1878 at a cost of £120. It seems, therefore, that the original cabin structure was either moved or a second hand structure from elsewhere used, and in the process it received a new gable type roof. By 1878, the LNW 'Type 4' cabin was the standard for new work and this had a gable roof. This particular cabin was still standing at the time of writing and operated a lifting barrier crossing on the very busy section of double track between Roade and Rugby.*

Plate 9.10 *A cabin of unusual design was this one at Wednesbury No. 2 which is something of a cross between the Types 2 and 3 designs of cabin and earlier types such as that at Horseley Fields. It was more conventionally shaped being 22 feet by 13 feet in plan. Another cabin of very similar design was Denbigh No. 1 erected in 1875. Like the majority of those early cabins which survived for any length of time the frame was replaced by an LNW one, the work being done in this case in 1898.*

Photo: M J Lewis

Plate 9.11 *This cabin at Milnthorpe was something of a curiosity. It is again a standard Saxby design but is the only example of the kind so far found on the LNWR. It is basically a modified form of the Type 2 cabin and was used in the north of England quite extensively during the mid 1870's, quite large numbers appearing on the Lancashire and Yorkshire Railway for example. In its normal form the design incorporated the Type 2 narrow top windows and a row of additional windows below the main ones. (An example is Moss Side cabin on the LNW and L&Y Joint line near Kirkham.) This simplified version (either being constructed that way or having the additional windows boarded out later) has boarding instead of the usual top and bottom windows. On the front of the cabin is the LNW nameboard, rather unusually for a timber topped cabin, this is a separate wooden affair rather than the normal arrangement of screwing the letters directly to the woodwork. The board has more rounded ends than those seen in* **Plates 9.3, 9.5** *and* **17.4.** *A noticeable feature is the steel staircase, these were an early BR(LMR) addition, replacing life expired timber ones. No doubt they were introduced due to the high price of good timber after the war. It was also hoped that the steel staircases would have a much longer life than the timber ones. Time has shown that they corrode in much the same way as the wooden ones rot and new replacements now are generally in timber. This photograph was taken in 1968 and shows only too clearly the sad state many cabins on the main line had fallen into by the time electrification and resignalling came along.*

and it was resolved that these should be slated over. As with all these things this took time to put into effect, the cabins only being altered when repairs were necessary. Bulkington still had its zinc roof when photographed in 1880 (**Plate 9.8**) while the type 2 cabin at Cockley Brake Junction was still sporting its in 1912! The majority of cabins which survived for an appreciable period of time eventually had their zinc roof covering replaced by slates.

The LNW commenced its own signalling work in 1874 and its own design of cabin (Type 3) began to appear (Chapter 10). This soon superseded the Saxby designs for most new work even when the installations were still made by Saxby. At this time Saxby and Farmer were in the process of revising their signal cabin designs and once again different designs were adopted in the north and south. Because of the adoption of the LNW's own standard design these new Saxby designs had no real impact on the LNW. Only one example of the new northern type Saxby cabin has so far been found and that was at Milnthorpe (**Plate 9.11**).

In the south Saxby and Farmer obtained a contract in 1874 to carry out the signalling work in connection with the quadrupling of the line between Willesden and Bletchley. For this work they adopted a variation of the type 2 cabin. This was structurally the same as previously, but small ornamental brackets were provided at the eaves, similar, but not identical, to those used on the type 1 cabins. This change was probably connected with the adoption of slates as a roofing material.

As might be expected in those pioneering days when the whole art of signalling was being learned and communications were generally poor, a number of cabins were built to designs other than those already described. Some of those which survived into recent times are illustrated in this Chapter. Penygroes, Wednesbury No. 2 and Bolton No. 1 cabins seem to show some movement towards the LNW type 3 standard cabin design. Bolton No. 1 cabin would, indeed, seem to be an early attempt at the type 3 design.

Figure 9.2 SOME EXAMPLES OF TYPE 1 CABINS SURVIVING INTO B.R. DAYS

Cabin	*Date*	*Size*	*Frame Renewed*
Adlington	1875	14′ 0″ x 12′ 0″	1918
Bay Horse	1869	14′ 0″ x 10′ 6″	1909
Bransty No. 1 (Whitehaven)	1874	16′ 9″ x 10′ 6″	1902
Christleton	1873	14′ 0″ x 12′ 0″	1890
Copley Hill No. 2	1872	22′ 0″ x 13′ 0″	1896
Dunham Massey	1872	14′ 0″ x 12′ 0″	1900
Lambrigg Crossing	1872	12′ 0″ x 12′ 0″	1915
Llysfaen	1868	17′ 6″ x 10′ 0″	1901
Penrith No. 3	1872	18′ 0″ x 14′ 0″	1884
Port Dinorwic	1872	14′ 0″ x 12′ 0″	1903
Port Siding	1872	14′ 0″ x 12′ 0″	1903
Shap Station	1872	14′ 0″ x 12′ 0″	1902
Willaston	1870	12′ 0″ x 10′ 0″	1877
Worleston	1868	14′ 0″ x 12′ 0″	1897

Figure 9.3 SOME EXAMPLES OF TYPE 2 CABINS SURVIVING INTO B.R. DAYS

Cabin	*Date*	*Size*	*Frame Renewed*
Boxmoor	1876	22′ 0″ x 12′ 0″	1902
Brandon and Wolston	1874	14′ 0″ x 12′ 0″	1899
Broxton	1872	12′ 0″ x 10′ 0″	1899
Bulkington	1873	12′ 0″ x 12′ 0″	1911
Coventry No. 2	1874	20′ 0″ x 12′ 0″	1887
Knighton No. 2	1872	14′ 0″ x 12′ 0″	1907
Penrhyn Sidings	1870	11′ 0″ x 13′ 0″	—

Plate 9.12 *This cabin at Penygroes was opened in 1872 in connection with the reconstruction of the line, the new standard gauge branch to Nantlle being opened in October of that year. (See also Chapter 16.) The structure shows a noticeable similarity to the later LNW standard 'Type 3' design but with detail differences. The cabin has a brick back wall, a most unusual feature in composite construction cabins on the LNW.*
Photo: D J Christensen

Plate 9.13 *The final photograph in this section illustrates the cabin at Bolton No. 1, erected in connection with the opening of the new Great Moor Street Station in October 1874. The structure appears to represent an early attempt at the Type 3 design of cabin. The front window layout is basically that used in the LNW standard cabins but the end details are not quite right! The picture is also of interest in showing one of the very few all-timber early cabins to survive into recent times.*
Photo: R T H Platt, 1963

Chapter Ten Signal Cabins—1874 to 1930

As already described, once the LNW had decided to do its own signalling, design work for the new equipment was put in hand. In addition to the obvious items, such as interlocking frames and signals, consideration was given to the question of signal cabin design and whether any benefits would accrue from the use of standard parts which could be mass produced. Saxby and Farmer had shown the way along this road by concentrating on standard designs of cabin (the types 1 and 2 described in Chapter 9). This process was taken a stage further by the LNW in evolving its own design. Since cabins need to be different sizes to suit the location and layout to be controlled, a standard design had to be capable of being varied to suit circumstances. It was realised that the most significant item in the signal cabin structure, and the one from which the greatest benefits of standardisation would be achieved, was the windows. The Saxby sliding windows used in the types 1 and 2 cabins were simplified into just two basic LNW types, the two window and three window units (**Figure 10.2**). Cabins of sizes to suit any number of levers could be produced by use of suitable combinations of these two standard window units.

In line with previous practice, a hipped style of roof was adopted, and the policy of using a brick base for the cabins, wherever possible, was continued. To provide light for the locking room a standard form of cast iron window frame was adopted. This was a direct copy of that used by Saxby and Farmer in their signal cabins. (The same design was later used by both the Railway Signal Company and the Lancashire and Yorkshire Railway for their standard signal cabins!) The result of all this work was what might be termed the type 3 design (**Figure 10.1** and **Plate 10.1**).

Manufacture of the standard parts in the timber shops and foundries at Crewe was a fairly straightforward process once the design work had been completed. The bricks for the cabin bases were produced in the brickworks at Crewe. A large number of cabins of this design were produced between its introduction, in about the middle of 1874, and the end of 1875. As is explained in Chapter 11, the LNW was not able to produce sufficient interlocking frames at Crewe in the early years to meet all its needs and Saxby and Farmer lever frames continued to be purchased. In most cases these were fixed in standard LNW cabins rather than Saxby ones as had been the case previously. There were exceptions to this rule, however, the most significant of which was the resignalling work for the Bletchley to Willesden widening carried out between 1874 and 1877. This work was done entirely by Saxby and Farmer under a special contract and the cabins provided were similar to the (Saxby) Type 2 design. Like the earlier type 1 and 2 cabins, the majority of the type 3 cabins were subsequently swept away in the great widening and enlargements of the 1880's and 1890's and few survived into BR days. **Figure 10.5** lists some of those which did, and as can be seen, the majority were small wayside cabins.

As with the signals, the cabin design was reconsidered in 1875/6. It was realised that the hipped roof was relatively costly due to the amount of fitting work required to the timber framework and finishes, while it also made maintenance more difficult. The cabin design was therefore altered, the hipped roof being replaced by a simple gable roof although the rest of the design remained unchanged. This new 'Type 4' cabin is illustrated in **Figure 10.6** and **Plate 10.3**.

Among the earliest type 4 cabins erected were Oxford Road Junction and Killay, both of which were brought into use in January 1876. The design became standard for all new work and continued to be used until the introduction of the 'type 5' cabin in 1903. The type 4 design was thus in use for rather more than half the life of the LNW Signal Department. Its life spanned much of the great period of railway expansion which was at its height during the 1890's. As a result many hundreds of cabins of this design were erected, and after about 1890 it was by far the most

Plate 10.1 *An LNWR Standard 'Type 3' hipped roof cabin at Monk's Siding, Warrington. This was opened in 1875 and is of size 'E'. The handrails along the windows were provided as a hand hold for the men when they had to stand on the window cleaning stage to clean the outside of the windows. The cabin door was originally placed next to the main windows near the centre of the end and the staircase parallel to the tracks. It had been moved to the left hand end, by the time this photograph was taken in 1972, to allow the staircase to be placed against the cabin wall, and was probably done to allow widening and alteration of the crossing. A special small window has been used to fill the space formerly occupied by the door. Since the photograph was taken the door has been moved again, this time to the opposite end of the cabin. The level crossing gates are of LNW pattern with both gas pipes and mesh guards. Curiously the small type gate has the large gate type of hinge post. An LNW type gate lamp, provided as a night warning for road and rail traffic, can be seen mounted on top of the gate. Note how the sidings behind the cabin have a separate crossing with their own hand gates.*

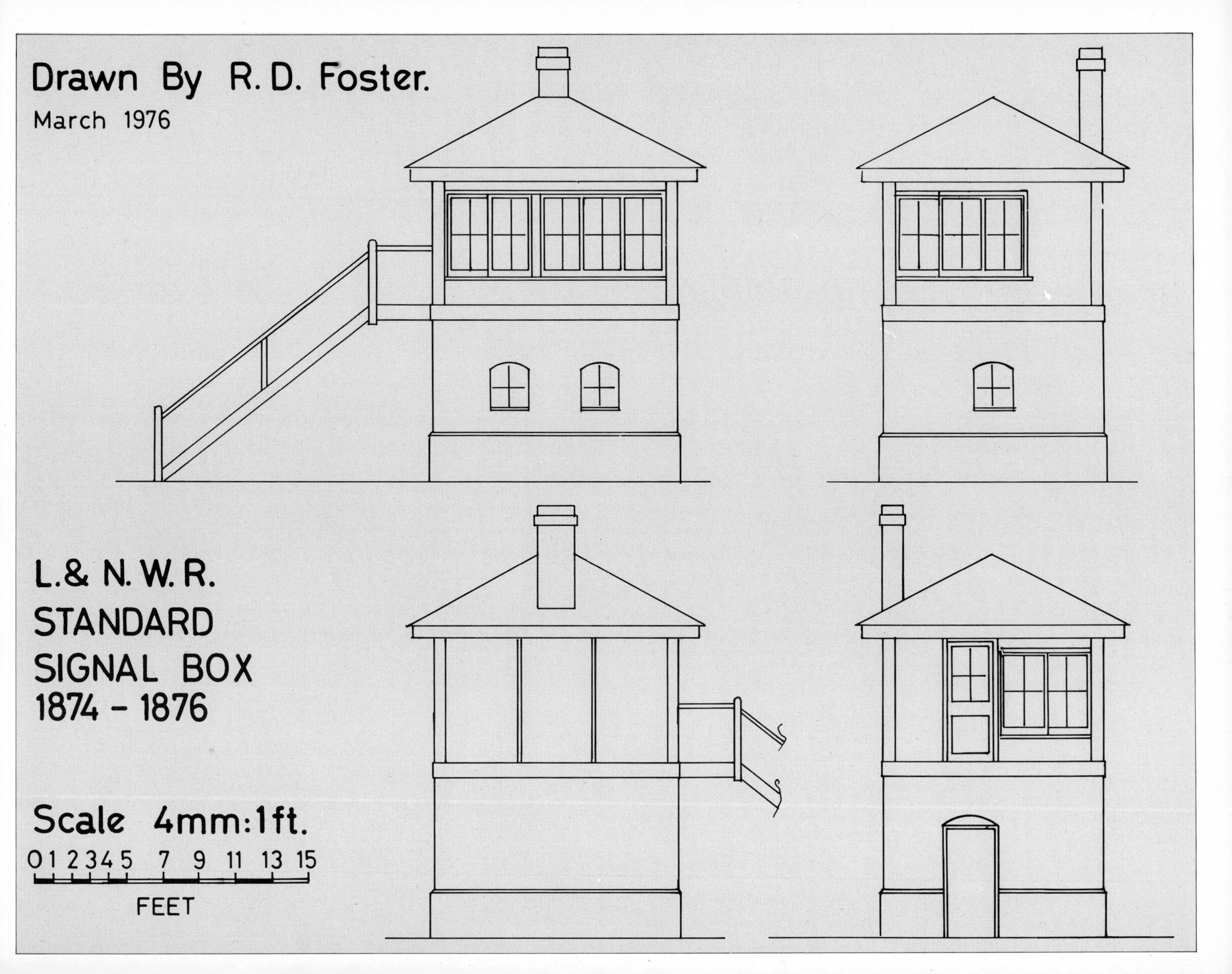

Drawn By R. D. Foster.
March 1976
L.& N. W. R.
STANDARD
SIGNAL BOX
1874 - 1876
Scale 4mm:1ft.
0 1 2 3 4 5 7 9 11 13 15
FEET

◁ **Figure 10.1** *A Cabin of 'Type 3' design. This one is shown with its brick chimney and is of size 'C'. The staircase has been omitted from the end view in order to show the locking room door. Scale of reproduction: 4 mm to 1 foot (1:76).*

ARRANGEMENT OF PARTS FOR FRONT OF SIZE 'C' CABIN

4' - 10½"

7' - 3"

4' - 6"*

2'-6"

END PILLAR

2 WINDOW UNIT

MIDDLE PILLAR

3 WINDOW UNIT

END PILLAR

SECTION THROUGH WINDOW UNITS TO SHEW ARRANGEMENTS OF FIXED AND SLIDING SECTIONS

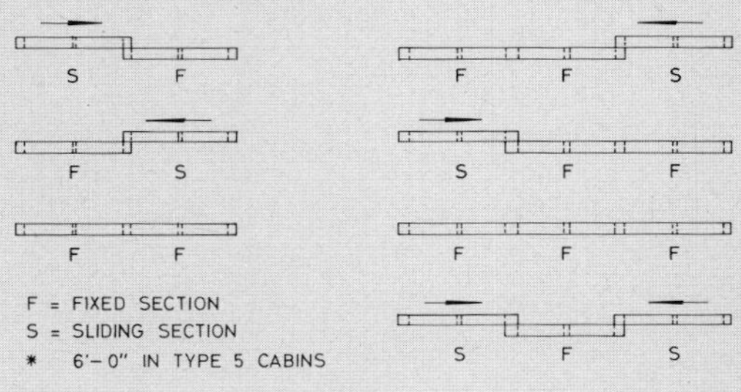

Figure 10.2 *Sketch showing the dimensions of the one, two and three window units. The sketches at the bottom show the way in which the arrangements of sliding and fixed sections in the Types 3 and 4 cabin windows could be varied to suit circumstances. The top sketch also shows the components (windows plus end and middle pillars) necessary to make up the front section of a signal cabin. The case shown is a size 'C' cabin but any size could be constructed from an appropriate combination of windows and end and middle pillars.*

common design of cabin found on the LNW and its successors.

Since the whole concept of the standard signal cabins on the LNW was based on the use of standard windows these merit a detailed description. The design evolved was based on the use of a standard window frame 2′ 6″ wide and 4′ 6″ high overall. These windows were not used singly (except for a few special cabins), but either in pairs (2-window units) or threes (3-window units). Like their predecessors (and most British signal cabins) the windows opened by means of a section sliding behind an adjacent one. This was the reason for using the windows in pairs or threes. In the opening version, the two frames overlapped by 1½″ to give a reasonably weathertight joint when closed. The length of the two and three window standard units were, therefore, not multiples of 2′ 6″, a two window unit being 4′ 10½″ long and a three window unit 7′ 3″ long. Since not all windows were required to be opened, fixed (or partly fixed) versions of the window units were produced. To ensure interchangeability and standard layouts, these fixed units were the same overall size as the sliding ones, **Figure 10.2** should make this clear. The figure also illustrates the combinations of fixed and sliding windows which could be found in the two and three window units. The sliding units were always mounted behind the fixed units (i.e. towards the inside of the cabin).

Windows were fitted along the full length of the front of LNWR cabins, timber pillars (end or middle) being

Figure 10.3 COMPOSITION OF STANDARD SIGNAL CABINS

Size Code 1	2	*Length*	*Nominal Number of Levers*	*Frequency of occurrence* No.	%	*Dimensions and numbers of window components* *End pillar* Size	No.	*Middle pillar* Size	No.	*2 window unit* No.	*3 window unit* No.
C	C	13′ 5½″	15	133	12	6″ sq.	2	4″	1	1	1
D	D	16′ 2½″	20	209	19	6″	2	3¾″	2	3	0
E	E	18′ 9″	25	200	18	6″	2	4½″	2	2	1
F	F	21′ 6″	30	142	13	6″	2	4″	3	4	0
G	G	24′ 1½″	35	98	9	7½″	2	4″	3	3	1
H	H	26′ 6″	40	68	6	7½″	2	4″	3	2	2
J	J	29′ 8″	45	37	3	7½″	2	5″	4	4	1
K	K	32′ 3½″	50	41	4	9″	2	5″	4	3	2
L	L	35′ 0″	55	30	3	9″	2	6″	4	2	3
M	M	38′ 7½″	60	42	4	9″	2	6″	6	7	0
N	N	44′ 0″	70	23	2	9″	2	6″	7	8	0
O	O	48′ 9″	80	27	2	9″	2	6″	7	6	2
P	P	54′ 1½″	90	24	2	9″	2	6″	8	7	2
R	R	65′ 6″	112	18	1.5	9″	2	6″	11	12	0
	S	76′ 3″	135	5	0.4	9″	2	6″	13	14	0
S	T	80′ 4½″	144	4	0.4	9″	2	6″	12	9	4
T	U	96′ 6″	180	8	0.7	9″	2	6″	15	12	4

Total sample size: 1109 signal cabins

Size codes A and B were for the 6′ x 6′ and 9′ x 9′ standard cabins. The width of all standard cabins in size codes C to U was 12 feet.

Figure 10.3 *Table listing the components required to make up the front section of a standard size signal cabin. Column 1 lists the original size code designations and Column 2 the codes used after the introduction of the 76′ 3″ size. The Column 2 designations are used throughout this book. The frequency of occurrence columns lists the number (or percentage) of cabins in a sample which were of each particular size.*

Figure 10.4 ARRANGEMENT OF WINDOWS IN STANDARD SIGNAL CABINS

Size	*Order of standard two and three window units in cabin front*
C	2 + 3
D	2 + 2 + 2
E	2 + 3 + 2
F	2 + 2 + 2 + 2
G	2 + 2 + 3 + 2
H	2 + 3 + 3 + 2
J	2 + 2 + 3 + 2 + 2
K	2 + 3 + 2 + 3 + 2
L	2 + 3 + 3 + 3 + 2
M	2 + 2 + 2 + 2 + 2 + 2 + 2
N	2 + 2 + 2 + 2 + 2 + 2 + 2 + 2
O	2 + 3 + 2 + 2 + 2 + 2 + 3 + 2
P	2 + 2 + 2 + 3 + 2 + 3 + 2 + 2 + 2
R	2 + 2 + 2 + 2 + 2 + 2 + 2 + 2 + 2 + 2 + 2 + 2
S	2 + 2 + 2 + 2 + 2 + 2 + 2 + 2 + 2 + 2 + 2 + 2 + 2 + 2
T	2 + 3 + 2 + 3 + 2 + 2 + 2 + 2 + 2 + 3 + 2 + 3 + 2
U	2 + 2 + 3 + 2 + 3 + 2 + 2 + 2 + 2 + 2 + 2 + 3 + 2 + 3 + 2 + 2

Figure 10.4 *The layout of windows in the standard size cabins were almost always made up with the same standard patterns or layouts of windows. These standard patterns are set out in this table.*

Figure 10.5 SOME EXAMPLES OF TYPE 3 CABINS WHICH SURVIVED INTO B.R. DAYS

Cabin	*Size Code*	*Date*	*Frame Renewed*
Betley Road	E	1875	1904
Brookhay Crossing	C	1874	—
Elmesthorpe	E	1875	—
Essington Wood	D	1875	1892
Fossway Crossing	C	1875	1890
Gowerton No. 1	C	1874	—
Great Barr	C	1875	—
Macclesfield Tunnel End	F	1875	—
Monks Siding	E	1875	—
Narborough No. 2	E	1875	—
Sandy No. 2	E	1875	—
Stafford No. 5	R	1876	—
Vulcan Bank	D	1875	1882

provided between the window units for rigidity and to support the roof structure. The arrangement of these components is shown in the diagram in **Figure 10.2.** Obviously, different sizes of cabins were required at different places to suit the layouts to be controlled. Cabins were constructed of standard lengths, which were determined by the combination of window units, the timber corner posts and the posts between the windows. **Figure 10.3** lists the standard sizes of cabins used on the LNWR, together with the number of levers they were intended for. Also listed is the number of basic components, and their dimensions (where appropriate), required to make a cabin of that size. **Figure 10.2** shows the parts required for a size 'C' cabin.

The standard sizes of cabins were each given a letter coding for reference purposes and these letter designations were widely used in paperwork within the Signal Department. Column 1 lists the sizes originally available when the cabin designs were evolved in the 1870's. In the 1890's it was felt that there was a need for an additional cabin between the 65 and 80 foot sizes. A new 76' 3" standard cabin was, therefore, introduced and designated size 'S'.

Plate 10.2 *Fossway Crossing, Lichfield. This photograph shows the back of the cabin and illustrates how the brick chimney was arranged in the timber portion of type 3 and 4 cabins. Where a stove was later provided, the brick chimney was removed down to floor level and the gap boarded over. The resultant narrow section of boarding is a feature of those cabins which have had chimneys removed. The boarding on the back of the later cabins which never had chimneys was normally in long sections.*

Plate 10.3 *Abergele, August 1968. This cabin was positioned between the up and down fast lines on this straight four track section in order to obtain the best possible sight along the line. It was opened in 1902 and is of size 'M' with the operating floor 8 feet above rail level, this being the standard height for the cabin floor (see* **Figure 10.7***). Note how one window in each alternate unit is made to open and that double handrails are provided over these windows. The brick base is of the simple flush type without panelling and the small lower windows give light to the lower portion of the cabin. In the foreground, on the left of the cabin, is the corner of the coal pen, another standard LNW product. To the right of the cabin are some ex-LNW carriages in use as Camping Coaches.*

The old S and T codes were redesignated T and U to produce the standard codes listed in column 2. All references to standard cabins in this book use the column 2 designations.

As can be seen, only one combination of two and three window units could be used to make any particular size of cabin. It will be noted that the two window units were used much more extensively than the three window units (12 sets of two and only 4 sets of three in the case of a size U cabin). Despite this, the windows were always (with only one or two very special exceptions) placed in the same combination in any particular size of cabin. These standard combinations are listed in **Figure 10.4**.

In addition to the standard window units described above some special units were produced to suit particular needs. These principally consisted of narrow or wide versions of the two window units and were used to allow windows to be provided across the full width of a cabin end where extra vision was required. The standard units could not be used to produce the standard 12 foot external width of a cabin. The dimension into which the windows had to be accommodated varied, of course, with the length of the cabin due to the different sizes of middle and end pillars. A six pane single window unit, equivalent to about 1½ standard units, was also produced and was again to be found in the ends of a few cabins. Where windows were required in the back of a cabin the non-standard length two window units (and occasionally an equivalent three window version) and six pane windows were sometimes used in order to make up the exact length of glazing required.

Very occasionally the six pane window unit was used in the front of a signal cabin. Several of the overhead cabins had this feature which was necessary in order to make up the special size of cabin required to accommodate the gantry structure. Apart from this the provision of anything other than the standard window units in the front of a cabin was very rare and, in fact, only 6 examples have so far been found (**Figure 10.9**, page 137), these representing only about 0.5% of the examples studied!

Windows were generally provided on three sides of a cabin to give the best possible view for the signalmen. In some cases it was considered necessary to make special efforts to provide the signalman with a good view. In some of these cases, particularly in cabin ends, the centre vertical glazing bars would be omitted from the appropriate window units and a large sheet of plate glass inserted. Examples of this practice occurred at Crewe Sorting Sidings Middle

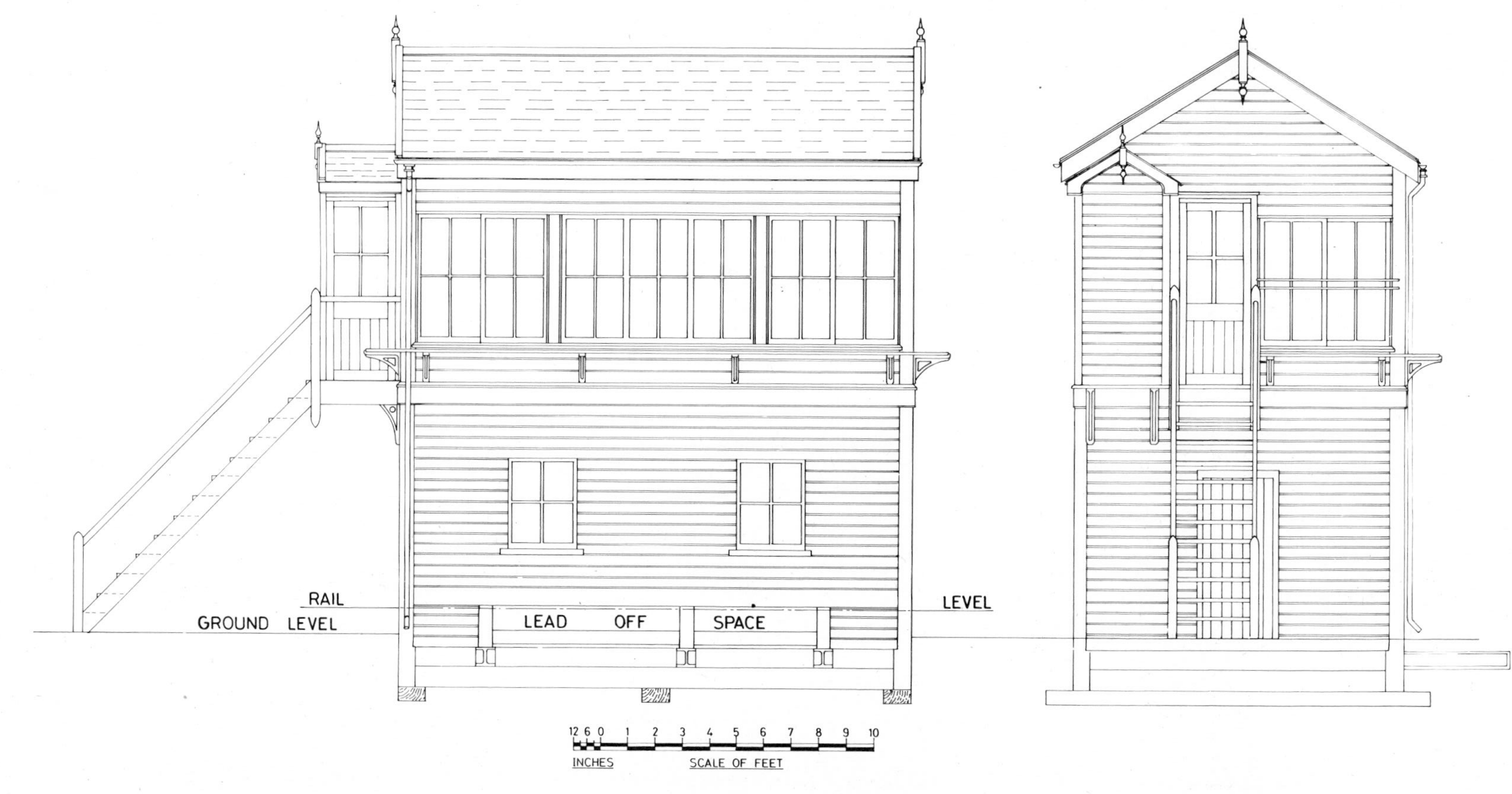

Figure 10.6 *Drawing of an All-Timber Cabin of 'Type 4', this one is of size 'E'. Where a brick base was required (as it was in the majority of cases) the timber structure below floor level was omitted and the timber top placed on top of a prepared brick base. The locking room windows on the all wood cabins varied somewhat in size to suit the location and design of that particular cabin and some cabins were fitted with quite large ones. It will be observed that the middle support to the cabin, visible in the lead off space, is not central. The normal size of frame for a size 'E' cabin was 25 levers and this was usually made up on a girder for 10 levers and one for 15 levers. The support is placed at the junction between the girders where there was an 11 inch space between the levers. This cabin has an elevation of 8 feet. Scale of reproduction: 4 mm to 1 foot (1:76).*

Plate 10.4 *Port Sunlight Sidings, March 1972. This cabin was opened in 1902 when this section of line was quadrupled. The freshly tipped ground on the edge of the embankment was not considered to be sufficiently consolidated to support a brick structure. The cabin is of size 'K' and the operating floor is 13 feet above rail level, rather high for a timber cabin. The cabin front shows a pronounced 'sag', something of a characteristic of big timber cabins. Note the special right hand leaf of the two window unit in the end of the cabin. The toilet at the top of the staircase is a modern addition.*

Figure 10.7 ELEVATION OF CABINS

Table showing a sample of LNWR standard signal cabins distributed by elevation (height of operating floor above rail level).

Elevation feet	*Number of cabins*	*Elevation feet*	*Number of cabins*
4	15	17	3
5	21	18	5
6	66	19	3
7	78	20	4
8	233	21	2
9	49	22	6
10	78	23	1
11	24	24	3
12	44	25	3
13	22	26	1
14	23	27	0
15	15	28	1
16	6	Number of cabins	706

Overhead type cabins not included in figures.

and Nuneaton No. 2. In some instances it was found that with the use of the ordinary window units the signalmen could not see portions of the layout or tall signals close to the cabin when stood at the levers. Additional glazing was, therefore, provided above the main windows in the cabin ends to give extra sight. Examples of cabins with these special additional windows included Colwich and Wolverhampton No. 2. At Chester No. 4 a set of six foot windows was provided for this purpose in the end of the cabin.

In some cases windows were required in the rear of signal cabins to give sight of roads approaching a level crossing or of sidings or running lines there. In these cases additional 4′ 6″ or 6′ 0″ windows (as appropriate to the cabin type) would be provided over an appropriate portion of the back of the cabin to produce a 'glass all round' cabin. In fact glass was rarely provided over the whole of the back and there was usually a boarded section where the stove stood and where the noticeboards were mounted.

It was, obviously, essential that the windows were kept clean in order to maintain the visibility. In the early days a variety of methods were adopted for carrying out this work. The sliding leaves and the adjacent sections of window could be cleaned from inside the cabin by leaning out. In other cases the windows were cleaned from outside by means of ladders or long handled mops. In June 1870 a requisition for a ladder to be used to clean the windows of the new Spon Lane (Oldbury) cabin was received. The Directors probably saw this as being the thin end of a very large wedge and refused the request asking if the cabins could not be designed so that the windows could be cleaned without the need for ladders. In August Mr Dick stated that it had been decided that in future the cabins would be constructed in such a way that all the windows would slide in order to enable them to be cleaned from inside. Mr Neele, the Superintendent of the Line, was to issue instructions that all existing cabin windows were to be cleaned by mop and only where this was impossible would the supply of a ladder be considered.

A few cabins were constructed, about this time, with opening windows as described above but an alternative solution was soon adopted. A small platform or stage was attached to the outside of the cabin just below the windows, and a handrail fixed along the front of the cabin at the same height as the horizontal glazing bars, double handrails being provided across opening window sections. This then enabled the signalman or porter to get along the front of the cabin and clean all the windows. The general practice with the Types 3 and 4 cabins was to provide opening (sliding) windows only where these were needed. This was usually at the ends and at selected places along the front to suit circumstances. A few cabins, usually where a lot of shunting was likely to take place, were fitted with a full set of opening windows but these were exceptions. With the introduction of the Type 5 cabin design in 1904 a reversion was made to the 1878 idea, all the windows being made to slide and no stage was provided.

Cabins below about 7 feet above rail level, or where clearances were limited, could not be provided with walkways for safety reasons and here the cabin windows still had to be cleaned by mop or a full set of opening windows provided.

In the case of the Type 4 overhead cabins something

more substantial was considered necessary and a proper walkway with external handrailing (see **Figures 10.11, 12** and **13**) was provided in most cases. In a few instances tall type 4 cabins of conventional construction were provided with similar fencing. In a number of other cases fenced walkways were provided in LMS or BR days as a result of complaints by the staff. An example of this was Ordsall Lane No. 4, where a walkway was provided in about 1936 as a result of representations made to the LDC by the signal box lads.

The standard cabins used by the LNWR (whether of type 3, 4 or 5 design) were of composite construction, that is, they consisted of a wooden top on a brick base. All timber cabins could be provided if necessary and **Figure 10.6** is a drawing of the type 4 version. Generally, all timber cabins were only provided in special circumstances and had to be ordered specially, hence they were in effect non-standard. The usual reason for providing a timber, rather than a brick cabin, was foundation problems. These could occur on embankments, particularly in the case of cabins provided in connection with new or widened lines where the ground had not had time to consolidate sufficiently to support the additional weight of a brick structure. The other main situation in which wood cabins were provided was in areas prone to subsidence due to mining. Here the railway often had to be built up and altered in order to maintain a reasonably level road. Over the years settlement could produce a difference in level of several feet. A timber structure was less susceptible to settlement and had the advantage that it could be lifted from time to time to bring it back to the correct position in relation to the tracks. Quite a number of all wood cabins were provided in circumstances of this sort and they were particularly common in the Lancashire coalfield area (around Tyldesley, Wigan and St. Helens). It also seems probable that a few were provided where temporary cabins were required or where it was thought that it might be necessary to move the cabin at some time. Despite these special uses the number of all wood cabins provided was fairly small and they represented only about 10% of all the cabins constructed. Indeed, the LNW seems to have regarded all wood cabins as more expensive than the brick ones. For example the new cabin at Crane Street, Chester erected in 1907 cost £78 more than the estimate. This was stated to be due to the necessity of providing an all wood cabin, rather than the composite one intended, due to the unsatisfactory ground conditions found, but possibly this was just an excuse produced for the benefit of the Directors!

A problem with all wood cabins was deterioration due to rot at ground level, thus cabins of this type generally had a shorter life than those with brick bases. This is, no doubt, the reason why so few all timber cabins of type 3 or earlier construction survived into recent times as certainly examples were built. In a few cases all timber cabins had their lives extended by removing the lower timber structure and inserting a brick base. Examples of cabins which received this treatment were Cheadle Village Junction and Hinckley.

It seems likely that all the type 3 cabins were fitted with slate roofs from new although it is possible that a few may initially have had zinc roofs like the Saxby cabins they replaced (see Chapter 9). Certainly from July 1877 onwards all new cabins had slate roofs.

Returning to the size of cabins, it may be worth outlining roughly how the size of a cabin necessary to work a given layout might be determined. The number of levers needed can be roughly estimated by counting the number of signal arms (including distant and disc signals), point toes, facing point locks, gong etc. that the cabin will be required to control. To this total an allowance for spare levers (about 10 to 20%) is added. The number of levers obtained can be compared with **Figure 10.3** to determine a suitable size of cabin. Chapter 16 describes some actual signalling layouts and this should assist in making the use of levers clear.

One or two considerations which help to fix cabin sizes deserve mention. Crossovers on the LNW were normally worked by two, rather than one, levers unless they were within say 50 yards of the cabin. This arrangement was an LNW speciality, and most other companies used a single lever for a crossover. It was adopted to reduce the load on the levers and so minimise wear and tear and maintenance costs. Level crossings (Chapter 8) generally required four

Plate 10.5 *Fir Tree House Junction, July 1968. The reason for using a timber cabin here is fairly obvious from the photograph. This cabin was in the complex of lines at Springs Branch, an area where mining subsidence was also a problem, and the nearby Springs Branch No. 1 cabin, a brick structure, showed a distinct 'list' in later years. The cabin controlled a junction on the high level lines where these passed over the main line; it was of size 'E' and was opened in 1891. Although it was only 6 feet above rail level on these lines, handrails were provided around the window cleaning stage because of the height at the back. The photograph also shows the way in which windows were provided in the back of a cabin where sight was required in that direction (referred to as having 'glass all round'). Note the timber coal pen at the left hand end of the cabin.*

Springs Branch No. 1 was a short distance to the north on the main line, but was too far away to work one connection on the down side just south of the high level bridge. This connection and associated signal were, therefore, worked from Fir Tree House with a bolt lock control from Springs Branch No. 1. The cabin, therefore, effectively controlled lines at two different levels, the rod and wire for the low level point and signal running down the side of the embankment. The adjacent cabin, Platt Bridge Junction, on the high level line went further and controlled the whole layouts on both the high level line and the Whelley line below. The cabin was at the high level to give adequate sight and the wires and rods again ran down the side of the embankment (see also **Plate 9.1***). Control of two levels of line by one cabin was treated a little differently at Duston West Junction, where a tall cabin was provided at the low level. This was elevated about eight feet above the high level lines thus allowing sight of both lines. The rod and wire runs were taken direct from the cabin, avoiding the need for sloping runs. The cabin had two lever frames, one for each line, and these were mounted at right angles to each other so that each was parallel to the line it controlled.*

Plate 10.6 *Longridge. This diminutive cabin was approximately 9 feet square and may represent an example of the standard size 'B' cabin. The front was made up of three single 2' 6" windows. It was opened in 1884 and, significantly, LNW records described it as a 'hut'. It is interesting to note how large the standard locking room windows look when fitted to such a small cabin. A pleasing feature is the mini-porch over the door. The number '6/50' on the front of the cabin refers to the last date on which the structure was painted. This cabin was of particular interest in that it was one of the LNWR cabins to be fitted with a Saxby and Farmer lever frame. The levers with their 'conventional' catch handles can just be seen through the windows as can the LNW booking desk. There was no gate wheel as the gates were worked by hand.*

Photo: M Christensen

levers to control the gates. Several feet of extra space was also required at one end of the cabin for the gate wheel (equivalent to about 5 levers). The LNW policy of 'Build to Last' should be borne in mind. In a few cases it was known (or expected) that some enlargement of the layout would take place in a few years. In this case the new cabin would sometimes be placed to enable it to control the future layout. The cabin and frame would be made large enough to accommodate the extra levers (either by means of space left in the frame or room for a frame extension). Inevitably, in a few cases the extensions were never done; on the other hand a cabin and layout might be installed only to find that the expected traffic did not materialise. Rationalisation of the layout (yes, it even occurred in LNW days!) could leave a cabin which was apparently too large.

In order to illustrate which were the most common sizes of cabins provided on the LNWR, the dimensions of over 1,000 actual cabins have been taken. These represent about

Plate 10.7 *Wolverton Works, October 1978. This cabin contained a 12 lever frame and was 10 feet square, being made up from a standard two-window unit plus a special six-pane unit. The retention of the LNW name on the front of the cabin will be noticed. This consisted of four inch high standard cast-iron letters screwed directly to the fascia board. The object just below the pinnacle on the end is a standard signal cabin ventilator and examples can be seen in many of the other illustrations. The cabin was provided in 1903 at the request of Mr C A Park, the Carriage Superintendent, in order to control shunting operations in a congested area of the works where considerable delays were being experienced in carrying out the work. The installation cost £310 and several of the signals were fitted with 'Crewe System' electric motors in order to prevent accidents to staff through tripping over signal wires. The cabin seems to be well cared for by its present owners, British Rail Engineering Ltd.*

Plate 10.8 *Crosfields Crossing, April 1972. This was one of a small number of cabins fitted with the type 5 six foot windows and a type 4 flat gable roof. These cabins fall into two groups, the first of which were constructed between 1898 and 1904, in advance of the introduction of the type 5 cabin. Large windows were provided where circumstances made it necessary to improve the signalmen's view. This occurred principally where cabins were fitted with the 'Crewe system' power frames (Chapter 14) which took up a great deal of space in the front of the cabin. The cabins at Gresty Lane and on the Crewe goods lines were of this type, while the tall Severn Bridge Junction cabin at Shrewsbury (erected 1903) was fitted with larger windows in order to allow the signalmen a view of the tracks near to the cabin. Crosfields Crossing falls into the second group and was one of several special cabins erected in 1913. It was probably a rush job due to fire or accident damage. Two of the others, Bridgefoot and Lamplugh, were curious in that they incorporated the station ticket offices within the cabin structures!*

80% of all the standard cabins in use in the last years of the LNW. They have been divided up to give the number of each size of cabin which are represented in the total (**Figure 10.3**). As can be seen the majority, some 60% of the total cabins, were in the range of sizes between 'C' and 'F' with size 'D' being the most common. The LNW seems to have become associated with the provision of large signal cabins, but as the figure shows this was not really so, only some 3% of cabins having more than 100 levers.

The siting and heights of cabins deserves some mention. The Board of Trade 'Requirements' for railways required that the signalman should be able to see all the points and signals under his control when he was standing at the levers. There were also limitations on the distance over which points (particularly facing ones) could be worked by rod (Chapter 15). These distances gradually increased over the years, sometimes enabling the duties of two cabins to be combined into one. Before the days of readily available and reliable electrical aids, the requirement of sight was of paramount importance. Great care was, therefore, taken in siting a new cabin to give the best possible sight for the signalman of the layout under his control. If necessary, to enable sight over bridges and buildings, or around curves, very tall cabins were provided. In other cases a squat cabin would be built to enable the signalman to see under the obstruction. Where layouts were on curves the position of the cabin could be arranged at the coincidence of the tangents from the various curves. In yards and stations tall cabins were often required to ensure that the signalman could see over vehicles or trains standing in sidings, platforms or on running lines. It should be noted that there was always a reason for the position and height of a cabin. Although the LNW was fond of tall cabins these were all provided for a reason and the extra expense was not incurred without careful consideration. The interlocking mechanism did have an influence on the height of very large cabins (see Chapter 11). The standard height (or elevation) of LNWR signal cabins was 8 feet (measured from rail level to operating floor level) and this dimension was used wherever possible. **Figure 10.7** lists the range of cabin elevations and the numbers of cabins of each height found from a statistical sample of cabins and clearly demonstrates that the standard 8 feet was the most common, only 5% of cabins having elevations greater than 15 feet.

It should be noted that, in a number of cases, the original reasons for the choice of a particular site and height of cabin no longer apply, leaving a cabin which is apparently curiously positioned, or of an awkward height. This can be caused by the removal of a level crossing, a bridge or building or by the erection of a new bridge or building which now obscures sight.

The standard prefabricated signal cabin top was 12 feet wide. Where a restricted site only was available such as between running lines or where there was insufficient land a narrow cabin with specially altered structure was sometimes provided. More commonly, the narrow base necessary was extended above the obstruction and a standard top used. This obviously overhung at the front or back (or both) and where the overhang was more than about a foot the top was usually supported on cast iron brackets. If possible the overhang was placed at the back of the cabin, but in many cases this was not possible due to the need to push the structure forward to give the signalman an adequate sight or to avoid encroaching onto adjacent property. A structure which overhung at the front could present problems since it resulted in the lever frame and interlocking being very near the front wall making maintenance difficult. Thus overhangs at the front of cabins were generally restricted to a foot or so. Occasionally this was not sufficient and something else had to be done. An example was Tile Hill Station cabin where the top structure had to overhang the base by about 5 feet. Here the lever frame was placed in the back of the cabin. On the LNWR placing the lever frame in the back of the cabin was only done in very special circumstances such as this (see also Chapter 11).

Where sites were very congested there could be quite considerable problems in finding sufficient space for the signal cabin, let alone finding it somewhere where the signalman would be able to obtain adequate sight of the layout. Here the LNW favoured the provision of an overhead cabin, the cabin structure being placed on a gantry structure over the tracks. This solution solved the problem of finding space and enabled the cabin to be placed where the signalman would be able to see the whole layout. Overhead cabins were, of course, expensive and so were only provided where the cost was thought to be justified.

In LMS and BR days maintenance problems began to be experienced with these structures and a few were removed and replaced by conventional cabins. In the

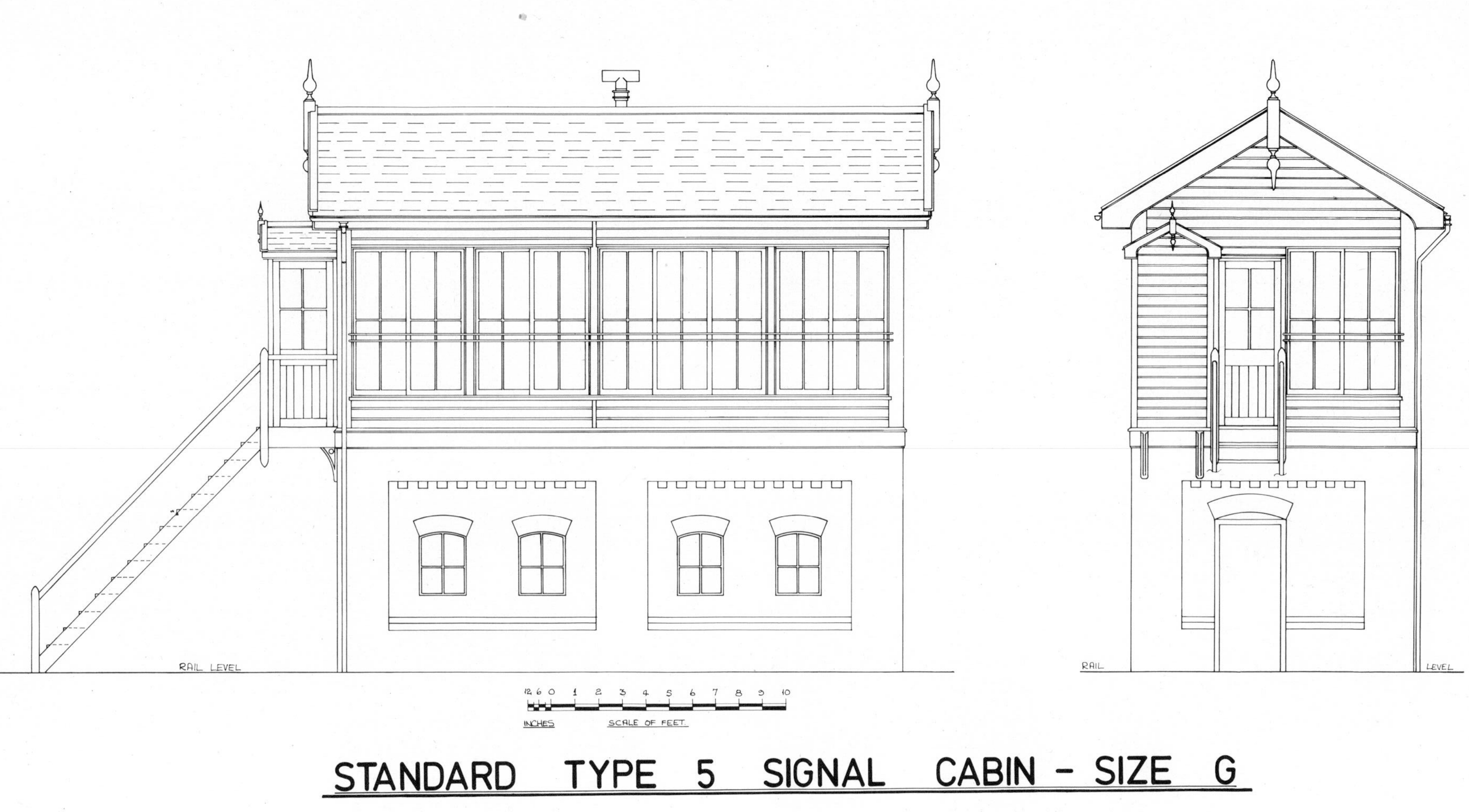

Figure 10.8 *A Standard Type 5 Cabin with a Panelled Brick Base. Note the use of double handrails along the windows, these are now some distance below the centre horizontal glazing bars. This cabin has an elevation of 10 feet. Scale of reproduction: 4 mm to 1 foot (1:76).*

Plate 10.9 *Brock, August 1972. The type 5 design of cabin followed the theme of the type 4, but with larger windows and an overhanging roof, this one being a size 'C' cabin. It has lost the pinnacle off the left hand end of the roof, at some time, possibly as a result of repair work. The wooden staircase has been replaced with a steel one. Note that double handrails are fitted in front of all the windows and that they are now some distance below the horizontal centre line of the windows.*

Plate 10.10 *Valley, July 1976. This was the first type 5 cabin to be constructed and was opened in October 1904. Again, the locking room windows in the all-wood cabins varied in size to suit circumstances and the height of the cabin. This is a size 'F' cabin and is elevated 8 feet.*

second world war these cabins were considered to be especially at risk in air raids and several were removed and replaced by LMS 'ARP' design cabins. Those at Manchester London Road, which could not be removed, were fitted with concrete 'hats' to protect them from incendiaries and flying shrapnel and debris. Some examples of overhead cabins are given in **Figure 10.15** (page 144).

In addition to the overhead cabins some special cabins on stilts were constructed. Here a normal all timber cabin structure was elevated a suitable amount (usually between 8 and 10 feet) on an open timber framework. This was generally done in rock cuttings where the arrangement saved the cost of excavating a space in the cutting side to accommodate the cabin. This stood on the timber framework at the front and directly on the rock or cutting slope at the back. Examples of this type of construction were Argoed, Menai Bridge No. 1 and Nine Mile Point No. 2.

Originally, heating for cabins of types 1, 2, 3 and 4 was generally by open fire, or a stove placed in the fireplace, and a brick chimney was provided. In the 1880's a change was made, for new work, to the use of a separate stove with a stove pipe style of chimney and the use of brick chimneys was discontinued. Over the years the majority of the timber topped cabins had their brick chimneys removed to reduce the load on the structure and the space in the back wall of the cabin was boarded over. Some large cabins were provided with a central heating system with a central (often at ground level) boiler and a system of hot water pipes and radiators.

Where layouts were extended or new signals provided there could sometimes be insufficient levers in the cabin to work the new equipment. In many cases, of course, the alterations were so extensive that a new cabin had to be provided, indeed the old one was often found to be in the way of the new work. In other cases the work was of a more minor nature and such a solution was not suitable. It was usually possible to extend the lever frame at one or both ends within the existing cabin structure in order to accommodate the extra levers. In a few cases this was insufficient and the cabin had to be extended. Normally the extension was made to match, as far as possible, the design of the existing structure and was usually made in some combination of the two or three window units (for types 3 to 5 cabins). **Figure 10.10** lists some examples of standard LNW cabins which were extended in this way.

In the early years of this century the Signal Department carried out a reappraisal of its practices and equipment. Where necessary designs were modified and modernised, although the majority of the equipment remained substantially unchanged. The most significant changes were in the design of the signal cabin and the introduction of the tappet locking frame (Chapter 11), although it should be noted that these two changes did not come into effect together.

Rather than design a completely new cabin, the successful principles of the types 3 and 4 cabins — prefabricated components and standard sizes — were retained. The existing design was, therefore, simply altered by substituting larger windows (six feet high instead of 4′ 6″) and redesigning the roof. The larger windows were introduced to improve the signalman's vision and helped to counteract the effect of increasing quantities of equipment being placed in the front of cabins (particularly on the block shelf) and the space taken up by the 'Crewe System' power frames (Chapter 14). The roof was made rather larger so that it overhung on all four sides, which no doubt helped to keep water out of the structure. Visually, the design was a great improvement over its predecessors and is very pleasing. **Figure 10.8** is a drawing of this new 'Type 5' design of cabin, while it is illustrated in **Plate 10.9**. The last two 'production' type 4 cabins, Mochdre & Pabo and Welham Sidings, were brought into use in July 1904 and the first 'Type 5' cabin appeared in October of that year at Valley (curiously an all timber structure). The Type 5 design remained in use for the remainder of the LNW's independent existence.

After the grouping the design was adopted as the standard for use on the Western and Central divisions of the LMS and examples appeared on the lines of the other pre-grouping companies which became part of these divisions.

Plate 10.11 *Crewe Station A, June 1971. Placing the cabin under a station roof sometimes caused headroom problems and where a conventional roof could not be accommodated a flat roof was provided, as in this example. The cabin has six foot windows and was constructed in connection with the station enlargements in 1906. A pleasing feature is the use of yellow bricks for the base to match the station buildings. Other examples of cabins with flat roofs were Crewe Station B and London Road No. 3 (Manchester).*

A number were erected on the lines of the old Lancashire and Yorkshire Railway and odd examples appeared on the Furness and North Staffordshire lines. The design continued in use until about 1929/30 when the LMS standard cabin was introduced.

The Type 5 design was, therefore, in use for nearly as long as the Type 4 had been (a little more than 25 years each). However, the majority of the signalling work had been completed by 1904 and hence the number of Type 5 cabins constructed was considerably less than the number of Type 4 cabins.

The Type 5 cabins were not fitted with a window cleaning stage or gallery and so the appropriate sections of all the window units were made to open to provide access for cleaning (see photographs). However, the basic window layouts were not changed and **Figures 10.2**, 3 and 4 also apply to type 5 cabins.

As with the Types 3 and 4 cabins, Type 5 cabins were normally constructed with a brick base. An all-timber version was also available but again they represented only about 10% of the total. A few overhead cabins were also constructed in Type 5 form (examples being Atherstone and New Mills).

The LNW standard signal cabin might be considered to be one of the most successful applications of prefabricated building techniques ever. It was produced in large numbers over a long period of time with few design changes. The cabins have proved very durable, many having been in use for upwards of 80 years. This is something of an achievement when one considers the vibration they are subjected to with every passing train and that their 'design' life was about 50 years!

Although the LNW does not seem to have suffered from vandalism in the same ways as railways do now, over the years the lives of a few cabins came to an abrupt end through fire. Mention might be made, briefly, of one or two cases that occurred.

Plate 10.12 *The signal cabin porch at Llanwrtyd Wells, October 1975. A few cabins in exposed locations were fitted with small porches in order to give some additional protection from the elements. In some cases the porches were fitted from new while in others the porch was added later. There was no standard design for the porches since only a few were constructed and each was arranged to suit the particular location. In some cases they were constructed integrally with the toilet, while in others they were separate structures. This particular cabin is not strictly LNW as it was not opened until the 4th December, 1928. Other examples of cabins with porches included Grayrigg, Penrith No. 1, Sugar Loaf Summit and Nantybwch No. 1.*

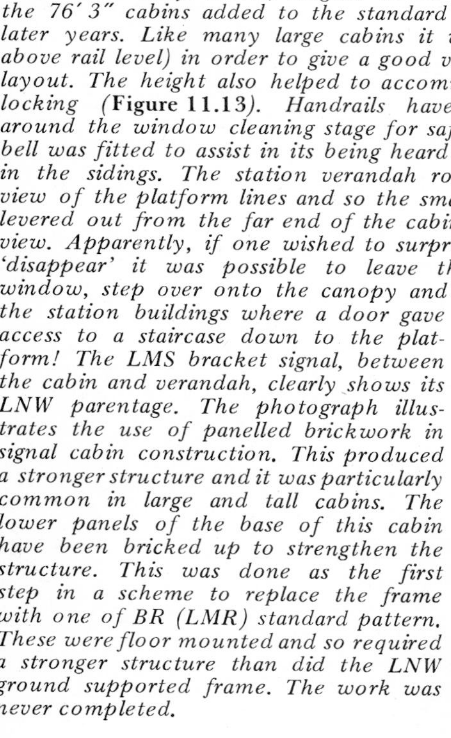

Plate 10.13 *Rhyl No. 2, August 1968. This was one of the 76′ 3″ cabins added to the standard range of sizes in later years. Like many large cabins it was tall (18 feet above rail level) in order to give a good view over the busy layout. The height also helped to accommodate the interlocking (***Figure 11.13***). Handrails have been provided around the window cleaning stage for safety. A very large bell was fitted to assist in its being heard on the station or in the sidings. The station verandah roof restricted the view of the platform lines and so the small bay was cantilevered out from the far end of the cabin to give a better view. Apparently, if one wished to surprise a colleague or 'disappear' it was possible to leave the cabin by the window, step over onto the canopy and walk along it to the station buildings where a door gave access to a staircase down to the platform! The LMS bracket signal, between the cabin and verandah, clearly shows its LNW parentage. The photograph illustrates the use of panelled brickwork in signal cabin construction. This produced a stronger structure and it was particularly common in large and tall cabins. The lower panels of the base of this cabin have been bricked up to strengthen the structure. This was done as the first step in a scheme to replace the frame with one of BR (LMR) standard pattern. These were floor mounted and so required a stronger structure than did the LNW ground supported frame. The work was never completed.*

Figure 10.9 EXAMPLES OF CABINS CONSTRUCTED WITH NON-STANDARD FRONT WINDOW LAYOUTS

Cabin	*Window Layout Used*	*Notes*
Chester No. 4	2 + 2 + 2 + 2 + 2 + A + 2 + 2 + 2 + 3 + 2 + 2 + 2 + 2 + 2 + 2 + 2 + 2	1
Copley Hill No. 3	2 + 2 + A + 2 + 2	
Greenfield Junction	2 + A + 2 + 2 + 2 + 3 + 2	
Severn Bridge Junction	2 + 2 + 3 + 2 + 3 + 2 + 3 + 2 + 3 + 2 + 3 + 2 + 3 + 2 + 2	2
Stockport No. 2	2 + 3 + 2 + 2 + A1 + 2 + 2 + 2 + 3 + 2 + 3 + 2	3
Willesden No. 3	A1 + 2 + 3 + 2 + A1	4

NOTES

A — Special 6 pane window unit, A1 — 6 pane window used in conjunction with a single (2′ 6″) window unit.

1. Possibly done to accommodate signal structures placed against cabin.
2. Tall type 4 cabin erected in 1902 with special 6 foot windows to give a better view for the signalmen.
3. The window layout here suggests an error was made in setting out the brick base for the cabin!
4. Special windows to accommodate small verandah roofs built over end windows, these being provided to shelter the signalmen while giving instructions to drivers and shunters.

Figure 10.10 EXAMPLES OF EXTENDED CABINS

Cabin	*Cabin Date*	*Original Size*	*Date of Extension*	*Extended by*	*Notes*
Bridge Street No. 1 (Northampton)	1907	F	1914	5′ 2½″	1
Coventry No. 1	1895	H	1915	5′ 2½″	2
Deepdale Junction	1876	E	1926	7′ 7½″	
Diggle Junction	1885	J	1894	18′ 9″	
Furness Vale	1887	D	1909	5′ 3″	
Harlescott Crossing	1882	C	1941	15′ 7½″	
Heatley and Warburton	1907	E	1913	7′ 7½″	
Hindlow	1892	E	1928	5′ 3″	
Leamington Avenue	1883	G	1899	7′ 7″	3
Leighton No. 1	1902	K	1927	7′ 7″	4
Leighton No. 2	1881	J	1927	12′ 11½″	
Llandudno Junction No. 2	1893	T	1921	7′ 9″	
Morecambe	1891	M	1928	12′ 11½″	
New Street No. 2 (Birmingham)	1885	K	1896	7′ 9″	5
Ordsall Lane No. 4	1885	O	—	5′ 4½″	
Preston No. 3	1880	G	1922	2′ Approx.	
Preston No. 4	1902	U	1909	4′ Approx.	
Salop Goods Junction (Crewe)	1901	E	c1939	18′ 3″	6
Soho Station	1882	D	1923	7′ 7″	
Sorting Sidings South (Crewe)	1901	G	c1939	15′ 7½″	6
Stockport No. 1	1884	P	c1910	—	7
Three Spires Junction	1914	H	1916	5′ 2½″	
Willesden High Level Junction	1884	E	1894	8′ 3″	8
Willesden No. 7	1879	N	—	10′ 9″	9
Willesden No. 9	1879	K	1906	12′ 11½″	
Wolverton No. 2	1882	J	1927	5′ 3½″	10

NOTES

1. Extension to house safety equipment in connection with extension of Northampton Corporation Tramways across the level crossing (tram signals and cut off switches for power supply).
2. In connection with the doubling of the Kenilworth Branch to Gibbet Hill.
3. Cabin knocked down in a shunting accident 9/1/1885, the brickwork being destroyed and the wooden top structure and lever frame damaged. The cabin was rebuilt and brought back into use on 12/1/1885.
4. Also special extension at other end for telephone operator.
5. Additional levers provided in connection with quadrupling from Grand Junction.
6. Crewe system power frame removed, additional space required to allow the installation of an LMS standard 4½″ centres mechanical frame.
7. Extended by 15′ 6″ at one end and 7′ 9″ at the other.
8. Replaced by new cabin of size L in 1930.
9. Frame replaced by LMS standard Tappet 1928.
10. Plus special narrow section.

Plate 10.14 *Farington Curve Junction, August 1972. The cabin shown here stood between the slow and fast lines, necessitating a narrow base which, for strength, was of panelled form and carried the operating floor above the loading gauge so that it could overhang the line, the top overhanging equally at the front and back. As can be seen there was an overbridge immediately behind the cabin which restricted sighting southwards. Fortunately, the bridge was much higher than usual due to the deep cutting and so the cabin was arranged to give a view, via the corners of the overhanging top, under the bridge, a neat solution to a rather difficult problem. A cabin looking over the bridge would have had to be enormous. The cabin had just received its delivery of coal which can be seen stacked in the coal pen in plastic sacks, a modern method used to avoid the time consuming task of unloading wagons by hand on the running lines.*

Wednesbury No. 3 cabin burnt down while closed for the weekend in March 1886, the fire which had been left alight by the signalman, having apparently fallen out onto the floor. It was decided that, rather than replace it, a key interlocking frame should be provided which could be operated by the shunter thus saving the cost of the signalman!

Pilkington's Siding cabin near St. Helens burnt down while closed on the night of 13th October, 1888, apparently due to the pointsman having left some lamps burning in the cabin. Unfortunately £11 7*s* 3*d* worth of clothing, stored in the cabin and belonging to some men who were working away from home, was also destroyed. This was not insured and the Company, rather reluctantly, agreed to reimburse the men to 2/3rds of the value of the lost clothing.

The cabin at Witton Goods was surrounded by factories and when the adjacent works, belonging to Messrs. Kynoch, burnt down on the 6th December, 1911 it took the signal cabin with it. The timber structure and block instruments were destroyed and the cost of reconstruction was put at £200. It is not recorded whether the LNW managed to recover this from Kynochs!

Plate 10.15 *Mostyn, 1976. The amount by which cabins could be made to overhang at the front was limited by the frame, whose interlocking and other apparatus had to fit inside the brick base. For this reason some cabins overhung at the back only, as in this case. Note the steep and elaborate staircase necessary to keep clear of the loading gauge and level crossing. The unusual arrangement of the windows in the base is worthy of note as is the layout of the windows in the back of this 'glass all round' cabin. Because of the space problems the coal and ash pens are at the opposite end of the cabin from the staircase.*

Plate 10.16 *Chester No. 6, July 1970. This cabin, like many of the overhead cabins, was a special size, the cabin structure itself being 57′ 4″ by 14′ 0″. The extra width was necessary to accommodate the special lever frames used in overhead cabins (Chapter 11). A cabin of this design had been erected at Leominster Station in 1901 and when this one was required at Chester the Leominster drawings were simply adapted and the nearly identical cabin was opened in 1903. Both cabins were fitted with 80 lever tumbler frames of the SK448 type and the operating floors were 22 feet above rail level. The down rods for the points and the signal wires were brought down in line with the support legs. The wide spacing of the latter necessitated deep lattice cross girders and these were made solid under the cabin itself. The walkway and staircase at Leominster were different from that at Chester, being arranged to suit the site (the cabin was placed above the platform). The toilet was attached to the back of the cabin and the arrangement of the rainwater down pipes and toilet soil pipe will be noticed. Behind the gantry structure are two timber fog huts; these had to be small to enable them to fit into the restricted width available between the tracks. The standard hut for locations like this was a mere 3′ 4″ by 1′ 6″ outside and must have provided scant protection for a man working out in the damp and cold. Overhead cabins were quite expensive and the installation at Chester No. 6 cost some £517 more than a conventional cabin of similar size.*

Plate 10.17 *Preston No. 2A, June 1971. When Preston Station was enlarged at the turn of the century, there was no room for a cabin to control the new portion of the station. The best site available was over the retaining-walled cutting of the steeply graded Docks Branch. Crewe Coal Yard cabin was sited over the cutting for the Down Independent Goods line in a similar fashion and the men at both cabins must have noticed it when a heavy freight train with the engine working hard against the grade passed underneath them.*

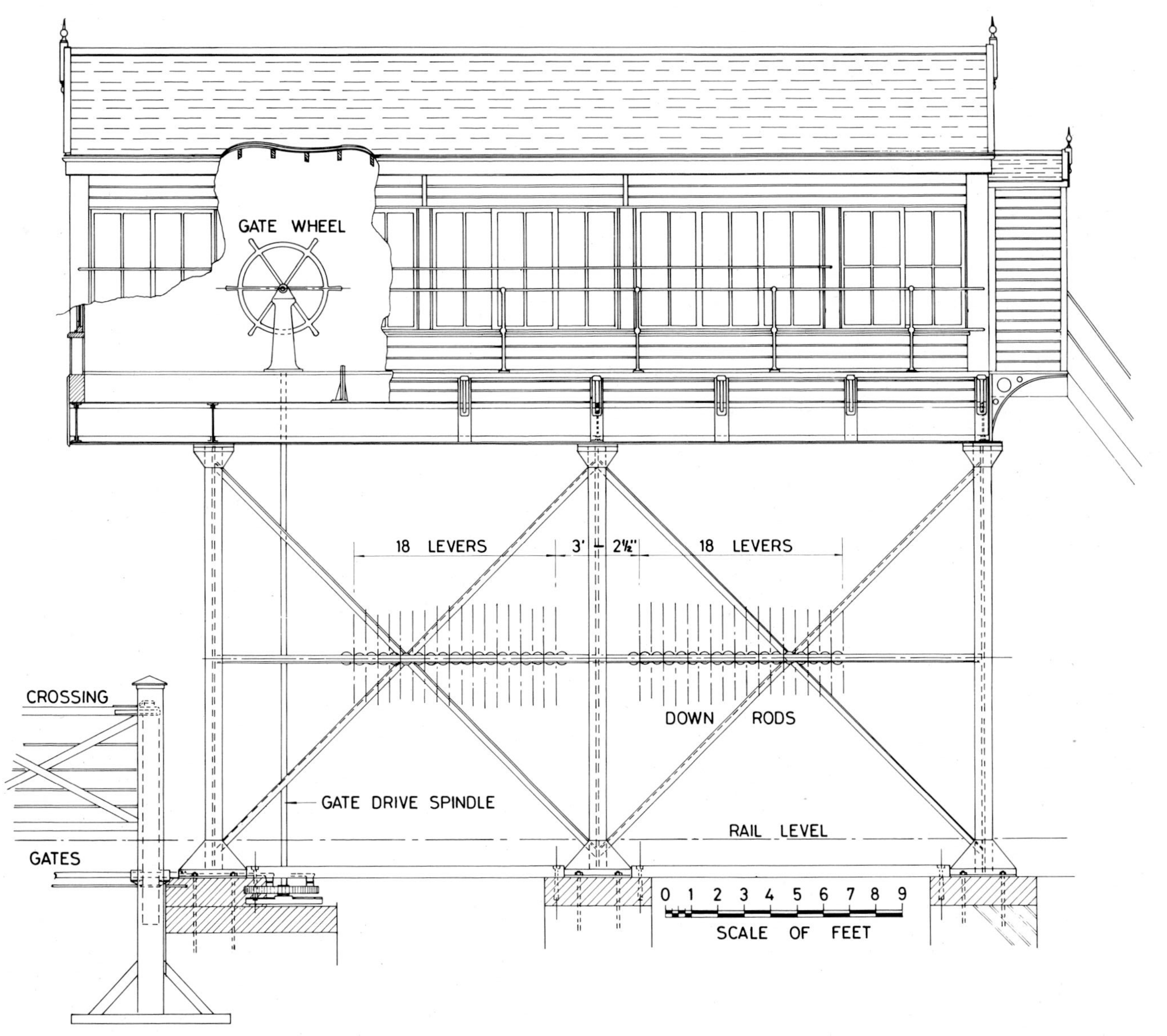
GATE WHEEL
18 LEVERS
3' – 2½"
18 LEVERS
CROSSING
DOWN RODS
GATE DRIVE SPINDLE
RAIL LEVEL
GATES
0 1 2 3 4 5 6 7 8 9
SCALE OF FEET

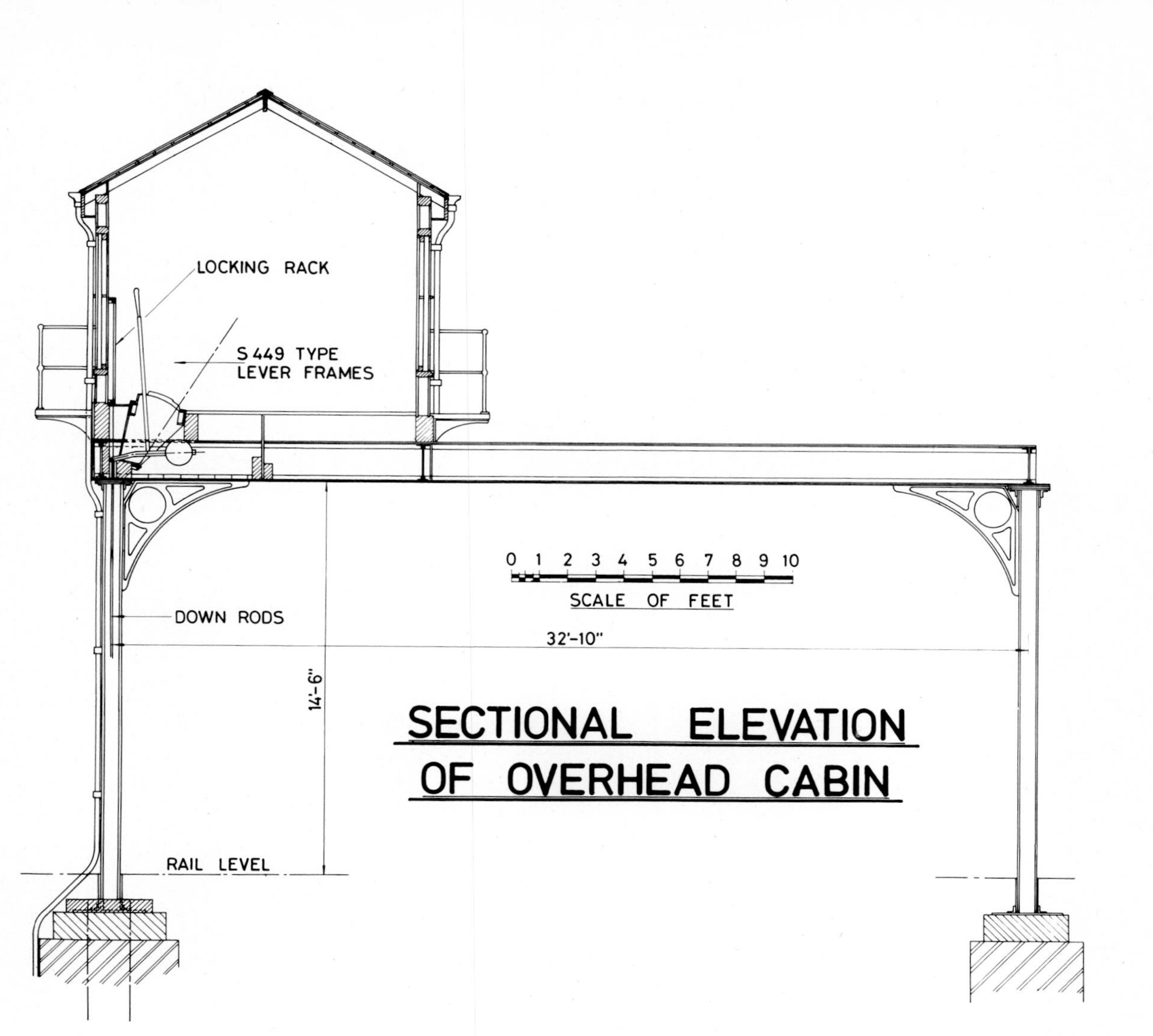

Figure 10.12 *Sectional Elevation of the Cabin at Wilderspool. This shows the arrangement of the walkways, the position of the cabin on the girders and the arrangement of the lever frame and locking racks. Scale of reproduction: 4 mm to 1 foot (1:76).*

◁ **Figure 10.11** *Scale Drawing of the Overhead Cabin Constructed at Wilderspool Crossing, Warrington in 1893. A portion of structure has been 'cut away' in the drawing to show the position of the gate wheel which was set at right angles to the crossing rather than parallel to it as was usual. Note how the cabin structure at that end has been cantilevered out over the crossing to give the signalman a better view of the road. The crossing was replaced by a bridge many years ago. The fenced walkway provided for window cleaning and maintenance purposes will be noticed. The window handrails (only single in this case) were not continued across the pair of windows at the right hand end since the opening leaf of these was used as the access route to the walkway. Care had to be taken in laying out the lever frame in an overhead cabin to ensure it would clear the supporting iron structure. The 36 lever frame was constructed on two girders for 18 levers each. These were not fixed together as in normal practice but separated by 3' 2½" in order to clear the centre support beam. Scale of reproduction: 4 mm to 1 foot (1:76).*

PAINTING OF SIGNAL CABINS

In LNW days the cabins were generally painted light stone (buff) and a medium brown (referred to as chocolate by some of Thompson's staff). The barge boards, finials, gutters and back boards, down spouts, window surrounds, doors, staircases, floor level fascia board and ironwork were brown. The window frames (both upper and lower storey) were white and the remaining woodwork stone colour. There were variations in this pattern from time to time and area to area while the shade of the brown colour seems to have varied somewhat. In an effort to prevent this happening A M Thompson sent out a memo in March 1885 asking the Inspectors to prepare themselves a board showing the standard colours so that they could ensure that all the future paintwork was kept to the same shades.

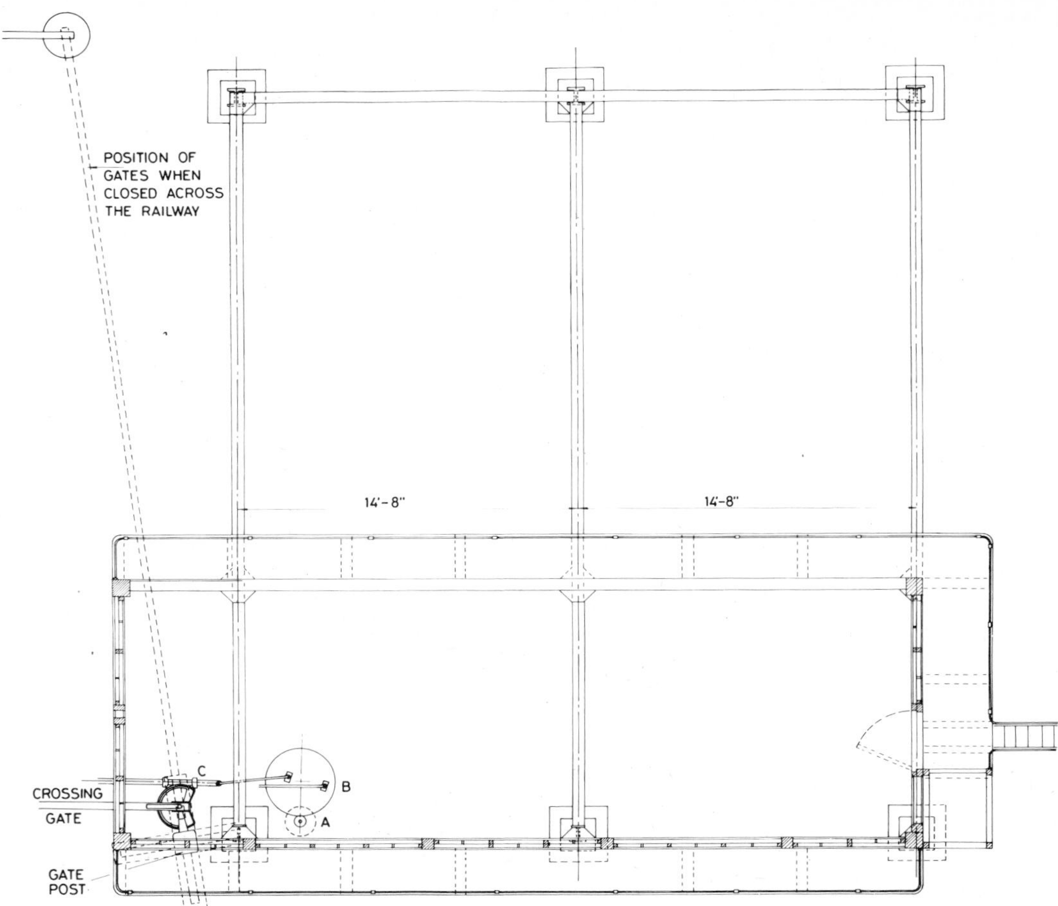

Figure 10.13 *Plan view of the Overhead Cabin at Wilderspool. The ground level gate operating gear has been included to give an idea of how this was accomplished. 'A' is the vertical drive spindle from the gate wheel. This has a small toothed wheel at its base which engages in the horizontal drive wheel 'B'. Rotating the gate wheel imparted a 'to and fro' motion to the two drive rods attached to wheel 'B'. At 'C' a toothed rack on the drive rod worked in a toothed quadrant attached to the foot of the gate, movement of the drive rod would thus cause the gate to open or shut. (See Chapter 8.) Scale of reproduction: 3 mm to 1 foot (1:102).*

They were asked to let Thompson know if the paint they obtained from Crewe varied from these colours. A set of sample colour boards were issued from Crewe as a guide again in August 1898. The stone colour was mixed by the men and in March 1885 the recipe was given as:—

7 lbs of white lead
½ lb of yellow ochre
½ oz of turkey umber

A slightly darker colour is specified in a memo of May 1898, when the recipe was given as:—

7 lb of white lead
2 lb of yellow ochre
1½ oz of turkey umber.

To add to the confusion, the latter was given as turkey red and this had to be corrected a few days later!

In the case of overhead cabins the gantry structure was generally painted in a similar manner to gantry and bracket signals (see Chapter 4). A memo sent out by Mr Thompson in October 1885 read:

> 'If you have any iron girder work supporting signal cabins etc., I want you in future to paint it light stone colour — as near as possible to the colour the PW Dept. use for station roofs etc.'

In practice, in later years at least, the girder work was normally turned out in a dark colour, brown, grey or black, the last two colours being the most common in LMS and BR days.

The cast iron letters of the signal cabin name were white and, at least from the mid 1890's, were usually accentuated by a painted red background. This was the same colour as the painted signal arms, two parts of red lead and one part of vermilion. Some of the painters, naturally, exercised a bit of individuality by embellishing the ends of this red panel in some way or other. An instruction, designed to put a stop to this, was issued in June 1900! The ends of the panels were to be finished as a half circle, thus;

(see also **Plates 9.3, 9.5, 9.8** and **17.4**).

A number of cabins in the Northampton/Peterborough

area which had managed to retain their LNW names were still to be found in the early 1960's with the lettering picked out in this way, although with the background simplified to a rectangular shape across the full width of the fascia board. Examples of this practice were Wellingborough Station, Tilton and East Norton cabins.

The interior of the cabin was painted the stone colour, while the block shelf, lockers, desk, internal ironwork etc. were painted vermilion red. In January 1899 Thompson sent out a memo indicating that he was not entirely happy about the internal painting of cabins. He felt it might be more cheerful if the ceiling was painted white instead of stone. After this the roof boarding was painted white

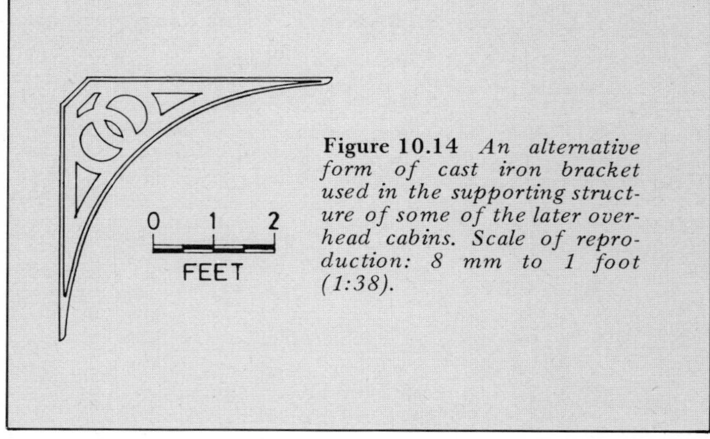

Figure 10.14 *An alternative form of cast iron bracket used in the supporting structure of some of the later overhead cabins. Scale of reproduction: 8 mm to 1 foot (1:38).*

Plate 10.18 *New Mills. A number of cabins of type 5 were also constructed in overhead form, and this photograph illustrates one of the smallest of these, New Mills, which was opened in 1910. The gantry only spanned one siding line and a light structure was therefore possible. This incorporates brackets of the* **Figure 10.14** *type. In a number of instances when overhead cabins (of both type 4 and type 5) were provided, advantage was taken of an adjacent structure to support one end of the gantry. This photograph illustrates one such case, use being made of the adjacent goods shed. Other overhead gantry structures employing this technique included Linthwaite, also supported by the goods shed, and Edge Hill No. 2 which was supported from the cutting wall. A bell bracket (without bell) can be seen on the corner of the cabin, while the LNW name lettering is still in place on the front of the structure.*

Photo: B E Timmins

Plate 10.19 *Boars Head Junction, June 1969. This cabin was sited in the 'V' of the junction, for good sighting. This site was, however, occupied by the station platform and the cabin had to be raised so that it did not obstruct it. Because the support structure had to be placed well back from the line, to give an unrestricted platform edge, the cabin overhung the iron structure by a considerable amount and special large brackets had to be provided to support it. It will be noticed that those overhead cabins with short spans between the supporting columns have quite slender cross beams. This cabin was opened in 1899 and had 16 working levers, the frame facing towards the branch line. The cabin was in an area subject to mining subsidence and over the years it gradually sank into the ground. By the 1940's it was in danger of fouling the loading gauge and something had to be done. The foundations were excavated (the footings were then some ten feet below ground level) and the whole iron and cabin structure jacked up to their original level and new foundations provided.*

although the roof beams and rafters continued to be painted stone colour. A similar treatment was applied to the Carbinoleumed cabins from November 1902 (with carbinoleum beams in that case).

The exposed parts of the lever frames were generally painted black although the levers themselves were painted distinctive colours to represent their functions as an aid to the signalmen. Charles Dick issued a memo on the 12th of January 1881 which defined the standard colours to be used on the LNW:

> 'It has come to my attention that the levers in all the districts are not painted the same. I have therefore decided on the use of the following colours:
>
> | | |
> |---|---|
> | Distant signal levers | green |
> | Home, starting and disc signal levers | red |
> | FPL levers | blue |
> | Bolt Lock levers | top blue/bottom black |
> | Scotch block levers | top blue/bottom black |
> | Gate lock levers | top blue/bottom black |
> | Wicket and gate stop levers | top blue/ bottom black |
>
> Point levers (not mentioned) were painted black.

The colouring was applied to the stem of the lever and the name and pull plates (except of course where the old Saxby brass plates were still in use). The catch block together with a short section of lever just above it and the loop handle were black (the top of the colouring was shaped, see **Plate 12.2**). The lettering on the name and pull plates was picked out in white (see also Chapter 11). The lever handles were left unpainted and were generally burnished (usually with emery cloth or wire wool) by the signalmen.

No evidence of any changes to these standard colours has yet come to light although there were possibly some additions to the list in order to meet changing needs (see Chapter 12 regarding the use of black and white stripes on levers). The LMS introduced a new set of standard colours in a memo sent out by Mr Bound dated May 1934:

Points, Scotches or Derailers	Black
Bolts, Bars (FPL's)	Blue
Signals other than distants	Red
Distant signals	Yellow
Wicket gates, Gate Stops and Locks	Brown
Asking, Permission, King, Route and Direction, Indicator and Gong levers	Green
Spare	White
Detonator placer	Black and white chevrons

From around the early 1890's a number of new cabins came from Crewe works with a wood preservative coating and these were not painted. The cabins so treated were referred to as the 'Carbinoleumed Cabins'. Carbinoleum was the name given to the oils distilled from coal tar at a temperature between 230 and 400°C, a principle constituent being anthracene oil. Carbinoleum Avenarius was introduced onto the wood preservative market in the 1880's by a Mr Avenarius and was still available in 1914. Application was made hot at 65 to 94°C either by means of a wire brush or by soaking in a tank. The exact colouring this imparted to the cabin is not known, but it seems likely it produced a dark overall colour. As with everything new, no-one was quite sure what to do about these cabins once they had got them.

Surviving correspondence gives us some insight into the various attempts made to find the right answer. The carbinoleumed cabins began to look rather tatty after about 18 months to two years. The usual frequency of repainting ordinary cabins was once in every three years. Memos to the effect that the carbinoleumed cabins should be revarnished externally more frequently than this were issued in April 1896 and April 1897. A memo of May 1897 stated:—

> 'Carbinoleumed signal cabins: There is no doubt that the inner portions of these cabins, including the levers, need only be painted and varnished say once in three years as a rule, but the outside window frames will have to be painted and varnished more frequently.'

It is not entirely clear what the word 'painted' meant in this context but it seems to imply a fresh coat of carbinoleum, since a memo of June 1898 stated:

> 'For the future the signal cabins will be coated with carbinoleum, but instead of varnishing them I propose to paint them the standard colour and we shall also deal with cabins already in existence when they come up for varnishing.'

However, even this was not the end of the matter, since it was found that the paint would not take properly onto

Figure 10.15 SOME EXAMPLES OF OVERHEAD CABINS

Cabins	*Date*	*Notes*
Acton Grange Viaduct	1893	1
Atherstone	1909	
Bangor No. 2	1923	2
Birmingham New Street No. 3	1885	3
Blackpool Street	1902	
Boars Head Junction	1899	
Camden No. 1	1905	1
Chester No. 3	1890	4
Chester No. 3A	1890	
Chester No. 6	1903	
Clifton Road Junction	1885	5
Crewe Coal Yard	1902	
Crewe No. 3 Scissors Crossing	1878	
Edge Hill No. 1	1881	6
Euston No. 1	1892	7
Huddersfield No. 1	1886	
Huddersfield No. 2	1886	
Kensington Middle	1910	
Linthwaite	1888	8
Leominster Station	1901	9
Manchester Exchange No. 1	1884	
Manchester Exchange No. 2	1884	
Manchester London Road No. 1	1908	
Manchester London Road No. 2	1909	
Melton Mowbray	1914	
Mossley No. 1	1906	
New Mills	1909	8
Preston No. 2	1880	
Preston No. 2A	1900	
Rugeley No. 2	1896	10
Smethwick	1891	6
Wigan No. 3	1894	
Wilderspool Crossing	1893	
Wilmslow	1908	

NOTES

1. Replaced by an LMS 'ARP' cabin.
2. Cabin perched on cutting wall.
3. Perched over footbridge, two SK80 lever frames in the open, small hut for signalmen.
4. Cabin perched on wall of station roof.
5. Special cabin over flyover line.
6. Supported on timber structure.
7. Special cabin under station roof.
8. Partly supported by wall of goods shed.
9. Replaced earlier overhead cabin.
10. Replaced by conventional type 4 cabin in 1903.

the carbinoleum! The instruction was, therefore, revised in February 1899:

> 'As we are not able to paint satisfactorily newly carbinoleumed cabins we will in future paint and varnish the cabins as we did before and in the course of 18 months or 2 years or so paint them our standard colours.'

(Another cure seemed to have been to varnish the cabin and apply the paint on the top of that). Fortunately the correspondence has left us with details of the way in which they were intended to be finished when new:

> 'Carbinoleumed surfaces, inside and outside:— Varnished. Sashes, inside and out, ground for name plates, stage and the brackets, launders (gutters) and downspouts, instrument shelf, cabin lockers and desk, ironwork inside the cabin, brackets, instrument shelf hangers; to be painted vermilion red, the same colour as for signal arms, and varnished.'

In LMS days, from May 1931, the external colours used were light stone and brown. The light stone was to BS (British Standard) Colour 61 of 1930 (BS381C/361 of 1948 and 1964). This was applied to the timber panels, window frames and underside of the roof. The brown was to BS Colour 12 of 1930 (BS381C/412 of 1948 and 1964) and was applied to the corner posts, facing and barge boards to the roof, steps, doors and frames and down spouts. A few cabins repainted during the second world war were turned out in grey.

At the same time (May 1931) revised instructions for painting the internal surfaces of the signal cabins were issued as follows:

> Dark brown to dado level.
> Main timbering above dado level to top of wall plate — Light Stone.
> Remainder, including sashes and roofing — White.
> Dark brown to be used on doors and windows where finger marks are likely to occur.

In British Railways times the standard colouring, at first, was light biscuit (BS Colour 381C/385) and gulf red (BS381C/473). The biscuit was applied to the mullions, timber panels, underside of the roof, window frames (including those to the lower storey windows in all-timber boxes). The corner posts, bottom sills, window sills, roof facings and barge boards, steps, doors and frames, guttering and down spouts were finished in gulf red. In some cases the window frames to the lower windows in brick base boxes would be biscuit, otherwise they would be white.

A change in livery was made in 1961, when the gulf red gave way to dark green (a very greyish green to the eye) to BS2660/4.051 of 1955, and the biscuit to mushroom (BS2660/4.047 of 1955). The window frames (both storeys) and glazing bars were painted white, with black for steps, gutters, down spouts and sills.

The 1970's brought further variations with the green replaced by black in some instances and rail blue in others, there are now many more local variations in colour than previously (not that things were ever quite standard!).

Plate 10.20 *Burneside Station, April 1968. This hut is basically a 'stretched' version of the S1355 (***Figure 10.17***) design and was 11′ 4″ long. The hut and lever frame, which was of the LNW Tappet type with 15 levers, were provided in 1922 as a replacement for an open platform ground frame installed in 1884. The cabin had full block post status (although usually 'switched out' in its later years). A prominent feature is the LNW nameboard which, this time, has rounded ends.*

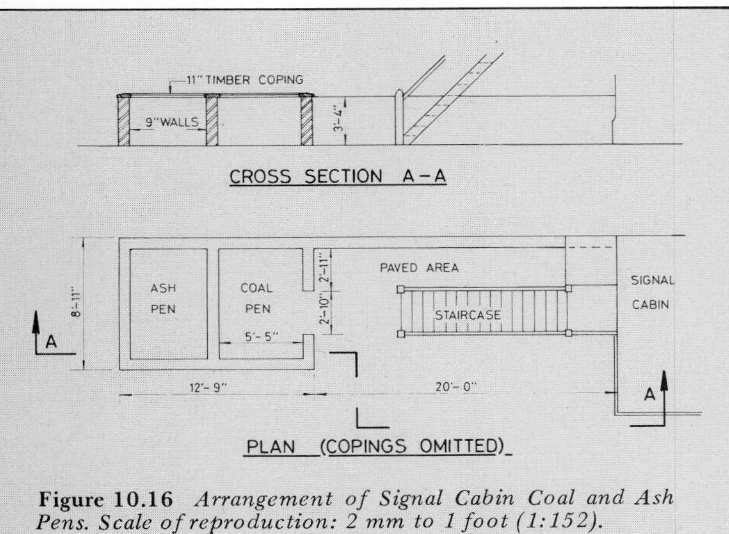

Figure 10.16 *Arrangement of Signal Cabin Coal and Ash Pens. Scale of reproduction: 2 mm to 1 foot (1:152).*

COAL AND ASH PENS

The comfort of the signalman must not be forgotten. The cabin stove or fire needed coal and produced ash and somewhere was needed to keep these. The majority of cabins (except those sited on station platforms) were provided with two pens, one for the coal and one for the ashes. The pens were usually sited near the foot of the cabin staircase, unless site conditions prevented this and the coal pen was generally nearest the cabin. The pens were usually constructed in brick with timber copings spiked on top, these being painted standard brown. A few pens were constructed in timber, usually where the cabin itself was all-wood or where the site was very restricted. The pens varied somewhat in size and position to suit the site and in a few cases the two pens were separated (for example Rugeley No. 2 which had one at each end of the cabin). **Figure 10.16** is a sketch of the brick pens at Market Bosworth and shows the most common arrangement, although the provision of a link wall between pens and cabin was only provided in some cases. This one acted as the railway's boundary.

Plate 10.21 *Hopton, January 1967. This cabin was on the Cromford and High Peak line and illustrates an alternative arrangement of the windows.*

Photo: M Christensen

Plate 10.22 *Little Sutton, February 1970. Little Sutton is an example of a larger type of hut and housed a 9 lever key interlocking frame installed in 1909. The hut was situated on the end of one of the platforms and controlled the running signals. The siding points for the goods yard were controlled by Annett's Keys as described in Chapter 11. As can be seen even the huts could be fitted with external bells. The 'H' shaped cowl on the stove pipe is a rather prominent feature.*

STANDARD SIGNAL HUTS

In **Figure 10.3** it will be noticed that the standard size codes listed commence at 'C' and one might ask what happened to 'A' and 'B'. These designations were used, of course, but as will be appreciated they were very small structures and so they are dealt with separately here. The original A and B size codes applied as follows:

Size A. 6 foot square to house 5 levers
Size B. 9 foot square to house 10 levers

The application in which these cabins could be used were, obviously, somewhat limited, being largely confined to intermediate block cabins, gate keeper's huts, cabins at very small stations and for ground frames. It is not absolutely clear what they looked like in their original form but it seems probable that they were of all wood construction, with a brick plinth in some cases. In practice these two sizes were not found flexible enough for all applications and numbers of huts were built to other dimensions to suit local circumstances. Since most of these were built to suit one particular application they varied somewhat in design and detail. Some were square in plan and some rectangular, some had a full length of windows in the front while others had only a small window. Roofs could be of hipped or gable type.

In July 1880 Mr Webb suggested to the Locomotive Committee that it would be sensible to adopt a standard design of wooden hut for use as mess rooms, stores, lamp rooms and offices. He considered they would be far superior to the old carriage bodies, which it had been the practice to use up to that time, while they should cost far less in repairs. The following month it was ordered that these standard cabins should be adopted for future work and the use of old carriage bodies discontinued. The huts came in three standard sizes 8 x 8 feet, 16 x 8 feet and 24 x 8 feet. As well as the applications already listed they even found use as platform shelters and booking offices at small stations.

It was soon realised that the huts could be adopted for use as signal cabins by fitting additional windows in the front and ends. The basic 8′ x 8′ hut derived in this way was adopted as standard for signal department work and effectively replaced the old size 'A' and 'B' cabins. Despite the adoption of this 'standard' hut it should be noted that the design was not nearly as standard as was the design of the standard size 'C' to 'U' cabins. The huts varied in detail from time to time and place to place. In addition, the huts had shorter lives than the more substantial large cabins and by their very nature they were often used in applications where temporary installations only were required. Thus changes occurred much more rapidly in the case of the huts than happened with the cabins proper.

With the introduction of the key interlocking apparatus on a wide scale it was realised that the 8′ x 8′ hut was ideally suited as an economical cover to the small frames. Many examples were installed, principally as ground frames, intermediate block cabins and crossing keepers cabins. **Figure 10.17** shows the standard form of 8′ x 8′ hut used for signalling purposes during the late LNW days. This could be stretched, if necessary, to give greater accommodation. As might be expected a standard range of cabin sizes and layouts were available and could be ordered by consulting a simple chart. The illustrations show some actual huts and give an indication of the variations that occurred in practice.

Not all of the huts were used to house the levers, in some cases they were merely used as a shelter and to house the telephone or other instruments while the levers were placed outside. In these cases an ordinary hut with small windows was often provided rather than one with full glazing.

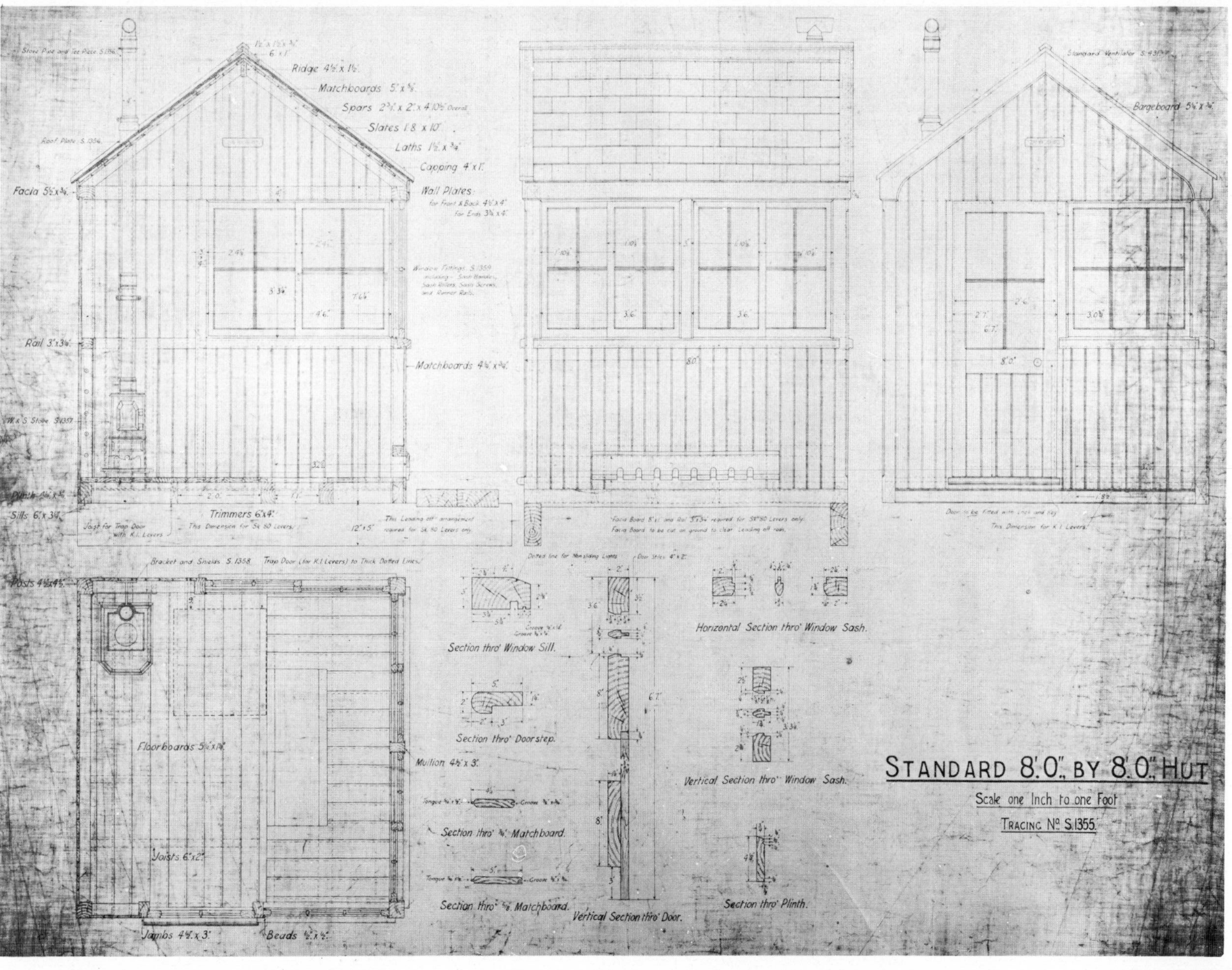

Figure 10.17 *Standard 8′ x 8′ Hut as used for small signal cabins, level crossing cabins and ground frames. As can be seen, it was primarily designed for use with SK80 or key interlocking (SK446) levers or frames. The design could be stretched to produce larger huts if required (see photographs). This drawing was prepared in 1914. Scale of reproduction: 7 mm to 1 foot (1:43).*

Chapter Eleven

Interlocking Frames and Ground Frames

The most costly and complicated single item in the signalling system was the interlocking frame. Webb recognised that if the LNWR was to be successful in its intention to produce its own signalling equipment a suitable design for an interlocking frame would have to be evolved that could be mass produced at Crewe. Design work was put in hand as soon as the decision to manufacture the Company's own equipment had been confirmed by the Board. It was recognised that the lever frame would have to be capable of mass production in the works while being robust and reliable in service. The manufacturing facilities available at Crewe were second to none and made possible the production of high quality components and the extensive use of steel. Experience had already shown that the interlocking frames would have to be well and strongly built to survive without excessive maintenance at busy locations. Thus Webb's philosophy in preparing the design was to –

> 'Keep predominently in view the advantages of having a strong machine, of the simplest possible construction, few parts, and these interchangeable, . . . large wearing surfaces, and the whole easily accessible for cleaning and repairs.'

By adhering to this philosophy, he was able to evolve a locking frame which would need little maintenance and have a long life. Webb patented his first designs on February 4th, 1874 (No. 442). Here some of the basic elements of the familiar LNW frame appeared, the hook rack and vertically mounted stud and bar locking.

The most important consideration and difficulty in designing a locking frame was to devise a means of actuating the locking mechanism so that it would remain tight, could not be fiddled and did not deteriorate with use. Locking attached directly to the levers was not always sensitive to slight movements of the lever. Similarly, direct action locking could be strained or worn by the large forces which could be placed on it by the leverage possible when the lever was moved. Many designers and inventors spent much time and effort in devising ingenious and curious means of overcoming the problem. The majority of these people patented their ideas and no one wanted to pay royalties to anyone else if they could avoid it, resulting in yet more designs. Webb was no exception to this and his patents contained a number of different methods of operating his interlocking, probably as much to protect his ideas from any attempts at copies as for their practical value. Further variations on the patent 442 theme were patented by Webb a few days later on February 7th (No. 494): this included a number of alternative methods of driving the locking, some manufacturing details and a facing point lock layout. The most significant items included were a system of channel rodding for actuating points and the loop or bow catch handles for lever frames, both of which were to become standard fittings on the LNWR.

In this first Webb frame the interlocking was driven by the catch handle rather than the lever. Operating the catch handle lifted the catch block out of the notch in the quadrant as usual (so allowing the lever to be moved). The catch block in turn lifted the hook rack to actuate the interlocking (see **Figure 11.1**). The interlocking mechanism itself consisted of horizontal steel bars driven from the hook rack via angle cranks. The interlocking was effected by means of studs mounted on the horizontal locking bars which engaged in the notches in the hook racks. (Stud and Bar Locking.)

This frame suffered from some problems however, the most significant being that the direct catch handle drive imparted a motion in both directions to the locking bars each time a lever was moved, and this made the interlocking of some functions rather complicated. In addition, the catch handle drive for the locking was said to infringe one of Saxby's patents and this caused further problems. Only a few frames of this type were produced.

The following year Webb patented some further ideas (No. 462 of February, 1875), the most significant of which was a new method of driving the racks. Here a 'Cam-Head' was formed on top of the rack instead of a hook, **Figure 11.2** is a section through this 'Cam-Head' frame. It was again a catch handle locking frame. Depressing the catch handle to release the lever swings the bell crank 'X' so raising, by about half its full travel, the cam head and rack. When the catch handle is released, at the end of the

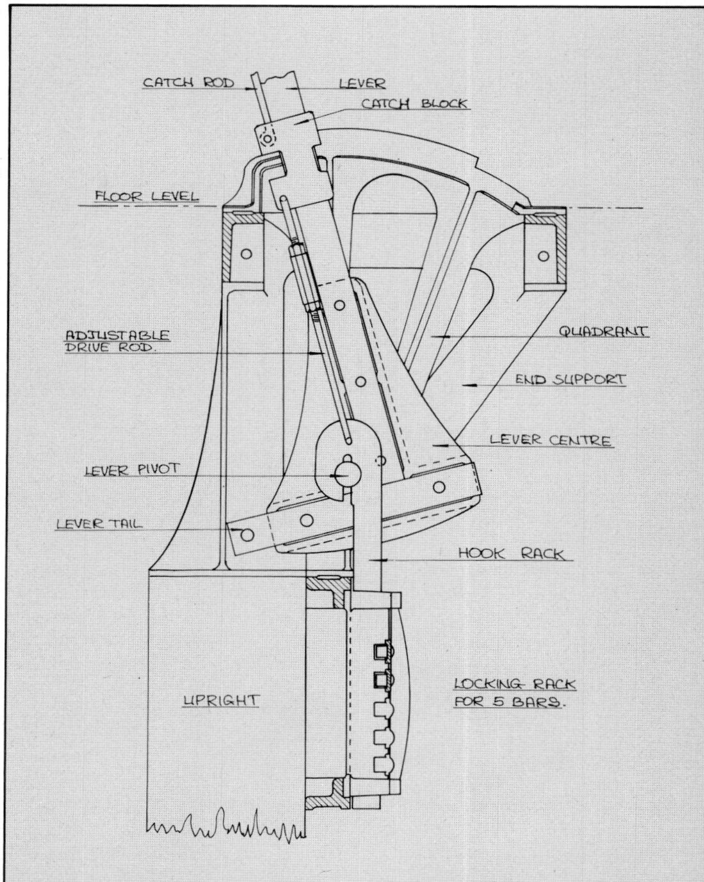

Figure 11.1 *Webb's original design of lever frame, which was of the 'catch handle' locking type.*

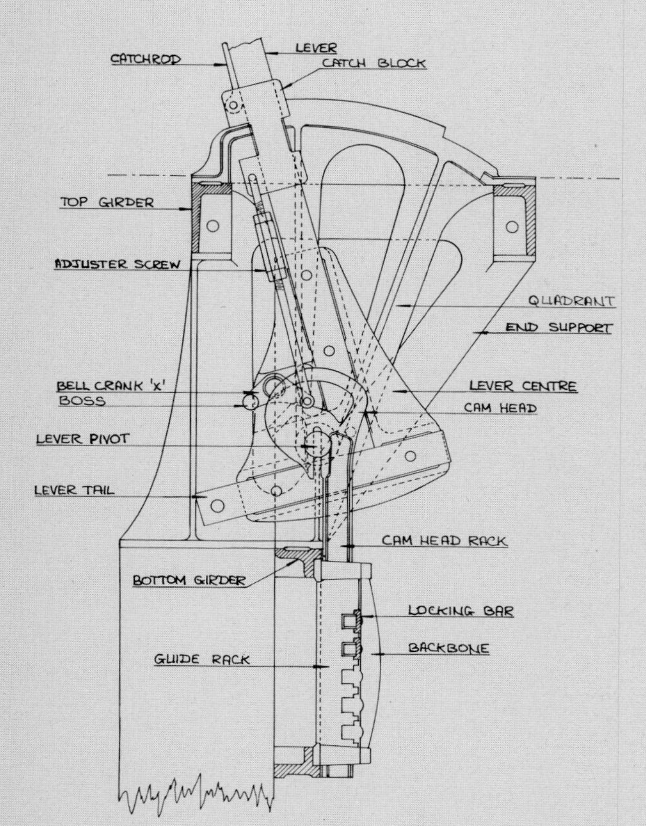

Figure 11.2 *The second design of Webb frame used on the LNWR. This was also of the 'catch handle' type but incorporated the 'cam-head' to give improved operation of the interlocking.*

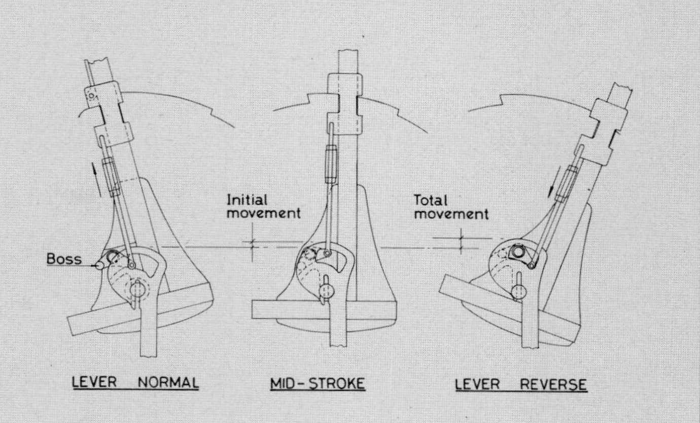

Figure 11.3 *Diagram showing the operation of the 'Cam-Head' arrangement. Depressing the loop (catch) handle lifts the cam-head rack by half its full travel. When the lever has reached the end of its stroke releasing the loop handle imparts the remaining upward movement to the Cam-Head rack.*

lever stroke, the crank is moved again causing the boss at its rear end to rise and lift the cam head through the remainder of its travel and so complete the interlocking, **Figure 11.3** should make this operation clear. This method of drive had the advantage that the locking bars were only moved in one direction for each lever stroke, while the locking was not fully completed until the levers were fully home. The majority of the parts of this 'new' Cam-Head frame were identical to those of the original frame thus saving the cost of new patterns. This also enabled the original frames to be altered to cam-head locking. About a hundred of these 'Cam-Head' frames were produced over the next eighteen months.

With the experience of those frames in service it was found that their performance was not entirely satisfactory, possibly due to wear in the locking drive causing the cam-heads to stick or not travel far enough to effect the locking correctly.

In June 1876 Webb patented a further design of drive for his locking. This was the well known 'Tumbler' system, a lever driven locking device this time, but arranged to incorporate many of the advantages of the catch handle drive. **Figure 11.4** is a drawing of the standard LNWR tumbler driven stud and bar locking frame (commonly known simply as the 'Tumbler' frame), while **Plate 11.3** illustrates the lever shoe, tumbler and its connection to the hook rack. Here we gain some insight into the true genius and ingenuity of Webb and his staff. The new actuation method only involved a couple of minor changes to the existing frame (and indeed all the other proposals). These were the modification of the quadrant casting to accept the tumbler guides, the casting of the tumbler, drilling a bolt hole for it in the lever, a reversion to the original design of hook rack, and a slight modification to the length of the drive rod from the tumbler (formerly from the catch block) to the hook rack. All other parts remained unchanged. Thus the tumbler system was interchangeable with the original apparatus, and it was a fairly simple matter to convert the cam-head frames to the tumbler type.

The 'Tumbler' frame soon proved itself to be reliable and effective and it was adopted as the standard for all new work. It was to remain the standard lever frame used on the L&NWR for thirty years and during that time over 1,200 new frames were produced, in addition to countless parts for renewals and extensions to existing frames.

The problems in arriving at a good and reliable design for the interlocking frame meant that relatively few frames were produced during the first couple of years, and these were by no means sufficient to meet the huge demand for new interlocking apparatus on the line. Locking frames, therefore, continued to be purchased from Saxby and Farmer (see Chapter 2). These were installed in standard LNW 'type 3' (and later 'type 4') signal cabins and generally worked the new LNW signals. In addition, such was the pace of change that many lever frames were removed while still quite new and these were, no doubt, re-used elsewhere. The delays and problems associated with the change over from the cam-head to the tumbler frame probably accounted for the shortage of new frames in the Autumn of 1876 which Edwards had remarked on.

Once the tumbler frame had been proved, production was stepped up, and by the early 1880's Crewe Works was able to provide all the new frames and spare parts required. The scale of this production and the distance the Company had travelled along the road to self-sufficiency can be seen from the fact that by 1884 about half of the 24,500 levers then in use were of LNW manufacture. Since there had only been just over 13,000 levers in use in 1874 it can be seen that output from Crewe largely represented new work rather than replacement of Saxby equipment.

Figure 11.4 is a drawing of the tumbler frame, this and **Figure 11.5** shows the naming of the parts and can be used to see how the mechanism operates. The frame is of the 'lever' locking type with no connection between the catch handle and the locking. The locking is driven by the

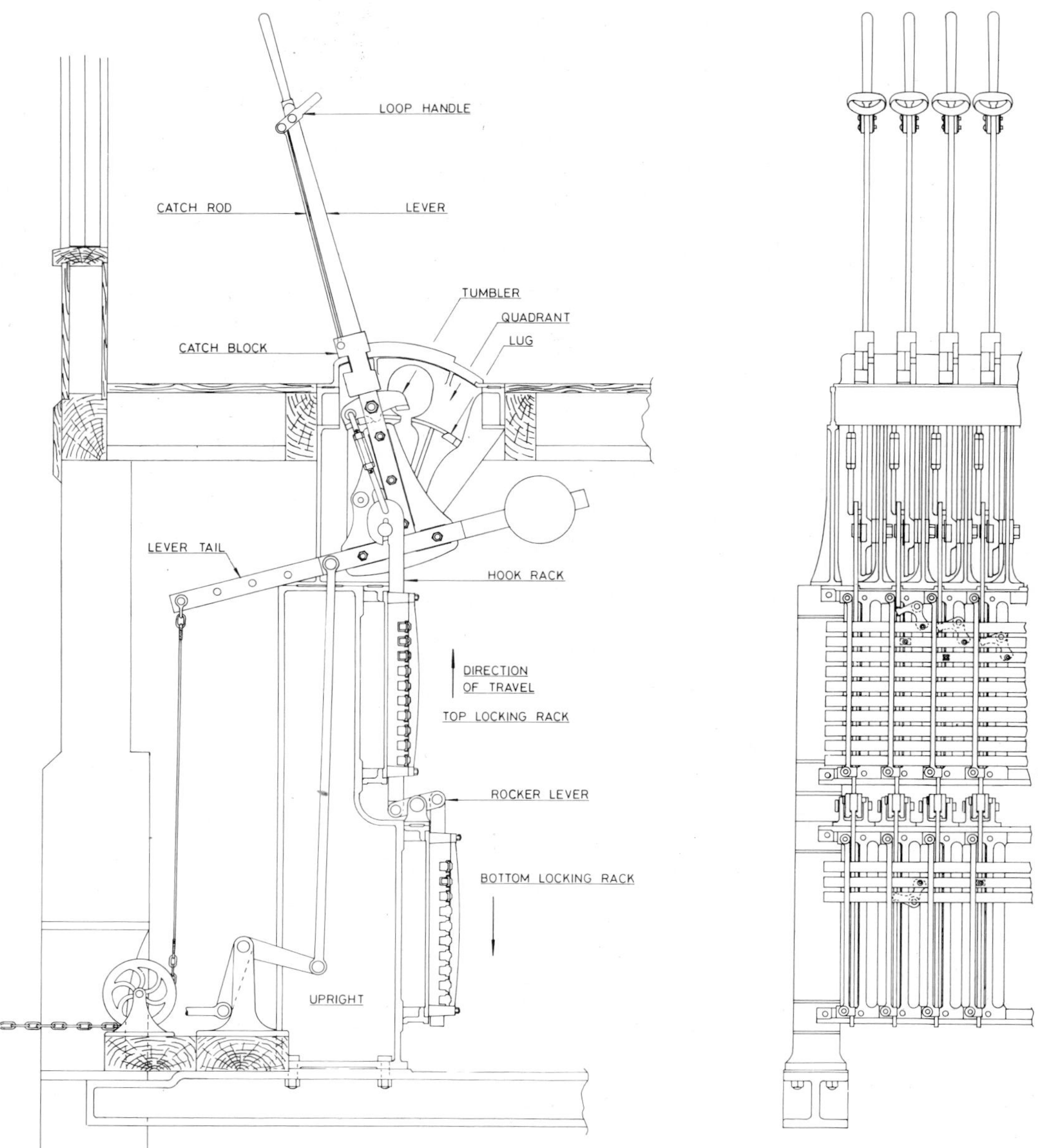

L.& N.W.R. STANDARD INTERLOCKING APPARATUS

— F. W. WEBB'S SYSTEM — CREWE WORKS —

Drawn By: R. D. Foster. December 1977

Figure 11.4 *Webb Tumbler Frame. This drawing shows a frame with double locking racks and illustrates the arrangement of rocking levers used to reverse the direction of movement of the racks. Note how the frame was entirely supported by the uprights. The ground level girders were used for fixing the lead-off timbers and in many installations, particularly later ones, these girders were extended through the front of the cabin to allow the fixing of external lead-off timbers. Scale of reproduction: ½ inch to 1 foot (1:24).*

Plate 11.1 *An LNW Tumbler Frame on a single girder for 15 levers at Aber, photographed in 1976. Originally, all the levers except Nos. 4, 5 and 12 worked, and in accordance with normal practice spaces were provided at these positions. The LNW used separate cast iron name and pull plates on its frames. The pull plates were attached to the levers and had the lever number at the top. Below this was listed, where applicable, the numbers of the levers which preceded it (i.e. those which had to be pulled to release it). Thus, in the photograph, before the distant signal lever No. 1 can be pulled, levers 2 and 3 (the home and starting signals) have to be reversed. The name plates were mounted on a board behind the levers. The LNW used a 'two-plating' system for these, the top plate showing the function of the lever in its normal position and the bottom plate the function in the reverse position. Levers which only have a reverse function (e.g. signals) were provided with a bottom plate only, while others, such as points, had two plates. Because of the arrangement of the plates, the descriptions often did not read clearly if the separate top and bottom plate descriptions were joined together as one phrase. The various plates were generally painted the same colour as the lever with white lettering, as seen here, although some frames could be found with white plates and black lettering. The pull plate on lever 13, incidentally, is a standard plastic BR (LMR) product and that on lever 15 is an LMS standard plate (these were derived from Railway Signal Co./Lancashire and Yorkshire Railway practice). Two LNW wire adjusters (Chapter 15) for the distant signal wires can be seen behind the frame near its ends. Behind them is the window shelf, formerly used for mounting signal and other repeaters. The board in front of the frame is another standard product and was provided to give the signalman a good foothold when pulling the levers. The piece of carpet over the centre of the frame is there to help reduce the draughts through the lever slots!*

tumbler which is connected to the hook rack (which is of the patent 442 pattern, rather than the cam-headed rack of No. 462) directly. The tumbler bears on a shaped lug projecting from the quadrant. Moving the lever a mere 1/8th of an inch out of the normal position causes the tumbler to ride over the top of the lug and lifts the hook rack through about half of its full travel thus 'starting' the locking and preventing any further moves being made until the lever movement has been completed. In the last 1/8th inch of the lever's travel the tumbler flips over the reverse position lug and so completes the movement of the hook rack (this moves upwards by 1 3/8ths inch in a full lever stroke), and effects the necessary releases. By this means the advantages of the catch handle system were retained with the strength of direct lever locking. The relative positions of the tumbler and lever centre ensured that no strain could be placed on the locking if an attempt was made to pull a 'locked' lever.

The upwards movement of the hook rack is transferred into the horizontal movement of the locking bars by means of cranks (**Figure 11.6**). Attached to the locking bars are studs which lock or release levers as required, this can be

Plate 11.2 *An under floor view of a tumbler frame, showing the arrangement of the girders, uprights and locking rack. This particular frame is mounted on a single girder for 12 levers and the locking rack can accommodate 10 bars (only those actually required are fitted). Wooden uprights have been used in this all timber cabin.*

Plate 11.3 *An under-floor view of a lever in a tumbler frame. At the top is the lower portion of the catch block and below this is the tumbler itself (from which the frame gets its name), which is bolted to the side of the lever. The top end of the drive rod for the locking is attached to the left hand end of the tumbler, and its lower end to the top of the hook rack, which uses the lever pivot pin as a guide. At the bottom of the picture, the top of the locking rack can be seen with the backbones which retain the horizontal locking bars.*

understood by studying the drawings and photographs.

The locking racks fitted to the frames were made of suitable size to accommodate the locking required and to allow some space for any additions or alterations which might be found necessary. It was found that the large locking racks imposed an appreciable load on the frame and made it heavy to work since the long hook rack had to be lifted each time a lever was pulled. An arrangement was devised whereby the direction of travel of the hook rack could be reversed and the loads equalised. This was done by placing cranks or rocking levers at the mid point of the hook racks. In this way the hook rack above the crank lifted when a lever was pulled while the section below the crank fell thus balancing the load, **Figure 11.4** and **Plates 11.4** and **11.5** should make this clear.

Plate 11.4 *A view of a set of double locking racks. This shows how the lower rack is set forward to accommodate the rocking levers which reverse the direction of travel in order to balance the weight of the hook racks and lower racks. A set of fish plates joining two sections of the horizontal locking bars can be seen in the foreground. These were provided to facilitate removal for cleaning, repair and alteration. Originally, the bars had been continuous but this was changed for new work in December 1887 and the Inspectors instructed to alter all their existing frames. Generally, the fishplated joints were made at the ends of alternate girders.*

Plate 11.5 *A close up detail of the rocking levers used between the top and bottom racks. A couple in the foreground are in the reverse position.*

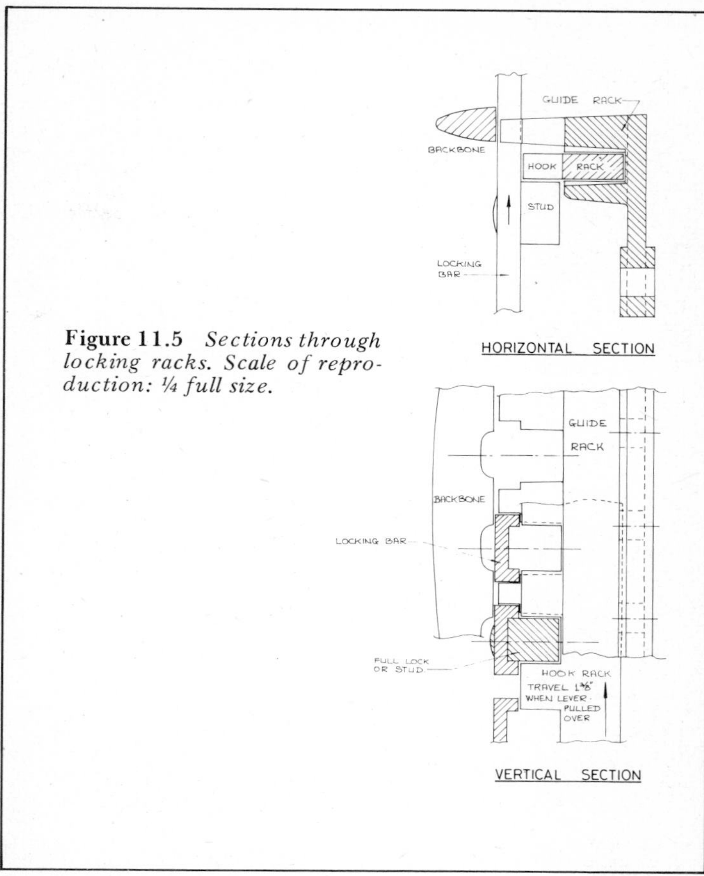

Figure 11.5 *Sections through locking racks. Scale of reproduction: ¼ full size.*

The first lever frame to be constructed with these cranks and the double rack arrangement was the large 144 lever frame installed at Crewe North Junction in March 1879. This had two racks for 38 bars each. The racks (single or double) were constructed in sizes for up to 38 bars each. In practice it was found that the large unsupported vertical length of the guide racks and backbones in the large locking racks allowed some flexing to occur which could result in breakages and other problems. Hence in later installations the locking racks were generally limited to about 26 bars in capacity and where more locking was required two or more locking racks were used. In some of the very large frames more than two racks were found necessary and a number of frames were fitted with four locking racks. The space required for the locking racks was one of the contributory reasons for the tall cabins found at large stations such as Rugby, Preston, Chester and Rhyl.

Much thought had gone into the design of the Webb frame. In addition to the considerations of ease of manufacture, the question of maintenance was taken into account. The frame was designed in such a way that individual parts could be removed for maintenance or repair without disturbing the rest of the mechanism. It was normal practice for worn levers or quadrants to be removed and returned to works for repair, their places being taken by refurbished ones from elsewhere. During the life of a frame the levers might be replaced several times.

Unlike many of the other types of lever frame in use at the time which were often fairly crudely made, the Crewe frames were a precision engineering job, advantage being taken of the skills and machinery available within the works. This coupled with their large and solid construction ensured that they would have long and trouble free lives. Because of this solid construction, the frames were quite heavy and unlike many other types were not supported on the signal cabin floor or structure. They were, instead,

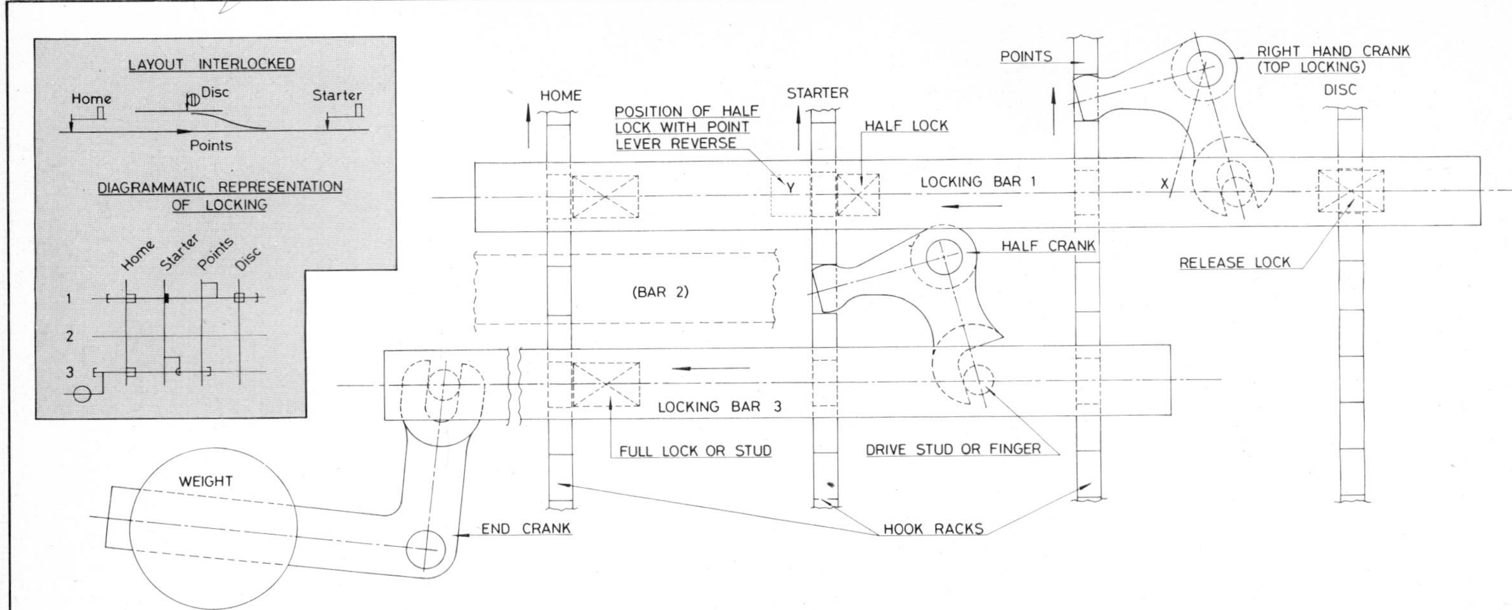

Figure 11.6 *Sketch showing a section of stud and bar (tumbler) interlocking. Locking bar 1 effects the interlocking necessary for the layout shown on the top left and illustrates the use of full and half locks. The locking on bar 3 illustrates a simple form of sequential locking. This prevents the home signal lever being pulled for a train until the starting signal lever has been replaced to normal after the passage of the previous train. The small diagram on the left shows how the locking was represented diagrammatically on a drawing.*

Plate 11.6 *A detail of the left hand end of a locking rack with a cast iron upright. The second bar from the bottom is a piece of sequential locking. The drive crank has one finger cut off to produce a half crank, the return motion being provided by the weighted crank mounted on the upright at the left hand end,* **Figure 11.6** *explains the working of this type of locking. The gap in the guide racks on the right is due to the presence of spaces in the frame.*

Figure 11.7 STANDARD GIRDERS

Size of Girder (number of levers accommodated)	8	10	12	14	15	16	18
Number of cabins containing at least one example of the girder	5	203	59	6	240	63	164
Total size of sample 607 cabins							

supported separately from the ground on timber uprights, the frame being totally independent of the cabin structure. These uprights were placed at intervals along the length of the frame. Between them the frame was supported on cast iron girders. These girders were made of standard lengths (see **Figure 11.7**) and all lever frames were made up of combinations of these girders. A 25 lever frame, for instance, would be made up of one girder for 15 levers and one for 10 while a 54 lever frame would consist of three girders for 18 levers. The locking racks were fixed directly to the uprights. Because of the space taken by the uprights and the fixings at the ends of the girders and locking racks it was not possible to have a lever at the joint between two girders. There was, therefore, an 11 inch space in the levers (which were normally mounted at 5½ inch centres) at the girder ends. Since this position could not be used for a lever it was not numbered, the numbering jumping from the last lever in one girder to the first lever in the next. This gap in the levers also allowed a floor joist to pass through the frame, thus strengthening the cabin structure.

From about the mid 1880's the use of wooden uprights was generally superseded for new work and cast iron uprights were introduced. These were of 'I' cross section and varied in height to suit the elevation of the cabin. These iron uprights were bolted to 'I' section girders at ground level. These girders were laid at right angles to the tracks across the width of the cabin (one girder being provided for each upright). The girders generally projected from the front of the cabin and were used for fixing the lead off timbers (both inside and outside the cabin). In this way the lever frame and the lead off for the point and signal connections formed one complete unit. After this wooden uprights were only used in some all-wood cabins

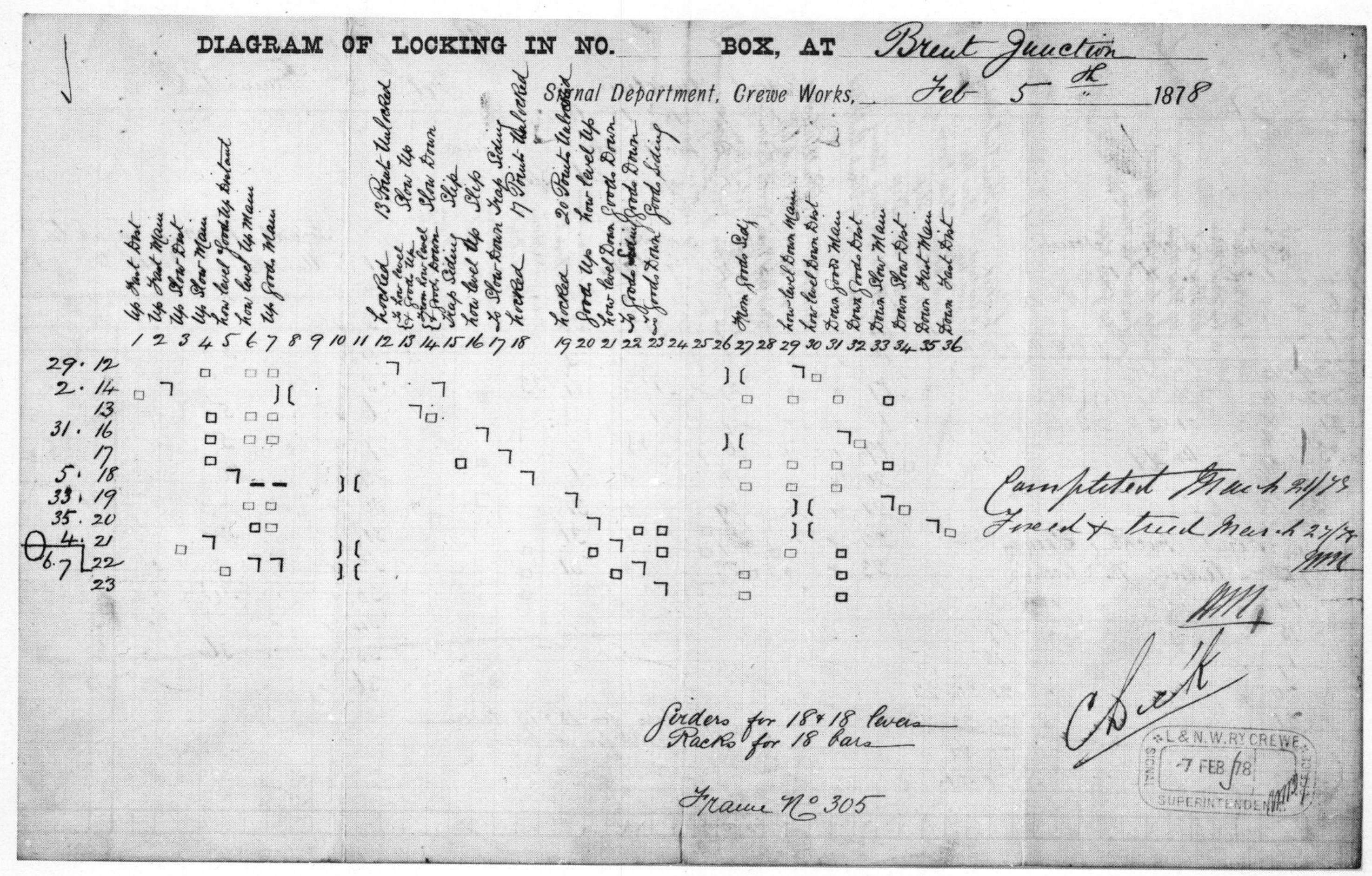

Figure 11.8 *Reproduction of an actual LNWR interlocking diagram, issued to the works for the construction of a new lever frame. This one was installed at Brent Junction, near Willesden, in 1878.*

where there were foundation problems. After about 1900 the wooden uprights used in a number of the old frames were replaced with new cast iron ones. The LNW did not provide spare levers in its frames to allow for additional functions, room was left in the frames but the lever and quadrant were not fitted, a sensible economy. The spaces for the levers were covered with plain cast iron cover plates. These could easily be removed to allow a lever to be fitted when this was required. Unlike the girder spaces, these unused spaces were numbered in with the working levers.

While the arrangement of the interlocking, mounted vertically below the levers in a separate room, aided maintenance and alterations it presented problems where there was insufficient space below the operating floor. In addition there were places where there was no room for a conventional signal cabin and where an 'overhead' type cabin was necessary to provide a satisfactory view for the signalman. In these cases a conventional frame could not be used. A special 'overhead' version of the tumbler frame was designed (**Figure 11.11**, SK449 type) where the interlocking was mounted above floor level. This type of frame was used in the 'overhead' cabins and other special locations. Since the interlocking was mounted on the wall behind the levers there was a limit to the size of the locking rack that could be fitted without obstructing the signalman's view through the windows. In cases where additional locking was required the frames were mounted in the back of the cabin so that the locking could occupy the whole of the back wall (**Plate 11.7**). This was one of the few instances where the LNW constructed cabins with the lever frame in the back away from the windows.

About 1890, to give additional flexibility in the design of the overhead cabins, two new types of 'overhead' frame were designed (SK447 and SK448 in **Figure 11.11**). These allowed the frame to be placed in the front of the cabin without restricting the signalman's view. All the overhead type lever frames were constructed on the girder principle with 11" gaps in the levers at the girder joints (subject to the details of the cabin structure – see **Plate 11.7**).

The tumblers did give a little trouble from time to time, mainly due to wear. In 1885 the District Inspectors were reminded that there was no point in replacing the tumblers on levers where insufficient movement was being imparted to the locking bars if the real trouble was wear on the quadrant casting. This was followed in December 1887 by a memo from Mr A M Thompson:–

> 'When the tumbler lever of our locking apparatus becomes badly worn it will, in many cases, be a

(continued on page 159)

Plate 11.7 *An interior view of Manchester Exchange No. 2 cabin, this was opened in June 1884 and closed in 1926 when the station area was resignalled. It was an overhead cabin and was fitted with a SK449 overhead type frame, the most common form of special frame. In this large cabin the double rack of locking (for 24 and 12 bars) took up the whole of the back wall of the cabin. The large gaps in the frame, containing the signalmen's lockers, were above the steel cross girders which supported the cabin and were a feature of most of the frames in overhead cabins. Placing the frame in the 'back' of a cabin was most unusual on the LNW and was only done in very special circumstances such as this (it was also done, however, in the case of some of the key interlocking frames and huts). The block instruments in this case were on the window side of the cabin, while some signal repeaters can just be seen, above the frame, mounted on boards in the roof.*

Figure 11.9 ARRANGEMENT OF GIRDERS IN STANDARD CABINS

Standard Cabin		*Arrangement of Girders in Cabin*			
		Most Common Arrangements		*Other Common Arrangements*	
Size Code	*Nominal Number of Levers*	*Number of Levers*	*Girders for*	*Number of Levers*	*Girders for*
C	15	15	15	18	18
		16	16	14	14
		12	12		
		10	10		
D	20	20	10+10	22	12+10*
		18	18		
E	25	25	15+10*	26	16+10*
		24	12+12	27	15+12*
F	30	30	15+15	32	16+16
G	35	36	18+18	35	10+15+10
H	40	36	18+18	38	15+15+8
		40	15+10+15*		
J	45	45	15+15+15		
K	50	48	16+16+16	50	16+18+16*
L	55	54	18+18+18		
M	60	60	15+15+15+15	64	16+16+16+16
N	70	72	18+18+18+18	64	16+16+16+16
				75	15+15+15+15+15
O	80	80	16+16+16+16+16	75	15+15+15+15+15
				80	16+16+16+16+16
P	90	90	18+18+18+18+18	90	6 girders for 15
R	112	112	7 girders for 16	105	7 girders for 15
S	135	126	7 girders for 18	135	9 girders for 15
				128	8 girders for 16
T	144	144	8 girders for 18		
U	180	180	10 girders for 18	162	9 girders for 18

*Also found with girders in a different order, the most common arrangement is shown.

Plate 11.8 *The largest tumbler frame ever constructed was made in April 1891 for Euston No. 2 and contained 288 levers in two rows of 144 levers mounted back to back. This photograph shows the frame erected in the works at Crewe for fitting up and testing. Four racks of locking (of 24+30+30+24 bars) were provided for each section. The cabin was quite low in order to allow sight under various overbridges and so two racks were placed under the frames while the other two were inverted and mounted on separate uprights a short distance away in order to reduce the height. Drive rods passed under the walkways to connect the two sets of racks. Even so, a pit had to be constructed below the cabin to house part of the interlocking. A number of other cabins, such as Birmingham New Street No. 5, had their interlocking partly in pits. Twist bars between the locking racks in the centre provide locking functions between the two sets of levers. The arrangement of the cross girders and uprights can clearly be seen in this illustration. The gaps in the levers at the end of each girder (occupied by an upright) can also be seen.*

Photo: Courtesy National Railway Museum

Figure 11.10 EXAMPLES OF SPECIAL ARRANGEMENTS OF GIRDERS

Cabin	*Number of Levers*	*Girder Arrangement as Built*	*Cabin Size*	*Date Erected*
Coundon Road	23	8+15	E	1877
Mostyn No. 1	40	10+10+10+10	K	1902
Bryn Junction	70	15+15+10+15+15	N	1929
Speke Junction	100	15+15+15+10+15+15+15	R	1907
Lancaster No. 3	82	15+18+18+18+15	P	1902
Hillhouse No. 1	104	16+18+18+18+18+16	R	1903
Euxton Junction	84	16+18+16+18+16	O	1894
Llandudno No. 2	86	18+16+18+16+18	O	1891
Chester No. 2	170	16+18+16+18+16+18+16+18+16+18	U	1890

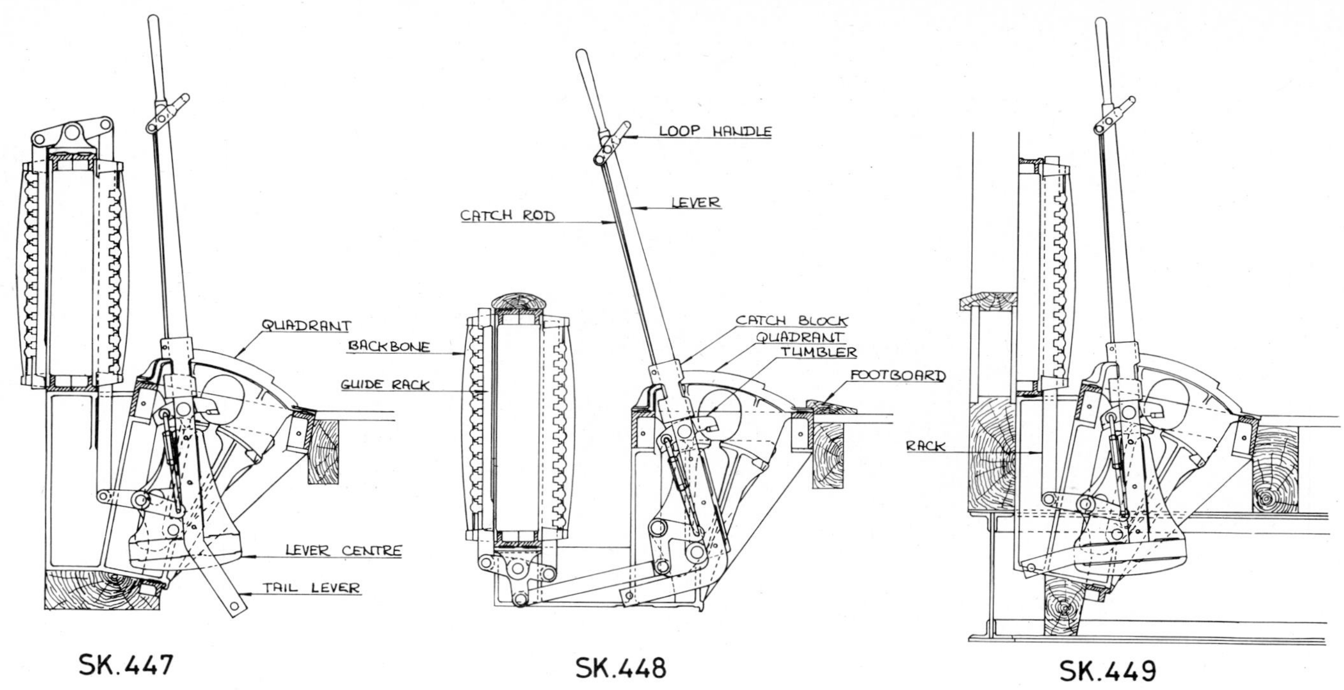

Figure 11.11 *The three types of tumbler frames used for overhead cabins. The interlocking was placed behind, rather than below, the levers so that the frame could be mounted in a cabin above the tracks. The Sketch 449 type was the original, and most common, form of overhead frame.*

Figure 11.12 USE OF LOCKING RACKS

Single Racks			*Double Racks*		
Number of Bars	*Number of Frames*	*Used on Frames of*	*Number of Bars*	*Number of Frames*	*Used on Frames of*
5	2	10 to 20 levers	10+10	1	40 levers
6	1	12 "	12+12	5	30 to 45 "
7	7	10 to 20 "	13+13	4	40 to 55 "
8	3	" "	14+14	5	" "
9	4	" "	15+15	3	45 to 80 "
10	24	" "	16+16	8	" "
11	6	12 to 36 "	18+18	4	" "
12	20	" "	20+20	1	64 "
13	3	16 to 36 "	22+22	2	80 to 90 "
14	14	" "	23+23	1	72 "
15	11	" "	25+25	1	60 "
16	10	" "	26+26	1	86 "
18	14	" "	28+28	1	90 "
20	17	" "	38+38	1	144 "
22	4	36 to 60 "	12+16	1	41 "
23	3	" "	22+20	1	68 "
25	3	" "	22+25	1	90 "
26	1	" "	15+13	1	54 "
28	1	" "	35+25	1	118 "
38	1	144 "			
Total 149 cabins in sample			Total 43 cabins in sample		

Plate 11.9 *The interior of Chester No. 6 cabin in March 1977. This overhead cabin was fitted with an SK448 frame and the interlocking can just be seen behind the levers. The divisions of the frame (15+25+25+15 levers) over the cabin support girders can be seen clearly here. Because of the space required for the interlocking, the frame was much further from the windows than was usual and to compensate for this the cabin structure was 14 feet wide. A wonderful selection of instruments can be seen on the block shelf. Those with sloping fronts are Tyer's clock type train describers (see Chapter 12).*

Plate 11.10 *A view of the back of the frame at Chester No. 6. This illustrates the arrangement of the interlocking which is partly above and partly below the floor. The fishplate joints in some of the locking bars can be seen in the girder spaces. Note also the stay rods provided between the back of the block shelf and the window pillars.*

saving to couple up the locking of the lever to the catch block by the existing screws. This of course cannot be done where a lever works a backlock, but there are many cases, for example, distant signals, ground discs and shunting signals which can be so dealt with.'

This was a reversion to the direct catch handle locking actuation proposed in Webb's first patent of 1874 (**Figure 11.1**). A number of distant signal levers with this type of locking remained in use until recent years.

Around the turn of the century the increasing complexity of working, additional traffic and safety considerations brought the need for more sophisticated or 'special' types of locking such as forms of conditional or sequential locking. Means were found to accomplish most special locking on the tumbler frame. However, probably a bigger problem was that many of the locking racks on existing frames were fairly full and it was difficult to fix additional locking. The two factors therefore acted as a spur to devise a means of easing the situation and in 1901 a double tray of tappet locking (the patent on which had expired in 1884) was designed which could be mounted below the locking rack on the tumbler frame and driven off the bottom of the hook racks (**Figure 11.14**). These were added to frames, where necessary, to house any additional or special locking.

Figure 11.13 EXAMPLES OF CABINS WITH SETS OF FOUR LOCKING RACKS

Cabin	*Levers*	*Racks for*	*Date*
Rhyl No. 1	90	15+15+15+15	1900
Llandudno Jct. No. 1	101	15+15+15+15	1897
Preston No. 5	126	15+15+15+15	1900
Hooton South	128	15+15+15+15	1902
Shrewsbury Crewe Junction	120	15+15+18+18	1903
Preston No. 1	162	15+15+20+20	1901
Rhyl No. 2	126	18+18+18+18	1900
Llandudno Junction No. 2	154	20+20+20+20	1898
Rugby No. 1	180	25+25+25+25	1884
Euston No. 2	144	24+30+30+24	1891 *

*Two frames.

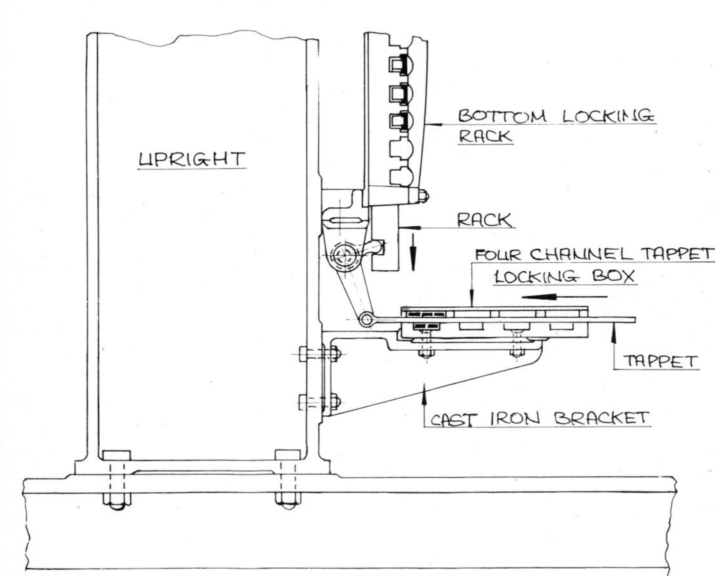

Figure 11.14 *Sketch showing the method used for attaching a tray of tappet locking to a tumbler frame. This example is attached to the bottom rack of a double rack frame. By a rearrangement of the drive crank they could also be used on frames with single racks.*

Once the tappet locking principle had been adopted for extensions to tumbler frames it was a fairly logical step to consider the design of a frame locked completely on the tappet principle. This was doubly so since the 'Crewe' system of all-electric signalling (Chapter 14) introduced in 1898 had included a miniature lever frame with tappet locking. In 1903 design work was carried out on a tappet locking frame for use on the LNWR which could be mass produced at Crewe. Some of the basic features of the Webb frame were incorporated in the new design. These included the principle of mounting the levers on girders which were supported from the ground by cast iron uprights, independent of the cabin structure. The lever was, however, placed in line with its pivot point instead of to one side, resulting in the lever standing nearer to the vertical position when normal and coming further forward when pulled. A return to 'catch handle' locking was made, the locking being actuated by a cam plate running between rollers attached to the catch block (**Figure 11.15**). This form of drive had been used in the Saxby 'Rocker' frame of 1874 where the cam plates were placed above floor level. It was also used in the Midland tappet frame, designed about the same time as the LNWR version, and the later LMS standard frames. The cam plate and lever shoe is illustrated in **Plate 11.12**.

The loop or bow catch handle was retained (uniformity of practice being one reason for this) but lengthened by two inches to give more leverage for positive working of the locking. In practice the catch handle (and catch block) would occasionally fail to go completely home and hence would not free the locking. Thus a signalman who could not 'get' the next lever he required could sometimes be seen walking along the frame lifting the catch handles to complete the locking (however this was by no means confined to LNW Frames!).

The newly designed tappet frame became available in addition to the traditional tumbler frame and the first was installed in November 1903 at Leighswood Sidings (interestingly about the time of Webb's retirement). A relatively unimportant place like Leighswood was probably chosen for the installation to enable experience to be gained of the frame in service and for any 'bugs' to be removed before any further installations were made. In the second installation, the LNWR rather went to the other extreme, the new Chester No. 4 cabin was fitted with a 176 lever tappet frame in June 1904. It will be noted that these first two frames were housed in type 4 design cabins. Only seven tappet frames were installed between 1903 and the spring of 1906, the majority being for large or special jobs where the tappet frame had advantages. Tumbler frames continued to be used for the majority of new work. After this some minor modifications were made to the design of the locking boxes and tappet blade drive. The first of the revised design of frame to be built was also the largest ever constructed! The large 288 lever frame (**Plate 11.8**) at Euston No. 2 was replaced by a double (144 plus 144 levers) tappet frame which was brought into use on 11th March, 1907. The new frames were mounted in the windows of the cabin rather than back to back to allow erection and partial fitting up to be done with the old frames still in use. The 'uniformity of practice' maxim of the LNWR management favoured retaining the existing numbering so as not to confuse the signalmen. In order to do this and re-use as far as possible the existing lead-offs and rodding runs, the new frames had to be numbered from right to left rather than conventionally!

From 1907 the tappet type of frame was used for practically all new work. About 400 new frames of the tappet pattern were made between 1903 and 1928 plus parts for extensions to existing frames and repair work.

Figure 11.15 is a sectional drawing of the tappet frame and shows the arrangement and naming of the parts. The tappet locking boxes have two channels for five locking

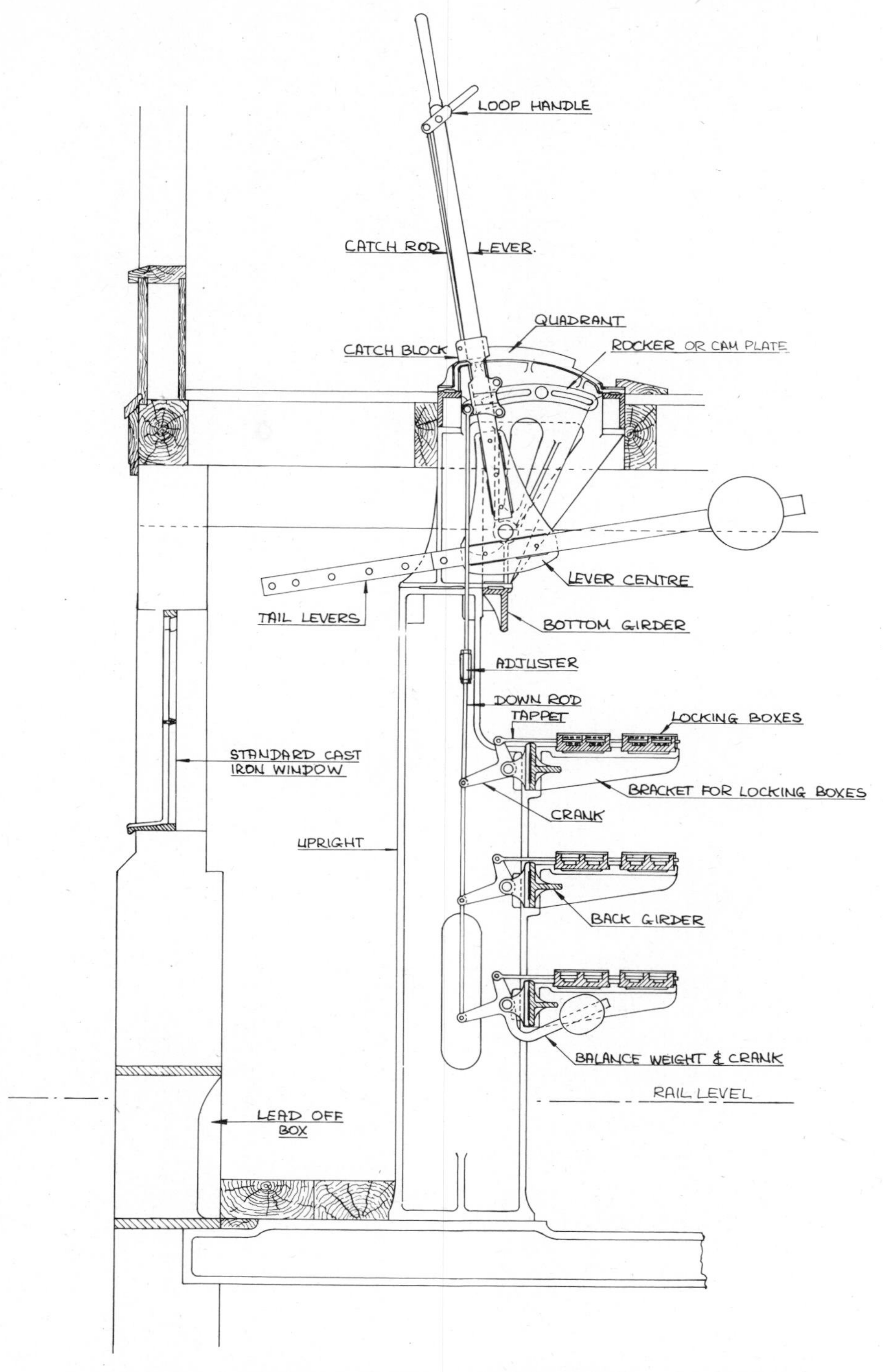

L.N.W.R. TAPPET FRAME

DRAWN BY R.D. FOSTER.

Figure 11.15 *LNWR Tappet Frame. This one sits on uprights for three brackets with three fixed. Note the balance weights on the bottom locking boxes. Scale of reproduction: ½ inch to 1 foot (1:24).*

Plate 11.11 *An LNW tappet frame on a single girder for 18 levers at Deganwy No. 2, photographed in August 1976. The outward differences between the tumbler and tappet frames can be seen by comparing this photograph with* **Plate 11.1**. *Again, only the working levers have been provided and Nos. 10, 11 and 14 are spaces (Nos. 9, 12, 13 and 15 have become spare in recent years). An LNW booking desk with its substantial cross-braced legs is placed near the door. At the left hand end of the window shelf is the stand which formerly carried an LNW arm and lamp repeater (Chapter 12), the functions of which are now provided by repeaters on the block shelf. Two LNW links or loop type lever collars are provided on hooks on the front of the block shelf.*

bars each. The boxes are mounted in pairs on cast iron brackets which in turn are bolted to the cast iron uprights. To allow room for additional locking (for example as a result of extending the frame) it was normal practice to install uprights with provision for more tiers of locking than was actually required. Thus in **Figure 11.16** the upright on the right is designed for fixing two brackets to support two tiers of locking, but only one has actually been fitted. This was described as 'uprights for two brackets, one fixed'. Since the down rods were continuous,

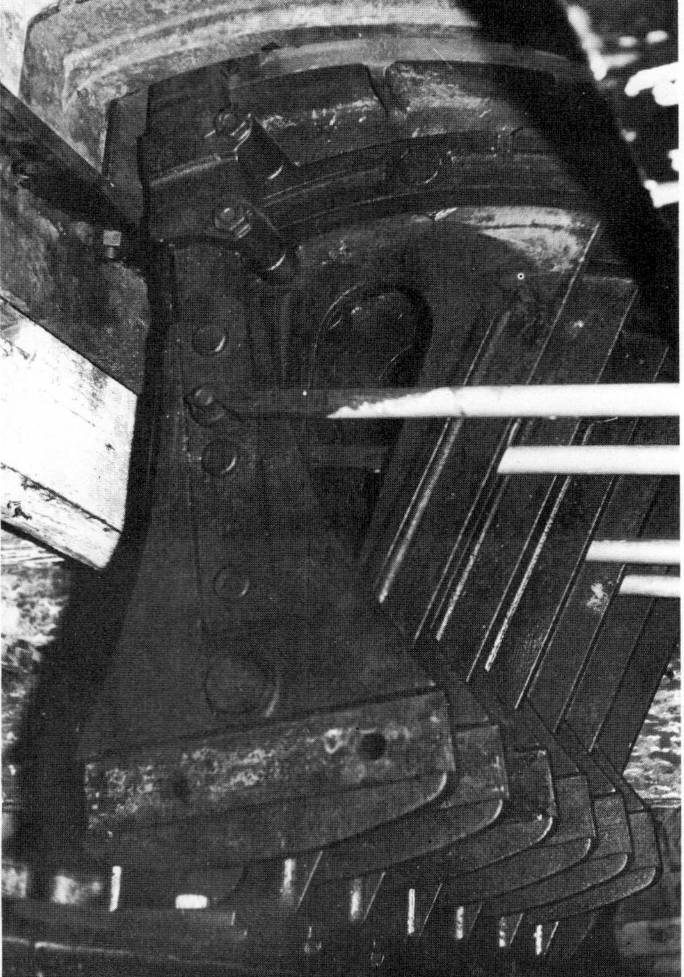

Plate 11.12 *A below floor detail of a lever in a tappet frame. The rocker or cam-plate, near the top, is driven between rollers on an extension of the catch block. On this type of frame the lever is in line with its pivot point. The horizontal, white painted, bars are connected to electric locks and contact boxes mounted under the floor. The LNW 'Northampton' Locks (Chapter 12) operated on rods of this type. The photograph makes an interesting comparison with* **Plate 11.3**.

Plate 11.13 *A photograph of the tappet locking at Ellesmere Port No. 2. The numbers painted on the fish-belly girders at the top are the lever numbers. The girders are for 15 levers each, producing a girder space between levers 30 and 31. Two tiers of locking boxes are fitted and the fixing positions for a third tier can be seen below them. The down rods which drive the locking are at the back and have been made long enough for all three tiers, adjusters being provided near the top. The balance weights, which ensure positive movement of the locking, are on the top boxes in this frame (only the top tier of locking was provided originally, the middle tier being a later addition).*

two tier rods would usually be fitted even though there was only one tier of locking. The frame in **Figure 11.15** has uprights for three brackets with three fixed.

One of the great advantages of the tappet frame was the reduced bulk of the locking. While this made little difference as far as the majority of cabins were concerned, where sites were restricted and large cabins were required it was a most useful feature. It was for this reason that the second tappet frame had been built for Chester No. 4. For maximum visibility a relatively low cabin was the most suitable due to the overbridge at the station throat. If a tumbler frame had been used a large pit would have been required under the cabin (see **Plate 11.8**) or the cabin would have had to be very tall to house the tumbler locking and give sight over the bridge.

Despite the more compact size of the interlocking in the tappet frame there were still situations where it could not be used in its standard form. A special arrangement of frame was devised in which the locking was turned around and placed behind the levers (**Figure 11.17**). Examples were installed at Atherstone in 1909 and at Bangor No. 2 in 1923 (**Plate 11.14**).

An advantage of the design of the LNW tumbler and tappet frames was that they could easily be extended if required by simply bolting on additional girders and adding new uprights. Levers could be added at either end of the frame as necessary (or where space was available). Those added at the left end were generally designated by letters rather than numbers to avoid altering the rest of the frame (see **Plate** 2.3). Quite a number of cabins had their frames extended at some time, in some cases this work also involved extending the cabin (see **Figure 10.10**). Extensions to frames constructed before 1890 seemed to be especially common partly because of the time the installations were in service and partly because the LNW seemed to be

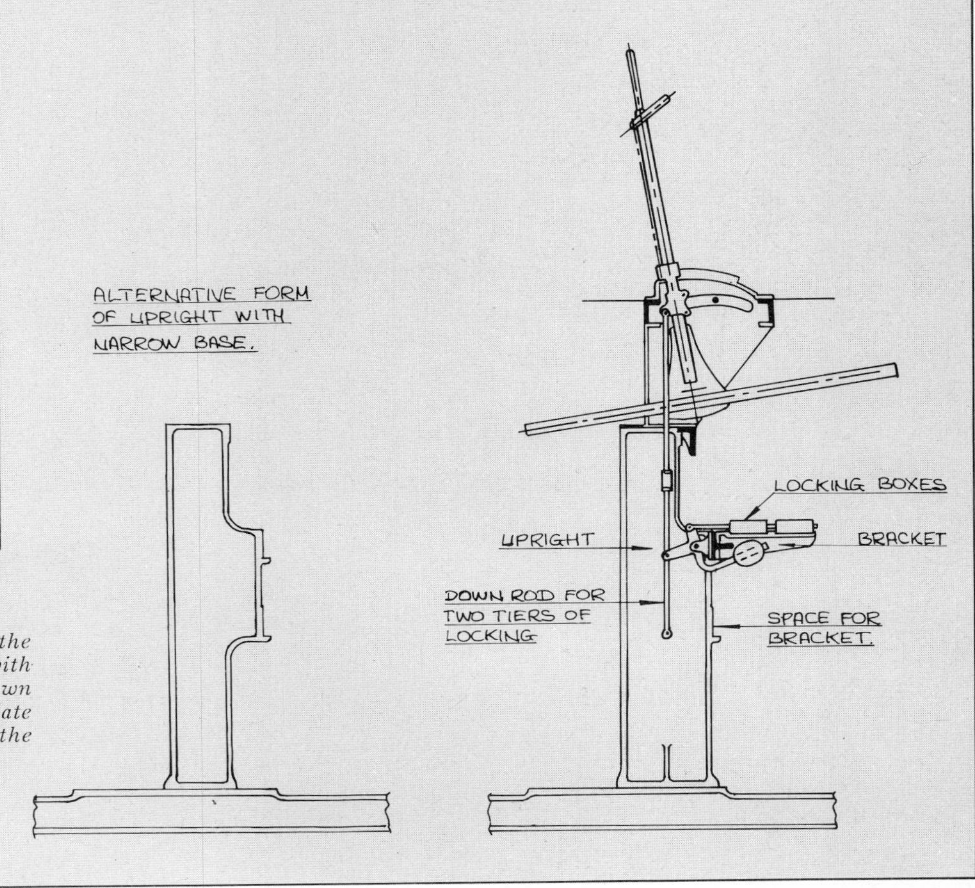

Figure 11.16 *Sketch showing the two types of upright used with tappet frames. Both uprights shown here are designed to accommodate two locking box brackets while the one on the right has one fixed.*

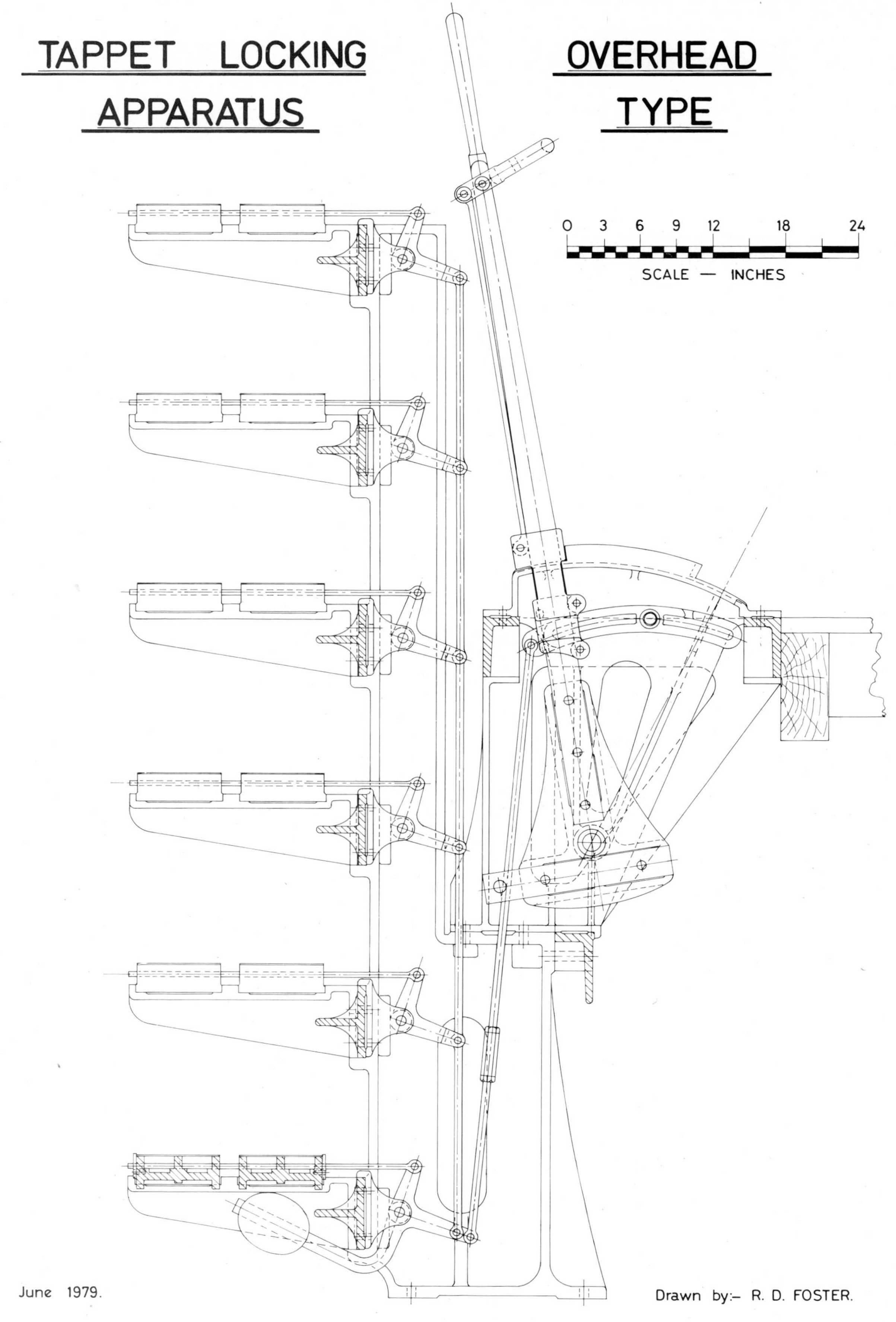
TAPPET LOCKING APPARATUS
OVERHEAD TYPE
0 3 6 9 12 18 24
SCALE — INCHES
June 1979.
Drawn by:– R. D. FOSTER.

Figure 11.17 *Overhead type Tappet Frame. The frames were normally constructed with uprights to accommodate the number of brackets required (plus one spare) only, working from the bottom upwards. Generally the interlocking fitted completely below floor level. No frames were constructed with as many tiers of locking as in this drawing! Scale of reproduction: 1 inch to 1 foot (1:12).*

Plate 11.14 *A view of the back of the overhead type tappet frame (**Figure 11.17**) at Bangor No. 2. This had uprights for four brackets and the bottom three were originally fixed. The top tier of these was removed in recent times leaving only the bottom two which are visible here, the space being used for fitting electric locks and contact boxes.*

fairly parsimonious in the provision of spare spaces in the frames in the early days. In later years more spaces were generally provided when new cabins were constructed.

Production of tappet frames continued after 1923 and in addition to installations on the former LNW lines, examples appeared on the lines of other railways which had become part of the Western Division of the LMS such as the North Staffs. and Furness. This situation continued until the LMS (REC) Standard Frame was introduced. Odd examples were constructed after this however. For example, in the late 1940's two large tappet frames were constructed, one to replace the bomb damaged frame at Birmingham New Street No. 5, and another of 186 levers to replace the tumbler frame installed at Preston No. 4 in 1902. The frame at New Street had been badly damaged in a bombing raid in October 1940, the cabin structure and 40 levers at one end being totally destroyed. The frame was 'temporarily' repaired by replacing the damaged levers by spares from stock. The cabin structure was replaced by parts from two spare LMS timber cabins kept in readiness for such an event at Stafford and St. Helens. The new structure was erected within four days of the raid.

Mention must be made of the fate of the large number of Saxby and Farmer interlocking frames installed on the LNWR. These included all those provided before 1874 and those provided between 1874 and the mid 1880's, while the new tumbler frame was being developed and production stepped up. Those provided prior to 1875 were of the spindle and other early Saxby designs while after the introduction of the 'Rocker' frame in 1874 new installations were equipped with this type of frame.

Inevitably many of the Saxby cabins and frames were displaced when stations were enlarged and lines widened and altered. As the quantity of LNW produced equipment grew the remaining Saxby equipment became non-standard, necessitating the retention of additional stocks of spares and additional training for the men. By the early 1890's many of the frames, particularly the pre-Rocker designs which were of fairly flimsy construction, were beginning to reach a stage where major repair or overhaul would be necessary. When this stage was reached it became the practice to renew the cabin and frame with standard LNW equipment. Where the cabin structure was in good condition and large enough for its duties the frame only would be replaced. This work reached its peak in the early 1900's and **Figures** 9.2, 9.3, 17.2 and 17.4 give an appreciation of the progress made.

By 1920 very few Saxby lever frames remained in use and mention might be made of one or two which survived. A spindle frame of 1870 was in use at Penrhyn Sidings, Bangor until 1954 (see Chapter 1). Four Rocker frames were provided for Wolverhampton Numbers 1 to 4 cabins in 1881 (of 45, 65, 45 and 50 levers respectively). Number 3 cabin was renewed completely in 1916 but the other three cabins retained their Saxby frames until the 1940's when they were replaced with LMS standard frames. The rocker frames installed at Cleator Moor Junction in 1879, Egremont in 1881 and Longridge in 1882 (all, of course, in standard LNW cabins) remained in use until closure.

Figure 11.18 TAPPET FRAMES; ARRANGEMENT OF UPRIGHTS AND BRACKETS

Uprights to Accommodate – Brackets	*Locking Brackets Fixed*	*Number of Cabins*	*Range of Frame Sizes*
1	1	9	10 to 20 levers
2	1	17	18 to 45 "
2	2	6	25 to 55 "
3	2	10	40 to 90 "
3	3	2	80 to 180 "
4	3	7	60 to 100 "
5	3	2	70 to 90 "
6	5	1	112 "

Total 54 cabins in sample

GROUND FRAMES

Even in the early days there was a need for ground frames with proper interlocking, as well as full signal cabins. These installations did not warrant the full time attention of a signalman but were worked by the guard or shunter. They were used to control intermediate sidings, level crossings, points which were too far from a signal cabin to be worked from it, and even small stations. The frames could generally be simpler in design and construction than the large interlocking frames although this was not always done. For example, some early ground, or open air, frames were of the Saxby spindle type.

When the designs for the LNW's own signalling equipment were being prepared it was realised that something would be required to fulfil the ground frame function. A ground frame of unique form was designed at Crewe and this was included in the provision of Webb's first patent for a full interlocking frame (no. 442 of 1874). This type of frame might, for simplicity, be described as the 'right-angle frame' because of the arrangement of the levers which were set out in three groups at right angles to each other forming, in effect, three sides of a rectangle (**Figure 11.19**).

One might ask why such an apparently curious arrangement was adopted. A problem which dogged designers of frames was the means by which the 'to and fro' motion of the lever or catch handle could be translated into the 'side to side' movement required of most interlocking mechanisms. In this frame Webb solved the whole problem by placing the levers for different functions at right angles. Thus the to and fro movement of one group of levers forms the side to side movement required to interlock another group. What are effectively tappet blades are attached to levers 2 and 7 and castings attached to levers 3, 4 and 5 either pass through notches in these bars or are held by the solid bar. Levers 1 and 6 are only interlocked with levers 2 and 7 respectively by means of lug locking. While the frame was simple and cheap to build and maintain the design limited the way in which it could be used. Levers 1, 2, 6 and 7 were intended as signal levers, numbers 2 and 7 were normally the home signals and 1 and 6 the distants. Levers 3, 4 and 5 were for points or siding signals. The normal use of the frames was to control a small siding or goods yard, for instance on a double line either a single trailing point using 3 or 4 levers (two running signals and one or two points) or a siding and crossover (2 signals each way plus two or three points). An installation which used one of these frames can often be recognised from a diagram by the 'backwards' numbering of signals 6 and 7. With a simple layout it was even possible to signal a station with one of these frames. An example of the use of a 'right angle' frame is described in Chapter 16. The most common type of installation occurred where the signal cabin had been placed at one end of the station (perhaps for a level crossing) and sidings existed at the other, out of range of rod working. Because these installations had their own signals (or more likely slotted the signals of the main cabin) no special release was required. Quite a number of these frames were installed during the first 20 years of the LNWR Signal Department. Examples of their use were for the goods yards at Clifton Mill and Wrenbury.

The limitations of the above apparatus were realised and there was an obvious need for something which was more adaptable and would have wider uses. If possible this apparatus too should be simple and rugged. Mr J E Annett of the London, Brighton and South Coast Railway devised and patented, in October 1875, a device which was both simple and adaptable. It consisted of a key shaped device (hence the term, still in use today, 'Annett's Key') which was normally kept in a 'lock' in the interlocking mechanism of a signal cabin lever frame. With the levers in suitable positions (usually normal, with the signals at danger) the key could be removed. The twisting action required to remove the key operated the interlocking and thus held the appropriate point and signal levers in position, to prevent conflicting moves, until the key was returned. The key could then be taken to a ground frame where it was placed in a similar lock to release the point and signal levers and enable shunting to take place. Here the key was 'locked' in the frame until shunting was complete and the levers had been returned to normal. The key was then returned to the signal cabin and placed in its lock to release the levers for signalling the ordinary traffic. The Annett's lock could, of course, be used to control other things besides ground frames. They could be fitted to practically anything which was likely to foul the running lines as a protection to traffic. Examples of their other uses were to lock level crossing gates, swing bridges and turntables.

Annett's Patent was bought by Saxby and Farmer in 1881 and they commenced manufacture of the system. The LNWR saw the advantages of the idea and a number of locks were purchased at a cost of £12 16*s* 0*d* each. Naturally, it was felt that they could be produced more cheaply at Crewe; an arrangement which would also enable them to be constructed to suit the Company's needs. Enquiries were made and in 1882 Saxbys stated that they would allow this to be done on the payment of a royalty of £4 each or a lump sum of £435 to cover the production of any number during the remaining 7¼ years covered by the patent. The lump sum payment was made and Thompson devised a 'Key Interlocking System' which could be manufactured at Crewe and used to interlock small stations, sidings and level crossings. Here some levers of very simple form were placed together as a small frame. The levers were interlocked by a small tray of tappet locking at floor or ground level. Annett's type locks were placed at each end of the frame as required, the whole being referred to as a 'Key Interlocking Frame'. The keys could be used to unlock single ground levers placed adjacent to the points they worked thus reducing installation and maintenance costs of the interlocking system. The levers in the key frame generally worked only signals and the system could be used to interlock a whole station. The levers, both those in the key frame and the single point levers, retained the foot treadle operation of the right angle frame, instead of catch handles, again cheap but effective.

The keys and locks too were simple in construction. There were three configurations or shapes of key. These were designated 'A', 'B' and 'C'. Keys 'A' and 'B' were generally used to control siding points and key 'C' for crossovers and level crossing gates. The keys had a description of their function cast onto the handle. These were generally 'Up Siding' or 'Down Siding' in the case of keys 'A' and 'B' and 'Crossing' in the case of key 'C'. Where the layout required it, more than one key of each configuration could be used. An example would be a layout where there was a level crossing locked by key. These normally required two keys, one for each pair of gates.

In about the mid 1880's the key interlocking frame was redesigned and the key locks were incorporated within the locking tray. The keys fitted into key holes cast into the locking box cover which was inscribed 'Key Interlocking System, Crewe Works' (see **Figure 11.20** and **Plates 11.18** and 19). This frame was also known as the Sketch 446 after its drawing number, while the single ground lever was Sketch 80. The quadrant casting for the SK446 lever had an extension at the rear for mounting the locking tray.

The key interlocking frame usually consisted of up to eight levers and these were generally used to work signals only (two or three in each direction), the points being operated via the keys and SK80 levers. Sometimes a pair of points situated near to the frame would be worked

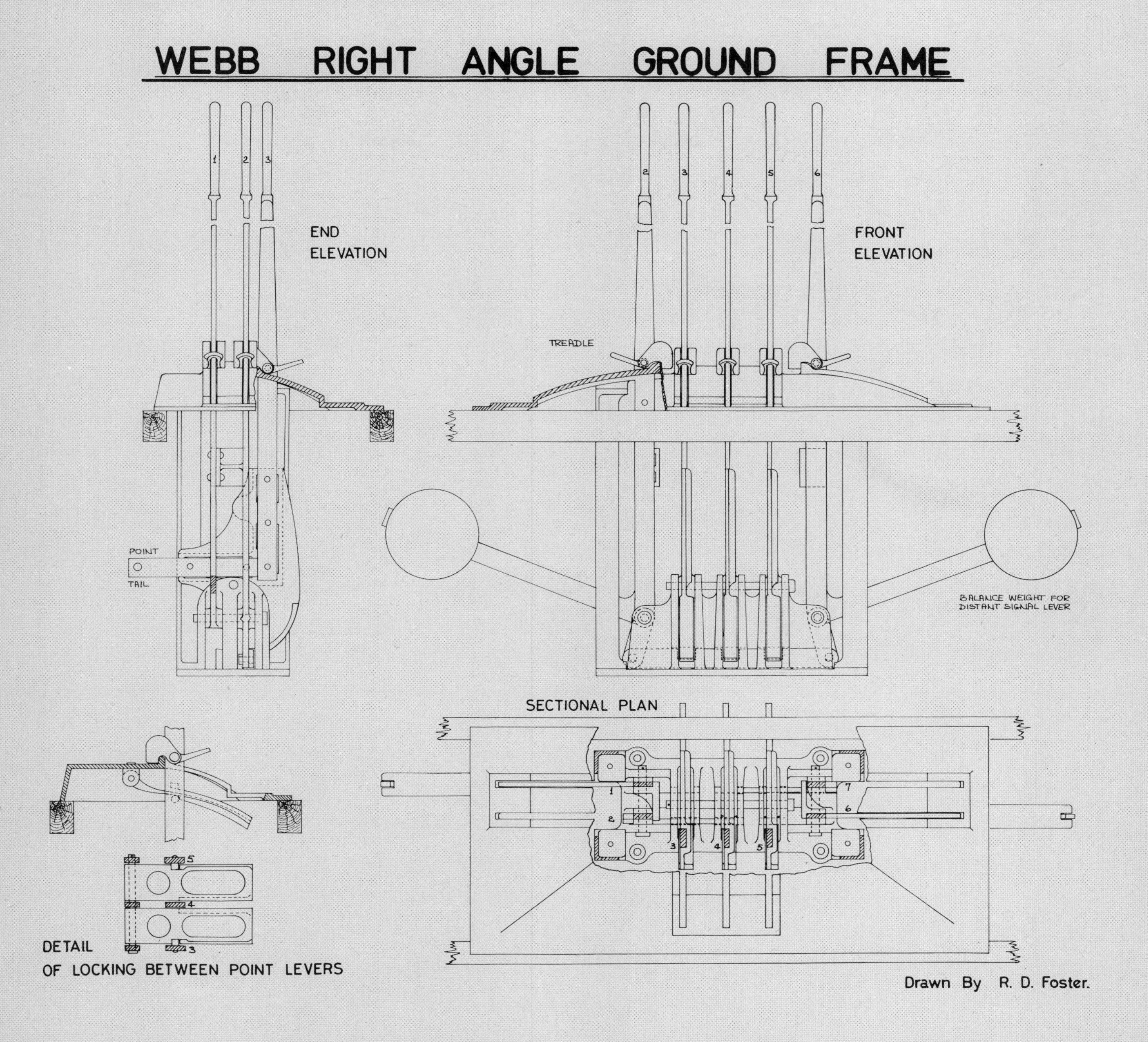

Figure 11.19 *F W Webb's 'Right Angle' Small Apparatus or Ground Frame. Foot treadles formed on the catch blocks were used to release the lever before it was pulled or replaced. Levers 1, 2, 6 and 7 were generally signal levers and 3, 4 and 5 point levers.*

directly from it, particularly in later years. A signalling layout using the key system is described in Chapter 16 and this should enable the operation of the system to be understood.

As already mentioned, the key system could be used to interlock a whole station. It was realised, apparently first by Mr Eddy, one of Mr Neele's (the Superintendent of the Line) staff that the system would form an economical method of interlocking small stations on the secondary lines. There was no reason why such installations should

(Continued on page 171)

Plate 11.15 *A single SK80 lever with an Annetts Lock at Millbrook, used to operate a crossover road. The lever is of the old LNW 'treadle' type.*

not be block posts if required (the instruments being placed in the booking office). In February 1884 Mr Findley reported to the Board:—

> 'It was proposed, by means of small locking frames, special keys and altering and improving some of the signals and trapping sidings to carry out an economical system of interlocking the points and signals on the following lines:—
> Denbigh, Ruthin and Corwen Railway
> Blaenau Branch
> Llanberis Branch
> and the Carnarvonshire Branch.'

Not only did the system save the cost of a signal cabin, interlocking frame and connections, it also reduced staff

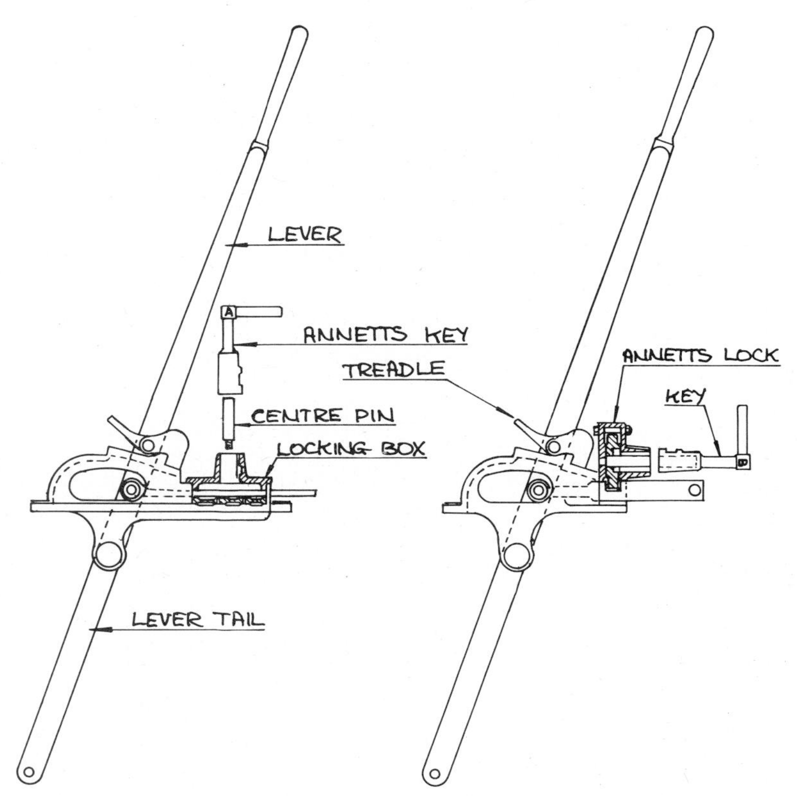

Figure 11.20 *LNWR standard ground frame levers as developed in the early 1880's. The difference between the two types of lever lies in the quadrant casting. The SK446 casting has an extension at the back to accommodate a horizontal tappet locking box. The SK80 casting is smaller and will only accommodate an LNW Annett's lock (or similar). Note the use of the simple foot treadle catch. In later years the levers were modified to accommodate the standard LNW loop handle.*

Plate 11.16 *A close up of the treadle, quadrant and lock on a SK80 lever showing how they were fitted together. On the original levers gravity was relied on to drop the catch block home. The spring arrangement shown here was introduced in 1908.*

Plate 11.17 *A pair of Annett's locks at Dyserth. This was a case where both Staff and Ordinary locks were used together and the whole of the station was interlocked by the staff and key locks attached to the individual point levers. No signals, other than the distant signal, were provided. The Train Staff which had a configuration 'A' Staff Key on it (Chapter 13) was placed in the left-hand lock of the pair in the photograph. This released the point lever behind it and allowed the points to be reversed. This action released the right-hand lock ('B – Down Siding') and allowed the key to be withdrawn to work the next set of points. With Key 'B' removed the first set of points were locked in position and the Staff was locked in the Staff Lock.*

Plate 11.18 *The SK446 frame was devised for use with the Key System. The example here is one of the old treadle operated frames (without springs) and was installed in April 1906. It was sited in the booking office at Claydon to enable the station staff to work it and to provide some protection from the elements without incurring too much expense! Three signal arm repeaters can be seen on the front of the shelf, while the middle two repeat the block indications for the benefit of the gatekeeper since it was no longer a block post. The Annett's Keys were placed in locks in the locking box which was just behind the levers. When this photograph was taken in 1973, the sidings had been removed and the keys working the points removed. Only the 'C' key for the gates remained. The LNW link (loop lever collar) could be dropped over the treadle as a reminder if required. Lever 4 has been renewed with a loop handle.*

Plate 11.19 *A five lever key interlocking frame at Derrington Level Crossing, with the cover removed to show the interlocking. The inscription on the cover reads 'Key Interlocking Crewe Works'. This one has four 'C' keys for the crossing gates. The keys fit over the vertical pins (the furthest one has part of a broken key on it) and engage in the circular locks. These are locked in position by the square or triangular shaped studs on the locking bars, and the tappet blades. With the levers reversed and the signals cleared as shown the keys would be locked in the frame to prevent the gates being unlocked. The keys had to be turned clockwise to release them from the locks. The frame has four levers fitted, these working a home and distant signal each way. The fifth quadrant was provided simply to accommodate the interlocking for the last key.*

Photo: M J Lewis

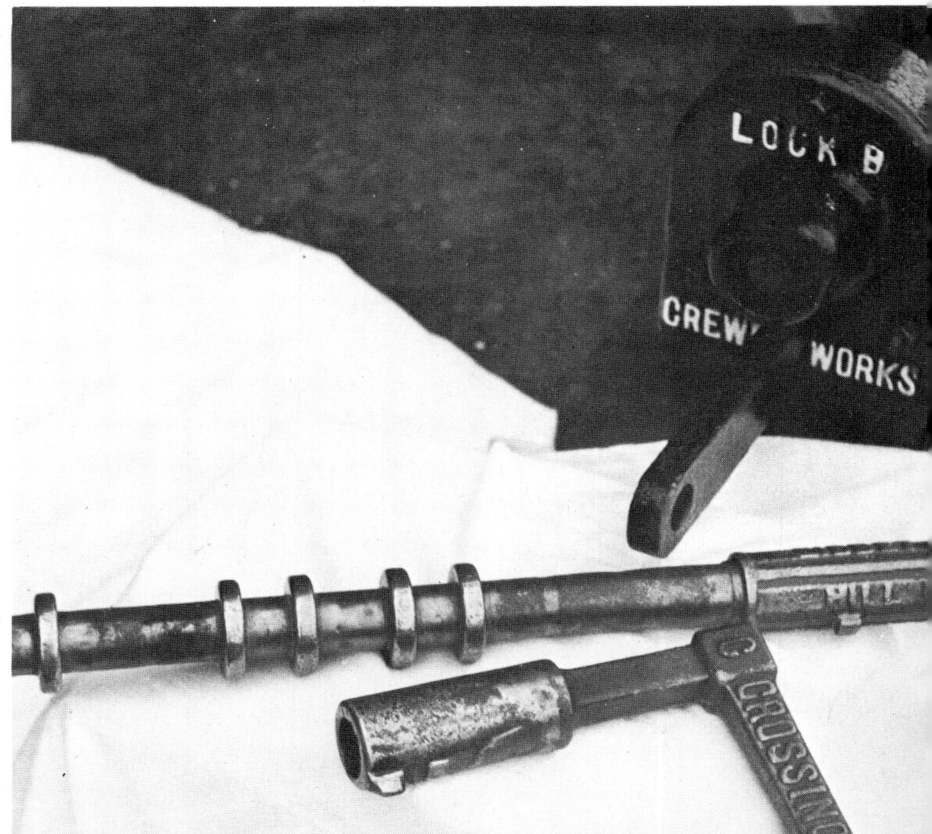

Plate 11.20 *The Annett's Key System. At the top right is a standard Annett's Lock of the type used by the LNW, this one being a configuration 'B' lock, used generally for sidings. In the foreground is an Annett's Key of configuration 'C', the word 'Crossing' conveniently covering both crossovers and level crossings! In the centre is a Webb and Thompson Electric Train Staff. The brass end casting incorporating the name of the section (Kenilworth Junction to Gibbet Hill), is formed at the same diameter as an Annetts Key and this one has the configuration 'A' key studs on it, a Staff Key of this type could be used to unlock a ground frame in the section. On the right is an ordinary key lock on a Sketch 80 lever.*

Equipment by courtesy of
S Robinson and M Christensen

Plate 11.21 *A pair of Annett's Keys in a key lock attached to a full size frame at Brock. They were provided in 1917 to lock the level crossing gates. The method of interlocking is illustrated in* **Figure 11.21**.

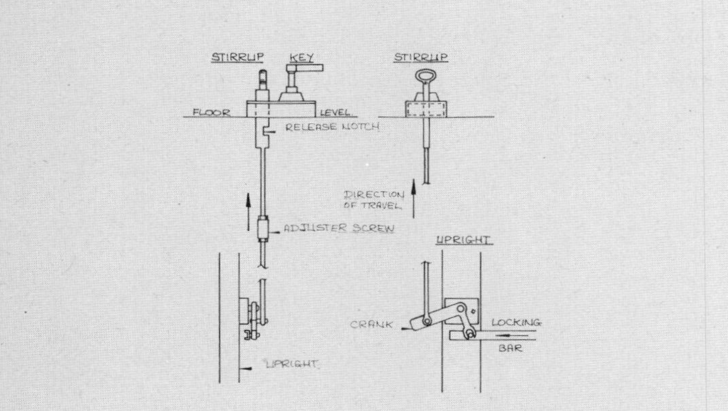

Figure 11.21 *Sketch showing the method of fixing an Annett's lock to a full size frame, in this case a tumbler type. A slightly modified version allowed the key to be fitted to a tappet frame. To release the key the stirrup was pulled up causing the locking bar to move and effect the necessary locking. When the key was removed the stirrup was held in the raised position until it was replaced in the lock.*

costs since the signalman could be used to perform other station duties between trains, and to assist with shunting operations. Signalmen who have worked at these key interlocking stations said that the work was often much harder there than at even quite large main line cabins because of the extra duties involved. In addition, they had to work out in the cold and wet, and the pay was very much less! These were sensible economies since the traffic on many secondary lines never really justified the extra costs that would have been incurred in providing full signalling.

The Board of Trade was not keen on the key system however since they considered that it did not comply with the principle that the levers should be concentrated at one central point. However, they had to concede that the principle of interlocking the points and signals was fully complied with. The LNW pointed out that the system would enable them to interlock the whole of their line much more quickly than would otherwise be the case and the Board of Trade, rather reluctantly, agreed to its extension. Once over this hurdle the LNW began to install the system on a large scale.

After the initial interlocking of the line had been completed the LNW did not abandon the key interlocking system but continued to use and even extend it. A number of existing signal cabins were removed and replaced with key installations. Lines operated largely by the key system included Oxford to Bedford and the Ingleton and Coalport branches.

A feature of the right angle, SK80 and SK446 levers was that there was no conventional catch handle. The catch block was extended to form a treadle in front of and at the base of the lever. The lever was released from the catch slot by depressing the treadle with the foot. This system reduced still further the moving parts making the levers cheap to construct and easy to maintain. Even the return spring shown in **Plate 11.16** was not provided until 1908. Like the large frames the catch block was heavy enough to return under its own weight. The spring was added to produce a more positive return action.

In about 1918 the levers were modified to incorporate the standard LNW loop handles and in this form they are still used today on the LM Region for ground frames. Many have been installed in recent years in connection with power signalling schemes.

About 1900 the LNW began to get more adventurous with the use of open ground frames, and some much larger installations were put in. These were still at country stations but instead of using a small SK446 frame with keys, a full size tumbler (or tappet) frame was provided and the points and signals were largely worked from the frame (the concentration the BOT had asked for). These installations were in effect proper signal cabins but without the cabin structure, and the instruments were again placed in the booking office. These were capable of dealing more quickly with the traffic as the time consuming job of carrying the keys about was largely eliminated. Such installations appeared, for example, at several places on the Afon Wen and Amlwch branches (where key interlockings were also found) and at Bethesda, Uppingham and Newport Pagnell. The signalman still assisted with station duties and the cost of a cabin structure was avoided.

The use of the Annett's Key was not confined to the key interlocking frames, it was also used with the full size frames. A special lock was devised to enable the keys to interlock with the tumbler or tappet apparatus. These were normally mounted at floor level at one (or both) ends of the frame (**Figure 11.21** and **Plates 11.21 & 22**). The keys were used for a variety of purposes such as those mentioned earlier.

Plate 11.22 *A large 'Ground Frame' at Groeslon, photographed shortly after the closure of the line. This consisted of an 18 lever tumbler frame mounted on a stage on the platform. The staff instruments were placed in the booking office and operations were carried out by the station staff. The level crossing gates were locked by Annett's Key, the lock for which can just be seen at the left hand end of the frame; a second lock at the right hand end released the points into the small goods yard. The wooden boxes mounted on the fence behind the frame contained the arm and lamp repeaters for the distant signals.*
Photo: D J Christensen

Plate 11.23 *A ground frame of the SK446 type at Lidlington, with space in the locking box for four gate keys. This frame incorporated a modern form of 'Lug Locking', a system dating back to the earliest days (Chapter 1). A bar of metal bolted to the home signal lever projects over the front of the distant signal lever to prevent it being pulled until the home signal lever has been reversed.*

Plate 11.24 *A modern form of the SK-446 frame, with a plain tappet locking box. This one is at Wednesbury and was installed in 1966.*

Chapter Twelve

The Block System and Signalmen's Instruments

Chapter 1 described the early evolution of the block telegraph system for signalling trains. As explained there, the block had been introduced on practically the whole line by 1884. This chapter takes a look at the instruments provided in the signal cabins in order to assist the signalmen in their work of controlling and regulating the traffic.

The double needle Clark type instruments of the first installations were superseded for new work and renewals by a variety of commercially available instruments, probably supplied initially by the Telegraph Companies and by firms

Figure 12.1 *The Standard Form of the Three-Wire, Three Position Block Instruments in use on the LNWR in the 1880's and 1890's. These were a direct adaptation from the speaking telegraph instrument. Note that the vertical position of the needle (line closed or blocked) is not named. Between them is a block bell in a tall wooden case. Bells of this type were standard on the LNW prior to the introduction of the Fletcher combined instruments and the type of bell illustrated in* **Plate 12.11**.

Plate 12.1 *A Tyers 3-wire 'tell-tale' or permissive block instrument for one line. This has an LNW style of dial face and instruments of this type were widely used on the LNW before the advent of the standard LNW instruments, quite a number surviving into recent times. This was the instrument placed at the advance end of the section and therefore has a commutator handle to work the block needle and description disc. The instruments with the commutators were normally referred to as 'Peggers', the non pegging instrument had no commutator or window. The photograph shows the instrument in the normal or 'Line Closed' position. In these instruments the commutator was locked by the spring plunger on the right hand side of the case. The plunger was depressed to release the mechanical lock which allowed the commutator handle to be turned to the right. This brought the words 'Line Clear' into the window and the commutator also pegged the needles in both this instrument and that at the other end of the section at 'Line Clear' by admitting a current to the line wire. The commutator was then locked in position until the plunger was again depressed. When the train entered the section, the plunger was depressed again and the commutator moved one more place to the right. This displayed 'Train on Line' in the window and reversed the polarity of the line wire current, deflecting the needles to 'Train on Line'. When a second train entered the section the plunger was depressed again and the commutator moved a further turn to the right. The block needle remained at 'Train on Line', of course, but the figure '2' was displayed in the window, indicating the number of trains in the section. This process could be repeated as required up to the capacity of the instrument (6 trains being the most common). As trains left the section the reverse procedure was followed and the commutator moved one place to the left for each departing train, (the plunger being operated before turning the handle). A separate pair of instruments would be provided for each line. Instruments of this design were also supplied in an absolute form. In this case the commutator only worked to three positions (Line Blocked, Line Clear and Train on Line). Tyers instruments did not incorporate bells or bell tappers within the instrument and these were in a separate case. An LNW tapper key and bell is shown in* **Plate 12.11**.

Plate 12.2 *This photograph of the interior of Rugby No. 1 Cabin (180 levers) was taken on the 8th September, 1898. As can be seen the block instruments are exclusively of the Tyers single needle type, similar to that shown in* **Plate 12.1.** *None of the standard LNW 'Fletcher' instruments had yet penetrated into this cabin, which had been constructed in 1884, when instruments of the type illustrated were standard. The instruments are all of the single, rather than double, needle type, a practice which was common at large stations no matter what type of instruments were in use. Between the instruments are wooden cased block bells. The lines to which the instruments refer and the cabins they work to or from are indicated by white labels attached to the instruments above and below the needles (or at the bottom in the case of bells). The large white labels at the bottom of the block instruments read "London and North Western Railway Company, Tyers Patent". A rather more modern instrument, a Fletcher electric train describer (***Plate 12.9***), can be seen in the centre of the shelf nearest the camera, while the instrument near the left hand end of the same shelf is a telegraph type route indicator (***Plate 12.7***). The use of short (rather than continuous) block shelves, just long enough to accommodate the instruments, will be noticed. Two layout diagrams are provided near the centre of the cabin, one for each of the two signalmen who normally worked this cabin. The lever frame is of the standard Webb Tumbler type arranged on girders for 18 levers each. The levers which appear white in the photograph are facing point lock levers and are painted light blue (the LNW did not normally provide spare levers in its frames). In the frame are several levers painted blue over black. These worked bolt locks on points controlled by an adjacent cabin. On the far top right of the photograph are two face discs in the normal (no indication) position, while along the back wall of the cabin is a fascinating selection of speaking tubes and their associated bells. The gas jet lighting will be observed (the incandescent mantle was a later innovation) as will the ubiquitous standard LNW booking desk and the bare boarded floor. The provision of linoleum was an LMS innovation; even so, it was obviously still not the done thing to wear one's boots in the cabin and one of the signalmen's outdoor boots can just be seen behind one of the lockers. By modern standards the facilities provided for the signalmen are distinctly spartan.*

Photo: Courtesy National Railway Museum

specialising in block telegraph instruments, particularly Tyer & Co. of Dalston, London. The most common type of instrument used was the single needle drop handle type which had been adapted directly from the speaking instruments (**Figure 12.1**). Separate instruments were provided for up and down lines and a separate bell was provided for communication between the signalmen. As firms like Tyers introduced their own designs of instruments these too were purchased (**Plate 12.1**).

Like the Clark instruments, the majority of these early instruments worked on what is described as the 'three-wire' system. Here three wires were provided between adjacent signal cabins on a double line, one wire working the up line needles at each cabin, one the down line needles and the third the block bells (although there had been no independent bells in the original Clark installations). All three circuits employed a common earth return. This was the simplest and most widely used block telegraph system. There was little chance of incorrect indications since the three circuits were independent. However, a number of railway managers and directors objected to the system on the grounds of the huge cost of stringing out the three wires over thousands of miles of railway. Much effort and ingenuity was exercised by inventors and railwaymen in devising a block system which would use less wire.

Edward Tyer and Mr Norman devised and demonstrated a one-wire block system before a Railway Clearing House Committee in February, 1870. Here one wire was used to work both the up and down line needles and the block bells by means of different current strengths and directions. Messrs Preece and Spagnoletti commented on the disadvantages of any single wire system for up and down lines as had Mr Martin, the LNWR Telegraph Superintendent. Preece, incidentally, had been involved with Clark in preparing the 1854 report. The one-wire block systems which were developed differed from the three-wire in that the needles could only be worked to two positions (left and right, to represent 'Train on Line' and 'Line Clear').

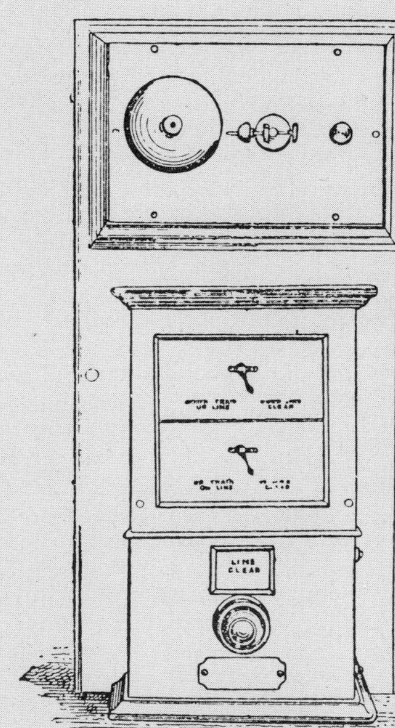

Figure 12.2 *Tyer's One-Wire Two Position Block Instrument as used on the One-Wire Block Sections of the LNWR. No 'Line Closed' position was obtainable with these instruments.*

This was not an important deficiency at first since, as described in Chapter 1, the third position ('Line Blocked') on the three-wire instruments was not generally used.

Many professional telegraph and operating officers did not like the one-wire block because of its relative complexity, the risk of failure or wrong indications and the fact that it could only show two positions. Unfortunately Tyer's demonstration came at a time when the LNWR was formulating its plans for adopting the absolute block system. The avoidance of expense by adopting one instead of three line wires had an obvious attraction for Mr Moon and it was decided to install the 'one-wire' system on some sections of line. Generally this was done on lines where there had been no previous installations of the block in either its absolute or permissive (time interval) form. The three-wire system continued to be used where it already existed and the 'permissive' sections were gradually converted to absolute working. Considerable lengths of one-wire block were installed on the line during the 1870's as the block system was extended, and by the late 1870's the length of one-wire block installations exceeded that of the three-wire.

At the same time consideration was given to the existing sections of three-wire block. Here it was realised that economy could be achieved by converting them to one-wire, the spare wires being utilised for communication circuits. In many cases the conversions were done as the existing equipment became in need of extensive repair or replacement, or where there was pressure for the provision of additional communication circuits. The first section to be changed from three-wire to one-wire was fittingly the portion of the original 'Clark Block' between London and Bletchley, the conversion being authorised in March 1873. Over much of this section one of the spare wires was set aside for block working on the two additional running lines and the other was used as a communication circuit to aid traffic working. The conversion work took some years to complete.

By the late 1870's the block system had been installed on the majority of the Company's lines and there was time to make improvements to the existing system. The LNW policy of uniformity of practice also came into play here and began to have its own influence on the choice of which type of block instruments were to be adopted for the renewal work. For a variety of reasons, therefore, work began in earnest in 1878 on the task of converting three-wire installations to one-wire.

For example, in October 1878 it was decided to convert the three-wire block telegraph between Rugby and Nuneaton to Tyer's one-wire system, both for the up and down main lines and the third line. A local speaking telegraph circuit was also established between the cabins at a total cost of £470 10*s* 0*d*. In November, it was decided to alter the block working at Walsall to one-wire 'to ensure uniformity of working'. January 1879 brought a decision to alter the line from Bletchley to Roade from three-wire to one-wire. Here one of the wires was utilised for the block circuits on the third and fourth lines which were then being made ready for opening. The third wire was used for a new speaking telegraph circuit.

Figure 12.3 SECTIONS OF LINE IN THE NORTH EASTERN DIVISION OF THE LNWR WHICH WERE WORKED BY THE THREE-WIRE BLOCK SYSTEM IN 1881

Crewe (Elton) to Cheadle Hulme
Ordsall Lane (No. 5) to Kenyon Junction
Bolton to Eccles Junction

Fairly good progress was, therefore, being made towards standardising on the one-wire block system and by the early 1880's a large proportion of the line was being worked on the one-wire system. **Figure 12.3** lists the sections of line on the North Eastern Division worked by three-wire block in 1881. The remainder was worked on the one-wire system with the exception of the station yard areas where there was, generally, no block working at all.

The absolute block system provided good and safe control of the trains on the open line but was too restrictive for working busy station areas where the trains would always accumulate. The block was not continued through the 'station yard' areas but was stopped at the cabin at each end. Communication between cabins in these station areas was, generally, by means of mechanical or electric gongs with the assistance of information provided by indicator discs (face discs) and sometimes speaking telegraph circuits. Trains and engines frequently shunted from one line to another and attached and detached vehicles making it very difficult for the signalmen to keep a tally of the number of trains in the section. Minor accidents were quite common through the signalman thinking the section was clear or forgetting the presence of vehicles. Some means was, therefore, required for controlling the traffic and reminding the signalmen of the trains.

The answer came at last at the beginning of 1879 when J W Fletcher devised and introduced the Tell-Tale telegraph instrument. Here a metal disc was attached to the commutator handle of the block instrument. On the disc was painted the names of the usual two (or three) positions of the needles plus the numbers 2 to 6 (or as necessary). These numbers denoted the number of trains actually in the section ('Train on Line' indicating the first one), the number or description appeared in a window above the handle (see **Plates 12.1** and **12.2**). The discs were placed in the instruments at the advance end of the section and could be advanced or stepped back by the signalman as trains entered or left the section as a reminder of the number of trains still occupying the section. These instruments were referred to as 'tell-tale' block instruments since they 'told the tale' of the actual state of the section. The term 'permissive' which is applied to this type of instrument today, could not be used since it was then still in use to describe the old time interval plus block system. It was not until about 1900, when the time interval system had long gone and was largely forgotten, that the term 'permissive block' began to be applied to the tell-tale working.

The new instruments overcame the problems associated with working the station areas and work was quickly put in hand on the installation of the system. For example, in March 1879 authority was given for installing tell-tale block in the signal cabins at the main stations between Bletchley and Stafford (Wolverton, Weedon, Heyford, Rugby and Lichfield). The station yard at Bushbury was converted to tell-tale working in May, 1879 at a cost of £33 and shortly afterwards £275 was expended on converting the three-wire block in use between Clock Face and Pilkingtons Siding on the Widnes and St. Helens line.

The tell-tale instruments were produced in both one-wire and three-wire forms, the one-wire instruments showing only two needle indications of course. Both types of instrument were manufactured by Tyer and Company, who also supplied them to other railway companies in large quantities. Meetings were held later in the year to devise a suitable set of instructions for working the new instruments. The question was discussed at an Officers' meeting in October 1879 and the following recommendation was made:—

> 'As it appears that the three-wire system enables the signalmen to give more complete indication of the state of the line where station yard working is in operation than is possible with the one-wire system. It is recommended that three-wire instruments be adopted. Mr Fletcher to substitute them for those of Tyer's one-wire pattern as opportunity occurs and for utilising the latter at other places.'

Generally the tell-tale installations were made in the three-wire form but a few one-wire installations were made. For example, in March 1880 authority was given to substitute Tyers one-wire tell-tale block instruments for the Tyers electric gongs in use between Shrewsbury Junction No. 1 and Crewe Bank (No. 2) cabins at Shrewsbury.

Diversity of practice, rather than uniformity, became the order of the day with both one and three-wire tell-tale and absolute block in use. One-wire continued to replace the three-wire installations on the absolute block sections while the reverse process was occurring in station and yard areas! Some places had the dubious privilege of having both systems in use at the same time. At Manchester the completion of the Ardwick and Longsight widening, in 1880, brought a change from the three-wire to one-wire on the main lines with three-wire tell tale being installed on the down loop line! Block working was instituted between Preston Nos. 4 and 5 cabins in the same year with one-wire absolute instruments on the fast lines and three-wire tell-tale on the slow lines.

The third ('line closed' or 'line blocked') position of the three-wire block needles was soon adopted as the normal indication. The instruments became truly three position and suitable regulations were framed for their use. This meant, of course, that the LNW was saddled with two sets of block regulations, one for the three-wire instruments and one for the Tyers one-wire instruments. As the importance of the third position of the needle was recognised, and as attempts were made to bring about uniformity of practice, the presence of two systems of block working became more and more of a nuisance. A number of individuals made attempts to devise a means of obtaining the third position with the one-wire instruments. In October 1884, J W Fletcher, by a clever electro-mechanical arrangement managed to obtain a half way (or vertical) position for the one-wire instruments. The system was installed for trials on the Buxton Branch. For some reason it did not find favour, and no further installations were made. The idea of a one-wire three position block was taken up and developed by Tyers who marketed it extensively. Indeed a number of railways, notably some of the smaller ones, adopted it as their standard.

Things continued for several years with both one-wire two position and three-wire three position instruments and regulations in use, but eventually it was realised that something would have to be done. A good one-wire three position block suitable for the Company's requirements was still not available and in the late 1880's it was decided to adopt the three-wire three position block as standard for all future work. When the one-wire block installations became due for renewal, renovation or alteration they were replaced with three-wire equipment. So as to maintain as much uniformity of practice as possible only whole lines, or sections of line, would be converted and not individual block sections. The new three-wire installations used either Tyers single or double needle instruments (**Plate 12.1**), or single needle telegraph style instruments (**Figure 12.1**). Generally, where the two different systems came together at a station or junction the division point was made at a simple block post before the junction rather than at the junction signal cabin itself, where the signalman had more to distract him.

About the same time, Mr G E Fletcher devised a three-wire three position block instrument in which the up and down needles and the bell were combined together in a single instrument. (**Figure 12.4**). As can be seen, the early examples had a distinct similarity to Tyers practice with the sloping front and suspended needles. The combined

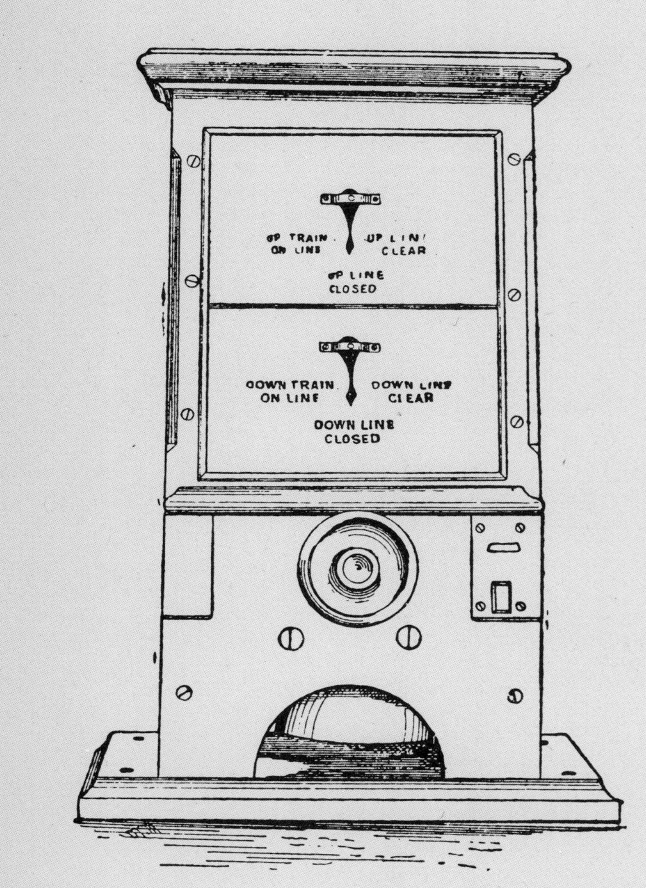

Figure 12.4 *The Prototype version of G E Fletcher's Three Wire, Three Position Block Instrument. The bell was placed inside the wooden case under the commutator with a semi-circular cut-away to let the sound out. Note the similarity of the instrument case with Tyers practice. This type of instrument had the advantage of saving space on the block shelf.*

Plate 12.3 *A standard LNW 'Fletcher' type combined block instrument manufactured in the LNW Telegraph Workshops at Stockport. The instrument combines the up and down line needles and commutator within one case while the bell mechanism has also been included and the bell itself suspended below the main body of the instrument. This combined arrangement saved a great deal of space on the block shelf, and so did not restrict the signalman's view of the line too greatly. In addition, it reduced costs since only one case had to be provided and shorter block shelves could be fitted in the cabins. This instrument bears the inscription 'LNW Ry. Tele. Dept. Stockport No. 1397' stamped on the side of the case. The number represents the serial number of the instrument and all LNW produced instruments had them. In later years, however, the inscription and number were stamped on the back of the case. This particular instrument is a double line absolute type of 'intermediate' design. It has the tall or full size style of case but retains the original pattern of cast iron feet. These were required to lift the instrument off the shelf to allow room for the bell which, of course, needed an open space in order that the signalman could hear it clearly. In the original instruments the tapper key was normally at the top of the commutator section of the case. The marks on the side of this instrument indicate that it was originally so fitted but the tapper has since been moved to the bottom. The instrument was in use at Anglesea Siding cabin when this photograph was taken.*

block had the advantages of reducing the space required for the instruments on the block shelf, therefore offering less obstruction to the signalman's vision and reducing the chance of error through use of the wrong instrument.

The new instrument was submitted for consideration in May 1888 and it was decided to adopt instruments of this type for new work and to gradually replace the existing instruments with them. Following complaints, the form of the instrument was modified in the autumn of 1891 by substituting longer needles to enable their position to be seen more distinctly. The wooden housing around the bell was also cut away to allow the bell to be heard more clearly.

The Telegraph Works at Stockport was opened in 1892 (Chapter 2) and production of instruments was commenced there on a small scale. The design of the instruments was altered, the casing around the bell was removed altogether and metal legs provided to support the main case. The first version of the standard 'Stockport' block instrument had an overall height (excluding bell section) of 18½ inches and was provided with cast iron legs or feet (**Plate 14.1**). Production of new instruments began in earnest about 1895. In about 1899 a tell-tale (permissive) form of instrument was introduced and in order to accommodate the disc and window arrangement and the electrical contacts it was found necessary to increase the height of the commutator section of the case. This increased the overall height of the case to 21 inches and this was adopted as the standard

Plate 12.4 *The Fletcher combined block instrument in its final and most common form. The cast iron feet have been replaced by tubular metal legs attached to a solid wooden base plate which also provided protection for the bell and increased the overall height of the instrument a little. No separate base plate was provided with the original type of feet and these were screwed directly to the block shelf (***Plate 12.3***). The tubular legs were utilised to pass the circuit wires from the instrument down into the block shelf, a neat and tidy arrangement. The tapper key is in the standard position, for these later instruments, at the bottom right of the case. The covered-in hole above it contained a red lamp or plunger which was provided in LMS days. This worked in connection with the 'normal contact' on the distant signal arm to ensure that the arm returned correctly to danger after each train.*

Plate 12.5 *A standard LNW combined arm and lamp repeater in a metal case. The inscription below the dial reads 'Signal Repeater, Fletcher's System, LNW Ry Tele Dept. Stockport No. 1230'. The combined arm and lamp repeater was, of course, patented by J W Fletcher whereas the standard block instruments shown in* **Plates 12.3**, *4 and* **13** *were devised by his son, G E Fletcher. The repeater illustrated is indicating that the arm is showing 'on' but that the lamp is 'out'. With the lamp correctly alight the 'out' flag in the lower window would disappear and be replaced by one indicating 'in'. A flag marked 'wrong' would appear in the upper window if the arm did not move fully to clear or return completely to danger in response to a lever movement.*

for all new production. An absolute version of the new tall case instrument is illustrated in **Plate 12.3**. The LNW made its own tell-tale instruments from this time onwards and was the only pre-grouping railway to do so. A further change in the design of the instrument was made soon after the turn of the century. The cast metal feet were replaced by four tubular metal legs and an integral wooden base plate. When the Signal and Telegraph Departments were combined in 1903 about 1700 standard block instruments were in service and by the time of the grouping this figure had reached over 4000. The standard case was used for all types of block instrument, single and double needle, absolute and permissive, pegging and non-pegging.

Work had continued on the task of replacing the one-wire block with the three-wire pattern and by 1905 practically the whole line had been equipped. **Figure 12.5** lists the sections of line where one-wire block was still in use. As can be seen no real effort seems to have been made, after this time, to eliminate the system entirely although an Officers' meeting of January 1913 had agreed that the one-wire block instruments were to be replaced by the three-wire pattern. At the grouping much of the one-wire block listed in **Figure 12.5** was still in use, but it was all replaced with three-wire (or in one case, one-wire three position – see Chapter 17) block in LMS days. New LNW block instruments continued to be manufactured for new work and to replace non-standard three-wire instruments, a process which continued throughout the LMS era.

ARM AND LIGHT INDICATORS

When signal and point levers began to be concentrated in raised cabins it was realised that it was important to ensure the cabin was placed so that the signalman could see all the signals under his control. This important principle was later incorporated in the Board of Trade requirements for the operation of passenger railways. At most places this

Figure 12.5 SECTIONS OF LINE WORKED BY ONE-WIRE BLOCK, MAY 1905

SOUTHERN DIVISION	
Verney Junction to Oxford	1-wire installation authorised 8/1880 to replace existing 'permissive' block between Bletchley and Oxford. 3-wire Tell-Tale block authorised 7/1888 between Bletchley and Winslow. Verney Jct. to Claydon converted to 3-wire between 1913 and 1918, remainder still in use in 1921.
Bletchley No. 2 to Bedford No. 1 and Sandy Station to Cambridge Goods Yard	1-wire absolute block authorised for Bletchley to Cambridge line 8/1880. Bletchley No. 2 to Fenny Stratford converted to 3-wire by 1909. Fenny Stratford to Woburn Sands converted to 3-wire between 1918 and 1921. Remainder still in use in 1921.
NOTTINGHAM, NORTHAMPTON AND PETERBOROUGH DISTRICT	
Yelvertoft to Market Harborough No. 1	1-wire block Rugby to Market Harborough authorised 8/1878 at a cost of £877, this remaining section still in use in 1921.
Market Harborough No. 3 to Yarwell Junction	1-wire block Market Harborough to Seaton authorised 8/1878 at a cost of £1025. Seaton to Wansford line opened 1879 and 1-wire block installed at a cost of £230. Seaton to Yarwell Junction converted to 3-wire by 1909.
Northampton to Market Harborough No. 1	1-wire block authorised August 1878 at a cost of £1540 in connection with the widening of the line. Northampton to Boughton Crossing converted to 3-wire in 1910.
Duston West (Low Level) to Northampton No. 1	Tyers 1-wire block authorised March 1880 (new line), converted to 3-wire between 1913 and 1918.
Welham Junction to Melton Mowbray South	LNW and GN Joint line (see Chapter 17) 1-wire block installed on opening of line. All still in use in 1921. Converted to Tyers 1-wire three-position block by 1942.
CENTRAL DISTRICT	
Ryecroft Junction to North Walsall Junction and Ryecroft Junction to Lichfield Road Junction	1-wire installations authorised 11/1878 and still in use in 1921.
Ryecroft Junction to Lichfield City No. 1	Converted to 3-wire between 1909 and 1913.
Lichfield No. 2 to Alrewas	Converted to 3-wire between 1909 and 1913.
Ryecroft Jct. to Rugeley No. 1 (Cannock Branch)	1-wire block authorised March 1876. Still in use in 1921.
NORTH EASTERN DIVISION	
Edgeley Junction No. 1 to Buxton No. 1	1-wire block showing 3 positions (the experimental installation of the Fletcher 1-wire 3-position block, had been on this line), converted to 3-wire by 1909.
Greenfield Junction to Waterloo Jct. (Oldham)	Converted to 3-wire by 1909.
CHESTER AND HOLYHEAD DISTRICT	
Whitchurch, Chester Jct. to Tattenhall Junction	Converted to 3-wire between 1918 and 1921.
Mold Junction to Denbigh No. 1	Installation of 1-wire block authorised 2/1877; still in use 1921.
LANCASTER AND CARLISLE DISTRICT	
Ingleton Branch	1-wire block authorised April 1881 (cost not to exceed £300). Conversion to 3-wire authorised November 1911 at a cost of £200; the work had been completed by 1913.

Authority was given in December 1912 to convert the majority of the remaining sections of line to 3-wire at a cost of £3270. Little of this work was actually carried out.

did not cause much of a problem, even for the distant signals which were originally only a few hundred yards from the cabin. Indeed, in the early days it does not seem to have been too unusual for the starting signal for one line to be almost opposite the distant for the other. Inevitably there were places where the distant signal could not be seen (it was not good practice to have hidden starting signals as this could result in trains being forgotten) and here some form of repeater was required in the cabin to show that the arm had responded to the lever. Initially this was done mechanically by running a second wire back from the arm to an indicator in the cabin (similar to the 'face disc' described in Chapter 15). However, electrical repeaters came on the scene very early on. A contact box was provided on the signal arm which passed suitable currents to a repeater in the cabin, so providing an indication of the position of the arm. In 1874 the Signal Department was authorised to remove the 162 remaining mechanical repeaters and replace them with electrical ones at a cost of £12 each.

A big step forward was made in 1884 when J W Fletcher patented his combined arm and lamp repeater. Here, by using different current strengths and directions it was possible to convey information on the position of the signal arm (arm on/wrong/off) and the state of the signal lamp (in/out) over a single wire to a combined repeater in the cabin. As the railway system became more complex and distant signals were moved further from the cabin to give adequate braking distances, more and more repeaters were required. Many hundreds of the Fletcher repeaters were, therefore, manufactured, first by outside firms and then by the LNW at Stockport and Crewe and most cabins boasted at least one example. The first repeaters produced were mounted in a wooden case (see **Plate 2.3**) but the ubiquitous metal case with its semi circular top and circular dial face was soon introduced (**Plate 12.5**). In 1891 it was decided that, in view of the number of failures that were being experienced with the old type repeaters, they should be replaced with the new (Fletcher) type. Those on the main lines were to be changed first. It should be noted that these

Plate 12.6 *The standard indicator case was used for a number of purposes other than for signal repeaters. This picture illustrates a pair of instruments (the top has been removed from the right-hand one to show the interior) used as block repeaters. They were placed intermediately on a block circuit to repeat the position of the needles for the benefit of level crossing keepers (or other purposes as appropriate). These instruments were constructed at Crewe, the Telegraph Department having moved there from Stockport in 1904. The standard metal case could also be used for track circuit indicators, VOL indicators, electric slot indicators etc.*

Photo: G H Platt

repeaters were not normally positioned on the block shelf as repeaters today would be, but either on the window shelf or behind the levers on tubular metal stalks screwed to the floor. In both cases the repeater was placed behind, or as near as possible to, the lever to which it applied. **Plate 11.11** shows one such stalk while window shelves are visible in **Plates 11.1** and **11.11**. The standard repeater case was also used to house a number of other electrical devices such as block repeaters (**Plate 12.6**) and slot indicators.

ROUTE (TRAIN) INDICATORS

One of the biggest problems for the signalmen on the approaches to and at large stations and junctions was knowing what train he had been offered on the block and where it was going. The usual means of overcoming this was for the driver of the train to give a coded whistle as he passed a specified signal cabin some miles before reaching the station or junction. The signalman there was then able to pass forward the destination of the train to the man in advance and so on. The signalmen at the station were thereby made aware of the route of the train some time before its arrival and were able to make the necessary preparations for it. This helped to minimise delays and enabled the signalmen to regulate the traffic. The messages could be transmitted forward by a number of means, the most common being via a speaking telegraph circuit or via special bell codes added on to the standard 'is line clear?' (be ready) and/or 'train entering section'

Plate 12.7 *At busy places where several routes existed, some means of advising the signalmen where the trains had to go was required, particularly where a good deal of additional shunting and other movements, not in the timetable, took place. Additional bell codes (routing codes) could be used, but these were momentary and could be forgotten. Local telegraph circuits could be used to give permanent information. This photograph illustrates two telegraph instruments adapted as simple three-position 'routers'. The one on the left was at the receiving end of a circuit from Grand Junction to Exchange Sidings, Birmingham, and provided the signalman at Exchange Sidings with a permanent indication of the route the next up train was to take at his cabin. In this case the choice was between its continuing along the main (London) line or being crossed over into the Adderley Park Sidings. The LNW made sure there could be no doubt about the ownership of the instrument! This circuit was installed in 1881 in connection with the introduction of 'Tell-Tale' block working between Adderley Park and New Street Station. The instrument on the right was the pegging end of a circuit between Preston Nos. 1 and 4 cabins and provided routing information for north bound trains.*

Equipment by Courtesy of P Jordan and M Christensen

Plate 12.8 *A Tyers 16 position train describer in use at Chester No. 4. This is the 'pegging' end of the circuit and was used by the signalman to provide routing information to the signalman at Chester No. 6. The 'peg' was pushed into the appropriate hole and the slide on the right hand side pulled out and released; the needles then moved to the pegged position. A needle was provided above the pegging dial and worked with that in the other cabin (No. 6), to show that the description had been correctly sent. In the photograph the instrument is pegged to 'G W Passenger Train' and this is repeated by the needle above. The descriptions make interesting reading, especially as the photograph was taken in 1977!*

bell signals. Both these methods had the disadvantage of being transitory and could easily be misinterpreted or forgotten in busy moments, while the speaking telegraph had the added disadvantage of being on a separate circuit with the instruments usually placed away from the block instruments. Both these methods were used extensively on the LNWR. Some railways (such as the Midland) transmitted the train or routing information via 'beats' on the block telegraph instrument needles (in a similar way to that used to transmit messages on the speaking telegraph).

There were obvious dangers in using the block instruments in this way, or for any other purpose than controlling the trains, and the LNW did not allow their block instruments to be used for transmitting messages.

At very busy places some sort of continuous indication of the destinations of trains was thought desirable. The first installations occurred in the late 1870's when indicating circuits were established between some cabins. Normally an adapted telegraph instrument was used which could be pegged over to indicate a destination (**Plate 12.7**) as required, the instrument being operated from the rear end of the section at the same time as the train was offered forward. In a number of cases spare line wires, resulting from the conversion of a three-wire block section to the one-wire system, were used for this purpose.

When the one-wire system replaced the three-wire block at Walsall in 1879 train indicators were introduced between the Park Street and Ryecroft Junction cabins on both lines, the up line indicators continuing to Bridgeman Place. At Earlestown, a new train indicator circuit was introduced between Manchester Junction and Newton Bridge at a cost of £13 in 1879.

Plate 12.9 *A selection of instruments on the shelf at Chester No. 6, all of which apply to the Fork Line between this cabin and Chester No. 5. The LNW combined block instrument on the left is a permissive instrument similar to that in* **Plate 12.13**, *but this time with double needles, and since the Fork Line could be worked on either the Permissive or Absolute (e.g. for passenger trains) block systems a brass flap marked 'Absolute' on one side and 'Permissive' (as shown here) on the other was attached to the case and acted as a reminder to the signalman of which system was being used (it was set manually). A few instruments were to be found with two flaps, one at the top for the top needle and one below it for the bottom needle. The middle instrument is a Tyers 9 position describer and is in the normal (no indication) position. On the right is a 9 position Fletcher electric describer in its metal case. This is a receiving instrument worked by Chester No. 5 and shows the destination of a train approaching from there.*

Plate 12.10 *These three instruments stood on the shelf at Chester No. 3A and are a group applying to the Fast Lines between this cabin and Chester No. 4. On the left is a 15 position Fletcher describer (pegging), here the peg holes were placed in the rim around the needle dial face instead of on a separate lower dial. The peg is just lodged in one of the holes and has not actuated the needles. In the centre is the block instrument for the Fast Lines; they could be used permissively for trains not conveying passengers and so the instrument is of permissive form. To add to the fun, the block shelf at Chester No. 4 was divided into 'Up' and 'Down' halves (this was in fact a BR alteration, see* **Figure 12.7***) and so this instrument worked to two separate single needle instruments there, one on the 'Up' portion of the shelf and one on the 'Down'. Two tapper keys have, therefore, been provided one working to each of the instruments at No. 4 cabin. On the right is the receiving end of a 16 position Tyers train describer which provides routing information for trains on the Up Fast line. On the far right is a separate bell of a more modern design than that shown in* **Plate 12.11**.

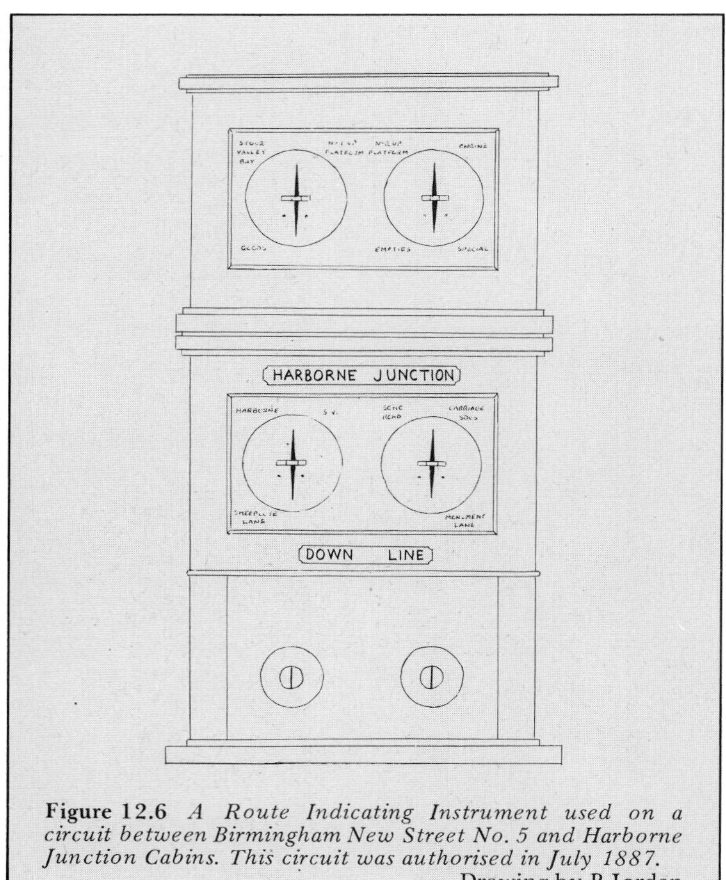

Figure 12.6 *A Route Indicating Instrument used on a circuit between Birmingham New Street No. 5 and Harborne Junction Cabins. This circuit was authorised in July 1887.*
Drawing by P Jordan

The obvious limitation of the indicating circuits was that generally only two or three different routes could be shown. Edward Tyer had devised a step by step telegraph instrument back in 1861. Here the needle could show any one of 27 positions to indicate all the letters of the alphabet plus a 'no indication' position. Further improvements were made in 1865, 1879 and 1893, the last two being specifically for use as train describers. Instead of letters of the alphabet a route or train type was placed against each position of the needle (see **Plate 12.8**). The train describers were made with different numbers of positions to suit requirements.

The first installation on the LNWR of Tyers new 1879 indicating instruments was put in at Birmingham New Street Station at the beginning of 1880. It worked between the Navigation Street and North End cabins and cost £35. A circuit was provided, soon after, at Willesden No. 1 to enable the shunters to communicate with the cabin. The train indicators at Walsall, installed in 1879, were replaced by these new Tyers clock-work train indicators at the end of 1880.

These Tyers instruments were electro-mechanical in action. In order to set the needles to a particular position the metal peg was pushed into the appropriate socket in the sending instrument. The needles were actuated by pulling the spring loaded slide on the right hand side of the instrument (**Plate 12.8**) and releasing it. This operated a make and break contact in the instrument which caused pulses of current to pass along the line wire. The needles at both the sending and receiving instruments 'ticked forward' step by step in unison with each other and the pulses until the sending needle reached the pegged position where a mechanical stop prevented further movement and both needles stopped. Removing the peg removed the stop and allowed the needles to continue to step around the dial in a clockwise direction until the vertical or zero position was reached. The instruments were then ready for the next description.

G E Fletcher devised and patented an all electric form of train describer in 1891. This was subsequently improved by altering the electrical arrangements in the receiving instruments to ensure that the needles worked together. The instrument was adopted by the LNWR and many were manufactured in the LNWR telegraph shops at Stockport and Crewe. They were quite distinctive in appearance (**Plates 12.9 & 10**). Instead of a wooden case, a circular iron casting was used which doubled as a foundation ring for the internal contacts and electrical equipment. Access for maintenance was via a removable cast iron cap at the rear. The instruments were manufactured in a number of sizes, the 9 (8 indicators plus the no-indication position) and 15 position versions being, perhaps, the most common. Some could be quite large: Nuneaton No. 2, for instance, boasted a 24 position one!

FLETCHER ELECTRIC LOCK

A problem in signalling was to provide a satisfactory and flexible means of controlling siding connections in the block section or which were too far from the signal cabin to be worked directly from it. A ground frame controlled from the cabin was provided to work such a connection. Mechanical means were available to provide the necessary safety and control over the operations of the ground frame (these are described in Chapters 11 and 15). They all had limitations, however, in the distance over which they could operate or in the time required to carry out the necessary operations.

J W Fletcher devised and patented an electric release for this purpose in 1881 and this was quite widely used on the LNWR. It consisted of an electric lock fastened to one of the levers at the ground frame working the points: this normally locked the lever normal and prevented the points being used. In the signal cabin a switch was mounted on a pedestal (or on the block shelf) behind the appropriate signal lever. Operating the switch locked the signal lever normal and released the lock at the ground frame so allowing it to be used. When work at the siding was complete the ground frame levers were returned to normal allowing the switch in the cabin to be turned to lock the ground frame and release the signal lever. Normal working was then restored. Indicators were provided in the cabin and at the ground frame to show whether the points were 'locked' or 'free' and electric gongs or bells were provided for communication between the cabin and ground frame.

The regulations for working the electrically locked sidings as they stood in 1884 are reproduced in full in Appendix 5. The general procedure described was that adopted where the frame was controlled from both the adjacent block posts.

SIGNALMEN'S REMINDERS AND SAFETY DEVICES

In theory, the combination of the block system and interlocking, used in accordance with the Rules and Regulations, should prevent the majority of accidents. In practice the weak links were often the signalmen and other staff who were only human and could make mistakes. Such mistakes have caused a fair proportion of railway accidents and this section looks, briefly, at a number of reminder devices introduced on the LNWR in order to reduce the opportunity for errors. From the signalling point of view the largest single cause of accidents was through signalmen forgetting trains or vehicles standing on the line. Following various accidents through oversight, culminating in one on the LNWR at Watford in 1883, a new Rule, designated 41A, was introduced into the revised standard Railway Clearing House Rule Book published later that year. This rule, briefly, required the fireman to proceed to the signal cabin to remind the signalman of the presence of his train when it was detained on a running line. This rule was renumbered 55 in the 1897 edition of the Rule Book and was perhaps the best known and most important of all the rules. Most of the safety devices described in this section were introduced primarily to assist in achieving the objects of this Rule.

SIGNING THE REGISTER

The keeping of train registers by the signalmen to record the times of passing of the trains (and subsequently of the block signalling process for each train) had been introduced on the LNWR at the end of 1870.

Despite the provisions of Rule 55 (41A as it was originally) signalmen occasionally forgot why the fireman was in the cabin or his presence could even provide enough distraction for an error to be made.

(continued on page 186)

Plate 12.11 *Originally, where separate bells were required (as they were, of course, with the old forms of instruments) the LNW used wooden cased instruments. These were no doubt supplied by instrument manufacturers such as Tyers. When the LNW began manufacture of its own electrical instruments a new form of separate bell was designed for production in the works and this is illustrated here. Like the standard block instruments the bell was mounted at the bottom with the mechanism above it. The similarity of the design with that of the original block instrument bases will be apparent; like the block instruments, tubular legs were used in later years. The mechanism was covered by a simple metal cover. A tapper key could be provided (as in this case) where return bell communication was required, otherwise the bell tapper or bell (as appropriate) would not be provided.*

Courtesy J R G Griffiths

Plate 12.12 *In modern practice it is usual to provide a block shelf of about the same length as the frame. This allows signal and other repeaters to be mounted on it (usually on the front) above the lever to which they apply. In LNW days this was not done and the shelf was only made long enough to house the block instruments and any other special equipment (such as the block switch). The signal repeaters were normally mounted on the window shelf or on pedestals behind the frame. This photograph shows perhaps the ultimate in short shelves at Llandudno No. 2. Only a short length of shelf (interestingly fitted with only single support rods) was provided at the centre of the cabin, beneath the diagram, to accommodate the single block instrument (it is a terminal station) and is dwarfed by the 80 lever frame. The separate section of shelf at the right hand end of the frame is a later addition for mounting some modern repeaters, plungers and the separate signal lamp repeaters.*

Figure 12.7 (Opposite) *The Block Shelf Layout at Chester No. 4 Signal Cabin as it existed in the early 1950's prior to the installation of illuminated diagrams. The lever frame in this cabin was quite large (176 levers) and so spaces have been left in it (between levers 53 and 54 and between levers 123 and 124) to allow the signalmen access to the windows. The frame is mounted on girders for 18 levers and the girder spaces can be seen along the line of the levers. All the block instruments have been grouped together at the centre of the frame (between levers 57 and 119) and in LNW days this was the only section of block shelf provided. All the remaining sections of shelf were added in LMS days to accommodate selector switches, additional track circuit indicators, sealed releases, lamp repeaters and so on, hence their rather 'empty' appearance. Because of the volume of traffic passing through Chester and the number of lines and routes, extensive use was made of route indicating instruments to assist the signalmen in their work. The instrument above lever 60 is a two position routing instrument of the telegraph type, while that to the right of it, above lever 63 is a Tyers type train describer (receiving end). The train describer above lever 68 is a Tyers pegging type, while that on its right, above lever 70, is of the Fletcher type. The block instruments above levers 76 and 81 have LNW track circuit indicators attached to their left hand sides. Above levers 73 and 90 are LNW 'separate bells' for bell only communication (***Plate 12.11***).*

In the 1930's 'call on' signals were added underneath many of the home signals at Chester. At that time practically all the levers at Chester No. 4 cabin were in use and there were insufficient spaces to allow all the new 'call on' arms to be worked by separate levers. They were, therefore, connected to the same levers as the main arms above them via an electrical signal selector. Plungers were placed on the block shelf above the signal levers (for example numbers 5, 8, 22, 156, 160 and 170) and by pressing these the signalman was able to pull off the call-on arm instead of the main arm.

It will be noticed that there are few lamp repeaters or signal arm repeaters on the block shelf. This was because the Fletcher combined arm and lamp repeaters were normally mounted on the window shelf and not on the block shelf. The small sketch at the top left shows the dimensions and positioning of the standard LNW block shelf. Scale of reproduction: 7 mm to 1 foot (1:43.5).

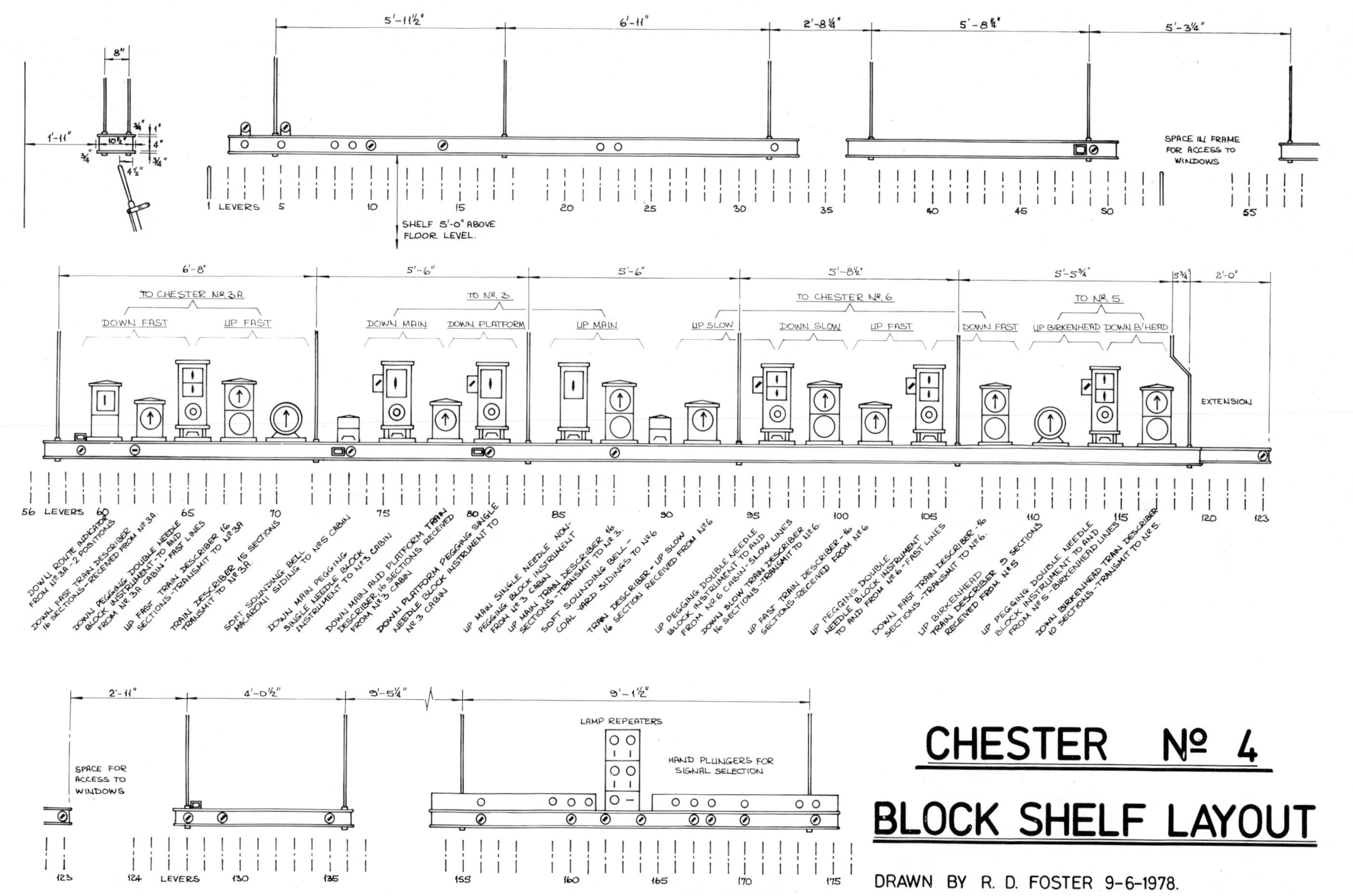

CHESTER Nº 4

BLOCK SHELF LAYOUT

DRAWN BY R. D. FOSTER 9-6-1978.

In the early 1890's a rule was introduced on the North Eastern Division of the LNWR that a fireman carrying out Rule 41A should sign the train register. This had the advantages of ensuring that the fireman complied with the rules as well as acting as an additional reminder to the signalman. The practice was introduced throughout the LNWR in 1894.

LINK OR LEVER COLLAR

This was perhaps the simplest possible safety device and was dropped over the lever and through the catch handle when the line was obstructed or blocked. The lever could not then be pulled until the link was removed and so 'reminded' the signalman of previous events. The most obvious uses of the link were to remind the signalman of a train standing at a signal or one which had been crossed over to allow a following train to pass. Usually a lever collar slips over the lever and sits between the lever handle and the catch handle thus wedging them and preventing the catch block being raised out of its notch. The loop handles on LNWR lever frames did not suit this arrangement, but a very simple and cheap loop or link was devised which slipped over the lever handle and through the loop handle (**Plates 11.11 & 12.14**).

Despite the apparently obvious advantages of the link many railway companies were very reluctant to introduce any form of reminder as it was felt that they would reduce the vigilance of the signalman and therefore have a negative rather than a positive effect. It took many years of public pressure to get them adopted on any scale.

On the LNWR the first steps towards the introduction of the link came in connection with the practice of crossing a train from one line to another to allow a following one to pass, the dangers of such an arrangement being fairly obvious! A number of accidents continued to occur despite the provisions of Rule 41A and, following the Norton Fitzwarren accident on the Great Western Railway in 1890, further efforts were made to reduce the risk of accidents. On the LNWR a special regulation was introduced to eliminate one of the practical difficulties of applying the rules.

> 'Rules 41A, 154A and 275A (later Rule 55); If after a train has been shunted onto the opposite line the engine is required to be detached either for the purpose of shunting or for any other cause, and the fireman is therefore unable to remain in the signal cabin he must, before the engine is detached, obtain from it the iron target which is used in front of the engine to denote the description of the train and place it on the lever of the home signal for the road occupied. This will act as a reminder to the signalman that the line is not clear and release the fireman to assist in the shunting. When the shunting is finished and the signalman is ready to cross the train to its proper line the fireman must go back to the signal cabin, and after obtaining the signalman's authority, withdraw the iron target from the lever on which it has been placed. In cases where engines are not provided with suitable targets a red flag must be tied to the signal lever.'

On the 1st of January, 1905 the signal cabins on the Central Division were provided with 'metal links' for use as a reminder to the signalmen. Their initial use was rather restricted, the regulations only requiring them to be placed on the levers in the event of the fireman having to leave the cabin, and not having a target with him. The link was soon introduced throughout the system and its uses were gradually expanded to cover all cases where such a device would be of assistance.

FIREMAN'S CALL BOX

As track layouts grew in complexity and signals were provided further and further from the signal cabins new problems began to be experienced with the provisions of Rule 55. At busy places it could be very dangerous for a fireman to cross the tracks to reach the signal cabin, particularly in darkness or bad weather. The distance between the train and the cabin meant that some time could elapse between a train coming to a stand and the fireman reaching the cabin. It was quite possible for the signalman to make a mistake during this period. Similar comments applied to the fireman's return journey, while the time taken could also lead to appreciable traffic delays. At times of heavy traffic or difficulty the signal cabin could become rather full of people, something which could inhibit, rather than assist, the signalman in his work.

In the early years of this century the LNWR Signal Department devised the Fireman's Call Box (**Figure 12.8**) to overcome these problems. A plunger was provided at the call box, which when depressed by the fireman caused a metal disc lettered 'Train Waiting at Signal' to appear out of a box attached to the side of the appropriate block instrument in the signal cabin. In most cases the block needle was also held at 'Train on Line'. A bell rang in the call box to indicate that the equipment had worked correctly. Provided the fireman heard the bell he was exempted from going to the signal cabin.

In the first installations the box was fixed to the signal post. This was soon found to be inconvenient since it often involved crossing several lines and the signal post could be difficult to get to. The box was, therefore, mounted on a pedestal as shown in **Figure 12.8**, and this was positioned, where possible, on the left hand side of the line to which it referred and at about the position the engine would come to a stand.

Trials of the apparatus were carried out in 1907, and as with most things, once the device had proved itself useful the LNW put in hand its introduction, on a large scale, throughout the system. Call boxes at Crewe North Junction were authorised in October 1908 and installations at 21 signal cabins in April of the following year. By the end of 1910 approximately 90 call boxes were in use at 42 signal cabins while work on another 55 installations was in hand. The War slowed things down but by the spring of 1918 there was a total of over 250 devices in use at 128 signal cabins, some of which had as many as 6 sets of apparatus.

To assist the train crews in determining if a call box was provided, and its location, an indicator lettered 'Fireman's Call Box' was placed near the call box. In most cases this was illuminated at night. (**Figure 12.8**).

In LMS days the indicators were removed and replaced by the familiar 'D' sign attached to the signal post.

'NORTHAMPTON' LOCKS

A weakness in the signalling system was that there was, generally, no physical connection between the block instruments and the interlocking. It was possible for accidents to occur through incorrect interpretation of the information given by the instruments or levers. It was not unknown for a signalman to make a mistake in working the block instruments or levers and to allow a second train into the section. He could, particularly on multiple-track lines, signal a train on the block instrument for one line and send the train on another. A number of systems or devices were introduced to combat the problem and provide a physical link between the signals and block instruments. Perhaps the best known and most comprehensive of these

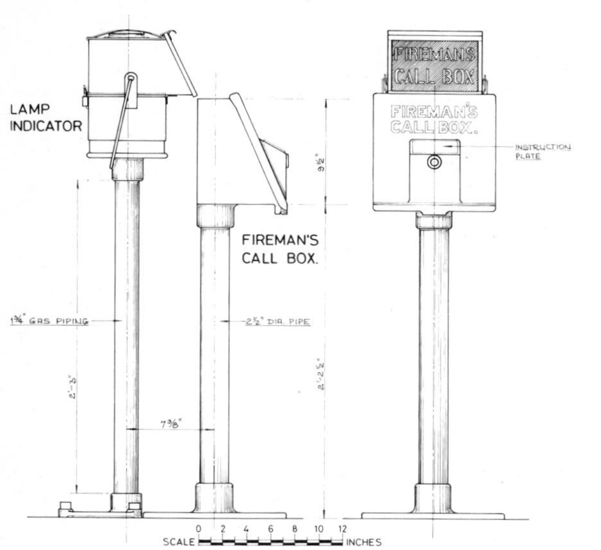

FIREMAN'S CALL BOX

DRAWN BY R.D. FOSTER. 11 NOVEMBER 1979

Figure 12.8 *Fireman's Call Box and Indicator. These were placed at ground level near where the engine would come to a stand if it had to stop at the signal. The instruction plate on the front read 'Instructions – Fireman to press plunger. A bell will ring when communication is made with signalman. If bell does not ring, fireman must walk to the box.'*

The lamp indicator behind displayed the words 'Fireman's Call Box' on an illuminated ground glass screen. This lamp indicator (lettered 'Track Circuit') was also used to indicate to drivers the presence of a track circuit and was sited in the same way as a Call Box. Scale of reproduction: 1/16th full size.

London and North Western Railway.

INSTRUCTIONS TO SIGNALMEN.

Electric Locks have been fixed on Levers Working the Signals as shewn below :—

Disley Station Box—Up Platform Starting Signal, Lever No. 3.
New Mills............—Up Advanced Starting Signal, Lever No. 17.
,, ,, ...—Down ,, ,, ,, Lever No. 3.
Furness Vale.........—Up Starting Signal - - Lever No. 20.
,, ,, ...—Down ,, ,, - - Lever No. 8.
Whaley Bridge......—Up Advanced Starting Signal, Lever No. 5.
Chapel-en-le-Frith...— ,, ,, ,, ,, Lever No. 15.
,, ,, ,, —Down ,, ,, ,, Lever No. 4.

The Levers will be locked in their normal position when the needle from the Box in advance stands at " Line Closed " or " Train on Line."

The Lock on the Lever will be withdrawn when the needle for the Box in advance points to " Line Clear."

When it is necessary to lower a Locked Signal for the purpose of " Switching Out " a Box, the Bell Signal (3—3—3) " Release Lock on Signal " must be sent to the Box from which the Signal is locked, and the Signalman there must repeat the Bell Signal (3—3—3); place his Indicator to the " Line Clear " position and keep it in that position until he receives the " Switching Out " Signal from the Box in rear. The Signalman in rear must not give the " Switching Out " Signal until he has lowered the locked Signal.

When it is necessary to test a locked Signal, the Signalman in advance must place the Block Needle to " Line Clear " before repeating the testing signal (5—5—5—5). When the testing is completed, the Signalman in rear must give the " Testing Completed " Signal (8—3). The Signalman in advance must acknowledge the Bell Signal (8—3) by repetition and place the Block Indicator in the normal position.

S. B. CARTER,
District Superintendent.

May, 1912.

Figure 12.9 *An LNW Notice for the installation of Northampton Locks at the stations on the Buxton Branch in 1912. These installations cost £11 per signal.*

was Sykes 'Lock and Block' and later the Midland 'Rotary Interlocking Block'. The LNWR did not consider that the lock and block would be suitable for use on their line, a view shared by most of the large 'northern' companies. The Sykes 'Lock and Block' was really only suited to railways where the majority of the trains passed through one section and on into the next. Elsewhere (for example where there was a significant goods traffic) the system did not offer any real advantage since the locking had often to be overriden by the signalman.

Consideration was given, however, to devising some form of link between the block and signals which could be installed where required to meet local circumstances. As often happens an accident provided the final spur to action. This was a minor collision at Northampton on the 20th of April, 1910.

At Northampton No. 4 the double track line from Birmingham split into four passenger lines and two goods lines. The signalman there sent an up coal train on the fast line to No. 3 cabin where it came to a stand in order to carry out some shunting. Some time later he accepted the 10.5 am passenger train from Birmingham to London and offered it to No. 3 cabin on the up slow line block instrument, the fast line still being occupied by the coal train. This was accepted but the signalman at No. 4 pulled off the signals for the fast line by mistake (the junction was still set for that route). The train proceeded onto that line under clear signals and collided with the rear of the coal train, seventeen people being injured.

The arrangement developed consisted of providing an electric lock on the starting signal lever which was linked to the block instruments so that the lever could only be pulled and the signal cleared with the block needle showing 'Line Clear'. Inevitably, the arrangement was christened the 'Northampton Lock'!

The first installations were made in the spring of 1911, when electric locks were fixed to the starting signal levers at the following places:—

Northampton No. 4	Colwyn Bay
Willesden No. 5	Connah's Quay No. 1
Rugby No. 7	Muspratt's Siding
Camden No. 2	Abergele
Heyford North	Camden No. 3
Loudoun Road	Crewe North Junction
Wolverhampton	Northampton Station

The total cost of these installations was £391.

Again, once the arrangement had been proved it was rapidly installed in large numbers throughout the system. In order to speed the work of introducing the device on a wide scale, an expenditure of £2,000 was authorised in January 1917. It was not until July 1920 that the regulations for its use were incorporated in the L&NWR Block Telegraph Regulations as Regulation 40. Prior to this the instructions had been displayed on the block cards in the cabins concerned.

It was realised that some indication of the levers locked in this way was required in the signal cabin. In 1916 it was decided to paint a horizontal black stripe, six inches deep, on those levers which were fitted with electric locks. This arrangement was quite satisfactory while the locks were limited to signals and facing point lock levers but ran into obvious problems when electric locks began to be fitted to point levers; in later years a white stripe was used.

TRACK CIRCUITS

The principle of the track circuit had been propounded way back in the 1870's. The problem was that the electrical equipment then available (particularly insulation) was not good enough to allow outdoor installations to be made that would operate reliably in all weather and ground conditions. The quality of the ballast used was not of the best (even on the Premier Line!) and track drainage was often poor so that, in many places, current would flow through the ballast between the rails almost as readily as it would through wheels and axles. An added complication was that the majority of carriage stock in Britain ran on wheels with wooden centres (the Mansell wheel) and would not operate track circuits anyway! The introduction of track circuits as a signalling device had, therefore, to wait until technology could catch up with ideas and produce something that would work reliably. This position was reached about the turn of the century and a few companies began installing track circuits to suit their own needs. It was necessary for these companies to bond across the wheels and axles of those vehicles which were fitted with wooden centred wheels. The tremendous amount of through running of vehicles from other companies caused problems and inhibited the large scale introduction of track circuits as well as making the first installations somewhat expensive.

There was no urgent need for track circuiting on the LNWR and in view of the problems they would cause little was done at first. Alfred Oldham was very much against the whole idea and did not think that track circuits could be made reliable enough for everyday service. Some investigations into the subject were made around 1907 and the Westinghouse Company prepared designs for track circuits at Birmingham New Street and several other places, and for the necessary wheel bonding.

The question of the use of coaching vehicles fitted with unbonded wheels (those which would not operate track circuits) on lines with track circuiting was raised at the Railway Clearing House in 1910. Following this, F A Cortez-Leigh sought approval for bonding all the Mansell wheels in use on the LNW to cover the running of LNW vehicles on other railways and also to allow for the introduction of track circuits on the LNW itself. It was estimated that there were about 31,000 pairs of wheels to be attended to at a cost of £2,196 (1/5d per axle). A further 2,400 pairs of wheels under West Coast Joint Stock vehicles would have to be dealt with at joint LNW and Caledonian expense. The work consisted of fixing a copper strip between the axle and tyre to provide electrical continuity. It was anticipated that the work would be done gradually as the vehicles passed through the works and so it probably took about three years to complete.

In April 1911, approval was given for the expenditure of £420 on the provision of some track circuits at Rugby. These were stated to be experimental installations and their performance was to be carefully monitored. As before, once the idea had been tried and proven, and its usefulness demonstrated, it was quickly and extensively applied. In October 1911, authority was given for the expenditure of £5,000, spread over the following two years, on the installation of track circuits at agreed places. A further sum of £5,000 was set aside in October 1912 for the same purpose and in November 1913, £10,000 more was made available. By the beginning of 1914 over 200 track circuits had been installed. The First World War and the arrears of maintenance it caused naturally slowed down installation work and the 300 figure was not reached until early in 1921.

On the North-Western, the track circuits were seen primarily as a device to assist in the requirements of Rule 55. Over 80% of the track circuits installed up to 1921 were provided in the rear of home or starting signals in order to give train crews exemption from Rule 55. This system had the additional advantage of enabling these signals to be placed further from the cabin if necessary. The block instruments were locked at 'Train on Line' where necessary with the track circuit occupied. The state of the track circuit was indicated in the signal cabin by means of a black banner indicator which was normally attached to the block instrument applying to the track circuited line (**Plate 12.13**). In a few cases the track circuits replaced Fireman's Call Boxes, but the majority were new installations. In some places track circuits and Fireman's Call Boxes were used together, a three position indicator being provided in the cabin (**Plate 12.13**).

The presence of a track circuit was indicated in the same way as that of the Fireman's Call Box. The illuminated indicator shown in **Figure 12.8** was provided and lettered 'Track Circuit' on the screen.

TRAIN ON LINE INDICATORS

Despite all the safety devices and provisions of the Rule Book occasional accidents still resulted from the practice of crossing trains from one line to another. Such accidents were always likely to be serious, as was horribly demonstrated at Quintinshill on the Caledonian Line on 22nd May, 1915, the signalman having forgotten a local passenger train which had been crossed from one line to the other to allow an express to pass.

Following this accident the LNW Signal Department immediately set about devising a means of preventing such a tragedy ever occurring on their line. Just eight weeks later, in July 1915, the drawings for the mechanical 'Train on Line Indicators' were completed. The basic idea came from J T Roberts, while the detailed design work was done by Percy Hardman. Roberts patented the device in 1917. Sets of the apparatus were installed in each district for trials and evaluation. In October 1916, it was decided that these had been successful and the expenditure of £2,000 was authorised for its installation at those places where the crossing over of trains was necessary. As far as practicable the practice of refuging on running lines was prohibited at cabins not fitted with the device.

The indicators were purely mechanical in action and were connected to the interlocking but were not linked to the block instruments. Two pointers (**Plate 12.14**) were provided near the ends of the lever frame at block shelf height, one for the down line and one for the up. If the crossover road lever(s) were reversed the indicators, which were attached via a linkage to the interlocking, moved from the 'Clear' to the 'Blocked' position and remained so after the point levers had been restored to normal. In the 'Blocked' position the indicators locked the appropriate signal levers at danger and hence prevented another train approaching. In order to release the signals the handle attached to the indicator had to be swung to the 'Clear' position by the signalman. This action was intended to remind the signalman of previous events. Naturally, the indicators moved to the 'Blocked' position whenever the crossover was used and not just when a train was crossed over for refuging. When two levers were provided for the crossover the indicators were linked separately to the appropriate levers.

Briefly, the process of operation was as follows. A train which had to be crossed over was brought to a stand

Plate 12.13 *The standard combined block instrument could be produced in a number of different forms to suit the particular installation. The interesting example shown here also allows a number of other forms of instrument used on the LNW to be illustrated. The main instrument is an LNW tell-tale or permissive recording instrument. The number of trains in the section is indicated by the number displayed in the window above the commutator, and the working of the instrument is similar to that shown in* **Plate 12.1**. *At many large stations the lines could not conveniently be divided into up and down pairs (there were usually different numbers of up and down lines in any case) and so it was common practice to use single needle instruments, one set for each line. As can be seen the single needle is accommodated within the standard double needle case. This particular instrument was from Preston No. 4 cabin where it controlled the down Platform 8 line from No. 3 cabin. When track circuits were introduced on the LNW indicators had to be provided in the cabin and it was decided that the best possible place for these was as near as possible to the block needle so that the signalman would see them each time he glanced at the block instrument. Generally, therefore, the track circuit indicators were mounted on the side of the block instrument case itself so that they would be more or less opposite the block needle to which they applied, and an example of such an installation is shown here. Of course in LNW days there was usually only one track circuit on any one line and so the method did not cause too many problems. (A few block instruments did exist with two indicators mounted one above the other). The standard rectangular wooden case could be used for other instruments and on top of the block instrument is a 'Vehicle On Line' indicator. This worked in conjunction with 'VOL' switches on the platform (operated by platform staff) and was provided to indicate to the signalman when vehicles had been left standing in the platform. An example of its use would be to protect a vehicle which had been detached from the rear of a train which had departed and left the vehicle on its own. The signalman could not always see the platform roads clearly due to obstructions. This 'VOL' indicator has been attached to the top of the block instrument in order to place it near the block needle. The idea of the 'VOL' indicator dates back to a nasty accident at Watford in October 1883, when an up express ran into some carriages which had been left on the main line and forgotten by the signalman. Following experiments at Watford and Crewe in 1886 it was decided, in December 1888, to introduce the equipment on the line generally. From this time on those stations and platforms where there were difficulties were gradually fitted up with the apparatus. On the left of the photograph is a third type of indicator which could be found in the standard wooden cases. This is a three-position train indicator showing 'Track Clear', 'Train Approaching' and 'Train Arrived'. The 'Train Approaching' position indicated that a train was occupying the track circuited portion of the line, while the 'Train Arrived' position of the needle indicated that the train had come to a stand at the signal and the fireman had depressed the plunger on the Fireman's Call Box (***Figure 12.8***), provided near the signal.*

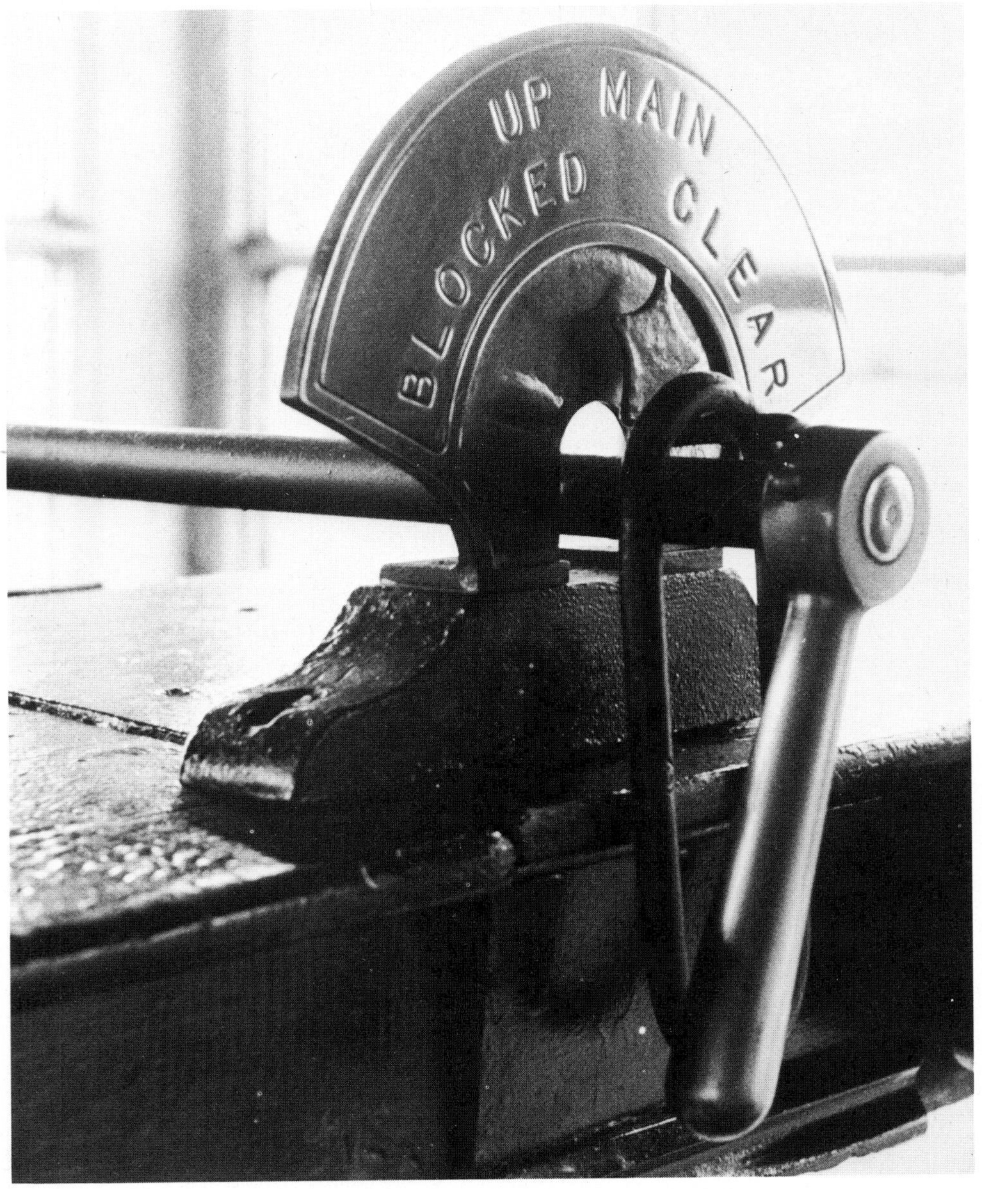

Plate 12.14 *An LNW Train on Line Indicator at Ty Croes. This is one of the block shelf mounting type. This one locked the up line signals and is in the clear position. The pointer moved to the 'Blocked' position when the crossover road was used and the signalman had to turn it back to 'Clear' with the handle before the signals could be lowered for another train. The signalman seems to have found that this one was also a useful place to hang the link.*

in advance of the crossover, and the crossover reversed. This moved both indicators to the 'Blocked' position and locked the appropriate signals on both lines at danger. When the train was on the other line, clear of the crossover, this was restored to normal. The indicators both remained at 'Blocked' and the signals remained locked. The signalman then operated the indicator handle for the line that was clear to release the signals and allow the following train to pass. The other indicator remained at 'Blocked' to protect the standing train. When it was clear for the standing train to proceed the crossover was again reversed (both indicators then showing 'Blocked') and the train sent on its way. The crossover was then restored to normal and when both lines were clear the two indicators were moved to the 'Clear' position to restore normal working.

The apparatus could be fitted easily to both tumbler and tappet frames, while the indicators could be either free standing or mounted on the block shelf. It was, normally, fitted in cabins where the practice of crossing trains over was likely to occur and large numbers were installed. They were most common on the secondary double track lines where there were few refuge sidings or loop lines but where it was quite common for trains to be overtaken by faster ones. They were also to be found at quite a number of small cabins on four track sections of main lines. Here a pair of indicators working with the slow or goods lines crossover would be provided to allow a slow train to be refuged safely on the other line while it was overtaken. Examples of this practice occurred at Balshaw Lane and Leyland on the West Coast Main line.

The regulations for working the indicators were added to the LNW Block Telegraph Regulations booklet in July 1920, becoming Regulation 41.

In LMS and BR days many of the indicators were replaced by track circuits and electric locks although quite a number of sets remained in service until the 1960's.

Chapter Thirteen The Working of Single Lines

Something of the difficulties of operating trains in the early days on double lines has already been described. As can be imagined these problems were compounded on a single line where there was always a risk of meeting something coming the other way which could have disastrous results. While the LNW was not noted for its single lines, it must be remembered that quite a proportion of its secondary lines had been built as single lines and were doubled later, thus adding to the scale of the problem in the early days.

A number of methods were tried on the single lines in an attempt to regulate the traffic safely. These included operation strictly by timetable, the use of a pilotman or pilot engine, or more simply, by ensuring that only one engine was working. All the methods had disadvantages through cost or a lack of flexibility to deal with late running or additional traffic. In most cases the systems did not provide an absolute safeguard and usually broke down when things were not going well, which was just the time when they were most needed.

Single line tunnels were a special hazard since the consequences of collision were obviously serious and there was little chance of a driver seeing an obstruction in time to stop. The Standedge tunnel was opened in 1849. This single line bore was over 3 miles long and obviously required special attention. Initially this was provided by use of a special pilot engine which was attached to each train. Since there was only one pilot engine there could only be one train in the section and security was achieved. To provide additional security and to positively identify the pilot engine, Mr Henry Woodhouse, the Line's Engineer and Superintendent, devised a train staff or pilot (**Figure 13.1**) which was to be carried with the engine. The Board of Trade Inspector, Captain Wynn, made an inspection of the tunnel in May 1850 and his report describes the method of working as it existed then.

> 'The mode of working the tunnel. An electric telegraph has been laid down through the tunnel and is extended on the Huddersfield side half-a-mile to the Marsden station, and on the Manchester side one and-a-quarter miles to the Saddleworth station. At either mouth of the tunnel are huts for policemen, which are supplied with telegraph instruments, as well as the Saddleworth and Marsden stations, and from these huts, wires extend to distant signals up and down the line and into the tunnel; these latter reach 600 yards into the tunnel, and show green and red lights. All trains are required to stop at the Saddleworth and Marsden stations, and a telegraphic communication takes place between these stations to ascertain all is right, before a train is allowed to proceed. As an additional precaution a pilot has been established, which consists of a stick having a cross piece on the top, with the words 'Standedge pilot' printed on it; no train or engine, or wagon is permitted to enter the tunnel, without the stick being with it, with the exception of two goods trains which pass through the tunnel at 1.25 a.m. and 5.30 p.m. The pilot (stick) is carried on an extra engine set apart for this especial purpose, but on the two occasions named it is borne by a policeman. The two station masters are, I consider, the chief responsible persons for the safe working of the tunnel. The traffic on the line last month amounted to seven passenger trains, and three goods trains each way per day.'

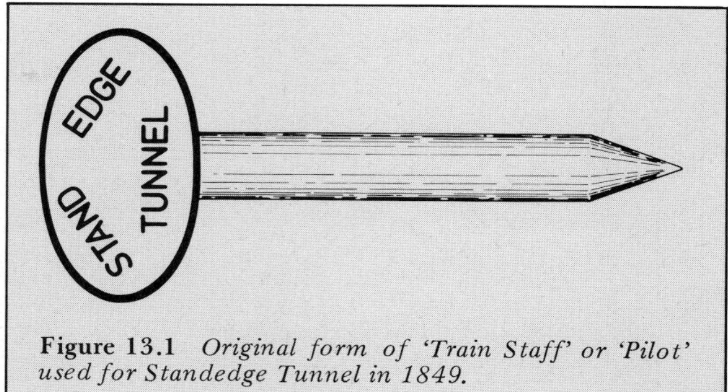

Figure 13.1 *Original form of 'Train Staff' or 'Pilot' used for Standedge Tunnel in 1849.*

It was found, however, that delays occurred through waiting while the pilot engine was attached and detached from trains, and particularly when it had to return to accompany another train in the same direction. Mr Woodhouse realised that the staff offered security in itself and the pilot engine was withdrawn, the staff being carried by the train engine. To further facilitate working, where several trains were to pass in the same direction in succession, the driver of each train was shown the staff before entering the tunnel. The staff was retained by the signalman until the last train in the sequence arrived and this one took the staff with it so that it could be used for a train in the reverse direction. At first no authority, other than the sight of the staff was given to drivers of trains which did not carry it. This was the first application of the train staff system in Great Britain. (Although it has been suggested that the first application was actually on the Coventry to Leamington branch).

Where there were several sections of single line together the staffs were painted distinctive colours so that the men could easily see that they had the correct staff for the section they were to travel through. As an additional aid it was resolved, in October 1865, that the staffs should be varied in form as well as colour.

The basic 'train staff' described above became widespread and most single lines were equipped with it in due course. The main problem with it was the reduced security afforded to the trains which did not carry the staff. There was always doubt as to whether the train really had had authority to proceed. The staff was therefore supplemented by a supply of printed paper tickets kept in two locked boxes, one at each end of the section. The boxes could only be opened by the staff which had a key attached to, or formed on, it. Where trains were required to proceed without the staff, the ticket box was unlocked with the staff, a ticket removed and completed by the signalman. This was handed to the driver as his authority to proceed. Since it was obviously possible to remove more than one ticket when the box was opened, the driver was still required to see the staff before proceeding. To aid recognition, in January 1883, it was resolved that the colour and shape of the train staff tickets should be identical to that of the train staff they supplemented. As a further precaution it was decided, in December of the same year, that in future the tickets would be printed on coloured card rather than using coloured inks to represent the colour of the staff. A train 'staff and ticket' box is shown in **Plate 13.2**.

Minor branches, particularly terminating ones, did not need this sophistication and the staff was used on its own.

Plate 13.1 *A pair of LNW ordinary train staffs. Both have standard (ordinary staff type) LNW Annett's Keys formed on the left hand end. The way in which the different configurations were achieved by forming the nibs on the keys in different positions will be apparent. The bottom staff has a configuration 'A' key and the top one a configuration 'B' key. These keys could be used to unlock the points at an intermediate siding or to unlock the ticket boxes (***Plate 13.2***) kept at each end of the section in order to allow staff and ticket working. To aid recognition and prevent the staffs being accidentally used for the wrong section the staffs for adjacent sections were generally made of different shapes (as are the examples shown here) and painted distinctive colours. The names of the two ends of the section were also marked on the staffs.*

Courtesy: Chasewater Light Railway

Plate 13.2 *A pair of LNW cast iron ticket boxes at Friden on the Cromford and High Peak line. The front one is of configuration 'A' and was for the section of line to Parsley Hay. The staff for this section is in the key lock and the inscription 'Parsley Hay' can be seen on the metal portion of the shaft. Turning the staff would release the lock and allow the lid of the box to be opened and a ticket withdrawn. To make absolutely sure there could be no mistake in the use of the boxes the wording 'Parsley Hay' also appears in the circular embossed device on the lid of the box. The box behind is of configuration 'B' and applied to the section of line from Friden to Longcliffe, the word 'Longcliffe' being cast on the lid.*

Photo: D J Powell collection

This developed into the familiar 'one engine in steam' principle of single line working.

The block system, whose application to double lines has already been described, had obvious attractions for use on single lines. Here the security of the block system in its absolute form should, in theory, prevent any chance of two trains occupying the same section of line. Thus some of the earliest installations of the 'Block' were on the single lines as is evident from **Figure 1.5**. Indeed, in a number of cases the 'Block' was used on the single lines before the train staff system. As time went on the two systems were combined and by the middle 1870's it had become normal practice to operate the busier single lines with both the block and the train staff and tickets. The combination of the two systems provided additional security since the 'Block' needles provided a visual reminder of the state of the line. Where trains were following each other on tickets the block was necessary to ensure that only one train occupied the section at one time and so prevent one train from running into the back of the preceding one. In November 1876, for example, authority was obtained to install the combined system on the Sirhowy line, 'It being desirable to work the line by combination of block and staff as is done on other portions of the LNWR.'

The block system was generally of the 'two-wire' pattern. This consisted of one block wire with single needle indicators at each end of the section (since there was only one line) both instruments being of the 'pegging' type. The second wire was used for the block bell circuit.

As with the double line block, a train could not be accepted unless the block needles were at normal and the commutator handles standing vertical (unless permissive working was allowed for following trains). A few sections of one-wire block were also installed but in June 1880 it was decided that in future the two-wire block would be used on all single lines where the block telegraph might be introduced. Several two-wire installations were authorised in December of that year:

- Northwich Branch (Sandbach–Middlewich–Northwich) two-wire block and speaking circuit at a cost of £180.
- Ebbw Vale to Ebbw Vale Junction at a cost of £53.
- Gower Road and Penclawdd at a cost of £87.

All three installations were to be in addition to the existing train staff working on these lines. As a result of the decision the LNW was able to standardise its single line procedures long before this was achieved on the double lines. A note in the LNW single line block regulations referred to the fact that operation of the block in no way absolved the signalmen of the responsibility to operate the train staff system correctly.

Things remained much the same for a number of years, although the drawbacks of the staff systems were well known. Perhaps the most serious problem was that from time to time the staff would be at one end of the section, while the next train would arrive at the other. Considerable delay could then occur while the staff was transferred or in waiting for a suitable train to take it through the section, but no better system was available. Relief came at last in 1878 when, following a request from the Caledonian Railway, Edward Tyer introduced his Electric Train Tablet System. A tablet (generally a flat metal disc) was adopted instead of the traditional staff, probably as much for the convenience of the mechanism as anything else. Here a number of tablets (rather than the single staff) were provided in two tablet machines one of which was placed at each end of the section. The tablets were electrically locked in the machine in a way which allowed only one tablet to be out of either of the two machines, at one time. When the tablet was put back into one of the instruments another could be obtained from either machine (in the first designs the tablet could not be returned to the machine it had been taken from). Generally there were no problems with the tablet being at the wrong end of the section and there were no tickets to bother about. A trial installation was put in on the line between Bedford and Sandy. The system was, however, not widely installed on the LNWR, although many railways adopted it as their standard (for example the Caledonian and Midland). The LNW Officers were most careful to ensure that diversity of operating practices did not occur unless absolutely necessary and it was felt that the tablet was so different from the traditional train staff that it could cause confusion and misunderstandings as to its purpose and use among the men. It is also probable that the arrangement by which the tablet could not be returned to the machine from which it had come (e.g. after shunting into the section – see **Figure 13.4**) was also considered to be a serious disadvantage.

The advantages of the system were recognised, and A M Thompson set about designing a system that would meet the LNWR's requirements. In 1888 he patented, jointly with F W Webb, the Electric Train Staff System. The Bedford line was again selected for the trial of the apparatus and a set of instruments were installed to cover the section between Bedford and Blunham. These proved successful and approval was given, in April 1888, to install another set of apparatus to cover the Blunham to Sandy section. This was followed in May by authority to install the system on the Banbury Branch. Interestingly, it was only at this point that the LNW wrote to the Board of Trade to request approval of the system – and then only for the Banbury Branch. The Inspecting Officers were invited to see the installation at Bedford.

An independent electrical expert, Major Cardew of the Electrical School, Chatham, examined the apparatus for the BoT and recommended a few minor modifications. These were carried out and the extension to Sandy was brought into use in November 1888. At the same time the LNW applied to the BoT for formal sanction for the Bedford to Sandy installations. Introduction of the ETS onto the Banbury Branch, planned for 1889, was delayed until September 1890 while a few minor problems with the equipment were sorted out.

Further adjustments were made to the design early in 1891 and approved by the BoT in June. The general introduction of the Electric Train Staff system then began in earnest, the busier sections of line generally being converted

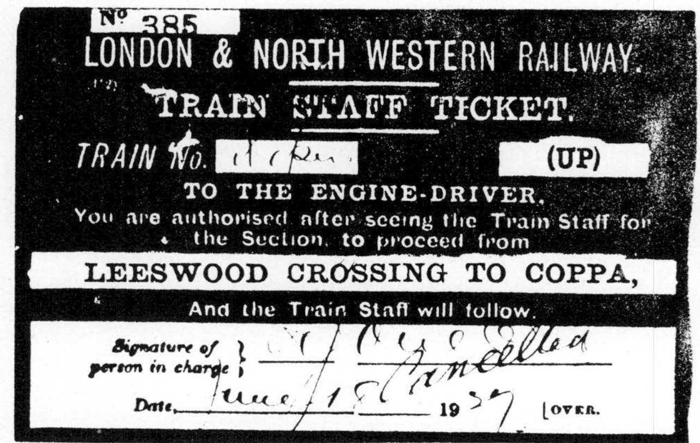
No 385
LONDON & NORTH WESTERN RAILWAY.
TRAIN STAFF TICKET.
TRAIN No. (UP)
TO THE ENGINE-DRIVER,
You are authorised after seeing the Train Staff for the Section, to proceed from
LEESWOOD CROSSING TO COPPA,
And the Train Staff will follow.
Signature of person in charge }
Date, 19 [OVER.

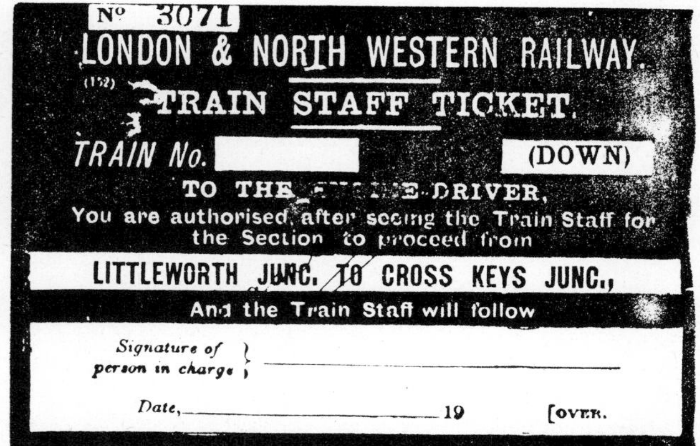
No 3071
LONDON & NORTH WESTERN RAILWAY.
TRAIN STAFF TICKET.
TRAIN No. (DOWN)
TO THE ENGINE-DRIVER,
You are authorised, after seeing the Train Staff for the Section to proceed from
LITTLEWORTH JUNC. TO CROSS KEYS JUNC.,
And the Train Staff will follow
Signature of person in charge }
Date, 19 [OVER.

Figure 13.2 *Examples of the Tickets used in the Train Staff and Ticket System of single line working. The ticket was filled in by the signalman (or person in charge) and handed to the driver, who handed it in on reaching the other end of the section. These examples were coloured black. In order to distinguish the tickets for adjacent sections some were coloured (for example dark red) while different shapes were also used. Instructions to the driver were printed on the back of the tickets. The tickets in this illustration were approximately 4½" by 3" in size.*

first (**Figure 13.4**).

The beginning of 1889 brought a letter from Edward Tyer complaining that the new apparatus infringed his own patent. Thompson considered that there was just enough in his claim to make it a doubtful policy to oppose it. Tyer had indicated that all he wished was for the Company to admit his claim and pay a nominal royalty of £2 per apparatus rather than get involved in litigation. Mr Thompson said that the LNWR effected a saving of about £60 on every set of apparatus they manufactured (against the cost of the Tyer equipment). It was, therefore, agreed to pay the £2 royalty during the continuance of the Tyer patent. Presumably payments ceased in 1892 when the patent expired.

Turning to the Electric Staff System itself, staff instruments are shown in **Plates 13.3** and **13.5** and some staffs in **Plate 13.4**. As can be seen the form of the ordinary train staff was retained. Rings were placed on the shaft to hold the staffs in the instruments and operate the electrical connections. A large number of staffs could be stored in each instrument so that there was no need for tickets. In addition to ensuring that only one staff could be removed from a pair of instruments controlling the same section of line it was also important to ensure that the staffs could only be placed in the correct instrument. There was always a danger that the signalman at a passing place, where there were two instruments, could inadvertantly place the staff in the wrong machine. Similarly there was the possibility of drivers proceeding into a single line section with the staff for another section, due to an error on his or the signalman's part. To prevent this, as far as possible, there were several different arrangements or 'configurations' of staff. A configuration 'A' staff would only fit into a configuration 'A' machine and could not be accepted into a machine of a different configuration. To assist the signalman and driver to recognise the staffs, each configuration had a distinctive colour and the names of the places at each end of the section were displayed on the end of each staff. The different configurations of staff were achieved by changing the position of the fifth ring on the staff. The instruments would only accept staffs with the correct combination of rings. The configurations and their colours in use on the LNWR were:—

Configuration A — Red
,, B — Blue
,, C — Green
,, D — Yellow

On a continuous single line each section would have a staff of different configuration to its neighbours (**Figure 13.3**). As can be seen, in theory it should be possible to operate the whole of the railway with just two configurations of staff, which are alternated. A third configuration was required occasionally, for example where there was a junction on the single line or where, due to piecemeal installation, a section to be converted adjoined an 'A' section at one end and a 'B' at the other. In practice the LNW's ETS installations were done in this form and 'C' and 'D' configuration sections were very rare. In 1911, for instance, there were just four such installations on the LNWR:—

Llandilo Bridge to Golden Grove — Green Staff
Blaenavon Furnace Sidings to Blaenavon — Green Staff
Beckermet Mines Junction to Beckermet — Yellow Staff
Cruckmeole Junction to Minsterley — Yellow Staff

Figure 13.4 lists some of the very first installations of the electric train staff system on the LNW together with the number of times a staff was removed from the instruments during a three month period. A point to notice is that in most cases the number of times a staff was taken out in one direction does not equal the number in the other. This rather disposes of the belief that the number of trains in each direction on most lines were equal. There can, of course, be many reasons for the differences. For instance, gradients could enforce short trains in one direction while several could be combined for return, similarly if loaded workings predominate in one direction and empties in the other. Light engines would, of course, normally work through coupled to convenient trains to reduce line occupation.

The LNW was not allowed to manufacture equipment for sale to other companies as this was regarded as unfair competition and was prevented by law. Indeed the LNW had itself been the cause of this situation when it incurred the wrath of the Private Locomotive Manufacturers in the early days of Webb by building some locomotives for the Lancashire and Yorkshire Railway. An injunction was

Plate 13.3 *The original form of Webb and Thompson electric train staff machine as manufactured by the Company for its own use. The instruments were made so that they could be floor mounted while the stem, or column was made of sufficient height to enable the operating portion to be at a convenient level to be observed and used by the signalman. The long support column of the instrument formed a convenient store for the staffs. As can be seen the capacity of the machine was limited to about 20 staffs while the use of a single column meant that only the top staff could be extracted. If the positions of the staffs were not changed from time to time some staffs could be used more often than others, depending on the traffic pattern, and this could result in differential wear. For most cases however this simple design was perfectly adequate.*

Photo: Courtesy The National Railway Museum

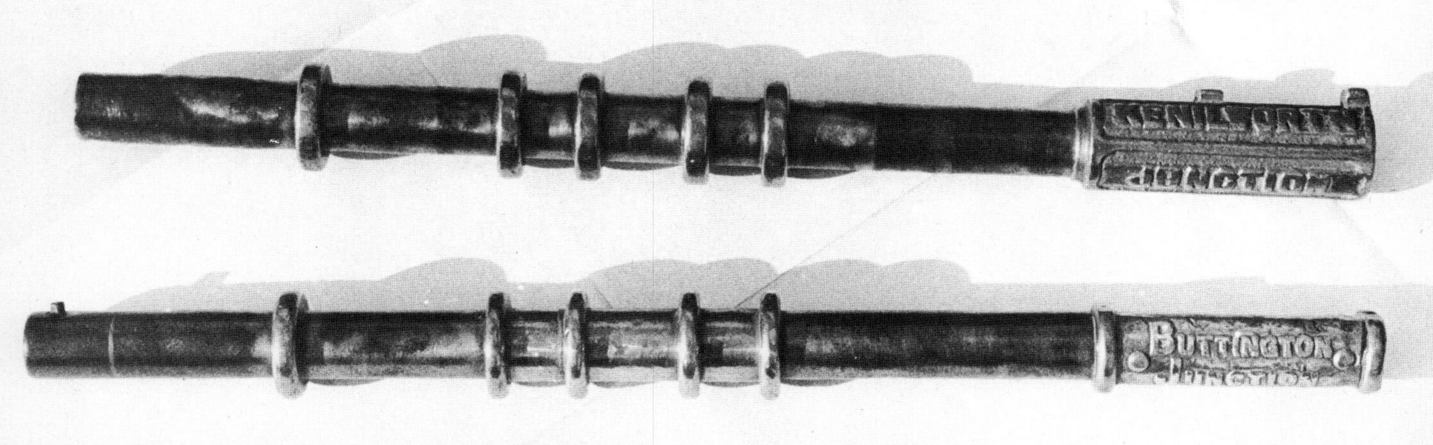

Plate 13.4 *A pair of large Webb and Thompson Electric Train Staffs. The top one applied to the section of line from Kenilworth Junction to Gibbet Hill cabin, and illustrates the normal style of lettering used on LNW staffs. The cast brass end incorporates an Annetts key (the two projections which engage in the lock can be seen at the top, above the word 'Kenilworth'). This was used to unlock the ground levers working a siding connection off the main running line in the section between the two cabins. The four rings in the centre of the staffs located them in the instruments while the position of the fifth, separate, ring on the left was varied to produce different configurations of staff. The staff at the bottom is from the Buttington Junction to Breidden section and no doubt the brass end was altered in 1928 when Middletown Station was renamed Breidden. On the left hand end of the staff is the stud used to secure the exchanging rings used on this section of line to speed up the process of staff exchanging (see* **Figure 13.6***).*

Courtesy M Christensen

placed on the railway companies preventing such practice and it is only in recent years that it has been lifted. A licence was granted to the Railway Signal Company (whose Managing Director, George Edwards had been the LNW's first Signal Superintendent) to manufacture the apparatus. The system was very popular and many thousands of instruments were sold both in Great Britain and overseas. **Figure 13.5** lists the companies known to be using the system in the British Isles in 1904.

The economical Annett's Key System (Chapter 11) was ideally suited for use on the single lines where traffic was sparse and cost savings were important. Since trains passing into the section for shunting outside station limits needed to have the section staff with them for protection, it was cumbersome to have to carry a separate Annett's Key to unlock the points. The LNW came up with a very neat arrangement whereby the end of the train staff could be formed into an Annett's Key where required (**Plates 13.4** and **11.20**), so avoiding the need for a separate key. This arrangement had been adopted for use with the ordinary train staff (in both the one engine in steam and staff and ticket variations) in the early 1880's and was quite extensively applied on the line. When the Electric Train Staff system was being designed it was realised that the Annett's Key system would have its uses on the lines to be operated by this method. Consideration was given to a design of staff which would accommodate a key in a neat and secure manner. The form of staff adopted was therefore quite large in order to allow the key to be formed on its end, and to make the staff strong enough to stand the additional handling it would receive. The length was also desirable to give the men enough of a hand-hold to operate the locks and to prevent it being 'mislaid' while shunting! This design criteria was another reason why the electric train tablet system was not thought suitable for adoption on the LNWR.

The electric train staff keys and locks were of the same form as the ordinary LNW Annett's Keys and locks (Chapter 11) and also came in three configurations, which were designated 'A', 'B' and 'C'. A key of any configuration could be formed on the end of a staff of any configuration. Thus a configuration 'A' staff could have keys of configurations 'A', 'B' or 'C'.

Although the ETS key was of the same design as the ordinary keys, the locks were cut differently so that a configuration 'A' staff key, for instance, would not operate an ordinary configuration 'A' lock. This produced a total of six different locks and ensured that accidents could not occur through the use of the wrong type of key. It also gave maximum flexibility since both types of lock could be used at the same location (**Plate 11.17**).

The keys used on the ordinary train staffs were of the same form, but again the keys were cut differently from the ordinary Annett's Keys and the electric staff keys. The

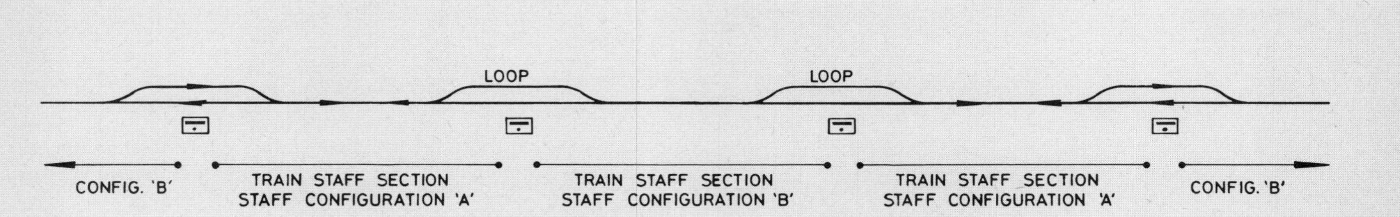

Figure 13.3 *Diagram showing how a series of adjacent train staff sections might be arranged using only 'A' and 'B' configuration staffs. Each staff station has only one instrument of each configuration so preventing a staff being placed in the wrong instrument.*

Figure 13.4 EARLY INSTALLATIONS OF THE WEBB AND THOMPSON ELECTRIC TRAIN STAFF

Location		Number of Instruments	Date Brought into use	Number of Times Staff Taken Out in 3 months to 31.12.1891		
				Down Line	Up Line	For Shunting
Bedford		1	18/3/1888	936	—	—
Blunham		2	18/3/1888 & 7/11/1888	943	938	40
Sandy		1	7/11/1888	—	934	—
Verney Junction	1	1	14/9/1890	853	—	—
Buckingham	1	2	"	760	858	5
Brackley	1	2	"	611	757	11
Cockley Brake	1	2	"	948	608	—
Banbury	1	1	"		957	1
Ebbw Vale	2	1	by 8/1890	—	978	28
Ebbw Vale Junction	2	1	"	1007	—	13
Rhymney Bridge	3	1	5/10/1890	1616	—	—
Rhymney	3	1	"	—	1494	5
Shackerstone Junction		1	4/5/1891	1091	—	13
Heather		2	"	1141	1131	105
Hugglescote		2	"	1442	1234	80
Charnwood Forest Jct.		1	"	—	1498	45
Cruckmeole Junction		1	7/6/1891	871	—	—
Westbury		2	"	870	867	4
Buttington		1	"	—	866	—
Sandbach		1	19/7/1891	1020	—	54
Middlewich		2	"	906	1068	238
Northwich		1	"	—	964	—
Gorseinon	4	1	"	1500	—	229
Gowerton	4	1	"	—	424	85
Killay	5	1	"	1548	—	50
Swansea Bay	5	1	"	—	1573	31
West Cheshire Junction		1	by 12/1891	—	1654	479
Holpool Gutter Bridge		1	"	1669	—	—
Knighton No. 2		1	18/10/1891	653	—	160
Llangunllo		2	"	836	824	10
Llanbister Road		1	"	—	652	41
Penybont Station		1	"	—	633	9
Penybont Junction		1	"	834	—	—

1. Authorised May 1888; 2. Authorised March 1890; 3. Authorised January 1890.
4. Line doubled 11/2/1894 and instruments recovered for re-use.
5. Line doubled 29/5/1892 and instruments recovered and re-used between Sirhowy and Nantybwch.

Figure 13.5 RAILWAYS IN BRITAIN USING ELECTRIC TRAIN STAFF 1904

Company	Company
Brecon and Merthyr	Taff Vale
Colne Valley and Halstead	North British
East and West Junction	Portpatrick and Wigtownshire
Furness	South Eastern and Chatham
Great Central	Burtonport
Great Western	Cork and Macroom
Hull, Barnsley and West Riding Junction	Cork Bandon and South Coast
Isle of Wight	Cork Blackrock and Passage
London and North Western	Donegal
London and South Western	Dublin Wicklow and Wexford
London, Brighton and South Coast	Great Northern (Ireland)
London, Tilbury and Southend	Great Southern and Western
Manchester and Milford	Londonderry and Lough Swilly
North Eastern	Letterkenny
North Staffordshire	Midland and Great Western (Ireland)
Rhymney	

usual three configurations, again designated 'A', 'B' and 'C', were available. In addition to their usual uses these keys were utilised to open the ticket boxes on the 'staff and ticket' lines. Needless to say a train having work to do at an intermediate siding locked by key on a staff and ticket line had to have the staff with it and could not travel with a ticket only.

The Board of Trade were very wary of the electric train tablet and electric train staff systems at first and for a number of years they required those companies who introduced them to sign undertakings that, if requested, they would return to the old train staff and ticket system. In fact both systems were found to suffer from remarkably few faults and there have been very few accidents as a result of their use. In fact those accidents which have occurred have been largely due to irregularities in working rather than fundamental flaws in the instruments.

In one or two isolated cases someone has discovered a means of fiddling the instruments and obtaining more than one staff or tablet. The signalman at Mitchelstown on the Great Southern and Western Railway, in Ireland, discovered that it was possible, by attempting to remove a staff 'very violently' and with some skill, to get more

Plate 13.5 *A two column electric train staff machine in use at Gibbet Hill (Gibbet Hill to Kenilworth section). This instrument was made by the Railway Signal Company who had the licence for manufacture of the system. The two column machines had the advantages of being able to store more staffs, so reducing the frequency at which the numbers of staffs had to be 'balanced' between the instruments at each end of the section, and also enabled the use of the staffs to be rotated in order to equalise wear.*

Photo: R P Hendry

than one staff out of the instruments. This practice came to light during an inspection in 1903, and was brought to the attention of the Board of Trade, who carried out a detailed investigation. After the investigator had been shown the 'technique' it was found possible to obtain additional staffs at a number of places by similar violent means. It was decided that the matter could not be left since the knowledge of how it was achieved could spread. The Railway Signal Company, who had supplied the instruments, devised a split armature arrangement which prevented additional staffs being obtained. The necessary modifications to the existing instruments cost only five shillings. A circular was, therefore, sent out by the Board of Trade in 1904 asking all those Companies using the electric train staff system to modify their instruments to prevent any such irregularity in the future. The LNW, in its usual independent way, modified its own instruments by a mechanical arrangement inside the instrument, rather than by fitting divided armatures.

The investigations on the Great Southern and Western Railway revealed the usual minor crop of other irregularities, such as the Stationmaster who did not know how to use the staff system installed at his station! It was also found that the train staff system was being maintained by the General Post Office, rather than the Railway Company, an arrangement which had not been sanctioned by the Board of Trade.

The irregular practices at Mitchelstown, fortunately, never caused an accident. Fiddling the electric train tablet instruments did cause a head on collision between two goods trains at Parkhall near Oswestry on the Cambrian Railways in 1918, both trains carrying the correct tablet.

The electric train staff system operated with a single line wire, and a separate block system was not necessary since security was provided by the staff instruments. However, the line wire currents were instantaneous rather than continuous. If there were level crossings in the section which were not staff stations and whose keepers required an indication of the state of the line, some positive indication had to be provided. In some cases bells or speaking instruments (later telephones) were provided while in others a 'block' circuit was maintained and operated from the staff stations in conjunction with the electric staff instruments. The needles were pegged at 'train on line' when a train entered section so that the indicators (**Plate 12.6**) at each crossing would indicate to the keeper that a train was approaching.

A number of Railway Companies did not like the electric train staff system because of the great bulk and weight of the instruments and staffs (a staff was 23 inches long and weighed 3 lb 9 oz). In 1906 the Railway Signal Company devised and introduced the miniature electric train staff by scaling down the size of both instruments and staffs (A 'new' staff being a mere 10¾ inches long and 11 ounces in weight). Again, the system was popular and many installations were made, the miniature electric train staff generally superseding the large staff for new installations. The LNW installed a few miniature instruments where new electric staff sections were required.

On the LNW staff exchanges were normally carried out by hand. However, devices to aid staff exchanges on the move were designed and used at a few places. For the large staffs, a metal hoop was provided. This clipped on to the end of the staff by means of a spring bayonet fitting which fastened onto a pin on the staff (**Plate 13.6**). A new type of exchanger hoop was designed for use with the miniature staff in 1920. This was also in the form of a ring, this time usually made of cane. The staff was kept in a leather pouch attached at one end to the ring. Appropriate receiving and delivering apparatus was placed near the signal cabin where necessary, to assist with staff exchanges. (See **Figure 13.6**.)

One or two special applications of the electric train staff system deserve brief mention. A curiosity of some single lines was the train staff station where trains could not pass. These were generally provided to shorten the sections and so allow trains, travelling in the same direction, to follow each other at closer intervals. Special instructions had to be issued to the signalmen to ensure that they did not accept two trains from opposite directions at the same time! For additional security, the LNW devised an electrical staff control box in 1908 to guard against such mistakes. This was connected to the two staff instruments at the station concerned. Holland Arms was an example of this type of installation.

Plate 13.6 *A large staff and exchanger hoop showing the spring bayonet fixing by which the exchanger was clipped onto the nib on the end of the staff.*

A problem with the electric train staff, tablet and token systems, was that all the staff stations had to be open whenever the line was open no matter what the traffic (which could be very sparse at night and on Sundays). This problem was eventually overcome by adopting long and short section working (**Figure 13.7**). By special, and quite elaborate, electrical and procedural arrangements it was possible to switch out an intermediate cabin (Goldington in the example), the 'short section' instruments being locked out of use while the 'long section' instruments were released to allow the linking of the two sections as a single long one (such as Willington to Bedford). The operating procedure is described in the figure. The design work for the Goldington installation, which appears to have been the first application of the idea, was carried out jointly by J T Roberts and Percy Hardman of the LNWR and W S Roberts of the Railway Signal Company in about 1923.

The introduction of the electric train staff system revolutionised the working of busy single line sections. Its application coupled with improved techniques of traffic management made it possible to move much larger volumes of traffic over a single line than had previously been the case. Thus the need to double busy single lines was considerably reduced and it is significant that the LNWR carried out practically no further doublings after the mid 1890's. Indeed they even singled a few sections of line (for example Seaton to Luffenham in July 1907).

Figure 13.6
ELECTRIC TRAIN STAFF EXCHANGING APPARATUS
LIST OF PLACES FITTED WITH APPARATUS IN 1911

Signal Cabin	*Apparatus*	*Line Applicable*
Cruckmeole Junction	R	Down
	D	Up
Westbury	R+D	Down
	R+D	Up
Middletown (Breidden)	R+D	Down
	R+D	Up
Buttington	D	Down

R = Receiving (picking up) apparatus;
D = Delivering (setting down) apparatus.

By 1931 the following lines had been equipped with receivers and deliverers.

Afonwen to Carnarvon (Large Staffs). Installed 1922.
Llanwrda to Llandovery No. 2 (Large staffs).
Builth Road No. 1 to Llandrindod Wells No. 2 (Miniature Staffs). Large Staff exchangers installed 1916. Sections converted to miniature staff 1917 and miniature staff exchangers installed.
West Kirby to Hooton (large staffs).

Plate 13.7 *A pair of miniature Electric Train Staffs ('M' Type) from the Coalport Branch. These had four fixed rings and the configuration was determined by the small collars placed against them. The Staff marked 'Hadley Junction' is of Configuration A and the one marked 'Stirchley' is of Configuration B.*
Courtesy J Pritchett

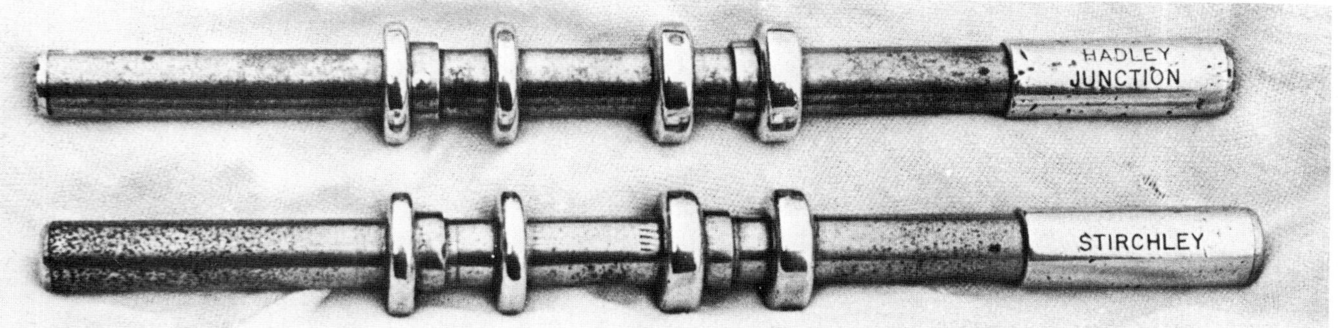

GOLDINGTON.

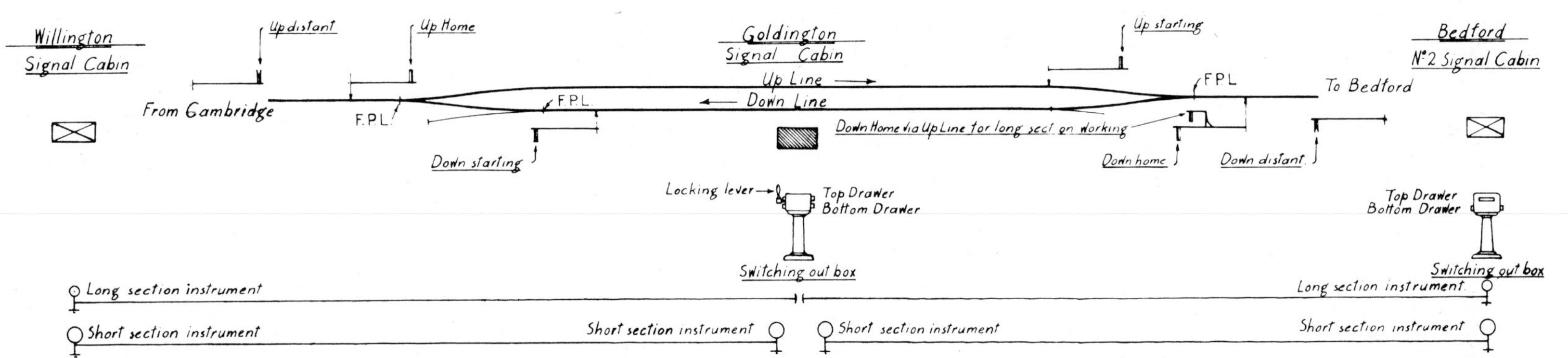

To Switch out Goldington Cabin

First set and lock the facing points at each end of the crossing station for the Up Line. Goldington then obtains permission from Willington to extract a short section staff and places it in the top drawer of the switching out box. The staff is then pressed halfway in drawer, releasing the locking lever which is then pulled right over. The staff is then pressed right home when the lever and staff become locked. This lever locks the points for the Up Line, the distant signals at danger & allows the Up home & starting signals and the down home bracket signal reading over the Up line, to be lowered. Bedford Nº2 then obtains permission from Goldington to extract a short section staff and places it in bottom drawer of his switching out box. This staff becomes locked when long section staff is withdrawn. Bedford Nº 2 can now obtain his long section staff on permission being given from Willington by Willington holding down long section instrument key. The staff is then placed in long section instrument enabling a train to be sent from either end of section Bedford Nº2 ~ Willington.

To Switch in Goldington Cabin

All signals at Goldington must first be put to danger. Bedford Nº2 obtains permission from Willington to extract a long section staff and places it in top drawer of the switching out box. This releases short section staff which is taken out of bottom drawer and placed in short section instrument. Goldington then obtains permission from Bedford Nº2 to extract a short section staff & places it in bottom drawer of his switching out box. This allows short section staff Willington ~ Goldington, in top drawer to be withdrawn halfway which then allows locking lever to be put back & both short section staffs to be withdrawn. The staffs are then placed in their respective instruments & short section working resumed.

Figure 13.7 *Switching out an Electric Train Staff Station. The diagram show the arrangement of the apparatus in the cabin concerned and in the two adjacent ones. The text below the diagram explains the operating procedure that had to be adopted in 'switching out' and changing from 'short section' to 'long section' working.*

Chapter Fourteen The 'Crewe' All Electric Signalling System

The LNWR was a pioneer in the use of power for signalling work and was considerably ahead of the times in adopting an all-electric form of signalling. Some of the most important centres were controlled by power signalling (such as Camden and Manchester London Road). The scope of the installations at Crewe, conceived at a time when power signalling was practically unknown and untried in Great Britain, shows a remarkable degree of confidence and forward thinking on the part of the Company while the scale and complexity of the work remained unequalled in pre-grouping days.

The rapid and continued expansion of traffic during the 1880's and 1890's brought with it increasing congestion and delays at major centres. Nowhere was this felt more acutely than at Crewe, the focal point of the Company's main line system. In 1894 attention was focused on the problem and schemes were prepared for enlarging the station and constructing independent goods lines which would avoid the station area and its flat junctions. Work on the goods lines and enlargements to the marshalling yards were put in hand soon after.

In the Signal Department, consideration was given to the signalling of the new lines and the enlarged station and yards. It was, of course, possible to provide mechanical signalling of the tried and tested LNW standard designs. Mechanical signalling at very large and complex layouts had disadvantages however. The signal cabins became very large (a 200 lever frame would take up nearly 100 feet) and involved the signalmen in the expenditure of much physical effort in walking up and down and pulling the levers. This distracted them from their primary functions of working the traffic safely and expeditiously. The space required by the rodding and wire runs from a large cabin could be quite considerable and it was often difficult to find sufficient space at busy and congested places. In addition, the rods and wires could be a hazard to staff working in the area.

These circumstances coupled with a knowledge that enlargements were likely to be required at other busy places in the future caused attention to be turned to possible alternatives to conventional mechanical operation. At this time there were no 'power' signalling schemes in use in Great Britain but one or two systems had been designed and installed abroad, notably in the United States. These generally used air or hydraulic power to operate the points and signals.

The Westinghouse Brake Company of America through its associated company, the Union Switch and Signal Company, had developed an electro-pneumatic system and was anxious to increase its sales by moving into markets such as Britain. At first they seem to have used McKenzie and Holland, the signalling contractors of Worcester, as agents or associates in the process of establishing themselves in this country. In the late 1890's Westinghouse set up its own British offshoot to carry out the work of adapting the designs for the British market. McKenzies were provided with copies of practically all the documents and drawings sent out by this Company during its first few years of existence and in about 1907 a Company titled The McKenzie, Holland and Westinghouse Power Signal Company was set up. During the 1890's discussions took place with the LNWR on the subject of the signalling for Crewe, and Westinghouse was asked to prepare preliminary proposals for a suitable power scheme.

As mentioned in Chapter 2, Thompson had a keen interest in electrical matters and had his own electrical staff at Crewe. In view of the LNW's strong 'do it yourself if at all possible' policy it is not surprising that design work for a power signalling system of its own was also put in hand. The basic elements of the design produced were patented jointly by F W Webb and A M Thompson in May, 1897. It is said, probably out of spite, that Webb insisted on an 'all-electric' design as he would have nothing to do with compressed air, after the poor showing of the Clark-Webb chain brake in comparison with George Westinghouse's air brake in the brake trials of 1875 and

Plate 14.1 *This photograph of the interior of Gresty Lane Cabin was taken in February 1899, only a few weeks after it had been brought into use. The form and construction of the two tier miniature lever frame mounted in sections or girders for 19 levers each (the three girders provided making a total of 57 levers) can readily be seen and studied. The system of lever numbering used in these frames is worthy of note, with odd numbers on the top row and even numbers on the bottom in the first section. The lever numbers were embossed on long brass strips fastened to the front of the quadrant plates. This system was only used on this, the prototype, frame and in subsequent installations individual brass numbers were fastened to the levers (***Plate 14.4***). This one was not altered, however, and the number strips remained in place until the frame was taken out of service (***Plate 14.2***). The cast metal name and pull plates for the levers have been mounted on the front of the block shelf (plates were not provided for the spare levers). The instruments on the block shelf are of interest. On the left is an LNW standard 'Fletcher' combined block instrument and bell: this is of the original pattern with short case, cast metal feet and with the bell tapper at high level. This was a permanent installation and it worked to the next cabin, Willaston, on the Shrewsbury line. The remaining two block instruments are of the older LNW/Tyers double needle type with separate tall case bells (compare with* **Plate 12.2***). These are temporary installations provided for working during the construction of the new goods lines and sorting sidings and the reconstruction of the passenger station. The centre one worked to the (old) South Junction cabin and the right hand one to Sorting Sidings North.* ▷

The photograph is also of interest in that all is not quite what it seems; the cabin had been opened to allow access to the construction sites for the new lines and consequently the layout is nowhere near complete. The name and pull plates on the block shelf have been provided for the final scheme, however, even though many of the points and signals concerned do not yet exist on the ground! It is just possible to see that this is so from the layout diagram (unfortunately partly obscured by one of the block instruments) which only shows the layout then in use. Those levers which were intended to control the missing functions are correctly painted white, as is most obvious in the case of levers 6, 8, 10, 12 and 14 in the photograph. The levers which were to be spare in the final scheme are, of course, also painted white. Those which were in use have their numbers painted on them in addition to the numbers mounted on the front of the frame.

Plate 14.2 *A close up detail of the frame at Gresty Lane taken in June 1977. This illustrates some of the changes that occurred over the intervening 78 years. The lever labels have been removed from the front of the block shelf to allow signal light indicators, repeaters and switches to be accommodated and they are now mounted on a board behind the top row of levers. A nine lever special section of frame has been added (numbered A to H and J) to enable additional points and signals to be worked from the frame, the work being carried out in 1913. In more recent years much of the space between the levers and the floor was used for additional electrical equipment, some of which is visible here. The difference in travel between the levers on top and bottom rows is also very clear in this photograph.*

their aftermath. Hydraulic systems suffered from problems in frosty weather and never seem to have been seriously considered for use in Britain.

The important consideration however was the fact that electric power would be freely available at Crewe from the Company's own power station. If this could be used to operate the signalling directly it would save the cost and complexity of the additional compressed air or hydraulic power plant that would otherwise be required for the signalling.

This was not the end of the matter however, as experiments with the Webb and Thompson system continued throughout 1897 and into 1898 as did consideration of outside manufacturers' products. In the summer of 1897 the Westinghouse Brake Company and Saxby and Farmer both loaned power systems (one electro-pneumatic and one hydraulic) for tests. These were still in progress at the end of the year and in January 1898 it was decided to purchase both plants at a total cost of £338 11*s* 2*d*. It was anticipated that the trials would need to be continued for some time and that the plants could probably be used to work some small station when the work was complete. In the event, this was never done.

Following discussions with the Board of Trade, provisional sanction was obtained, in May 1898, for an experimental installation of the Webb and Thompson power system at Gresty Lane Sidings, Crewe. Detailed design work for the installation was put in hand, Johnny Bean and Jack Smith carrying out most of the work.

Meanwhile, the Westinghouse Company had been successful in obtaining an order for their electro-pneumatic signalling system. This was for an installation at Granary Junction on the Great Eastern Railway (who were, of course, users of the Westinghouse Air Brake). Design and installation work for both schemes proceeded throughout most of 1898. At the LNWR Locomotive Committee meeting on the 13th of January, 1899 Thompson was able to report that the installation at Gresty Lane had been completed during the last four weeks. Although no actual opening date has so far been found it would seem likely that the cabin was brought into use as soon as it had been completed so as to allow access to the construction sites for the new marshalling yard and independent goods lines. The cabin at Granary Junction was brought into use on the 15th January, 1899. It would seem that Gresty Lane was, by a rather short head, the first power signalling installation in Great Britain.

The power frame at Granary followed American and European practice in that the functions were controlled by rotating handles rather than levers. The LNW policy of uniformity of practice was followed in designing the new 'Crewe' power frames and miniature levers were adopted as the means of control. The levers were mounted at 3½″ centres and to further reduce the space required, the levers were normally arranged in two rows or tiers, one above the other. The levers in the lower row were placed midway between those in the upper, producing a frame which effectively had levers at 1¾″ centres. The frame was therefore very compact and enabled the signalmen to concentrate their minds fully on the trains. The levers were placed at about waist level, for ease of working, and the frames were divided into sections with uprights at the end of each section or girder. As with the mechanical frames, the uprights occupied the position of one lever, in this case on the bottom row. Hence each section consisted of 19 levers, 10 on the top row and 9 on the bottom. Again the space was not numbered since, of course, it could not be used. In the case of the power frames this produced a curious effect. The first section in a frame commenced with lever 1 in the top tier, 2 in the bottom and so on, giving odd numbers on top and even numbers below. At the end of the girder, there was no lever in the bottom tier and so lever 20 was next to 19 on the top. Thus the second section of 19 levers had even numbers on the top tier, the third had odd numbers on top and so on (see **Plate 14.1**). Like the mechanical frames, the power frames were supported from ground level by the uprights which were also used to support the interlocking, switchgear and check-locks. The frame sections themselves were supported on cast iron legs bolted to the uprights at operating floor level.

The travel of levers in the top tier was approximately double that of those in the lower tier and they were generally used for points, the greater movement allowing the lever to be 'check-locked' in position at mid-stroke until the points were proved home. The bottom tier levers and the remainder of those in the top tier were used for signals. The interlocking and electrical equipment was placed below floor level to keep it out of the way of the signalmen.

Interlocking was mechanical, using the tappet principle. This was the first use of the system for a large installation on the LNW, a mechanical frame with tappet locking not being introduced until 1903, (although tappet locking had been used in the Key Interlocking frames for some time). The tappet locking trays or boxes were supported on brackets from the uprights and were placed just below operating floor level. The locking was rather smaller than that used on the mechanical tappet frame, since the levers were closer together and there was less mechanical strain. The number of locking trays provided varied to suit the installation. Below them were the electrical switches and check-locks.

When it had been decided to adopt power operated points and signals consideration was given to what form the latter should take. The desire of the LNW Officers to avoid diversity of practice and ensure that the signals seen by drivers presented a uniform appearance wherever they were has already been mentioned. This philosophy was adopted for the 'Crewe System' work, and standard LNW semaphore signal arms and rotating ground discs fitted with solenoid motors (**Plate 14.9**) were used. The motors pushed the arm or disc to the 'off' position when energised and these were balanced so that the arm or disc would return to danger when the current was switched off or in the event of a supply failure. The solenoid motors were normally mounted on the signal posts just below the arms in order to keep the connections simple and to reduce the weight of the push rod to be lifted. On disc signals, the motor operated directly on the balance lever.

Plate 14.3 *The interlocking, switch and check lock equipment at Gresty Lane in June 1977, much of the equipment being identical in pattern to that installed in this cabin in 1898/9. The cast iron uprights at the girder ends are an obvious feature and these are also used to mount the locking boxes and support frames for the electrical equipment. At the very top are the six tiers of tappet locking boxes and the tappet blades can be seen projecting from them. Below the mechanical locking on the down rods are the electrical switches which consisted of spring carbon contacts bearing on carbon blocks. Just below these are a row of check-locks, consisting of two electro-magnets, one operating with the points normal and the other with them in the reverse position. These worked on locks on the down rod to ensure that a lever movement could only be completed when the point had gone fully home (and was correctly bolted if necessary). At the bottom is another row of electric switches, note how the down rods are jointed between each function to allow easy and quick replacement of parts. In later frames the switches were all placed below the check locks to ensure that the switches could not be operated incorrectly as a result of faults or due to slack or play in the down rods.*

◁ **Plate 14.4** *This photograph of Crewe South Junction cabin was taken in July 1907, very shortly after its opening. The 247 lever frame (once again on girders for 19 levers each) has been divided into three sections to allow the signalmen access to the windows. The lever number plates are mounted on the levers themselves, (compare this with the system used at Gresty Lane,* **Plates 14.1** *and* **14.2**), *while the name and pull plates are mounted on the block shelf but are now engraved in a white material, like that used to name the block instrument functions, rather than being of cast brass. The Crewe Works plate can be seen on the end of the frame. The signal arm and lamp repeaters are placed on special shelves or stalks behind the levers since it would not be possible to see them easily if they were mounted in the usual place, on a window shelf. Twenty-one LNW combined block instruments are visible on the block shelf. These are of the later standard pattern with tall cases and tubular metal legs. The tapper keys, however, are still above the commutator. As was usual at large stations the majority of the instruments are of the single needle pattern. On the first section of the shelf are a number of indicators with three or four circular windows and a bell at the top. These were platform departure indicators and were worked by the platform Inspectors to inform the signalman when the train was ready to depart, the bell sounding to attract his attention. A 'flag' appeared in the appropriate window to indicate which route the train was to take. The descriptions on the four position indicators read, from the top; 'N.S. Line', 'Stafford Fast', 'Stafford Slow' and 'Salop', the last three indicators having the 'N.S. Line' indication omitted. A number of Fletcher clock-type train describers are also visible, two on the third shelf being extremely large! Note the lack of floor covering, the arrangement of the internal staircase, the electric lighting, and the tie rods which give rigidity to the cabin structure.*

Photo: Courtesy National Railway Museum

Plate 14.5 *A view of the frame in Crewe Station A Cabin taken in June 1977. This is an 'overhead' electric frame and is of the original type. These frames had a single row of levers and were produced in sections for 13 levers each: this cabin has two girders, producing a total of 26 levers. The ends and lower portions of the frame are boxed in which gives the whole thing a much neater appearance. This was done to protect the electrical equipment, much of which was mounted above floor level, from damage (and, conversely, to protect the signalmen from electric shocks). The lever name and pull plates are still mounted on the front of the block shelf in this cabin. The devices mounted under the shelf are standard BR (LMR) indicators which show the positions of the points and the aspects being displayed by the signals. The 'bulge' in the frame, behind the levers, was provided to accommodate the check-locks.*

Plate 14.6 *A view of the back of the frame at Crewe Station 'A'. At the bottom is the top tappet locking box mounted just above floor level, and above it are the electric switches. The check locks are out of the picture, above the switches, and are mounted in the bulge in the frame behind the levers (***Plate 14.5***). The arrangement of the centre upright should be clear and a Crewe Works plate is again provided on the end of the frame.*

Figure 14.1 (Opposite) *A drawing of the second type of overhead power frame as used at Manchester London Road. The locking boxes were all below floor level, and only those necessary for the particular installation were fitted. The check locks and switches were in the space between the levers and the operating floor.*

Plate 14.7 (Opposite) *The interior of Manchester London Road No. 2 Cabin, photographed in 1957. This was an overhead cabin and the frame is again of the overhead type. This time it is of the second design as illustrated in* **Figure 14.1.** *These frames also came in girders for 13 levers each and again the ends and lower portions are covered in to protect the equipment. Like the frame at Crewe South Junction this one has been divided into sections to leave passageways for the signalmen to gain access to the windows. Like the overhead mechanical cabins these gaps also allow for the girder structure which supports the cabin. Provision for the lever name and pull plates has been incorporated in the design of the frame and these are mounted in front of the levers they apply to. An interesting selection of instruments are visible on the block shelf.*

Photo: Dr I W Scrimgeour

It should be remembered that daylight colour light signals were not developed in this country until the 1920's.

The installation at Gresty Lane worked on 110 Volts D.C., and current was provided by the Company's own power station (which was situated in Pedley Street). The signal motors required a 'flash' current of about 15 amps (rather less for a ground disc signal) for a fraction of a second to reverse the signal arm. When this reached the 'off' position a switch operated and reduced the current to about 2 amps, which was sufficient to hold the arm in the 'off' position. Despite this it was said that after an arm had been 'off' for a considerable period of time (e.g. where a cabin was 'switched-out') the solenoid motor assembly became hot enough to fry an egg!

The points too were operated by magnet motors, separate normal and reverse magnets being provided side by side on one side of the points in the motor assembly. The magnets were of solid cast steel. A momentary current of between 20 and 30 amps was required to shift the switches, and as can be imagined, operation was very swift. A separate magnet and detector lock was provided to lock the switches in position.

The experiments at Gresty Lane were most successful and it was decided to adopt the system as standard for power signalling work on the L&NWR. Additional installations were, therefore, made in connection with the new goods lines and sorting sidings at Crewe in 1901. The volume of equipment required for this scheme was too large for the LNW to manufacture itself in the time available and some of the outdoor equipment was provided by the Railway Signal Company.

Following experience with the installations at Crewe some redesign work was done on both the indoor and outdoor apparatus. The positions of the check-locks and switches on the cabin apparatus were interchanged so that the former came above the latter, thus reducing the risk of faulty operation.

In order to reduce the high operating currents the operating voltage was increased to a nominal 220 volts. The use of magnet point motors was also discontinued and a new system of point operation introduced. A 800 r.p.m. motor was used to drive the switches via a gear, clutch and cam assembly. An operating current of about 15 amps was required and the motor could be arranged to work the

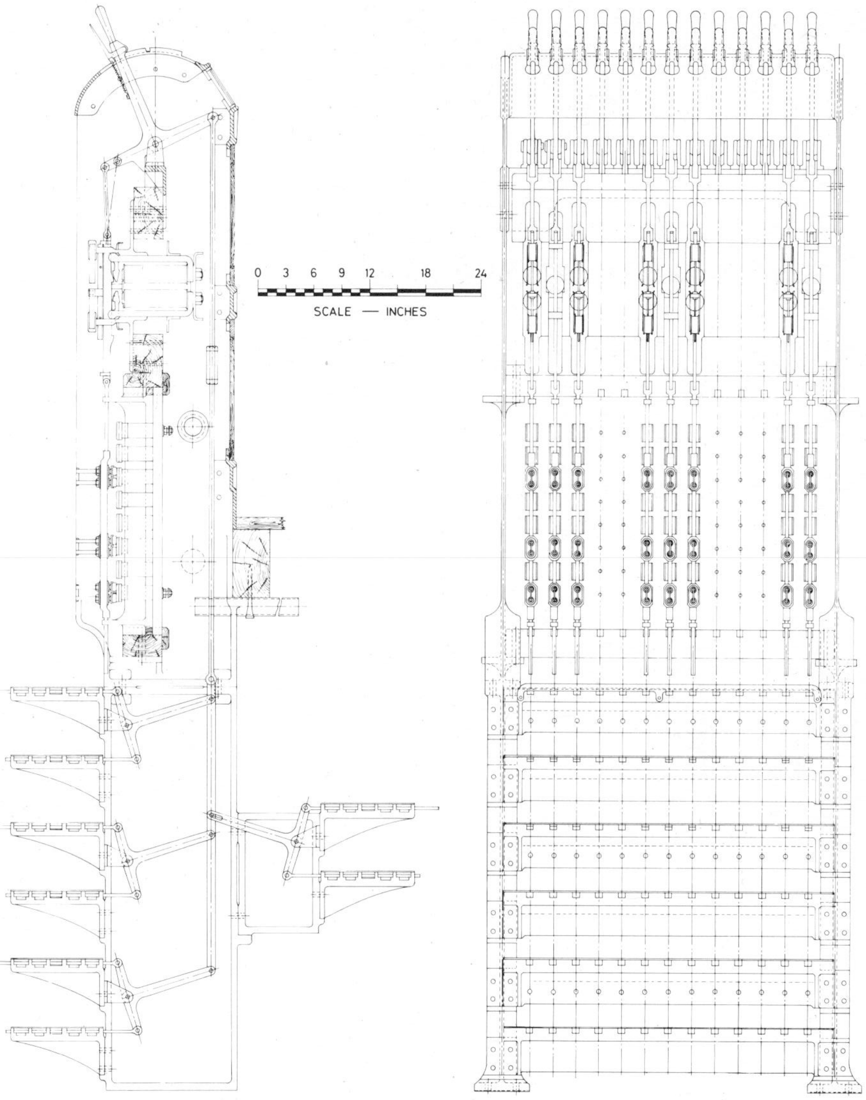

0 3 6 9 12 18 24
SCALE — INCHES

ELECTRIC POINT AND SIGNAL APPARATUS — 220 VOLTS
OVERHEAD TYPE — WEBB AND THOMPSON'S PATENT

DRAWN BY R. D. FOSTER June 1980

locking bar and bolt if required. A 110 volt version of the motor was also manufactured (with a correspondingly higher operating current) and in later years gradually replaced the original magnet motors fitted to the Crewe Yard points, the motors on the lines used by passenger trains being changed first. The last magnets were not removed until the mid 1920's when, as a result of relaying, it was found that the new standard points were too heavy for the motors. Some complaints were received from the signalmen about the longer operating time of the new motors!

In an attempt to eliminate, as far as possible, the risk of injury to shunters and other staff Thompson insisted that the covers of the point motors, detector boxes and other apparatus were made to stand no higher than the level of the top of the sleepers. This was not strictly necessary since the majority of the layouts controlled by the Crewe System cabins were electrically lit at night. The wiring was also at ground level, the single core heavy cables running in trunking which was filled with bitumen compound.

The system lived up to its description of 'all-electric' for all the signals were electrically lit. Switches were provided in the cabins to allow the signalmen to switch on the lights when this was necessary. Because of the blue tint of the 'green' spectacles used to colour correct the light from oil signal lamps, these electrically lit signals gave a noticeably blue-green light at night when the arm was in the 'off' position.

Placing the locking and switchgear below floor level had the advantages that it allowed more working space in the cabin while the equipment was out of the way of the signalmen and could be maintained, repaired and altered without obstructing the operating floor. However, it was realised that there would be problems if an overhead cabin was required. A special frame was, therefore, devised for use in this situation, with the locking, contacts and check-locks mounted above floor level behind the frame itself. (**Plates 14.5 and 6.**) Chapter 11 described how the same problem was overcome for the mechanical frames. Because the electrical equipment and interlocking was above the operating floor the front and ends of the frame were covered in, as protection for the signalmen, to keep dust and dirt out and against accidental damage to the equipment. Because of the confined space available only a single row of levers was provided. These were spaced at 2½" centres and the frames were constructed in units of 13 levers. These girders were the same length as those of the ordinary type.

In connection with the widening of the line between Euston and Camden approval was obtained, in March 1904, for the installation of power signalling at a cost of £29,500. In addition, it was decided to take the opportunity to install electric lighting in the area and to replace the gas lighting at Euston with electric light. A power station was to be erected at Camden to supply the power and the existing electric lighting in the Euston Hotel and Offices was to be connected to it instead of taking power from the Borough of St. Pancras. The estimated cost of the electric lighting work was put at £38,000. Four new all electric signal cabins were provided in 1905 and these worked on the new 220 volt system. Two of the cabins were of the overhead type and were fitted with overhead type lever frames. Further installations of the system followed at Crewe in 1906/7.

The largest cabins fitted with all-electric frames were Crewe North and South Junctions which had over 500 levers between them. At the conclusion of the enlargements at Crewe in 1907 there were nine cabins working on the Webb and Thompson system, having a total of over 1,000 levers (see **Figure 14.2**). Because of its many associations with Crewe, the system became known as the 'Crewe System of All-Electric Signalling'.

Plate 14.8 *An LNW solenoid signal motor. The solenoid itself is in the circular housing. When energised, the armature raised the push rod on the left and pushed the arm to 'off'. The balance weight assisted this action. The arm, balance weight and motor were balanced to ensure that the arm would return to danger when the power failed or was switched off. Below the balance lever is the switch and contact box.*

Photo: Courtesy National Railway Museum

Following experience with the overhead type power frames at Euston, Camden and Crewe these too were redesigned (**Figure 14.1**) so that all the functions could be operated by a common down-rod as with the ordinary frames.

At Manchester London Road, powers were obtained to widen the line from Ardwick Junction to the station in 1898. The space available on the viaduct approaches to the station for signal cabins and rodding and wire runs was very limited and so power signalling was adopted in the station area (both London Road and Mayfield) and it was not surprising, therefore, that the 'Crewe System' was used (although a mechanical cabin was provided at Ardwick Junction). Power was obtained from the existing LNW power station. Nos. 1 and 2 cabins were of the overhead type with the new 'overhead' type power frames and were brought into use in 1908 and 1909 respectively (**Plate 14.7**). A third cabin, No. 3, with 26 levers was placed under the station roof to supervise movements within the platform area.

The enlargements at Manchester were carried out on the north side of the line and considerable re-arrangement of the Great Central Railway approaches was required, necessitating resignalling of their lines. The GC adopted their usual system of low-pressure pneumatic signalling for this work and an overhead cabin was provided, at the end of one of their platforms, to operate it. This signalling was carried out by the British Pneumatic Railway Signal Company at the LNW's cost (£5,650 plus £228 for the signal gantry at the station throat). This was a nice reversal of the events at Rugby some 14 years earlier! (**Plate 6.9.**) The new cabin was brought into use in October 1909. The signal gantry was built to the standard LNW iron gantry design by the GC's contractors.

Plate 14.9 *A power operated semaphore signal and ground disc at Manchester Mayfield photographed in December 1959. The arrangement of the arm, push rod and motor should be clear. The motors were normally mounted near the signal arm in order to keep the weight of push rod, which had to be lifted by the solenoid, to a minimum. The photograph also shows the modified form of contact box used in later installations and just below this is a more modern stencil type indicator. This signal was clearly made up of second hand parts, the post having been cut down from a taller one and fixing holes for a front ladder can be seen. The arm still contains the fixing holes for the distinguishing ring but has been shortened for its new duty. The rotating disc at the foot of the signal post is also electrically worked, the solenoid motor being mounted on the base plate of the disc and tucked under the head. Some further examples of electrically operated discs can be seen in* **Plate 7.4.**

Photo: G H Platt

Plate 14.10 *A combined home and lower distant signal at Manchester London Road photographed in March 1953. This illustrates the arrangement of arms, push rods and motors used on this type of signal, note also the ladder at the front of the post. The Rule 55 diamond indicates, in this case, the presence of a track circuit which was, of course, a later addition. The LNW did not use this symbol nor were there any track circuits here when the signalling was commissioned in 1909 (Chapter 12). The photograph also illustrates very clearly just how dirty signals could become in busy city areas.*

Photo: M N Bland

The presence of two different systems of power operated signals side by side at Manchester led to some curiosities where the signals controlled movements between or across the two lines. For instance, the low pressure pneumatic signal at the Manchester end of the down platform at Ardwick was a starting signal with a lower distant arm. It was worked by the GC's Ardwick No. 1 cabin and was slotted mechanically by the LNW cabin at Ardwick Junction to protect the Lancashire and Yorkshire's line which crossed the GC metals to join the LNW line to London Road. The distant arm was worked from London Road No. 1 'Crewe System' cabin and was fitted with the usual solenoid motor. This, of course, had to be slotted by the top arm – mechanically and pneumatically!

The outdoor signalling in the power operated areas was laid out, in all cases, along conventional lines. The signals on the ground and arrangement of levers in the cabin were much the same as would be found in a mechanical installation. Separate levers were provided for each signalled route, no attempt being made to use one lever for a series of diverging routes and allow the electrical equipment to 'select' which signal arm came off from the lie of the points. Facing points and facing point locks were worked by a single lever however. Track circuiting was not provided (see Chapter 12).

In addition to the complete power installations, a number of motor worked signals were installed at Euston to reduce the danger to staff from signal wires in that busy and congested area (see also **Plate 10.9**).

In connection with the construction of the 'Watford New Line' the junctions at the north end of Camden were completely remodelled to eliminate conflicting movements

Plate 14.11 *A gantry of power operated signals at Euston Carriage Sidings (No. 4 Cabin). Since it only spanned two tracks this is an all timber type and as was usual on the LNW it is of modified bracket signal type (Chapter 6). Note the arrangement of the doll ladders and the guy wires. At the foot of each post is an electrically operated disc signal.*

Photo: British Rail

by the provision of a series of flying and burrowing junctions. It was realised that the existing Camden No. 2 cabin would be in the way of the altered lines and plans were drawn up to construct a new and larger all-electric cabin to replace it and to work the new layout. However, before this could be constructed the old cabin got on fire on the morning of the 16th of January 1920 and was completely burnt out. Although the cause was not positively identified, it was presumed to be due to some electrical fault. The replacement value of the cabin and its contents was put at £2,245 although, as it was soon to be taken down, its actual value was only that of the materials which could be recovered from it — some £200. A temporary cabin and signals were provided and brought into use later the same day. A more substantial temporary cabin, capable of working the traffic until the new permanent installation could be got ready was brought into use on the 24th of January.

The new cabin was brought into use in July 1920 and contained a 114 lever frame. By this time the LNW was using track circuiting on a quite extensive scale and a large part of the layout was track circuited right from the start. This was, of course, necessary in the case of the 'electric lines' since they were largely in tunnel and could not be seen by the signalmen. An 'illuminated' diagram was provided in 1922 to assist the signalmen, one of the first such installations on the LNWR.

The long tunnels on the electric lines also caused problems in providing suitable signals. Colour light signals were designed and installed in 1922 at a number of locations in the Camden and Loudoun Road (South Hampstead) areas, these being the first such installations on the LNWR.

It has been said that the 'Crewe System' was rather prone to fire and this is not particularly surprising when one considers the high currents used and the poor qualities of the insulation materials then available, particularly when exposed to damp. In fact, apart from the incident mentioned above, the problem was not serious and was largely confined to fires in the cable runs on the 220 Volt installations (it will be noted that all the original installations at Crewe were in all-wood cabins). These were caused by breakdowns in insulation through damp, or by rats gnawing through the lead sheathing of the cables. For some reason incidents occurred at Crewe South Junction more frequently than at any other cabin. Fireproofing work was carried out on most of the 220 volt installations in the early 1920's, after which no further trouble was experienced. The work included rearranging the cable runs and termination arrangements.

Because of the scale of the installations at Crewe it was decided that it would be advisable to appoint someone who could devote his whole time to the care and maintenance of the installations. Sub Inspector Joe White was chosen for this duty and his wage was increased from 54/- to 60/- per

Plate 14.12 *A power operated gantry signal at the north end of Crewe Station. This controlled departures from Platform 2 and Bay 8 (later numbered 2A). The four arms slung under the gantry (to give sight under the station canopy) apply to Platform 2 (the track below them under the gantry), and read (left to right) to Chester, Liverpool (Slow Line), Liverpool (Fast Line) and Manchester. These arms are bridge arms of the S1513 (***Figure 7.6***) type suspended on metal brackets from the underside of the gantry; note how dirty the arm situated above the track has become. The arm on the left hand post refers to the Bay 8 line, which is the track to the left. Since this is only a subsidiary line only one signal arm has been provided even though there are the same four routes available as from Platform 2. To provide information on which route is set there is a route indicator mounted on the gantry above the signal. This is of an all electric type devised by A M Thompson, and consisted of a series of vertical slats or vanes which could be rotated. The vanes were of metal pressed into a flattened 'U' shape to form three sides of a square. With the open end exposed (painted vermilion) no indication was displayed (the position shown in the photograph). A solenoid motor, mounted behind the vanes, could rotate them through 90° to present one side of the vanes to a driver. The exposed sides of the vanes were painted so that the pattern of colours produced a large figure or letter to denote what route was set. In a similar way other solenoid motors could rotate the vanes by 180° or 270° to produce a total of three indications plus the 'no indication' position. If more indications than this were required, or more than one number was necessary, two indicators were mounted side by side as has been done with the signal in this photograph. Separate levers were provided in the cabin for each route. The indicator illustrated here displayed the indications C, LS, LF, and M to represent 'To Chester', 'Liverpool Slow', 'Liverpool Fast' and 'Manchester' respectively. Note the stay rods attached to the right end of this gantry and the facing point locking bar mounted partly on the point switches to allow maximum use of the platform line.*

Photo: J P Richards

week on his appointment in April, 1913. Joe acquired a thorough knowledge of the installations and could usually locate the cause of a failure within a few minutes.

As already mentioned, the LNW was not allowed to sell equipment to other Companies. A licence was, therefore, given to Saxby and Farmer to market the Crewe Power Signalling system. They did not seem particularly interested however, and the licence was soon transferred to the Railway Signal Company. In the event only one scheme was sold, an installation being made at Severus Junction, York, on the North Eastern Railway, in 1903. The lack of orders was not necessarily a condemnation of the system, but more a product of the times. Most installations were fairly new at that time and there was little incentive for spending money on fancy new power systems when the existing arrangements were adequate and in good condition.

The market for any sort of power system was thus very small. In addition, everyone was anxious to promote their own pet systems and avoid using anyone else's!

It will be noted that only one new installation was made after 1909 (Camden No. 2) and this was made necessary by the need to remodel the layout there, to accommodate the 'new line' junctions. The reasons for this were similar to those mentioned above. Power signalling was only justified when major remodelling or enlargements were carried out at large centres. By 1910 the LNWR had completed most of this work.

Because of the strategic importance of the centres controlled by 'Crewe System' signal cabins, and the need to provide spares to help with the maintenance of the remaining installations, the frames at Salop Goods junction and Sorting Sidings South were removed just before the outbreak of the Second World War and kept as spares in case of bomb damage to the other installations. Standard LMS mechanical frames were put in the two cabins which had to be doubled in length to accommodate them. The huge installations at Crewe North and South Junctions were replaced by 'bomb-proof' concrete structures, fitted with new Westinghouse miniature lever frames, a couple of years later. The overhead cabin at Camden No. 1 was replaced by an LMS 'ARP' brick and concrete cabin in 1940 which was fitted with one of the spare two-tier all electric lever frames from Crewe. At Manchester, the three cabins disappeared in 1960 when the London Road Power Box was brought into use as one of the first stages in the Euston–Manchester and Liverpool electrification and modernisation. Basford Hall marshalling yard at Crewe was modernised in 1961 and the cabins there replaced with power panels. By 1970, only two cabins remained in use, Crewe Station A and Gresty Lane.

Of the frames made spare during the war, part of one of the station cabin frames was reconditioned and installed in a temporary cabin at Manchester Mayfield in 1960 in connection with the stagework of rebuilding and resignalling the London Road Station area.

Power signalling schemes, in whatever form, generally have a shorter useful life than mechanical equipment, before repair work becomes uneconomic. The LNW estimated the life of the Crewe System frames at 90 years, while their mechanical frames were considered to have 'infinite' life. These long lives were possible because the frames were designed to allow worn or damaged parts to be replaced easily. In the event, the longest lived frame was, curiously enough, the 'experimental' one at Gresty Lane with a service life of just over 80 years. It has now been removed to the National Railway Museum for preservation. The signal cabin remains in use, equipped with a modern panel.

Although Westinghouse were not able to supply power signalling equipment to the LNWR as they had hoped, they did in fact benefit indirectly from the resignalling work. One of the Westinghouse Companies were the contractors for supplying the equipment for the power station at Camden which, among other duties, provided the power required to work the new signalling.

Figure 14.2 'CREWE SYSTEM' ALL-ELECTRIC SIGNALLING INSTALLATIONS

Signal Cabin	*Number of Levers*	*Girders*	*Frame Type*	*Date Opened*	*Remarks*
Crewe area Installations					
Gresty Lane (No. 1)	57	3x19	2T	1-1899	First installation in use.
Salop Goods Junction	57	3x19	2T	3-1901	Frames removed at beginning of World War 2.
Sorting Sidings South	76	4x19	2T	6-1901	Both timber cabins.
Sorting Sidings Middle	152	4x19 4x19	2T	8-1901	Two 76 lever frames arranged in the windows to enable the signalmen to work between them.
Sorting Sidings North	95	5x19	2T	10-1901	
Crewe North Junction	266	14x19	2T	11-1906	Frame divided into two to allow space where the 'Spider bridge' passed through the cabin structure.
Crewe Station 'A'	26	2x13	O/H	2-1907	Flat roofed cabin.
Crewe Station 'B'	26	2x13	O/H	2-1907	Flat roofed cabin.
Crewe South Junction	247	13x19	2T	6-1907	Frame divided for access to windows.
Other LNW Installations					
Euston No. 3	52	4x13	O/H	5-1905	First overhead frame.
Euston No. 4	76	4x19	2T	5-1905	Later Euston Carriage Sidings.
Camden No. 1	52	4x13	O/H	7-1905	Replaced by ARP cabin (see below).
Camden No. 2	95	5x19	2T	8-1905	Replaced by new cabin (see below).
London Road No. 1	117	9x13	O/H	12-1908	Frame divided to allow access to windows.
London Road No. 2	143	11x13	O/H	11-1909	" " "
London Road No. 3	26	2x13	O/H	11-1909	Flat roofed cabin.
Camden No. 2	114	6x19	2T	7-1920	For new junctions.
Miscellaneous Installations					
Severus Junction, York	133	7x19	O/H	1903	North Eastern Railway. Manufactured by the Railway Signal Company.
Camden No. 1	57	3x19	2T	6-1940	Second hand frame from Crewe. LMS 'ARP' Cabin.
Manchester, Mayfield	38	2x19	2T	4-1960	Second hand frame from Crewe, temporary installation, closed 9-1960.

2T = Two tier ordinary type frame; O/H = Overhead type frame.

Chapter Fifteen — Miscellaneous Equipment

This chapter looks at some of the items of signalling equipment which cannot conveniently be dealt with under the headings used in the remainder of the book. The items covered are, therefore, distinctly miscellaneous and are described separately there being no common origins and development which can be traced in a general text.

TURNTABLE BOLT (FIGURE 15.1)

Drawing No. 1 in the Signal Department's 'S' series covered a bolt lock for turntables and this seems an appropriate place to start this chapter.

Where the movement of a turntable (which could be for locomotives or more commonly for wagons in goods yards) could cause a running line to be fouled it was necessary for the signalman to have control over its movements to ensure the safe passage of traffic. The simplest method of achieving this was to provide a mechanical bolt which would hold it in position. This would usually be connected to a lever in the cabin where it could be interlocked with the running line signals. When it was safe to use the turntable, the lever could be pulled to withdraw the bolt and allow it to be used. If a train needed to pass on the adjacent line the turntable had to be returned to the normal position, it then being held in place by reversing the bolt lever. Many LNW goods yards had wagon turntables and an appreciable number of these fouled running lines when used. Examples occurred at Brandon and Thrapston (see Chapter 16). Other uses for the bolt were to hold swing bridges and goods yard cranes in position.

POINT RODDING

Where points were worked from a signal cabin they were normally worked mechanically by rodding. The majority of railway companies used round rods. These could either be solid or a hollow tube (most commonly gas piping). The former was quite expensive and heavy while the latter could suffer from undetected internal corrosion. A problem common to both was the amount of blacksmith's work required to make joints and attach fittings to the rodding. F W Webb was aware of these shortcomings and put his mind to designing an alternative for use on the LNWR. In 1874 he patented his design of 'channel' rodding. This was a steel 'U' (channel) shaped section (used inverted to prevent water being trapped in it). It could easily be bolted together by means of fishplates, and standard fittings could be bolted on without specialist work. (**Figure 15.3**.) The rodding was manufactured and rolled in the steel works at Crewe and was turned out in large quantities. In 1903, for instance, it was being produced at the rate of 6,000 yards per month. It was cut into 18 ft lengths for transport and handling. The rods ran in roller guides which were normally placed at nine foot intervals.

At first the rodding, roller guides, and fittings were painted. After manufacture, the rodding was treated before leaving the works by heating and dipping in oil. When installed it was painted with red lead. For subsequent applications the recommended treatment was one coat of red lead followed by a coat of red oxide. Galvanized rodding was introduced in October 1888 and from July 1889 all the material turned out from Crewe was of this type. Generally this galvanized rodding was not painted

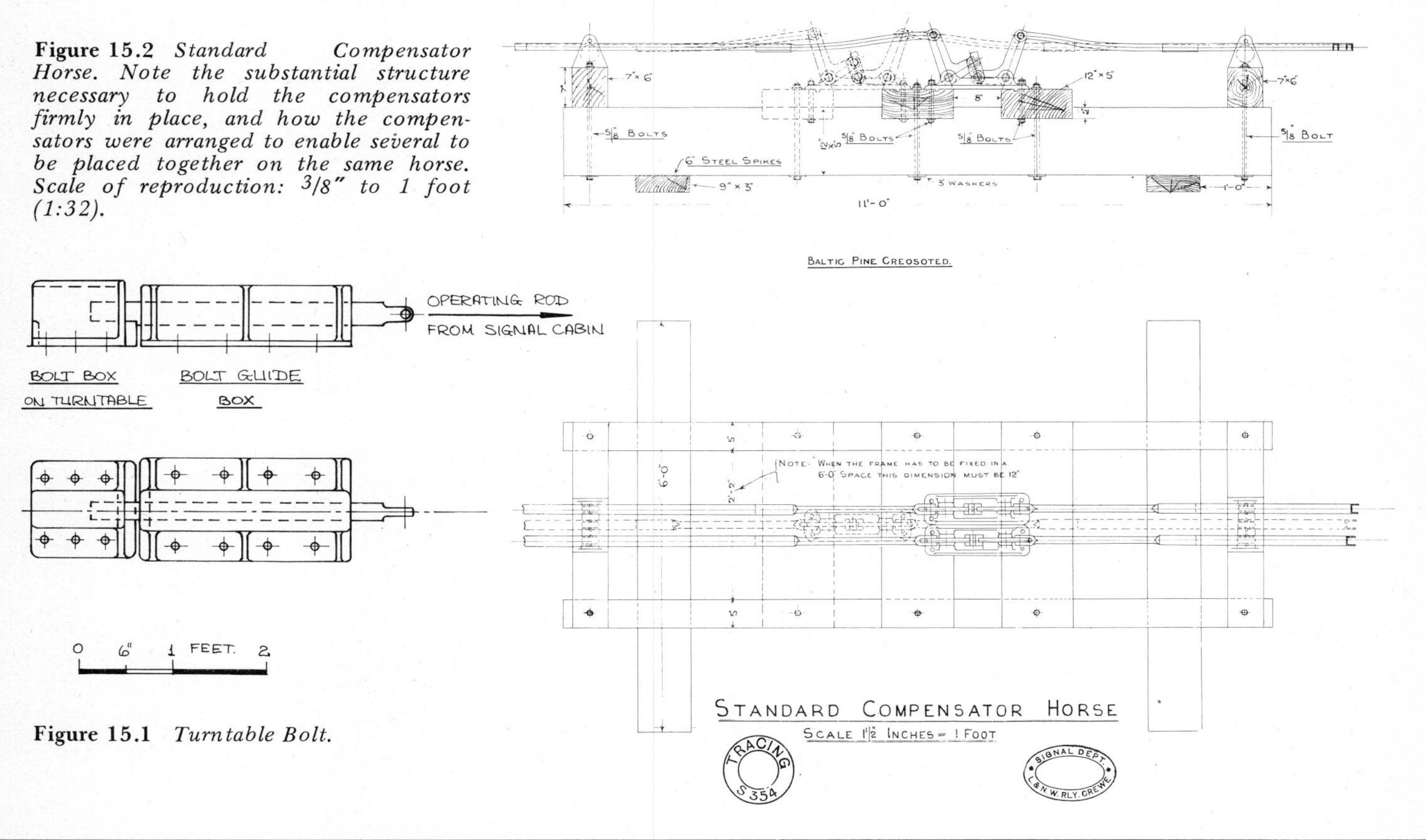

Figure 15.2 *Standard Compensator Horse. Note the substantial structure necessary to hold the compensators firmly in place, and how the compensators were arranged to enable several to be placed together on the same horse. Scale of reproduction: 3/8" to 1 foot (1:32).*

Figure 15.1 *Turntable Bolt.*

until the galvanizing began to break down, after which the above treatment was applied.

The 'Webb' channel rodding was adopted by the LMS as its standard and in due course by British Railways and it is still in extensive use today.

A problem with working points and other equipment by rod from a cabin was expansion and contraction of the rodding due to changes of temperature. This, of course, could throw the equipment out of adjustment. The problem was generally overcome by dividing the rodding at its mid point and putting in a device which reversed the direction of movement. This device, known as a compensator, was able to absorb the expansion and contraction and thus transmit the same movement to the points under all conditions. Many devices were produced in the early days to get around patent royalties and to improve the mechanisms. The LNW adopted a compensator in the late 1890's (**Figure 15.2** and 3) which was similar to those in use today although it was mounted vertically. **Figure 15.2** illustrates how the compensator was fixed in the rodding run and the arrangements necessary to prevent it from moving. The drawing also shows how several compensators could be mounted on the same base (or horse).

FACING POINTS

From the beginning facing points in running lines were recognised as a hazard. If they were out of adjustment the closed switch might not be tight home against the stock rail leading to the possibility of a train taking the wrong path and becoming derailed. Points could move under trains due to the signalman operating the lever prematurely (it was sometimes possible to 'beat' the interlocking) or due to some defect. Objects such as couplings hanging from trains could catch in the points and alter the position of one or both switches. For these reasons, in the early days it was normal to apply a speed restriction to trains passing over facing points. Because of this the signals controlling routes over facing points normally worked to 'caution' only and not to 'clear' (see Chapter 3). The problem of safety on facing points was brought home to the railway world, and the North Western in particular, on 1st August, 1873 when the night Scotch express became derailed on facing points at Wigan. This resulted in the rear vehicles being piled up on the platform while the front of the train escaped unharmed and was able to continue on its journey. Facing points therefore tended to be avoided where this was practical. However, many locations existed where facing points were required to enable the traffic to be worked, most obviously at a junction between two lines. Here something was required to minimise the risks. A step in the right direction had been made in 1867 when Messrs Livesey, Edwards and Jeffreys introduced the locking (or lift) bar and this was adopted for practically all facing points. The lift bar was placed on the approach side of the points and was worked by a separate lever which locked the point lever and signals as appropriate. The bar consisted of a piece of 'T' iron a little longer than the wheelbase of the longest vehicle. The bar was placed against one of the rails so that the wheel flanges would bear on its upper surface. It was arranged to lift when the lever was pulled. If a train was standing on the bar it could not be lifted and so the lever was locked in position and this in turn locked the point lever. The bar did not cover the eventuality of the point switches being incorrectly set or out of adjustment. However, this deficiency was overcome by Mr Saxby who introduced the facing point bolt or plunger lock in 1870 which held the switches in position by a bolt through the stretcher bar. This was then used in conjunction with the bar, both being worked by the same lever.

The apparatus worked in the following way. The signalman moved the points to the road on which the train was to travel and then pulled over the lever which actuated the lift (locking) bar and bolt (facing point lock lever) thus securing the switches in position and releasing the signals. (If the switches were not fully home the bolt would not go in and the signals remained locked at danger.) Pulling the signal lever locked the facing point lock lever in position and hence held the points locked. However it was often possible for the signalman to restore the signal lever to normal, thus releasing the FPL lever, before the train had completely cleared the points. While the train was passing over or standing on the points the flanges of the wheels held the lift bar in the lowered position preventing the FPL lever being operated. The bolt was thus held in position and the safety of the train was ensured.

A problem was that accidents could sometimes occur if the rod working the points broke or the switches became detached from the stretcher bar. The LNW adopted a design of facing point lock layout devised by F W Webb in 1876. This was rather a complicated apparatus (replacing an even more complex arrangement devised in 1874) and was designed to bolt the two switches separately. This arrangement was adopted to avoid the problem which could occur on points with a single bolt in the stretcher bar. If this broke, the bolt would often only hold one switch leaving the other free to move under a train. The Webb bolt ensured that both switches were in the correct positions before it would go fully home. Most other solutions proposed to this problem suffered from the same problems of complexity. About 1882 the LNW therefore changed over to a simple stretcher bar and bolt. Detector locks (which had been introduced in 1871) were added in the signal wire runs, to ensure that both switches were in the correct positions. Here separate rods were taken from each of the switches to a detector mounted on the ends of the sleepers. The rods ended in flat notched bars. The notches lined up when the switches were correctly positioned and allowed a weighted lever in the signal wire run to pass through and thus allow the signal to be cleared. If either of the switches were out of position the signal could not be cleared. A facing point layout is shown in **Figure 15.4**. Note the use of interlaced sleepers, these were cheaper and easier to handle than long timbers, but made maintenance difficult.

Because of the dangers of facing points the Board of Trade imposed stringent restrictions on the distance over which they could be worked mechanically from a cabin. This restriction had a profound effect on the way in which the signalling was laid out and resulted in a number of signal cabins being required close together at large stations and yards. Over the years the restriction of distance was gradually relaxed and this allowed the cabins to be placed further apart. The changes made it possible to abolish a number of cabins by adding their functions to an adjacent cabin or constructing a new central cabin to replace two or three existing ones. This work was only done in a few cases, usually when other alterations or renewals were required. Most locations continued to reflect the rules and practices in force at the time of their installation.

DISTANCE FROM THE CABIN OVER WHICH FACING POINTS COULD BE WORKED MECHANICALLY.

Year	1874	1877	1885	1900	1908	1925
Distance (Yards)	120	150	180	200	250	350

CLEARANCE BARS

At busy and complex locations additional safety devices were necessary to avoid mishaps. One of the most common sources of danger was through a busy signalman forgetting, momentarily, a train and allowing another to approach on a conflicting route. In complex layouts where the signal could be some distance in rear of the points it protected it was sometimes possible to replace the signal as soon as the

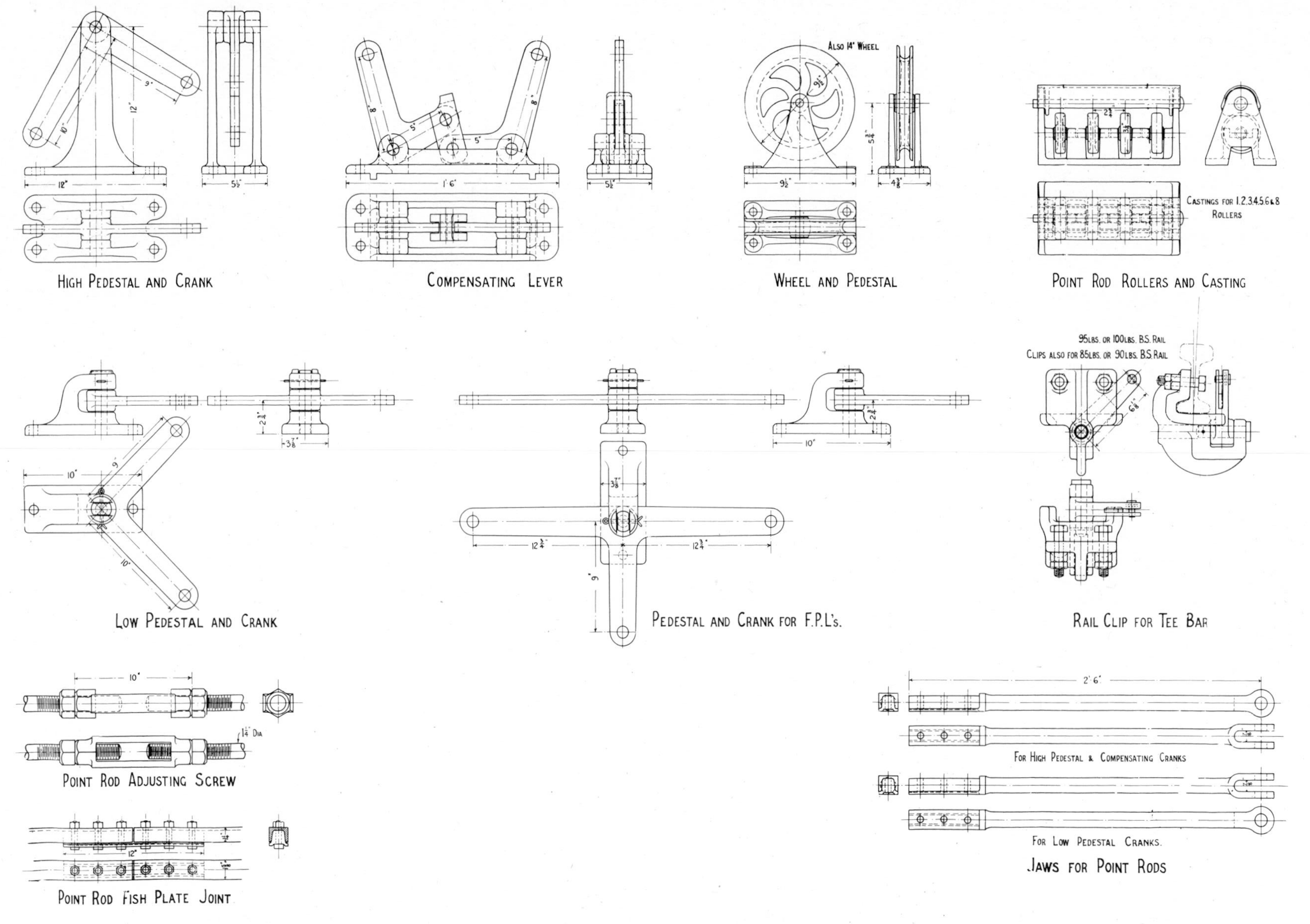

Figure 15.3 *A selection of wheels, cranks and fittings used for point rodding and wire runs. The cost of some of these items in late LNW days might be of interest. Point rodding cost 1/2d per yard, a compensating lever 7/9d while a 10" wheel and pedestal was priced at 2/-. Scale of reproduction: 1 inch to 1 foot (1:12).*

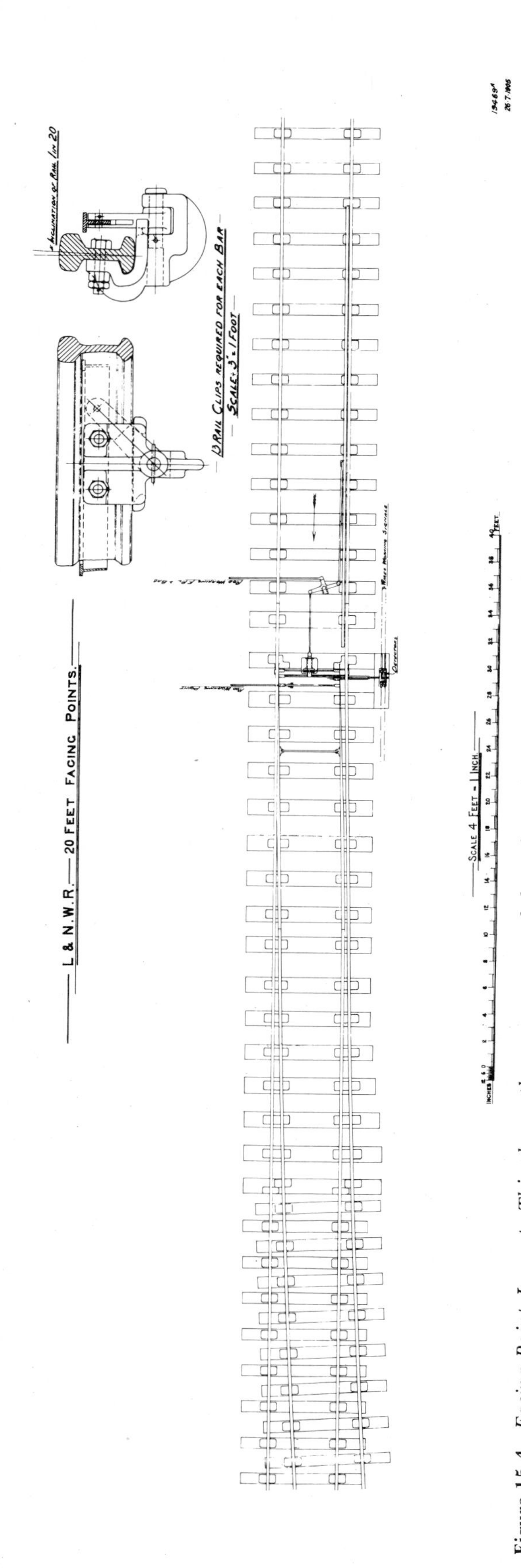

Figure 15.4 *Facing Point Layout. This shows the arrangement of the point switches and the operating rod from the signal cabin. The switches were connected separately to detector locks mounted on the sleeper ends. The facing point lock bolt and lifting bar were worked directly via a 'T' crank. This was the basic form of facing point layout used by the LNWR from about 1882 to about 1920. In later years the point lock connections were altered so that the bolt was driven via the lift bar rather than directly. Scale of main drawing: 2mm to 1 foot (1:152).*

engine had passed it thus releasing the points and enabling them to be pulled before the train had cleared. The most common solution to the problem was to make use of the principle of the lift bar which was used in conjunction with the facing point lock. These were used in a number of ways as intermediate facing point lock bars, worked by lever and locking the points, or as clearance bars worked by levers in the cabin which in turn locked the points. One form of the latter was the Park and Pryce train protection bars described in Chapter 17, a number of which were installed on the LNWR proper. Several were used at Birmingham New Street when that station was rebuilt in the mid 1880's. In modern practice the problem is solved by providing a track circuit, occupation of which holds the points locked in position.

A development of the mechanical clearance bar was to use the bar itself to operate an electrical switch. This had the advantages of doing away with the mechanical connections to the cabin and enabled a continuous indication to be given by means of an electrical indicator in the cabin. An electric lock could be provided to hold the appropriate levers in position. **Figure 15.5** shows the early form of Electrical Clearance Bar introduced on the LNWR in 1913. The bar was balanced so that it remained in the raised position. When a train passed over, it was depressed and operated the electrical switch which was fastened to the sleepers. The bars could also be used as 'depression bars'. These were used, for example, near the end of bay platform lines. A vehicle left at the buffer stops would stand on the bar and operate an indicator in the signal cabin to remind the signalman of its presence, as he was often unable to see it. Depression bars are still used in these situations since track circuits are not always reliable where vehicles stand for some time, and where the rails could become rusty.

MIDWAY RELEASE

Where points were too far from a cabin to be worked from it they were often worked by a ground frame. This had to be controlled from the main cabin to ensure that the points were only used when it was safe to do so. The most common means of control on the LNWR was the Annett's Key system, described in Chapter 11. Another form of release was the bolt lock where a rod was taken from the cabin to the frame where a bolt, a smaller version of the turntable bolt already described, locked the necessary levers in position. In the early days on the LNW bolt locks were normally worked by wire rather than rod. Following an accident attributed to the faulty operation of a wire bolt lock it was decided, in February 1877, to adopt rod working as standard.

However, in most cases the ground frame was too far away for control by rod. Rods were, therefore, taken from levers in both ground frame and cabin to a point midway between them (hence the term 'Midway Release'). Here a locking device was provided to enable one lever to lock the other in position. Thus with the lever in the cabin in the normal position the ground frame would be locked out of use. With the lever reversed and the ground frame in use, the lever was locked in position to prevent a conflicting move being signalled. A 'Midway Release' is illustrated in **Plate 15.1**, and as can be seen it is a fairly simple device. Another use was where one signal cabin worked a connection in a line otherwise controlled by another. A midway release link was provided between the two cabins to produce the necessary interlocking to ensure the connection was only used when it was safe to do so.

LINEMAN'S BOARDS

When interlocked signal cabins and the block telegraph (in some form or other!) began to be installed throughout the system it was realised that some means was needed for the signalman to summon the services of a lineman when some part of his equipment was defective. The speaking telegraph was installed on many lines, but it tended to be used for station to station communication and many signal cabins were not included in the circuits. Some cabins had the telegraph but in many cases these were special circuits for regulation of traffic and communication within yards, and they often did not extend in the right direction to be of any use in summoning the lineman.

Drivers of trains had to keep a careful look out when passing signal cabins in case the signalman wished to exhibit a hand signal to them. These signals could, for instance, supplement the fixed signals or indicate that the train was required to stop for traffic purposes. A system was, therefore, devised of hanging two boards on the front of the cabin to indicate that the equipment was in order or that assistance was required. The telegraph and electrical equipment was generally maintained by the Telegraph Department staff and the interlocking and signals by Signal Department staff. One board therefore applied to the telegraph equipment and the other to the signal equipment. The two boards were of different shapes to enable the drivers to distinguish them. The LNWR used oval and diamond shaped boards (see **Plates 2.1, 9.8** and **17.9**) one side indicating 'in order' and the other 'defective', as listed below:—

Board	*Shape*	*Colour*	*Meaning*
Signal	Diamond	Plain White	In Order
		Plain Red	Defective, Lineman Required
Telegraph	Oval	Plain White	In Order
		Plain Black	Defective, Lineman Required

These shapes and colours applied on the LNW, North London and the North and South Western Junction Railways.

Plate 15.1 *A Midway Release with the cover plate removed. In this illustration the bar at the back (worked by a cabin to the right) is locked in position. The front bar is holding it via the sliding lock which in turn slides between the two square stops. In this case the cabin on the right is the controlling cabin and the one on the left the subsidiary cabin or ground frame. When the photograph was taken the ground frame was in use and the release lever was holding the main cabin's release lever to prevent a conflicting move being made there. A wire is just visible attached to the left hand end of the back bar. This worked an indicator (face disc) in the ground frame to indicate to the person there when the release lever had been pulled to enable the frame to be used.*

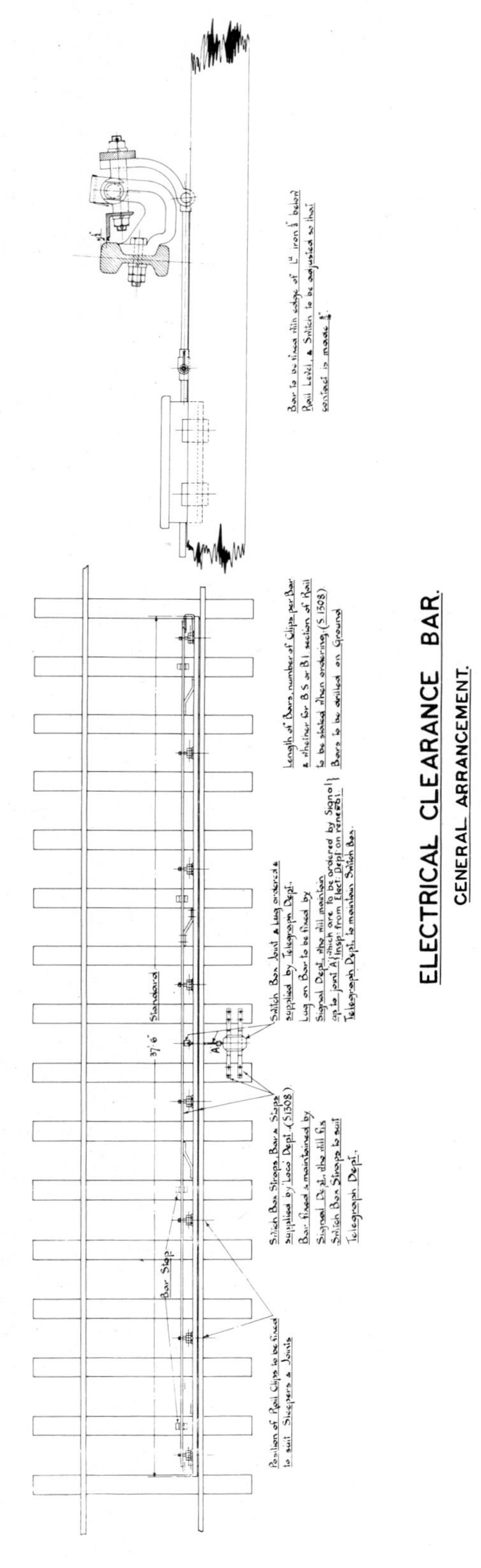

Figure 15.5 *Electric Clearance Bar. The clearance bar consists of a bar against the rail which was depressed by the wheel flanges. The weight of this was balanced by a second bar, the whole assembly pivoting on clips attached to the rail. The bar operated an electrical switch at about its centre point. Scale of plan: 1/8" to 1 foot (1:96).*

When passing a cabin the driver was expected to observe the boards and when he saw one in the 'defective' position he was expected to inform the stationmaster, at the next station where he was scheduled to stop, of the circumstances so that the necessary assistance could be summoned.

With improvements in communications and easier and quicker methods of obtaining assistance, the system slowly fell out of use after the turn of the century and the practice was officially abandoned on the LNWR at the end of 1911. Despite this a few cabins still had no telephone.

BELLS

Before the widespread use of the telegraph and telephone the signalman was often the only person who knew where the trains were. It was desirable therefore to provide him with a means of informing the station staff and passengers of the approach of a train. Most cabins were close to the station platforms so a bell of some description would serve the purpose adequately. Some cabins were equipped with a hand bell which was rung from the window or door.

The bells were especially useful where a train was approaching the platform away from the station buildings, since it was necessary to give the staff some advance warning of its approach to enable them to reach the platform before the train stopped. The bell was also helpful in attracting attention during shunting and other manoeuvres.

Where the bell was used frequently, or where a larger bell was required to enable the sound to be heard, a bell was fixed permanently to the outside of the cabin. It was normally placed above the door or windows, where it could be conveniently reached by the signalman. Usually a series of ringing codes were used to cover different situations. The messages covered would vary according to local circumstances but the most common were "Up Trains Approaching", "Down Trains Approaching" and "Assistance Required at Signal Cabin". **Figure 15.6** is a drawing of the signal cabin bell and an example is illustrated in **Plate 15.2**.

GONGS

The railway is of essence a long and straggling affair leading to problems in communication between the men working at different locations. The telegraph was obviously the answer over long distances and between stations. More locally, say from one end of a station to the other, between shunters in a yard or between a signal cabin and ground frame, this was an expensive solution (both in first cost and maintenance).

The signal cabin bell described above was limited by the distance over which it could be heard. An obvious method of extending its range was to place the bell near the point where it needed to be heard and to work it from elsewhere. This could be done by means of a wire and lever. **Figure 15.7** shows the original form of 'warning bell' used on the LNWR. A disadvantage was that it was difficult to send messages with this type of bell since its ringing could not be fully controlled. The idea of the mechanically worked bell was combined with the principle of the single stroke electric bells used in block signalling to produce the single stroke mechanical gong. (**Plates 15.3** and **15.4**). This could readily be used to transmit messages by means of laid down codes. As far as possible these codes were standardised and used throughout the LNW. There were inevitably variations to suit local circumstances and the purpose for which the gong was provided, and no doubt there were a few unofficial ones as well!

The gongs were fairly large in order to ensure that they could be heard and were fixed at the appropriate places in the yards, on station platforms, at ground frames or in signal cabins. They could be mounted on a wall or a separate post. In some cases communication was only provided in one direction, for example between signalman or shunter and engine driver to inform him it was clear to make the next move. In other cases communication was provided in both directions, an example being between a signal cabin and a ground frame. **Figure 15.8** illustrates the way in which the gongs could be used while the plates illustrate some actual examples. Some examples of gong message codes are given on page 220.

In **Figure 15.8** case 'A'; gongs are provided between a signal cabin and a ground frame released by it. The gong from the cabin was used to inform the man at the ground frame when it was clear for the points to be used and when shunting must be stopped. The man at the ground frame could communicate with the cabin by means of his gong lever to inform the signalman when he wished to use the points and when the movement was complete and the points restored to normal. In case 'B' a gong was sited near the end of a shunting line where the engine would come to rest after drawing forward for a shunt move. When the road was set for the next move to be made the signalman sounded the gong to inform the driver that it was safe to set back. Such a gong need not be operated from a cabin, and many were operated by the shunter from a lever at a suitable point on the ground.

Plate 15.2 *A Signal Cabin Bell at Woburn Sands.*

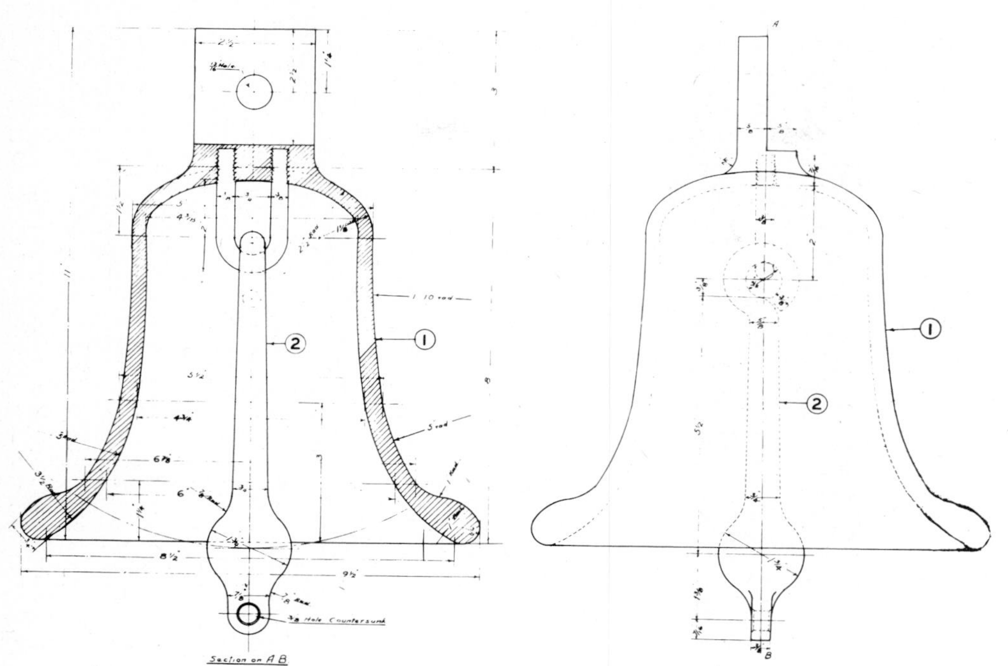

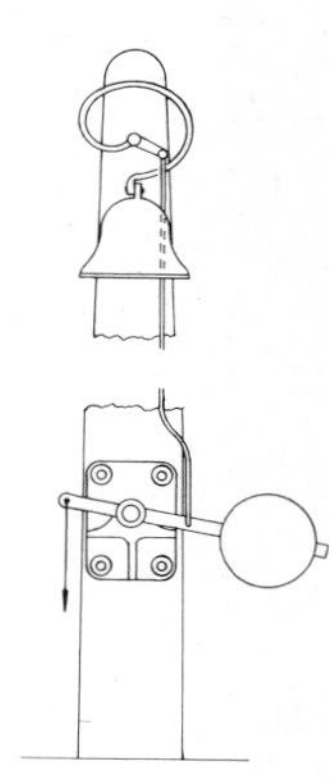

Figure 15.7 *Warning Bell. This type of bell was used to give warning (e.g. of the approach of a train) at a point some distance from the cabin and was in use during the 1870's and 1880's.*

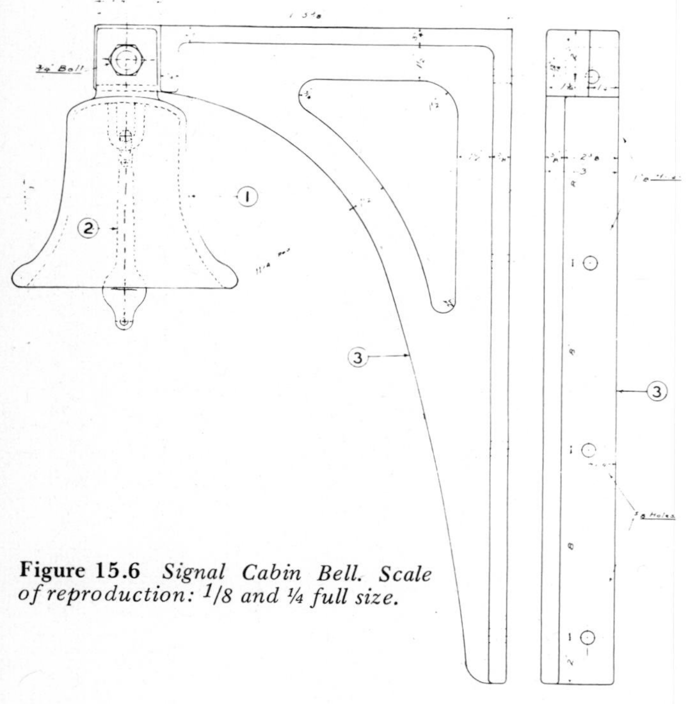

Figure 15.6 *Signal Cabin Bell. Scale of reproduction: 1/8 and ¼ full size.*

Plate 15.3 *A gong in a signal cabin. These were normally placed behind the frame under the windows. This one is on a separate board standing away from the wall but many were attached to boards (some of which were long enough to accommodate several gongs) which were fixed directly to the front wall of the cabin. The gongs were normally placed near the levers which affected them and sometimes the lever for the 'return gong communication' would be directly in front of the gong. This example was at Kensal Green Junction.*

Plate 15.4 *A shunting gong at Valley. The signal cabin at Valley was adjacent to the level crossing and a long way from the goods yard points. A gong, worked from the cabin, was placed adjacent to the points to enable the signalman to communicate his wishes to the driver or shunter. The sketch 80 lever on the right provided return communication from shunter to cabin via a similar gong placed in the cabin. The frame on the post just above the gong contained the instructions for use of the gongs and a list of the codes to be used in communication. In some cases a hand lever was provided on the gong post to provide the return communication.*

EXAMPLES OF GONG CODES

(a) SUTTON COLDFIELD
Gong from end of bay platform (run round points ground frame) to signal cabin

Engine requiring to run round	1
Work complete – restore bolt lock	2

This last only to be given when the engine is clear of Aston end of crossover and the points are restored.

(b) NEWPORT
Gong from signal cabin to platform

Up train approaching	3
Down train approaching	2
Assistance required at cabin	4

(c) GOWERTON No. 2
Gong on down platform worked from cabin

Clear to set back from down line to Llanmorlais Branch	2

Gong adjacent to branch line, worked from cabin

Clear to set back from branch line to up platform	1

(d) SHUNTING GONGS IN TUNNELS AT BIRMINGHAM NEW STREET
Mechanical shunting gongs were fixed in the Stour Valley Tunnel and in the old tunnel at the Proof House Junction end of the station.

Move forward	1
Move back	2
Stop	3
Move back very cautiously	4

(e) STANDARD CODES FOR SHUNTING GONGS
Where mechanical Gongs were in use for regulating shunting operations the LNW issued instructions that a standard code was to be adhered to. This was the standard Railway Clearing House code.

Move forward	1
Move back	2
Stop	3
Ease couplings	4

The LNW stated that no local code was to be allowed to clash with these general signals, although the codes in (c) and (d) above and other local codes in use at the same time would appear to have done so!

TUNNEL GONGS

Where signals were situated in or very near the mouth of a tunnel a means was often required of indicating to the driver of a train that he was approaching them. The simplest way of achieving this was by means of a mechanical tunnel gong. This consisted simply of a treadle which was connected via a crank to a large hammer. The treadle was depressed by the wheels of a passing train, causing the hammer to strike a sheet of thin metal mounted on a frame attached to the wall of the tunnel. The resulting din attracted the drivers attention and enabled him to be ready to look out for the signal. In 1911 they were in use at the following locations:—

TUNNEL	*LOCATION*
Primrose Hill	Slow lines – 150 yards inside the tunnel at both ends.
Kilsby	12 yards south of the down distant signal for Kilsby Tunnel North End cabin. This one sounded only if the signal was at danger.
Morley	50 yards on the Batley side of the down distant signal. 76 yards on the Churwell side of the up distant signal.
Gildersome	50 yards on the Huddersfield side of the down distant signal.
Huddersfield	North Line – 100 yards on the Springwood side of the down home signal.
Standedge North Line	50 yards on the Diggle side of the down north line distant signal (251 yards from the Marsden end of the tunnel).
Standedge South Line	50 yards on the Diggle side of the down south distant signal (240 yards from the Marsden end of the tunnel).
Standedge North and South	50 yards on the Marsden side of the up distant signal (617 yards from the Diggle end of the tunnels).
Grotton	Up line – 50 yards on the Greenfield side of the disc signal.
Clifton Hall	50 yards on the Patricroft side of the up distant signal for Clifton Hall No. 1 cabin.

The gongs or 'clanging plates' in Primrose Hill Tunnel were installed in 1888 to replace purple marker lights.

Plate 15.5 *A face disc in the normal position, with the disc horizontal so that the message is hidden. Mounting the disc on a board above the windows was the most common arrangement since the view of it was not obstructed by the levers. The drive rod is on the left. The message on the disc can just be seen and reads 'Down Distant Off'. This disc was in Three Spires Junction Cabin and was worked by Beldam Gates Cabin in connection with the 'Distant Indicator Working' system (Block Telegraph Regulation 34).*

FACE DISC

Where several cabins existed close together there was usually a need to provide visual information of various types between the cabins. Before the advent of reliable and cheap electrical aids this was generally done mechanically and the information displayed in the cabin (where possible behind or above the appropriate lever) by means of the Face Disc (**Figure 15.9**). Where a signal was slotted by two cabins it was often desirable to indicate to the men (or one of them) that the other had pulled his lever. A connection was taken off the signal wire (which often passed nearby) to the cabin where it worked a face disc. These stood normally horizontal so that the face was not visible, and when the lever was pulled the disc moved to the vertical position to reveal the appropriate wording, for example 'Down Home Slot Off'. A common, and long standing, function was in connection with 'Distant Indicator Working'. Where cabins were close together there were often difficulties in obtaining an adequate braking distance between distant and home signals for the second and subsequent cabins (even where distants for successive cabins were placed under stop signals of preceding cabins (**Figure 3.8**)). Rather than provide a great deal of complex slotting it was a common practice to apply a local rule that the man in the first cabin was not to pull off his distant signal for an approaching train until the men in the other cabins had pulled theirs. This practice was covered by the LNW and LMS Block Telegraph Regulation 34 and page 117 of the 1960 B.R. Regulations. A positive indication was needed of when this had been done and a face disc, usually lettered 'xxx Distant Off' (**Plate 15.6**) was provided in the first cabin and worked off the next cabin's distant signal wire.

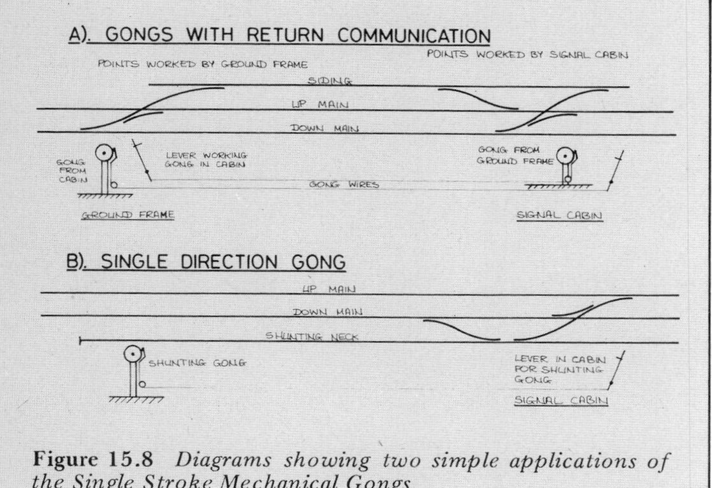

Figure 15.8 *Diagrams showing two simple applications of the Single Stroke Mechanical Gongs.*

At large stations it was sometimes difficult for the signalman to see whether platforms were occupied and it was possible to forget trains (particularly where some vehicles had been detached and left behind). One of the main functions of cabins such as Euston No. 1 and Birmingham New Street No. 3 was to act as a look out post under the station roof to assist the signalman at the station throat. When a platform was occupied or obstructed a lever was pulled to operate a face disc in the main cabin 'xxx platform occupied' as appropriate. Other uses of face discs were between two signal cabins or signal cabin and ground frame where one bolt locked a connection worked by the other.

Face discs in one form or another go right back almost to the beginning of signalling on the LNWR. They were even used in the earliest days, before block instruments (absolute or permissive) became common, particularly in stations and yards where cabins were close together, for indicating the approach of a train from one cabin to another. These origins could be seen in the way some of the discs were lettered as this memo from Mr Dick in January 1879 shows:—

> 'I note that many Face Discs in cabins in connection with slots are incorrectly lettered "Line Clear" instead of 'XXXXX Slot Off', please alter them.'

WIRE ADJUSTERS

The methods by which expansion and contraction of point rodding was counteracted have already been mentioned. While the adjustment of signal wires was not as critical as it was for point rodding, the change in length could be considerable. This can be appreciated when it is remembered that some wires could be three quarters of a mile or more in length.

In the early days adjustment of signal wires was achieved by the simple means of dividing the wire at a convenient point and attaching a piece of chain with a hook on the end to one of the wires. The hook was passed through an 'eye' attached to the end of the other wire and hooked into the chain at a position which gave the required length of wire. Adjustment was made by unfastening the join, pulling the wire tight and attaching the hook again at a suitable position.

Early in 1869 the LNW bought the rights to use a more sophisticated form of wire adjuster and it was resolved to apply these to the distant signals at Winwick, Walton and Crewe North Junctions. It was recommended that the

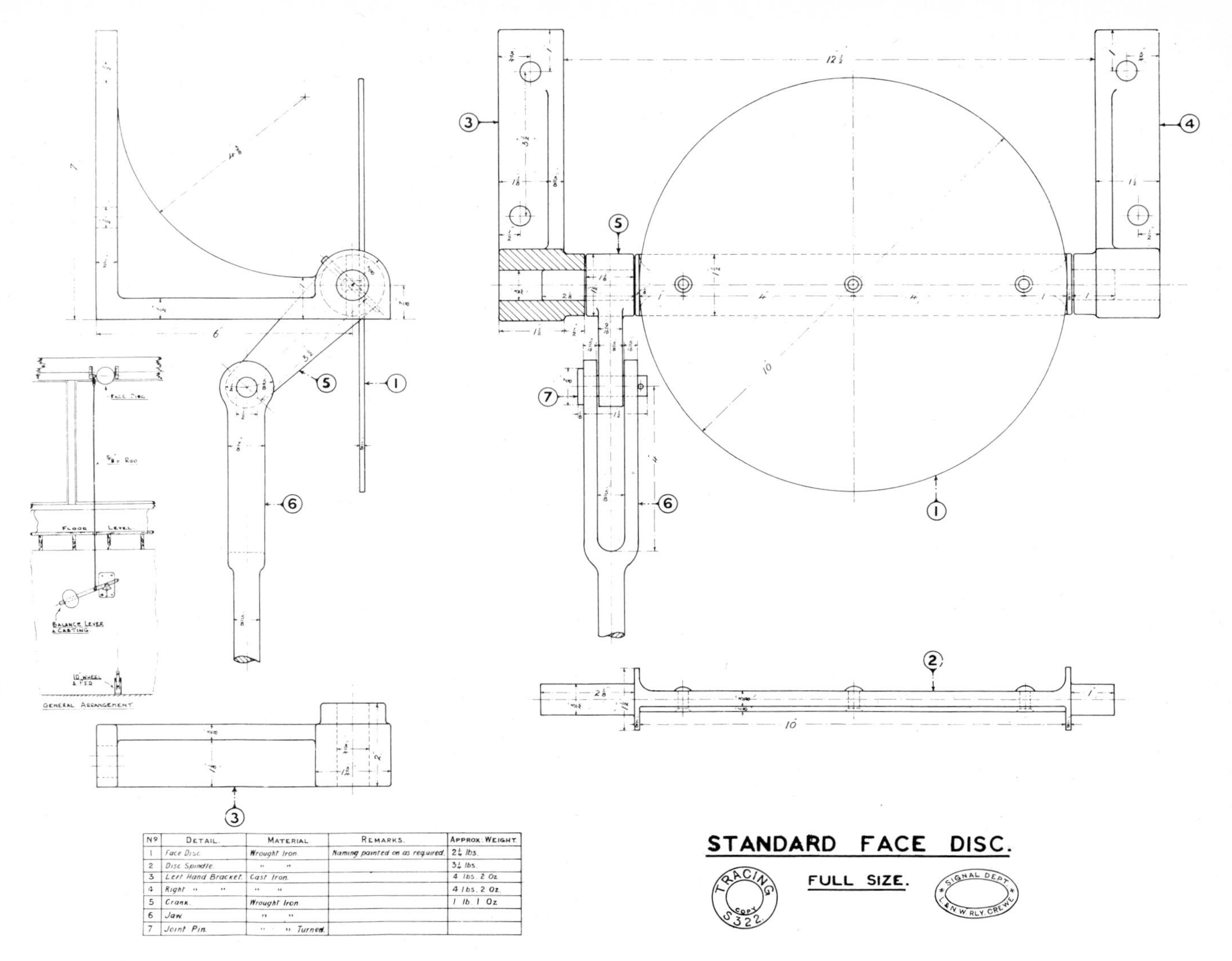

Nº	Detail.	Material.	Remarks.	Approx: Weight.
1	Face Disc.	Wrought Iron.	Naming painted on as required.	2¼ lbs.
2	Disc Spindle.	" "		3¼ lbs.
3	Left Hand Bracket.	Cast Iron.		4 lbs. 2 Oz.
4	Right " "	" "		4 lbs. 2 Oz.
5	Crank.	Wrought Iron.		1 lb. 1 Oz.
6	Jaw.	" "		
7	Joint Pin.	" " Turned.		

STANDARD FACE DISC.

TRACING COPY S322

FULL SIZE.

SIGNAL DEPT. L.&N.W. RLY. CREWE

Figure 15.9 *Standard Face Disc. The message was painted on the face disc itself (Item 1) which is shown in the drawing in the displayed position. The disc moved through 90° when not in use. The small sketch on the left shows how the apparatus was fixed in the signal cabin. They could also be found mounted below the windows or on a pedestal behind the levers. Scale of reproduction of main portion of drawing: ¼ full size.*

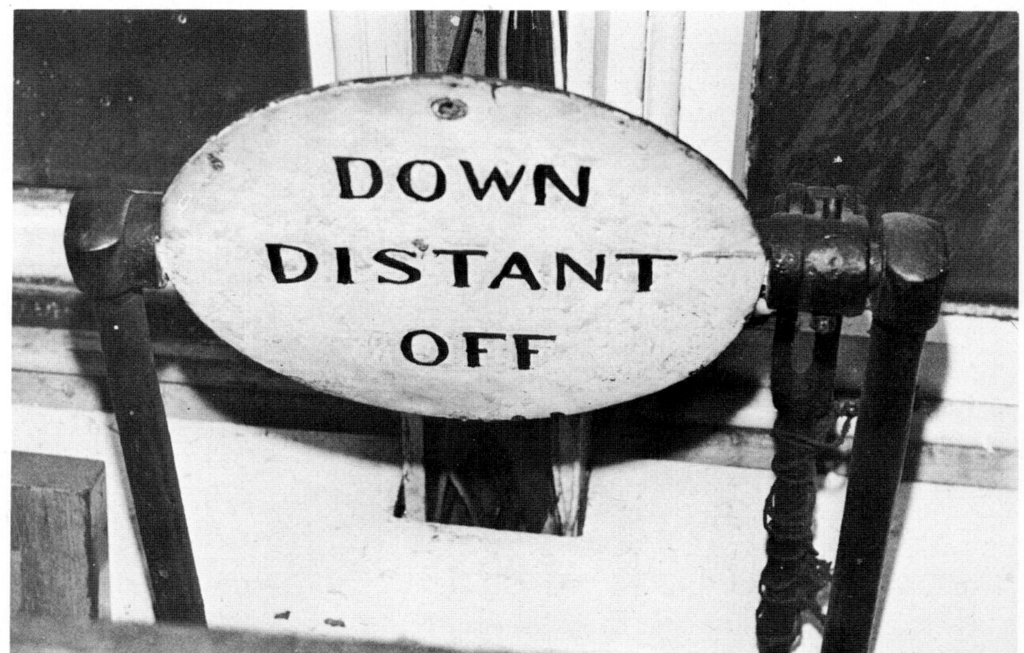

Plate 15.6 *A face disc in the vertical or operated position with the message revealed. This indicated that the distant signal lever at the next cabin had been pulled and that it was in order for the signalman in this cabin to clear his distant.*

Plate 15.7 *Not all face discs were mounted above the windows and this one at Willesden High Level Junction was mounted on legs from the floor. This cabin is of Type 5 with large windows and there was insufficient space to mount the disc on the wall below the windows, in a similar manner to the gong in* **Plate 15.3**, *as was done in the case of some Type 3 and 4 cabins. The disc illustrated here is shown in its operated position in* **Plate 15.6.**

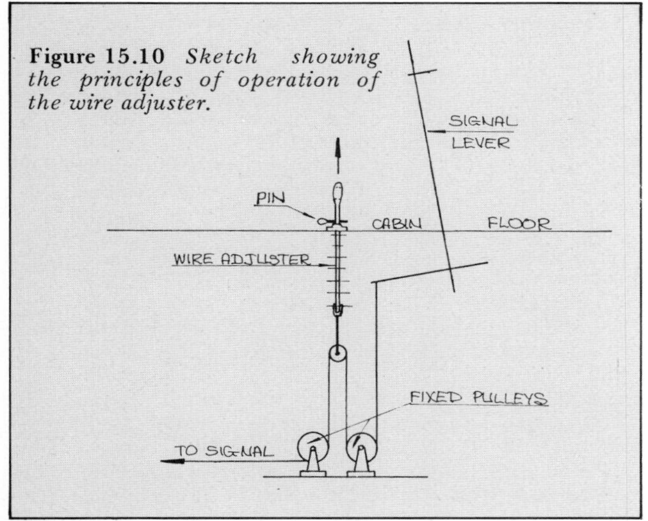

Figure 15.10 *Sketch showing the principles of operation of the wire adjuster.*

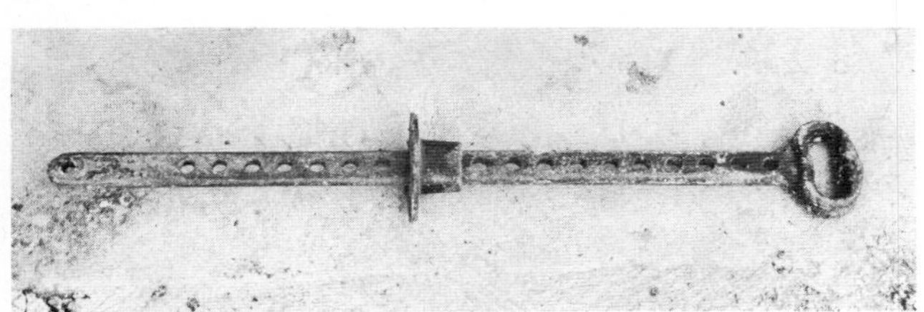

Plate 15.8 *An LNW wire adjuster removed from the cabin to show its very simple construction.*

Plate 15.9 *Two wire adjusters at Anglesea Siding, showing how the adjuster was pinned in the required position. They were generally painted the same colour as the lever with which they worked and some had the lever number painted on the top of the handle.*

apparatus be applied to all new distant signals. The Company developed a simple form of stirrup wire adjuster (**Plates 15.8** and 9) which could be fixed in the signal cabin to enable the signalman to adjust the signal wire without leaving the cabin. To tighten the signal wire the handle was pulled up the required distance and a pin pushed through the appropriate hole in the shaft to hold it in position. The reverse process was used to slacken the wire in cold weather or at night. The working of wire adjusters can be seen from **Figure 15.10.**

In later years wire adjusters of this type were provided for almost all distant signals plus those stop signals which were an appreciable distance from the cabin. This was not always the case and it was not until 1887 that they came into widespread use as this memo dated 17th October, 1887, from Mr Thompson to his District Inspectors, shows:

> 'I am anxious to provide wire adjusters for all distant signals. We cannot do them all at once so please advise me which are most important.'

In long wire runs it was difficult to obtain a sharp enough pull at the signal to move the arm cleanly to the 'off' position. A weighted lever (**Plate 15.10**) was, therefore, incorporated in the wire run as a counterweight to assist in keeping the wire tight. This assisted the balance weight on the signal in pulling back the wire when the lever was returned to normal and guarded against the possibility of the signal sticking in the 'off' position.

MULTIPLE LEVER DISTANT SIGNALS

Wire adjusters and intermediate balance levers assisted in keeping the apparatus in correct order and the signalman in operating signals which were a long way from the cabin. In a few cases, however, these aids were not considered enough. This occurred where a distant signal was an unusually long way from the cabin or the arrangement of the wire run was particularly awkward. In the days before the availability of motor worked signals the LNW adopted a rather unusual solution to this problem. The difficult signals were arranged to be operated by more than one lever. The principle was that the first lever took up the slack in the signal wire and the second, or last, lever actually moved the arm to the 'off' position. Use of this method probably arose from the same philosophy, of reducing wear and tear on the equipment, as had produced the system of working the two ends of a crossover by separate levers (Chapter 10). Some examples of this practice are listed in **Figure 15.11**. The operation of mechanically worked signals over such long distances was not always satisfactory, particularly where slotting was involved or the wire runs were complicated. In later years the LNW installed a number of motor worked distants where there were difficulties. Examples included several distant signals in the Wigan area which were converted in 1917. Motor worked up outer distant signals were installed at Watford No. 2 in 1920, these being operated by switches on the inner distant signals. The down distant signal at Stechford was converted the same year. This particular signal is of interest in that it was formerly a multiple lever slotted signal similar to the one at Colwyn Bay listed in **Figure 15.11**. Despite this the majority of the signals listed in the table remained mechanically worked until quite recently.

Figure 15.11 EXAMPLES OF CABINS HAVING DISTANT SIGNALS WORKED BY TWO OR MORE LEVERS

Cabin	*Signal*	*Number of Levers Used*	*Notes*
Bradley Junction	Down South Distant	2	1
	Down North Distant	2	1
Colwyn Bay No.1	Up Fast Distant	2	2
Deganwy No. 1	Down Main Distant	2	3
Duston West Junction	Down Distant	3	4
Helsby	Down Main Distant	2	
Lichfield City No. 1	Down Distant from Walsall	2	
Maryport Level Crossing	Up Distant	2	
Weedon No. 2	Down Outer Distant	2	5
Whitchurch Cambrian Junction	Down Distant	2	

NOTES:

1. Below Kirkburton Junction starting signals.
2. Slot on Fast line distant for No. 2 cabin, which was approximately 1600 yards from No. 1 cabin.
3. Below Llandudno Junction Crossing down main starting signal.
4. The distant at Duston West was on the High Level Line. It was sited at the south end of Hunsbury Hill Tunnel and was about 1 mile 140 yards from the cabin. This was considered to be better than providing something in the tunnel itself.
5. Slot on Weedon No. 1 Down Distant, 1 mile 55 yards from No. 2 cabin.

In all other cases the distant signals were between 1,400 and 1,700 yards from the cabins.

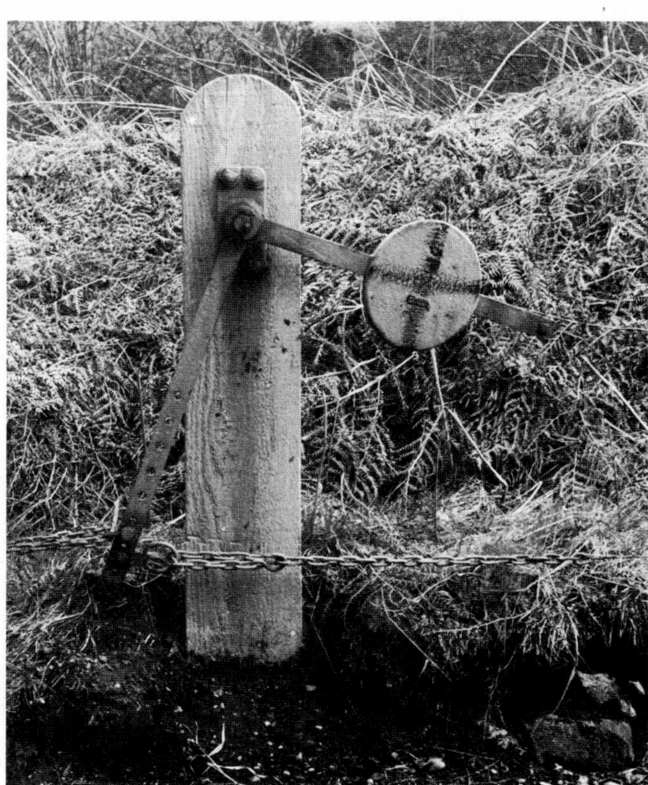

Plate 15.10 *A wire assister, or counterweight, at Hednesford No. 3, working in the distant signal wire. The cabin was to the right and the signal to the left.*

FOG MACHINES

Fogs (and falling snow) were the bane of the railwayman's life. Extra precautions had to be taken to guard against accidents. Perhaps the most obvious one was the provision of a fog signalman at many signals (particularly distant signals). His job was to assist the driver in finding and interpreting the signals in fog which, of course, could obscure completely, for all practical purposes, the normal fixed day and night signals. Platelayers were used for this work and could be called out for duty whenever the signalman thought this was necessary. There were set arrangements for relieving the men after the end of their duty period if the fog persisted. The fogman was provided with a small cabin (often very small, the special hut used in the restricted 10 ft space between tracks was a mere 3′ 4″ x 1′ 6″ (**Plate 10.16**)) and a brazier to give him some warmth. They were usually sited a little in the rear of the signal where the man could see its position and attract the drivers attention before he reached it. The fogman placed a detonator on the line when the signal was 'On' and displayed an appropriate hand signal to the driver of each approaching train.

These arrangements were, of course, expensive and took the men away from their proper duties. This was not too serious in the case of an occasional fog but it was not unknown for fog to persist for a week or more continuously in some city areas. There was, however, very little that could be done as the safety of the trains always came first. One way in which some economy in the number of men employed on the work could be made was by arranging for one man to 'fog' several signals. This could easily be done where the fog signalman was near enough to see all of them. Where the signals were too far away to be seen in fog, mechanical indicators were sometimes provided. These were connected to the signal wire and repeated the positions of the arms where the fogman could see them. Electrical indicators could also be found at some locations. There were problems with a man fogging signals applying to more than one line. He was required to put down a detonator whenever the signal arms were 'on' and remove it when they moved to 'off'. There were dangers in his crossing running lines in fog to do this (added to which the sleepers were usually wet and slippery).

The first moves towards providing equipment to assist the fog signalmen on the LNWR came in about 1890 when Mr Woodhead of the Permanent Way Department devised and experimented with some fog machines. These were mechanical devices which enabled the man, by means of a small lever, to place (and remove) a detonator on a line some distance away. Chains, wires or point rodding connected the operating lever to a lever arrangement clamped to the rail where the detonator was placed on top of the rail or removed from it. This enabled the fog-signalman to fog more than one signal and line, thereby economising on the manpower required. Woodhead patented a number of different types of fog machine in 1891 and 1892, several of which found use on the LNW. By the early part of 1893, 144 Woodhead fog machines were in use, enabling 49 fogsignalmen to be dispenced with.

The most common types of machine were the one, two and four shot varieties (**Figures 15.12** and **13**). The number referred to the number of detonators which could be placed on the line before the machine had to be replenished. An eight shot machine was also manufactured, this differed from the smaller machines in that once a detonator had been put on the line it could not be removed again. The machines were initially intended for use by fogmen at signals but their usefulness was soon realised and many sets of levers were fixed inside signal cabins and worked by the signalman. Initially they were only to be used between the time a fog came on and the time the fogsignalmen took up duty. Later this restriction was removed and the signalmen could use them whenever necessary.

The levers provided in the cabins were basically similar to those provided for outdoor use although there were some detail differences. The drive, for instance, was horizontal in the outdoor type but had to be vertical for use in a cabin. The small levers were generally placed at one end of the cabin adjacent to the lever frame. The position varied somewhat from cabin to cabin, depending on the space available. This was particularly the case where levers were installed in existing cabins.

The machines were not without their problems. Initially some difficulties were experienced, when they were first being installed, in obtaining the correct travel on the operating wire or chain to ensure the detonator would move fully onto and off the rail when required. Further problems occurred with the introduction of the North London and New Line Electric services. It was found that the hoods protecting the detonators alongside the rail fouled the trip cock levers on the electric trains. Detonator placers on these lines had, therefore, to be fitted with modified covers.

Reproduced in **Figure 15.14** is a portion of the instructions issued to the signalmen for working the machines. These are taken from the 1916 edition of the LNWR Appendix.

Plate 15.11 *A pair of LNW single shot machine levers at Workington Main No. 2. Note the standard cast iron name plates provided for them.*

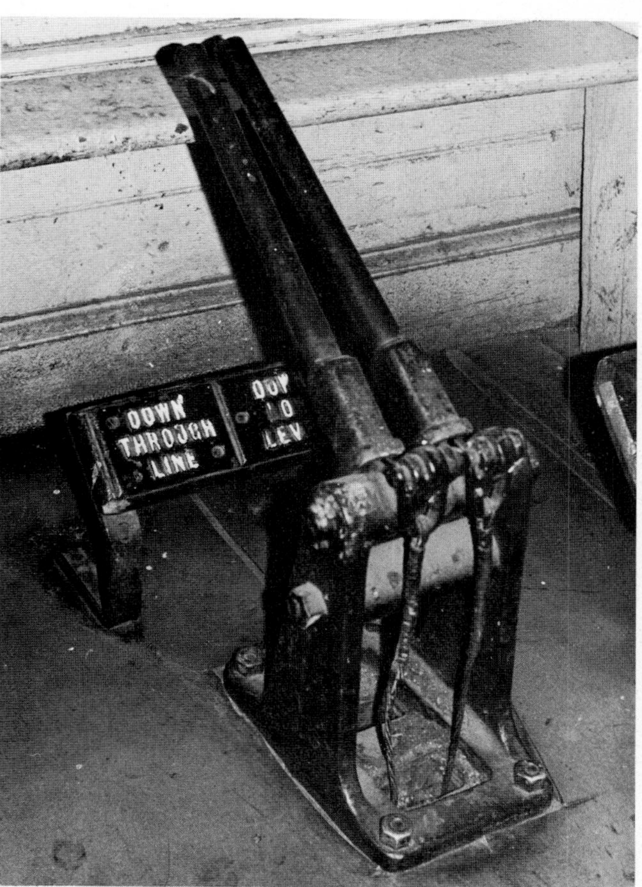

Plate 15.12 *A pair of shot machine levers in a 2 shot machine frame at Kensal Green Junction. The machine has, however, been used to work shots or detonators on two different lines producing, in fact, two single shot installations.*

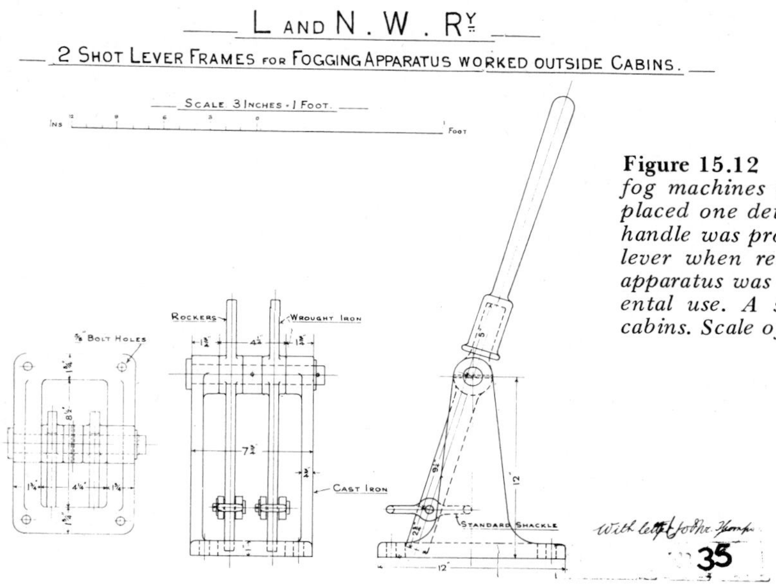

L and N. W. Ry.

2 Shot Lever Frames for Fogging Apparatus worked outside Cabins.

Scale 3 Inches - 1 Foot.

Rockers — Wrought Iron — Cast Iron — Standard Shackle — ⅝" Bolt Holes

With letter to Mr Thompson

35

Figure 15.12 *Two shot fog lever frame used for operating fog machines at ground level by fog signalmen. Each lever placed one detonator on the rail. One removable operating handle was provided and this was placed on the appropriate lever when required. The handle was removed when the apparatus was not in use to prevent unauthorised or accidental use. A slightly modified version was used in signal cabins. Scale of reproduction: 1 inch to 1 foot (1:12).*

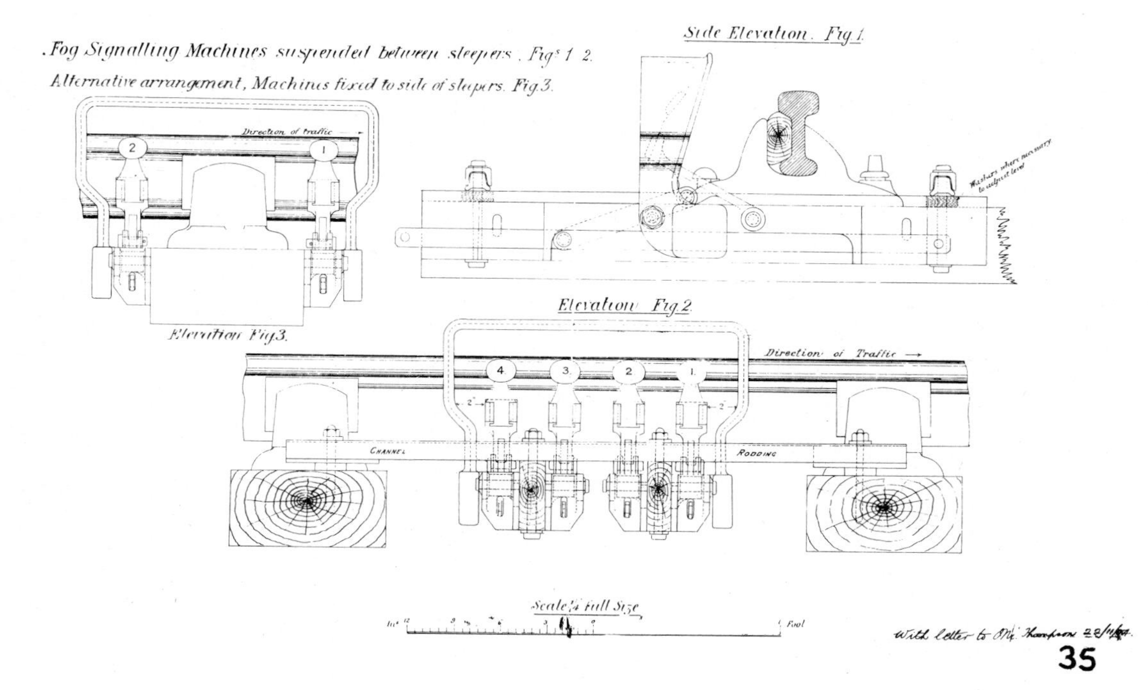

Figure 15.13 *The business end of the fogsignalling machine or detonator placer. The detonators were fixed in the layers (placers) and normally stood off the rail within the protection of the hood. When the shot machine lever was operated the layer swung on its pivot and placed the detonator on top of the rail where it would be exploded if a train passed over it. Scale of reproduction: 1 inch to 1 foot (1:12).*

USE OF DETONATOR LAYING MACHINES WORKED FROM SIGNAL BOXES, TO PLACE DETONATORS ON THE RAILS.

1. These machines are provided at certain places to enable the Signalmen, without leaving the Signal Boxes, to carry out Rule 85 during foggy weather, or at any other time when it is found necessary to do so either by day or night.

2. The District Traffic Inspectors are to satisfy themselves that the Signalmen, Fogmen, Relief Men, Gangers, Platelayers, or other men concerned, understand the working of the machines and the process of "charging," that is, placing the detonators with "layers" in the appliances adjoining the rails.

It is important that the movements performed in working in the Signal Boxes should be made smartly but not violently, and that the lever whether in the "on" or "off" position is to be moved to the full extremity of the frame.

3. **8-Shot Machines.**—Where a machine of "8-shot" power is provided, it is to be worked by the Signalman as described in paragraph No. 1, but in foggy weather, when the Fog Signalman arrives at his post, the Signalman will cease to use the machine, and, unless specially instructed to the contrary, remove the lever after the machine has been set back to the first or No. 1 rocker.

When a Signalman has once put a detonator on the rail by working the lever from the "off" to the "on" position, he cannot afterwards withdraw it, and when the Train which has exploded the detonator has passed the Signal Box, the Signalman must at once transfer the lever to the rocker next in succession in the frame, and in case of fog must repeat this operation for each Train until the lever has been twice across the four rockers, and the eighth or last detonator has been exploded, when the lever must be left on the rocker until the machine has been re-set and re-charged. When a fog clears off the Fogman must leave the machine fully charged.

4. **4, 2, and 1 Shot Machines.**—Where 4, 2, and 1 shot machines are provided, they are to be worked by the Signalman as described in paragraph No. 1. A Signalman may withdraw the detonator for future use if he finds it unnecessary to fire it and is satisfied that it has not already been exploded.

5. **Charging.**—The Signalmen will be responsible for seeing that the machines are constantly charged, and when they find it necessary to use detonators they must take the earliest opportunity to get the machines re-charged, and the levers set back to the starting point, so as to secure the advantage of having the full reserve of unexploded detonators at their command. If it is necessary to re-charge at a time when the services of the Permanent-way Ganger or a Platelayer are not available, the Signalman must call upon the man appointed by the Traffic Department to perform the duty, unless he is in a position to re-charge the machine himself.

6. **Testing of Machines.**—Except where special instructions are issued to the contrary, the machines must be tested daily by the Ganger; for this purpose the Signalman must work the machine, and the Ganger must see that it is in working order, making any adjustment that may be necessary by means of the adjusting screws or wire strainers, and a record of the testing should be entered in the Train Register Book, and both the Signalman and the Ganger must sign their names under the words "Machine tested," a note of the time being also inserted.

7. **Cleaning, Adjusting, Maintenance, Repairs, and Oiling.**—The Permanent Way Department will maintain and carry out repairs to all parts of the machines outside the Signal Boxes, including the return wires up to the point at which they are connected with the chains of the leading off-wheels situated in the basement of the Signal Boxes. The Ganger must at all times see that all such parts of the machines are kept in good working order and free from rubbish, &c., and that they are cleaned weekly; he must also adjust, where necessary the levels of the appliances fixed to the sleepers to suit the wear of the rail.

If a return wire is found broken, either inside or outside a Signal Box the Ganger must temporarily repair it, in accordance with Rule No. 260 (E) and report to the Permanent Way Inspector.

The Signal Department will maintain and keep in working order the lever frames, pedestals, rockers, wheels, chains, or any other fittings inside the Signal Boxes, and when repairs are required the Signalman must advise the Chargeman.

Non-freezing oil to be used for lubricating all parts outside Signal Boxes.

8. **Renewal and Testing of Detonators.**—The Gangers must see that the detonators and layers are renewed weekly by the Platelayers on the day they clean the machines. All detonators removed from the machines to be taken to the Signal Boxes, and kept there by the Signalman in a dry place for not less than four weeks before they are replaced in the machines; they must also be tested according to Rule 77, paragraph (C), and the result recorded by the Signalman in the Train Register Book.

9. **Pliers for withdrawing Layers.**—Each Signal Box must be supplied by the Permanent Way Department with a pair of suitable pliers to facilitate the withdrawal of "layers" from the tumblers.

10. **Machine thrown out of Use.**—If for any purpose any part of a machine is temporarily thrown out of use by the Signal or Permanent Way Department, the man in charge of the work must advise the Signalman, and the latter must make an entry of the fact in his Train Register Book. Both he and the man in charge of the repairs must sign their names, and the time must be recorded.

11. **When Machine is brought into Re-use.**—When the repairs are completed, the Signalman, after receiving an assurance from the man in charge that the work has been done, must test the machine, and if found to be all right, then enter in the Train Register Book the words "Machine in order," and both he and the man in charge of the work must sign their names under the words, a note of the time being also inserted. (G.C., 3548.)

Figure 15.14 *Abstract from the regulations for working fog machines printed in the LNWR Appendix 'A' to the Working Time Tables dated April 1916.*

Chapter Sixteen Signalling Layouts

This chapter looks at some station layouts to indicate how the signalling was laid out on the ground. Actual installations have been chosen rather than inventing 'typical' layouts as it is felt that these will be of more interest and lasting value. This does have disadvantages, however, since not all situations can be covered. In addition, the solution to a particular problem adopted at one location was not necessarily that adopted elsewhere. Practically all layouts suffer some restriction, such as limitations of space or difficulties of sighting, which require a 'local' solution and consequently are seldom 'typical'. The layouts illustrated and described in the Chapter should nevertheless give readers a good insight into LNW signalling practice.

Unless otherwise stated, the diagrams represent the layouts as they appeared in the 1920's and 1930's, but in most cases they would have changed little since LNW days. The majority of the examples are relatively small. These have been chosen deliberately since they are easier to describe and understand. The principles outlined can be used in building up or understanding larger layouts. In all cases the numbers adjacent to the points and signals are the numbers of the controlling levers in the signal cabin. The numbers in brackets near the foot of the signal posts in **Figure 16.2** and **16.4** are their distance in yards from the cabin.

Figure 16.1 is an LNW drawing of 1878 for the installation of a new seven lever ground frame at Kenilworth. This was provided in connection with the construction of a new siding alongside the single line forming an extension of the passenger loop. A new disc signal (3) was also provided to control exit from the siding. The new frame was of the Webb 'Right-Angle' type (Chapter 11), hence the seven levers and the numbering of the left-hand home signal as 7 and the distant as 6. This layout serves to illustrate the rather curious state of affairs which could exist, particularly on the branch lines, prior to the 1889 Regulation of Railways Act. The layout here originally consisted of a single line with a simple loop for crossing trains and a single siding, with no trap point, for goods traffic. There were no signals protecting the loop or siding and the points were all apparently worked by hand. This layout dated from the time of opening of the line when adequate protection was considered to be provided by the train staff system. The original frame referred to on the drawing was presumably installed in connection with Lockhart's Siding.

The Regulation of Railways Act of 1874 required more stringent standards of signalling for new construction and the new siding had to comply with these. The siding was therefore protected by fixed signals (1, 2, 6 and 7) in each direction. Trap points were provided to prevent vehicles running out of the siding (and Lockhart's siding). The point and signal levers are concentrated at one point and are correctly interlocked. This was all in accordance with the 1874 Act but hardly in the spirit of it since the original layout remained with practically no interlocking and virtually unprotected. Things did not remain in this state for too long however. The line was doubled and proper signalling, including a 30 lever signal cabin (page vii), was provided in 1883. The drawing also serves to illustrate just how small and simple the majority of stations were in those days. Local freight traffic did not start to develop in any quantity until the mid 1880's. The three-figure numbers by the various points were their distances, in yards, from the lever frame.

Where signalling alterations were proposed, these had to be approved by the Officers concerned, and the stamp for their signatures can be seen in the bottom left hand corner. Some well known names and initials can be found. Besides those specifically named, there are the initials of Richard Moon, the Company Chairman, and Charles Dick the Signal Superintendent. Mr Webb was not concerned with this side of operating matters and neither his name, nor that of the Chief Engineer, appear.

Figure 16.2 is an example of the signalling at a small station on a double track line. Three signals in the down direction (Distant, Home and Starting) were provided. This was the most usual arrangement. The home signal was placed near the fouling point for the crossover and yard points (7 and 8). The starting signal has been placed just in advance of the platform so that it could act as starting signal to trains standing in the station. On the up side there were four signals. An Outer Home signal (21) has been added in the rear of the platform so that it could protect a train standing in the station. The Board of Trade, in its requirements for new work on passenger lines, laid down that trains standing in stations should be protected by fixed signals, hence signal 21. The requirement was a relic of the days before the block system and the station signal era, but remained in force well into this century.

As was the usual practice, trailing connections have been taken from each running line (points 7/9 for the up line, with 12 and 14/15 for the down line) to the sidings. Facing points for this sort of movement were very rare. This was partly because of the dislike of facing points already referred to, and because it was also operationally most convenient. By the use of trailing connections a freight train with traffic to detach could simply draw past the points and push back the required wagons into the yard (leaving the rear of the train on the main line). Outgoing traffic could be picked up by the same process. This made shunting simple and quick and obviated the need for running round. When the work was complete the train proceeded on its way. Two connections were provided in the down line (points 12 and 14/15); this arrangement enabled the yard to be shunted and wagons to be put in and removed from the goods shed without the engine having to pass through it (a considerable fire risk).

The up line connection has had a slip connection (8) added to it to form a trailing crossover between the running lines. The arrangement and lie of the points was the usual one adopted in pre-grouping days. In later years the normal position of the slip connection points was reversed so as to lie normally for the crossover. Both ends of the crossover would then be worked by the same lever (7 in this case), points 8 becoming single ended. The LNW normally arranged double ended points, such as crossovers and those which connected running lines with sidings or loops which were some distance from the cabin, so that the two ends were worked by separate levers. This has been done with points 7/9 and 14/15. It reduced the weight on the levers which in turn reduced wear and tear on the equipment and hence maintenance costs. In addition, it allowed the signalman to use the running line points as a trap point to intercept vehicles running away in the wrong direction while keeping the yard points normal to prevent vehicles escaping from the sidings on to the main line. Thus points 15 could be reversed to intercept vehicles running away on the down line from the Windermere direction, while points 14 remained normal to intercept any vehicle running away along the siding.

In LMS days, disc signals 10 and 11 were fitted with yellow faces and lamps to signify that they only applied

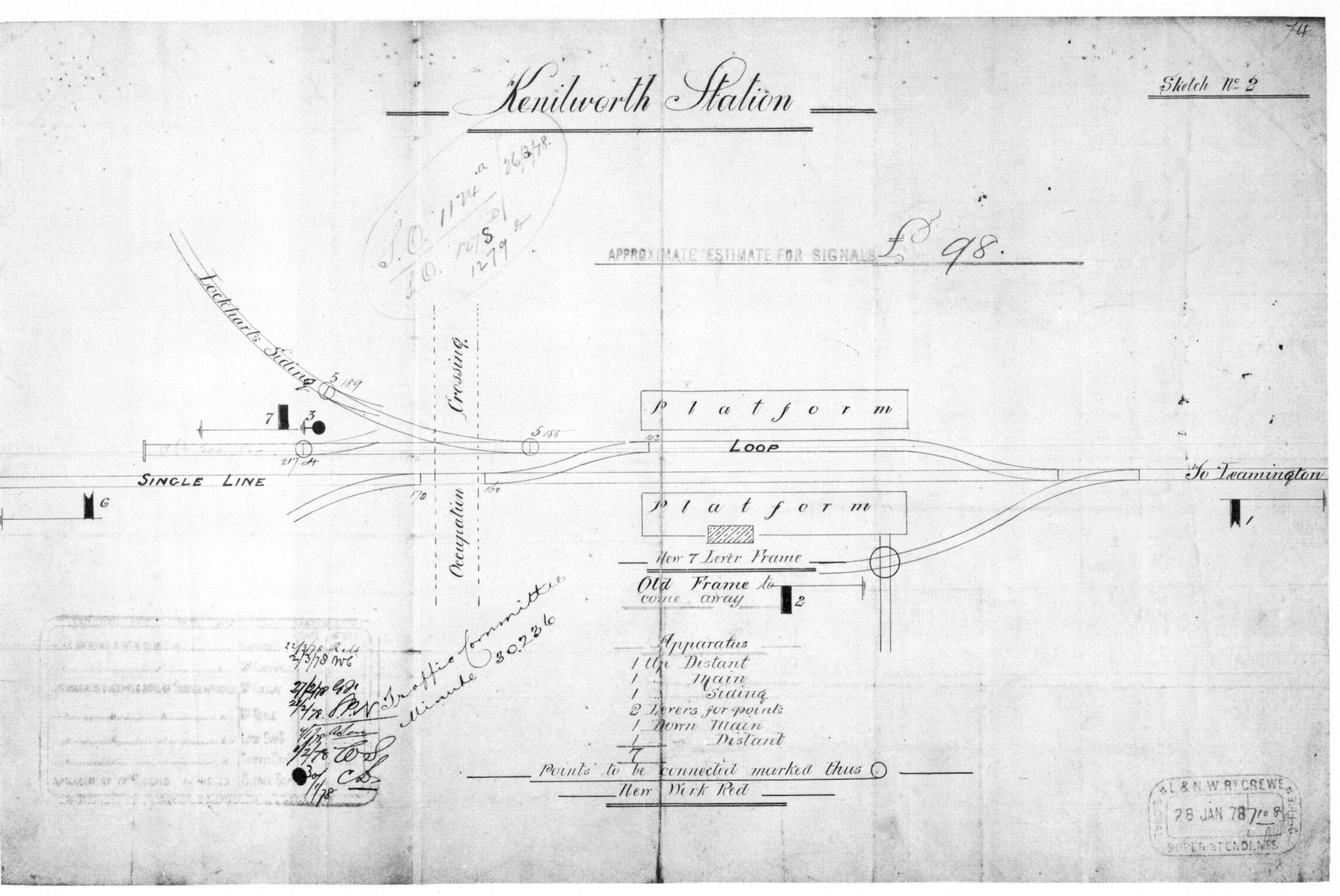

Figure 16.1 *An LNW sketch for the installation of a Webb 'Right-Angle' lever frame at Kenilworth in 1878. The work was expected to cost £98: this covered the provision of a new lever frame and a new disc signal plus connecting up the signals and points to the frame.*

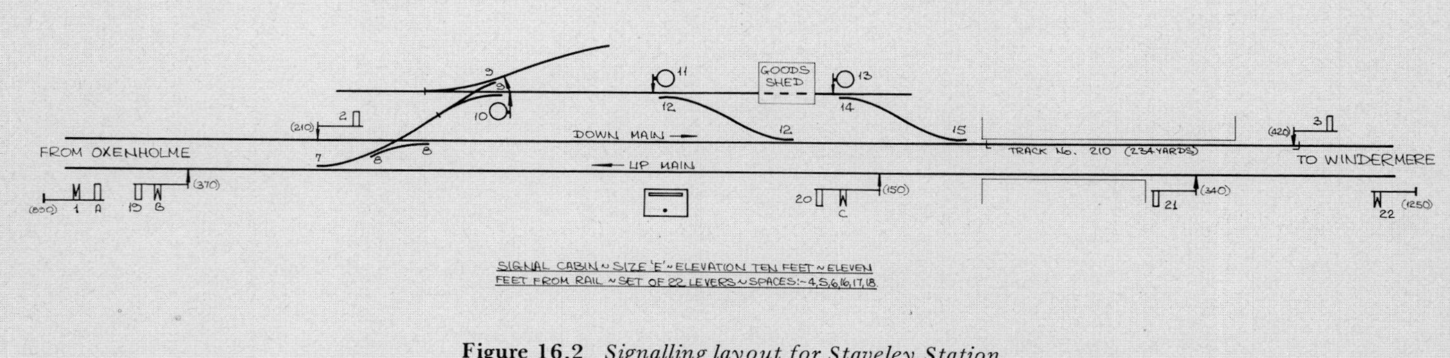

Figure 16.2 *Signalling layout for Staveley Station.*

to movements to the main lines. Shunting could continue past them when they were in the 'on' position provided the points were normal (i.e. along the siding).

The signals lettered A, B and C apply to Staveley Level Crossing. Signal A is the down home signal protecting the crossing and B and C are the up distants for the crossing. Distant B was too near the crossing to give adequate braking distance and so an outer distant (C) was provided under signal 20 (see **Figure 3.8**).

As already mentioned, signal 3 has been placed to act as a platform starting signal. This has resulted in it being over 420 yards from the cabin, rather more than the recommended maximum of 350 yards. While this was the best place from an operating point of view it carried the danger that a train could draw up to it, and being so far from the cabin could be forgotten by the signalman. Due to the curvature of the line here the presence of the station and goods shed obscured the view of the train from the cabin. For this reason a track circuit has been provided in the rear of the signal. This would operate an indicator in the cabin (**Plate 12.13**) to remind the signalman of the presence of the train. For record purposes the LNW numbered its track circuits, as did the Midland. The LMS continued the practice, using the Midland numbers as a base. The old LNW numbers had 2 000 added to them in 1926 to continue the sequence. The blank numbers between the two series were then filled up as new track circuits were installed.

Figure 16.3 illustrates a country station on a secondary double track line. As has already been mentioned, the LNWR soon realised that savings could be made in both installation and operating costs by not providing a conventional signal cabin at such stations. The block instruments were kept in the booking office out of the weather and interference from the public. In the simple key interlocking system used at Sedbergh, levers were provided for the signals only. With the signals normal (i.e. at danger) keys could be taken from the frame to release one lever ground frames adjacent to the point or set of points they worked. This arrangement was quite adequate as the signalman or shunter would be on the spot dealing with the train anyway. The majority of these frames were open to the elements but a few gained huts at some time or another, Sedbergh obtaining a second hand one in the 1940's. Further economy has been achieved by mounting signal arms 2 and 6 on the same post.

Signals 3 and 5 are sited in advance of the siding points to prevent the possibility of a misunderstanding whereby a driver who had completed shunting ran out on to the

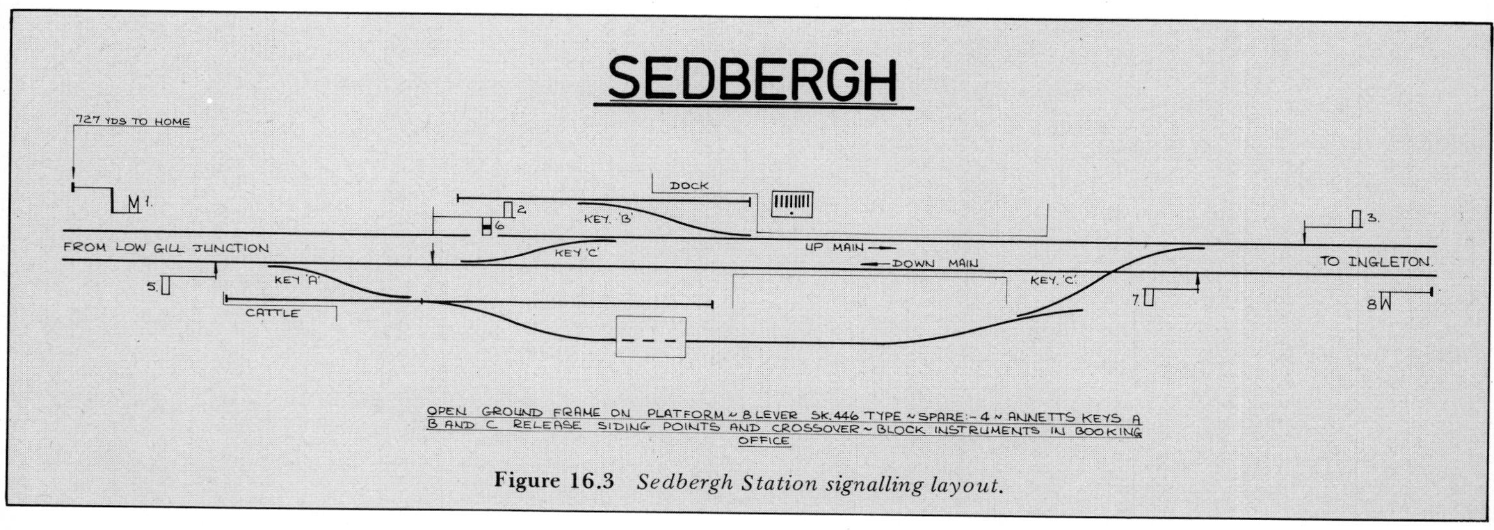

Figure 16.3 *Sedbergh Station signalling layout.*

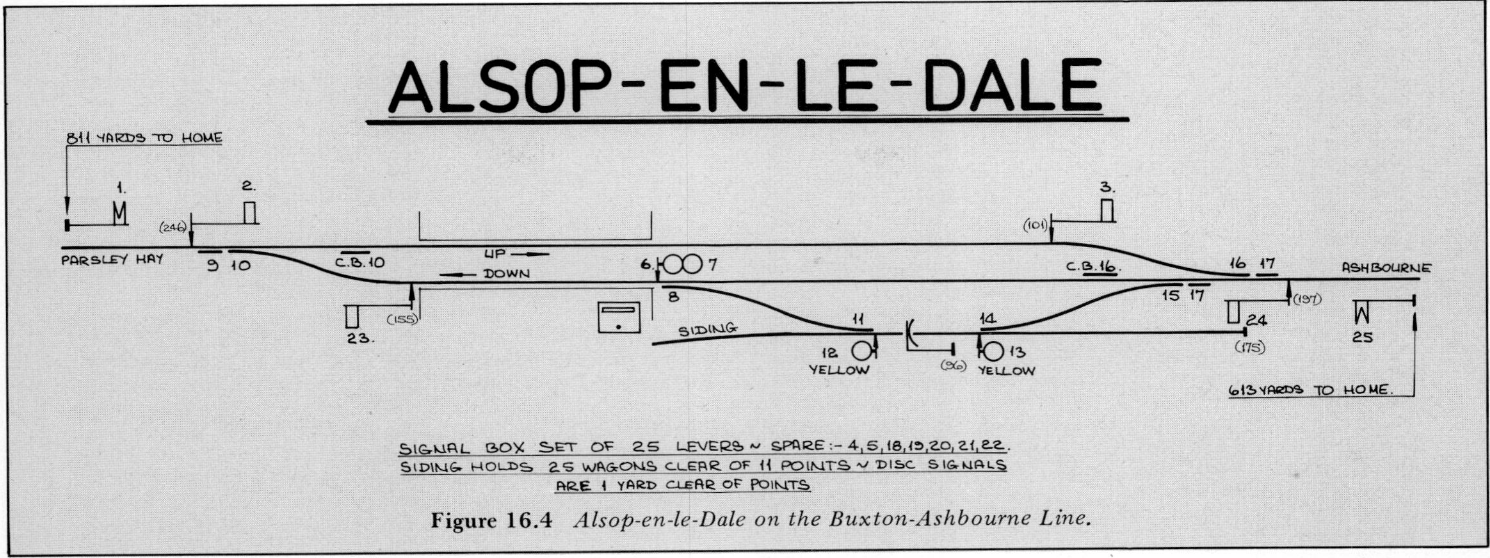

Figure 16.4 *Alsop-en-le-Dale on the Buxton-Ashbourne Line.*

main line to clear the points and then continued into the section (which could be occupied) thinking he had the 'right-away'. With signals 3 and 5 in advance of the points it was possible to drop a train out of the sidings and up to the signal to await a clear road without any danger of its continuing into the section.

Figure 16.4 illustrates a simple crossing station on a single line branch. This one dates from 1899 when the line was opened. Discs 12 and 13 in the yard applied to moves from the yard to the down main and had yellow faces, fitted in LMS days, to indicate that they could be passed at danger when the points were normal, so that shunting could continue clear of the main line. (See Chapter 7).

Clearance bars 10 and 16 work with the respective points at each end of the loop. These were intended to ensure that a train in one of the loop lines was not standing beyond the fouling point at its rear end when the points were reversed to allow a train on the other line to proceed. If a vehicle was still standing on the bar (which like a facing point lock bar must be longer than the wheelbase of the longest vehicle) it would not be possible to reverse the points.

A facing connection off the down line into the yard was provided here. Often only one connection would be provided at single line stations since the engine could get around its train by using the loop and so work the yard regardless of its direction of travel.

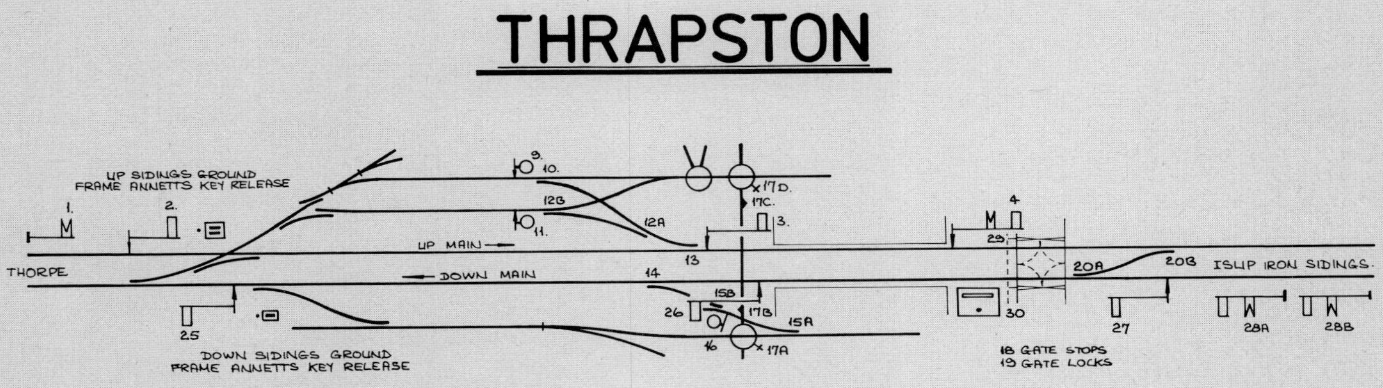

THRAPSTON

UP SIDINGS GROUND FRAME ANNETTS KEY RELEASE
THORPE
UP MAIN
DOWN MAIN
ISLIP IRON SIDINGS.
DOWN SIDINGS GROUND FRAME ANNETTS KEY RELEASE
18 GATE STOPS
19 GATE LOCKS
SIGNAL BOX ~ SET OF 30 LEVERS ~ SPARE:- 5,6,7,8,21,22,23,24.

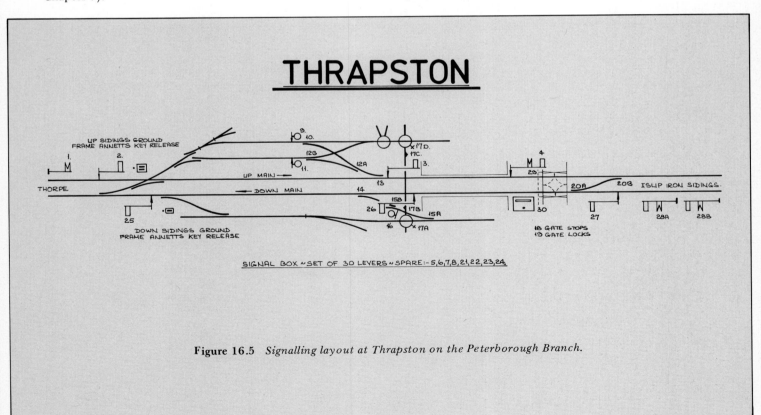

Figure 16.5 *Signalling layout at Thrapston on the Peterborough Branch.*

Figure 16.5 shows the layout at quite a large country station. The necessity of supervising the level crossing has resulted in the cabin being placed at the end of the station away from the yard. Ground Frames were therefore necessary to control the connections at the left hand end. These were released by Annett's Keys, which were normally locked in the lever frame at the signal cabin. Removal of one of the keys to operate one of the frames would lock the appropriate running signals at danger to prevent another train approaching while shunting was in progress.

A feature immediately apparent are the wagon turntables in the up and down sidings connected by a line passing across the running lines at right angles. Traffic on the main line was protected by lever 17. This bolted both of the turntables in position (17A and 17D) and so prevented them from being turned. (The simple act of turning a wagon end for end could easily foul the running line.) As an added precaution 17B and 17C are scotch blocks which would stop anything from the stub siding running across the table and onto the line. Originally only the scotch blocks were provided but in 1897 the turntables were altered by removing one set of rails and bolts were installed as additional protection for the main line. Such turntables were a common feature of the LNWR goods yards and were necessary because the Company had many goods vans with doors on one side only. These often had to be turned around to enable them to be loaded or unloaded against a dock or in a goods shed. The right angle crossings were common in early days, indeed many large stations had them for carriages. The majority of the crossings over the running lines were removed during the 1890's and early 1900's to enable line speeds to be increased and to reduce wear on stock and track. One at Brandon on the main line to Birmingham for instance was removed in 1903. This one at Thrapston survived well into LMS days however. The down distant signal number 28A was under the Islip Sidings Starting Signal, but because this was too near to the level crossing to provide an adequate braking distance a second arm (28B) was provided under the Islip home signal.

Figure 16.6 illustrates a medium sized terminal station. Oxford was at the end of the cross country line from Cambridge. It was double track from Bletchley but two platforms were quite adequate for the passenger traffic (about a dozen trains each way per day). The goods yard was quite extensive however.

There was a canal near the station and the line crossed this only a few feet above water level, necessitating a swing bridge. Special measures had to be taken to protect this and ensure that a train could not approach when the bridge was open for canal traffic. This added to the complexity of the layout and made the station rather awkward to operate. Lever 16 was a bridge bolt and held the bridge in position and alignment when it was used for rail traffic. A problem with moveable bridges was taking the point and signal connections across. In most cases these ran across the bridge itself and had to be physically disconnected and reconnected each time, a time consuming process. Mechanical means could be used for the point rods but these do not seem to have been very common. A shackle joint was generally used in signal wires. At Oxford, a small bridge at a higher level, clear of the boats, was provided for the point and signal connections.

Bethesda (**Figure 16.7**) is an example of a simple LNWR terminal station and a number of other small terminals on the line were of this form. Because the goods yard and loop points were some distance apart, separate signals were provided to protect them. Economy was achieved by mounting the starting signals on the same posts. This was an example of the 'larger' open frame installations, a 10

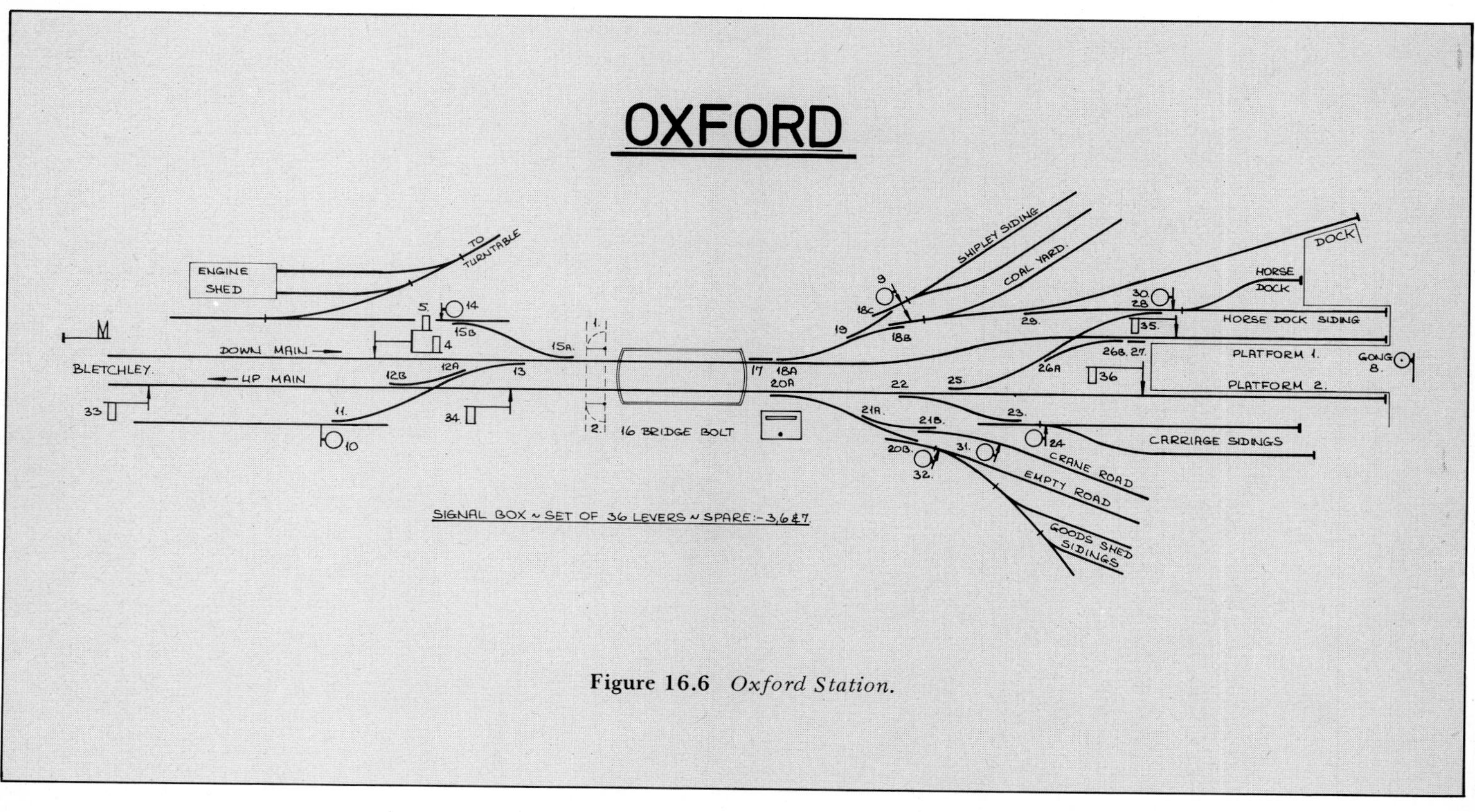

Figure 16.6 *Oxford Station.*

BETHESDA

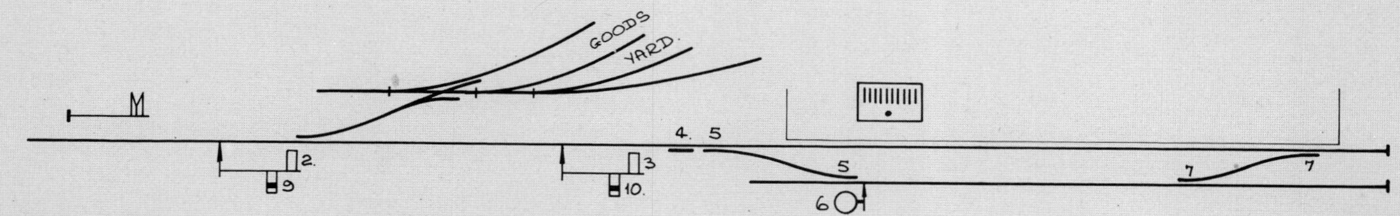

OPEN GROUND FRAME ON PLATFORM ~ SET OF 10 LEVERS ~ SPACES 1 AND 8.
SIDING POINTS RELEASED BY ANNETTS KEY 'C'.

Figure 16.7 *Signalling at Bethesda on the Branch from Bangor. The lever frame was installed in 1884.*

PENYGROES

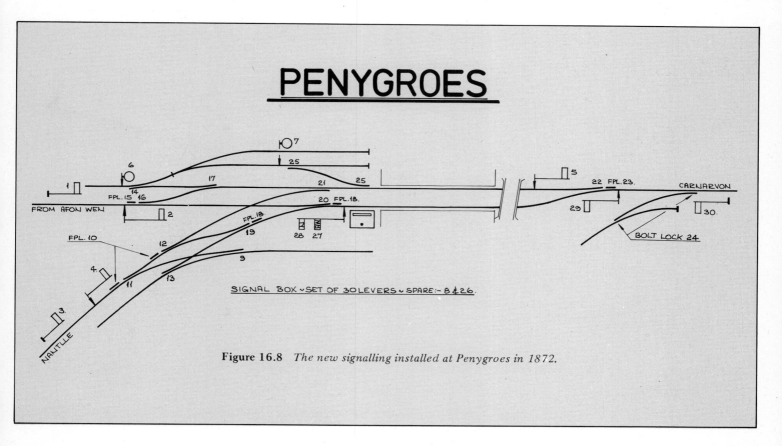

SIGNAL BOX ~ SET OF 30 LEVERS ~ SPARE:- 8 & 26.

Figure 16.8 *The new signalling installed at Penygroes in 1872.*

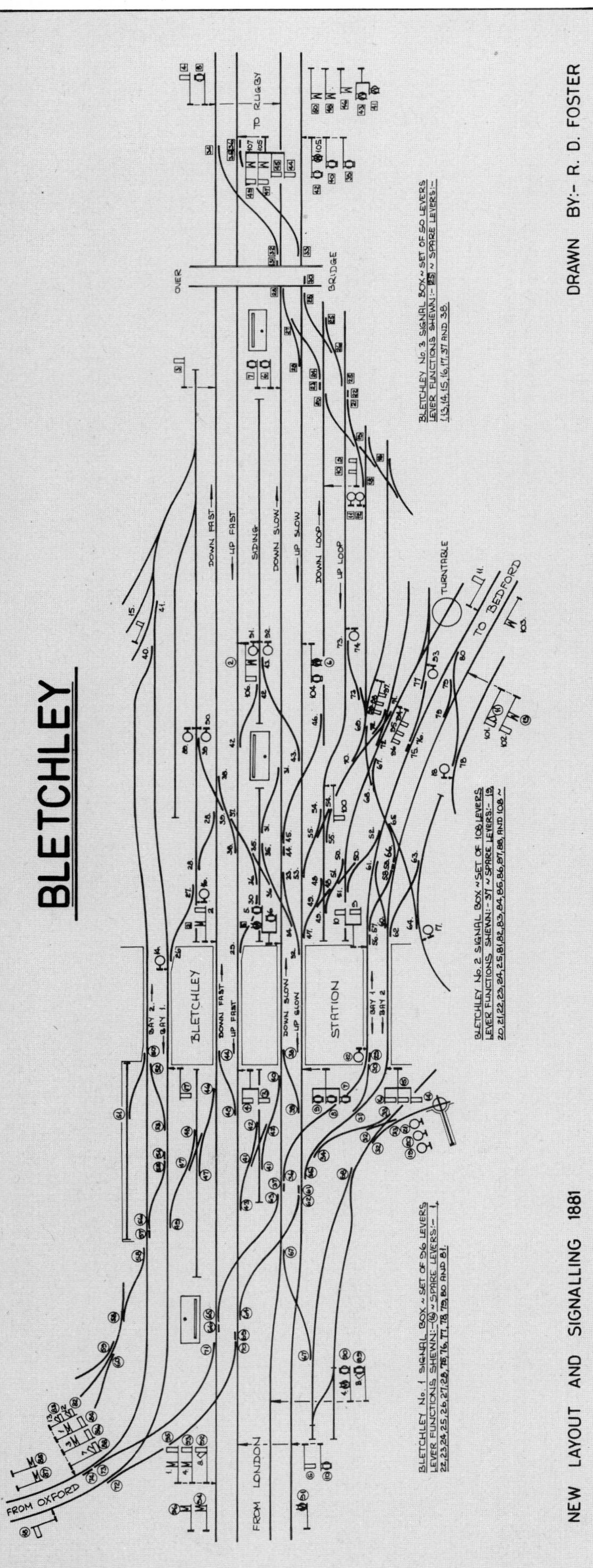

lever tumbler type frame being used. This was raised up above platform level to provide room for the interlocking and a better view for the signalman.

Both Oxford and Bethesda have fixed distant signals on the approach to the terminal. The use of a fixed, rather than working distant signal in such circumstances had become the preferred practice at about the turn of the Century. The caution signal acted as a landmark for the driver to remind him where he was and to enable him to bring his train under control as he approached the home signal and station area. In earlier days it was common practice to provide working distants and it is noteworthy that both frames have spares or spaces where the distant levers would have been.

Figures 16.8 and **16.9** illustrate two layouts installed new during the earlier days of the LNWR. Penygroes was a new cabin opened in 1872 when the standard gauge Nantlle branch was opened (it had previously been narrow gauge). Board of Trade regulations required single line junctions to be made in double track form and this was done here. The junction signals 27 and 28 show the old arrangement of mounting the arms one above the other according to the convention of top arm reading to the left hand route, and so on, the bottom arm reading to the furthest right hand route. Another early practice is seen in that the names of the routes are painted on the arms. Signals 1, 3 and 30 were in fact distant signals, although shown with the same form of arm as the home or stop signals. The drivers were expected to know which were which. The distinctive 'fishtail' form of the distant signal arm was not introduced until 1877 (Chapter 3).

Figure 16.9 illustrates a large station on the main line with three signal cabins. The layout and signalling were introduced in 1881 when this portion of the line was widened to four tracks. The basic track layout changed little until electrification. At the north end, the yard was greatly extended later by the LNWR and additional signal cabins provided to work the new layout. The, then common, practice of providing separate posts for splitting junction signals will be noted. Stability, construction and cost considerations seem to have limited the use of bracket and gantry signals in the early days. The practice of placing both slow and fast line signals together on one side of the line is also illustrated (see also Chapters 4 and 5). Note that No. 2 cabin has distant signals under No. 1 cabin's home signals for the down fast and slow lines, but slots No. 1 cabin's home signals for the Bay 1 line. This was necessary since that line was worked in both directions between the two cabins.

Mention was made on page 59 of the general LNW policy of placing the arms of junction or directing signals for through routes at the same height. The signals at Bletchley were set out in this way. Where signal arms applied to movements to bays and goods lines — for example the up home signals at Bletchley No. 3 reading to the Up Loop and yard (arms 39, 40, 44 and 45) — they were placed at a lower level.

The use of distinguishing rings on the signal arms which apply to the slow lines will be noted. A study of the diagram will show which signals were fitted with rings where there were parallel lines and alternative routes ahead. The signals installed under this scheme were of the 1876 types (Chapter 3) and a number of them were still in use in the early years of this century. The use of facing point lock bars and bolts on points passed over in a facing direction can be seen.

Figure 16.9 *New track layout and signalling installed at Bletchley in 1881.*

Chapter Seventeen

Signalling on the Associated and Joint Lines

A delight of the pre-grouping railway scene were the sections of line which belonged to two or more Companies. Many of these had a character of their own because of their cosmopolitan nature and often independent management. Practices varied widely from line to line, some reflecting almost entirely the equipment and practices of the dominant partner. In other cases they displayed a curious mixture of all the owning companies practices while yet others went very much their own way.

The joint lines added colour and variety to the railway scene, but since they do not fit conveniently into any category they often receive scant coverage. The next few pages contain a review, of necessity rather brief, of the major sections of line in which the LNW had an interest. These largely illustrate practices which were peculiar to those sections of line. It is not possible, in the space available, to illustrate or mention every such line and I hope that those whose favourite line has not been included will not be too disappointed.

17.1 LONDON AND NORTH WESTERN AND GREAT WESTERN JOINT LINES

Probably the largest and most important series of joint lines in which the LNWR had an interest were those shared in some way with the GWR. The most extensive and most important were the Shrewsbury and Birkenhead Joint sections. These lines merit a quite detailed survey following which the other sections of joint line are mentioned briefly.

SHREWSBURY AND BIRKENHEAD JOINT LINES

The joint lines in the Shrewsbury (Shrewsbury to Hereford, Welshpool and Wellington and Branches) and Birkenhead Districts have a common history as far as signalling is concerned and can be considered together. The meetings of the Joint Committee of LNW and GW Directors who managed the lines were often attended by Sir Daniel Gooch and Richard Moon, both of whom were said to be very powerful Chairmen and who would make every effort to protect their own Company's interests. One can imagine that some of these meetings must have been very lively affairs indeed!

Engineering matters were all administered from an Engineer's Office in Birkenhead, Mr R E Johnson being the Engineer for many years. During the 1860's, 70's and early 1880's the LNW and GW seemed to have had their hands full in coping with work on their own lines and consequently left the Joint Staff very much on their own.

Signalling work was generally put out to tender, the Company submitting the lowest tender (subject to satisfactory conditions) carrying out the work. Some of the early signalling was inevitably somewhat variable in character and could be rudimentary. The Shrewsbury and Hereford line was little more than a country branch line in the early years and it was not until about 1870 that any real attempt was made to signal and interlock the stations. A few installations had been made, for example a Saxby and Farmer signal cabin on stilts was provided at the junction with the Bishop's Castle Railway when this was opened in 1865 (see 'The Bishop's Castle Railway' by Edward Griffith).

Plate 17.1 *A typical example of one of the early 'joint line' all-brick cabins, at Leominster South End. This cabin was originally built to control a level crossing, but this was removed after a few years and replaced by the bridge seen in the background. The cabin remained, however, to control access to some sidings. Note the great width of the cabin and the fact that this particular example is almost exactly square in plan and has a nice pinnacle surmounting the hipped roof. The cast iron locking room windows were of similar type to those used on the LNW but were somewhat taller. Since closure of the station cabin this cabin has been renamed Leominster and the name plate shortened accordingly.*

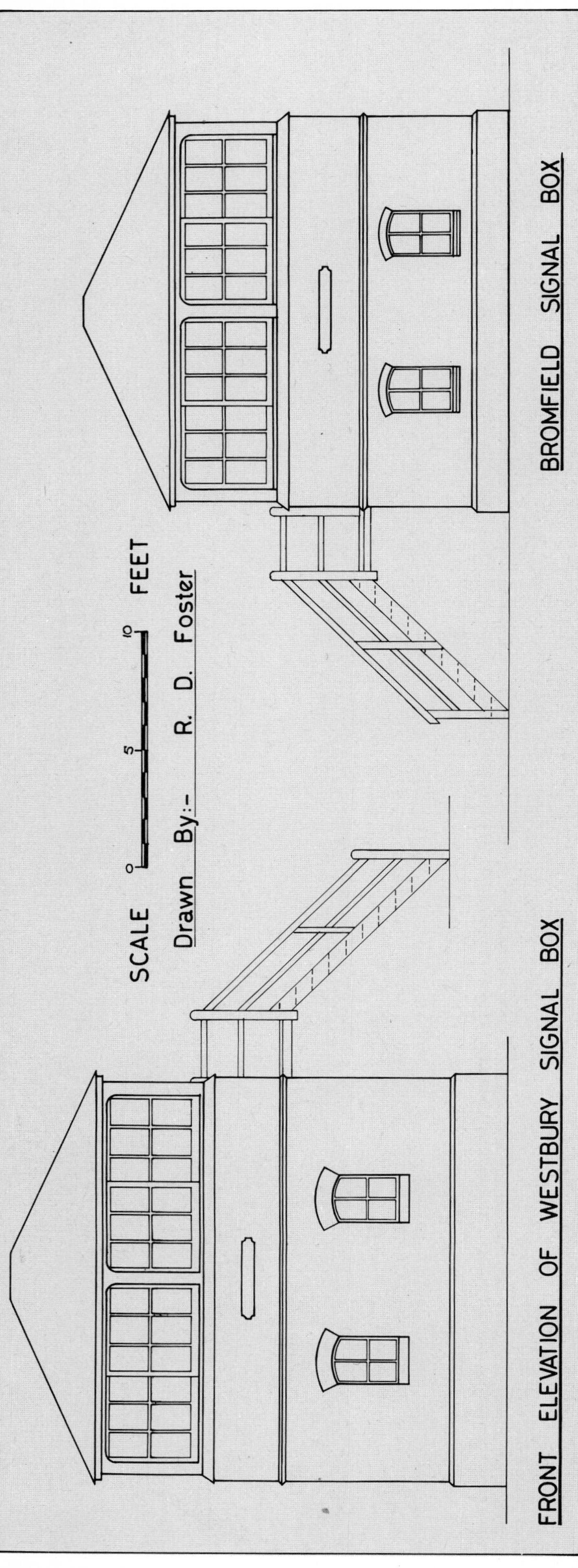

A report on the Hereford line signalling was prepared in November 1871. As a result, in January 1872 Saxby and Farmer patent gates were ordered to be provided for the level crossings at Marshbrook, Craven Arms and Onibury, the necessary signals and signal cabins being included. The following month authority was given for the expenditure of £5,416 on installing the block system on this line and carrying out the interlocking at those places which had not yet been done. Of the individual stations, expenditure of £500 on signalling at Leebotwood was authorised in August 1872. The following May, Saxby and Farmer's tender of £619 18*s* 3*d* for signalling work at Bromfield, and Stevens and Sons tender of £1,543 for signalling at Shrewsbury were both accepted.

By about 1870, the joint line had evolved something of a 'house style' of its own as far as signal cabins were concerned. These brick cabins had a Saxby influence in their design and were basically similar to the 'Type 1' Saxby and Farmer cabins found on the northern portion of the LNWR, although they differed in detail. It seems that the design was specified in the contract for each job and examples appeared all over the joint lines.

The cabins tended to be square or nearly square in plan and this led to many of them being unusually wide, as can be seen from the dimensions given in **Figures 17.2** and **17.4**. No examples now exist north of Chester but several are still in use on the Shrewsbury District. The width of the cabins, allowing the fitting of new equipment, and their sturdy construction were no doubt reasons for the survival of a number into recent times. In all cases however, the original lever frames have been replaced by the standard equipment of one or other of the owning Companies.

In January 1880 it was decided to standardise the Block Signalling Regulations on the Joint Lines. GW Regulations were adopted for the Shrewsbury District and LNW for the Birkenhead lines.

Returning to signal cabins and signals, approval was given in 1880 for the enlargement, rebuilding and resignalling of Wellington Station. The four new cabins were of a new design, with an overhanging roof and small top windows. They again had a distinct Saxby and Farmer appearance and were similar to the cabins they were erecting on the Brighton line at this time. All were fitted with the well-known Saxby 'Rocker' type lever frames.

Not long afterwards, work began on enlarging Hereford Station, and tenders were invited for the necessary signalling work. Six tenders were received, the Contractors and their tender figures being:—

Railway Signal Company, Liverpool	£2,950
Saxby and Farmer	£3,205 14*s* 9*d*
McKenzie and Holland, Worcester	£3,250
Railway and Electrical Appliance Co.	£3,500
Gloucester Wagon Company	£3,648
J. Tweedy and Co.	£5,050

The tender of the Railway Signal Company was accepted in January, 1884. Johnson had obviously specified the design of certain of the equipment in order to keep the signalling on his line reasonably standardised. 'Saxby' style signal cabins similar to those at Wellington were therefore constructed, and all were fitted with Saxby 'Rocker' frames. The signals however were standard Railway Signal Company products. The signal cabins at Wellington and Hereford, like the earlier designs, tended to be wide if circumstances permitted (see **Figure 17.5**).

Figure 17.1 *Scale drawings of the signal cabins at Bromfield and Westbury. As can be seen the two are almost identical. The heights were varied to produce the elevation required while the width of the window panes were altered to suit the exact length of cabin required. The remaining elevations of Westbury are shown in* **Figure 17.3**.

Plate 17.2 *The largest of the standard joint line cabins to survive into recent times was at Woofferton Junction. The layout here was enlarged in 1889, and rather than build a new cabin the existing one was extended by the LNW in a matching style as shown in* **Figure 17.3.** *A new frame with 55 working levers was provided for the enlarged cabin. The extension was made at the left hand end of the cabin and is just detectable in the photograph.*

These schemes were very much a final fling for the joint line and in June 1884 Mr Findley of the LNWR suggested that the signalling work should in future be carried out in the Birkenhead District by the LNWR and in the Shrewsbury District by the GWR. Messrs Webb (LNW) and Owen (GW) were asked to report on the subject. In August 1884 Sir Daniel Gooch explained that there would be a difficulty in adopting the suggestion owing to the GW Company not having a separate Signal Department staff as the LNW had (the maintenance of signalling equipment was carried out by the Permanent Way Department, on the GW). Mr Moon stated that the North Western would be prepared to undertake the work in both districts. This offer was accepted and it was agreed that the LNW would take over the installation of new work and maintenance of the existing equipment from the 1st of January 1885. It was estimated that the altered arrangements would effect a saving of £1,150 per annum in wages

Figure 17.2 EXAMPLES OF SHREWSBURY DISTRICT ALL BRICK CABINS

Cabin	*Length*	*Width*	*Frame Type*	*Installed*	*Notes*
Bromfield	16′ 6½″	15′ 0″	W.4″ VT.5B	24-4-1956	
Church Stretton	16′ 7″	13′ 7½″	LNW Tumbler		
Craven Arms Junction	27′ 5″	14′ 1½″	W.4″ HT.3B	9-10-1910	
Dorrington	15′ 8″	13′ 8½″	W.4″ VT.5B	21-9-1941	
Ford Bridge	15′ 0″	13′ 1″*	W.5¼″ S.		1
Leominster South End	15′ 2″	15′ 1″	LNW Tumbler	1901	
			W.4″ VT.5B	4-7-1941	
Marshbrook	15′ 7½″	13′ 7″*	LNW Tumbler		
Onibury	17′ 4½″	11′ 5″*	LNW Tumbler		
Shelwick Junction	15′ 6″	15′ 6″	W.5¼″ VT.5B	11-2-1942	1,2
Westbury	17′ 0″	15′ 1″	W.4″ VT.3B	13-1-1916	
Woofferton Junction	25′ 7½″	16′ 8″	As originally built		3
Woofferton Junction	36′ 10½″	16′ 8″	LNW Tumbler	1889	
			W.4″ HT.3B	2-2-1914	

W.4″ VT.5B = GW 4″ centres frame with vertical tappet locking of 5 bar type.
W.5¼″ S = GW 5¼″ centres frame with stud locking.
W.4″ HT.3B = GW 4″ centres frame with horizontal tappet locking of 3 bar type.

NOTES:
* – Width restricted by site conditions.
1 – Frame probably second hand when fixed.
2 – Converted from Stud locking.
3 – Cabin extended in 1889 to accommodate a new, larger frame – see next entry, **Figure 17.3** and **Plate 17.2**.

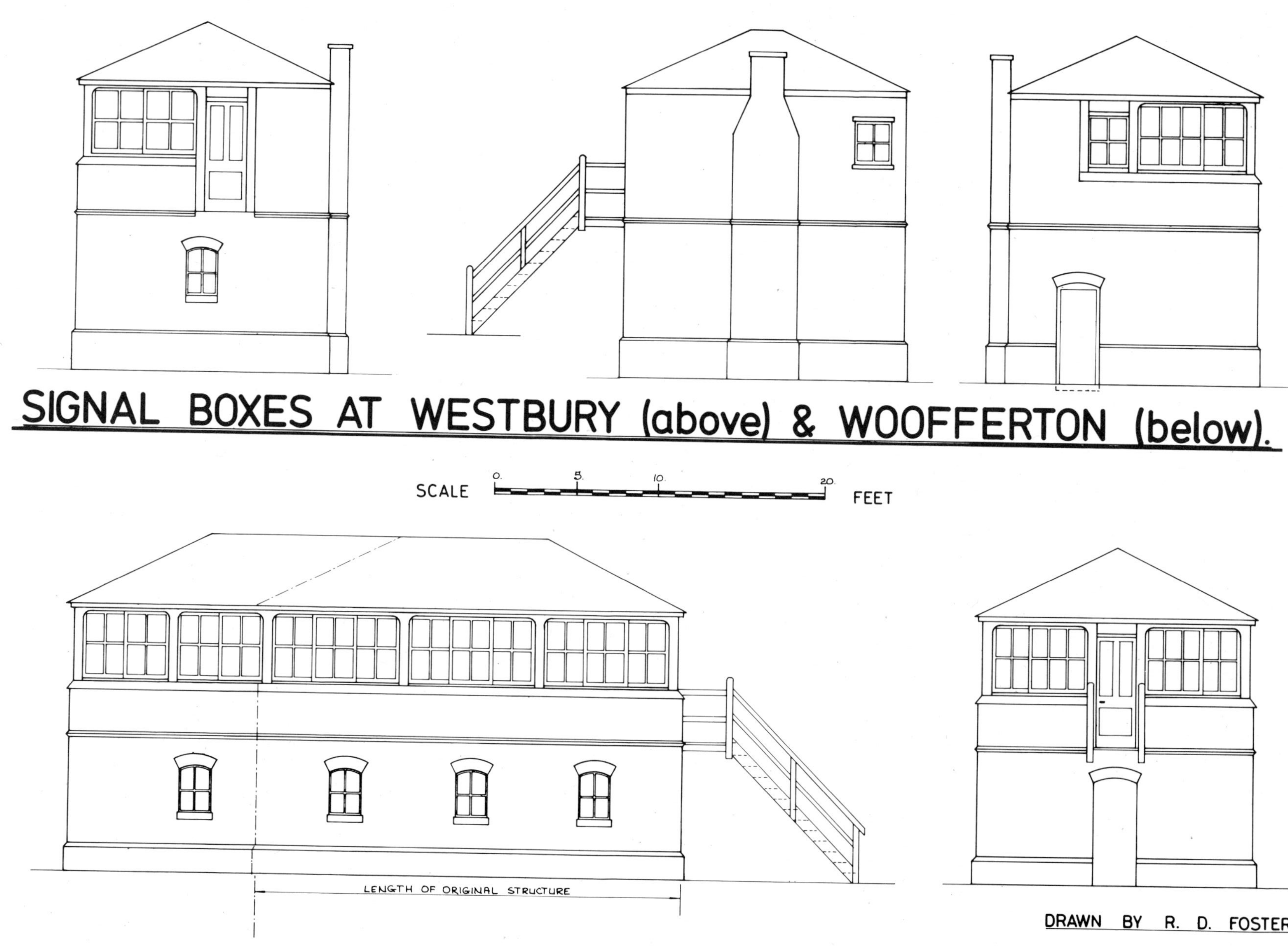
SIGNAL BOXES AT WESTBURY (above) & WOOFFERTON (below).
SCALE
0.
5.
10
20.
FEET
LENGTH OF ORIGINAL STRUCTURE
DRAWN BY R. D. FOSTER

Plate 17.3 *An early cabin of different design was this one at Chester No. 5 (Brook Lane) erected in 1874; when built it had 'more than 50 levers'. However, as the layout grew and more signals were provided the cabin became too small. Rather than build a new cabin (it occupied the best available site) the existing one was extended twice, once in 1908 and again in 1915, to accommodate the extra levers required. The cabin was originally 28' 11" by 15' 1" and the first extension increased the length by 7 feet and the second added a further 10 feet; both were made at the right hand end as seen in this photograph. A LNWR Tappet frame was provided in 1905 and this too was extended by adding 10 levers at the time of the first extension and a further 23 levers at the time of the second. The LNW went to some trouble to match the existing structure and the window frames etc. were specially made. As can be seen they made a good job of it. The stone window sills of the original were reproduced in timber on the extensions. Of interest are the McKenzie and Holland style roof pinnacles or finials: the GWR used this firm of signalling contractors quite extensively on their own line. The original contractor for this job is not recorded but it seems probable that it was McKenzie and Holland. Note how the large locking room windows have been bricked up in recent times.*

and that the only expenditure necessary would be £60 in fitting up the vacant store shed at Craven Arms (see Chapter 2 and **Figures** 2.3 and 4). Mr Johnson retained responsibility for the work and the LNW Signal Department was regarded simply as a joint line servant.

At this time there were 104 signal cabins on the Joint Lines with a total of 1987 levers and Mr Johnson had an Inspector and 55 men who carried out the maintenance work. The Inspector was appointed Sub-Inspector in the new Craven Arms LNW District (Chapter 2 and Appendix 1), the services of 39 men were retained and the rest dispensed with. The Shrewsbury and Wellington line was absorbed into the Stafford District and the Birkenhead lines into the Crewe and Warrington Districts.

Figure 17.3 *Westbury and Woofferton Cabins. The drawing of Woofferton shows the cabin after it was enlarged by the LNWR. The dotted line indicates the original size of the structure.*

Figure 17.4 EXAMPLES OF BIRKENHEAD DISTRICT ALL BRICK CABINS

Cabin	*Length*	*Width*	*Opened*	*LNWR Frame Installed*	*Notes*
Capenhurst	11' 7"	11' 7"	1869	1901	1
Dunham Hill	13' 4"	13' 4"	1873	1901	1
Dunkirk	11' 7"	11' 7"	1880	—	
Guilden Sutton	11' 4"	11' 4"	1873	1900	
Mickle Trafford	15' 0"	15' 0"	1874	—	
Mollington	11' 7"	11' 7"	1873	1902	1
Norton	12' 0"	12' 0"	1870	1920	
Upton	11' 4"	11' 4"	1869	1900	

NOTES:
1; Replaced by LMS 'ARP' style signal cabins during world war 2.

From this time onwards standard LNW equipment began to appear as renewals and alterations became necessary. The most obvious effect was the appearance of the characteristic LNW signals. In some cases new LNW arms were fitted to existing posts. This occurred at Hereford for example when the use of red and green lights for signals was adopted, the remaining single spectacle RSC arms being replaced with standard LNW ones. These looked a little strange fitted onto posts with large RSC ball and spike pinnacles. Block working continued to conform with the 1880 arrangement and GW 'Disc' block was in general use on the Shrewsbury District.

As lever frames wore out (or sometimes when layouts were altered or enlarged) these too were replaced with new ones of LNW manufacture (for example at Leebotwood — see also **Figures 17.2** and **17.4**). In other cases new LNW cabins were provided, some of the first examples to appear being Coleham (1885), Birkenhead Town (hut of 1889), Rock Ferry No. 2 (1891), Ledsham Junction, Ledsham Sand Siding, Godscroft, Frodsham Station (all 1892), Frodsham Junction and Daresbury (both 1893).

The quadrupling of the line between Ledsham and Birkenhead in the 1900/02 period swept away many of the old Joint line cabins on the Birkenhead District and some 14 new cabins of LNW standard design were provided in the course of this work. Other extensions and alterations

Plate 17.4 *A number of the early cabins managed to retain their LNW style nameboards into recent times. These consisted of metal letters screwed to a small shaped wooden board, as is illustrated by this one at Bromfield which was typical of the style used on the joint line. The shape of the board makes an interesting variation on the types provided on the LNW proper (see Chapter 9).*

Figure 17.5 EXAMPLES OF 'WELLINGTON' TYPE JOINT LINE CABINS

Cabin	*Date Erected*	*Size*	*Type of Frame*	*Date*
Wellington No. 3	1881	27' 4" x 12' 0"	Saxby Rocker	1881
	*	35' 0" x 12' 0"	LNW 5½" Tappet	1913
Wellington No. 4	1881	27' 3" x 15' 3"	Saxby Rocker	1881
			W.4" VT. 5B.	1954
Aylestone Hill	1884	36' 11" x 15' 5½"	Saxby Rocker	1884
			W.4" VT. 5B.	1938

*Cabin extended in 1913, see **Figures 5.6** and **5.7** in 'LNWR Portrayed' by J K Nelson.

Plate 17.5 *Aylestone Hill Cabin at Hereford was erected in 1884 and is typical of the 'Wellington' design of cabin used on the Shrewsbury and Birkenhead Joint lines in the last few years of independent signalling work. The design clearly owes a lot to Saxby and Farmer's work with the overhanging roof and narrow top windows. However, as explained in the text, this particular example was provided by the Railway Signal Company. Aylestone Hill cabin was renamed Hereford in 1973, when the other remaining cabins in the area were closed and working concentrated on this one.*

Plate 17.6 *Mention was made in Chapter 15 of the use of Lineman's Boards placed on cabins in the early days to indicate whether the lineman was required or not. This photograph, taken at Woofferton, shows the imprint of the telegraph lineman's board stained into the brickwork (through weathering) on the front of the cabin. Note the hook still in position for attaching the board. The board itself had been in position, although disused, until about 1970, hence the clear mark. The 'T' shape was punched out on these Great Western pattern boards.*

made inroads into the old cabins on the rest of the District and by 1910 only a handful remained (**Figure 17.4**).

The turn of the Century also coincided with the peak of activity on the Shrewsbury lines with LNW cabins being provided at Bishop's Castle Junction (1901), Leominster (1901), Marsh Farm Junction (1903) and Shrewsbury (Four cabins during 1900/4).

In 1903 the maintenance arrangements were revised and it was decided that the signal work should be split between the two Companies. From the 1st of January 1904 the GW took over maintenance on the Shrewsbury District Lines. A further change was made on the 1st of January 1909. In connection with the retirement of Mr Johnson, it was decided to abolish the Joint Engineer's Office and transfer the work to the two Companies' District Engineers. The LNW took charge of the Birkenhead District and the Shrewsbury (exclusive) and Wellington and in consequence the signal work on the latter line was transferred back to them. The GW took the remainder of the Shrewsbury District.

Renewals and alterations were carried out using the appropriate Company's standard equipment. These arrangements continued after the grouping. After nationalisation, signalling practice followed that of the Region to which the individual sections of line were allocated. As can be seen from **Figure 17.2**, quite a lot of modernisation work was done on the Shrewsbury and Hereford section during World War 2, when the line was of strategic importance as an alternative route to avoid congestion and bombing. Much of this work was paid for by the Government.

VALE OF TOWY JOINT

This line was dealt with in a similar manner to the Shrewsbury and Birkenhead lines, the LNW taking over the maintenance from 1/3/1886. From 1/1/1904 the GW took over the maintenance of the southern section of the line.

WELSHPOOL STATION

Although the Shrewsbury and Welshpool Joint line actually terminated at Buttington Junction, both the LNW and GW had interests in the Cambrian Station at Welshpool. This was enlarged in the late 1880's and the LNW provided the two new signal cabins and signals. One of these cabins is still in use at the time of writing (although the frame has been renewed).

THE WEST LONDON AND WEST LONDON EXTENSION RAILWAYS

The West London Railway from Willesden to a point just south of Kensington (Addison Road) Station was Joint LNW and Great Western property. The remainder of the line, the West London Extension Railway, was the Joint property of four Companies, the LNW and GW as before, together with the London and South Western and London, Brighton and South Coast. Originally signalling work had been in the hands of the Great Western. From the 1st of July 1874 the signalling work for both lines was transferred to the LNWR.

The LNW received eleven signal cabins: some were described as being in pretty good condition, although the rest were very old. With the cabins came two men and a lad who maintained the signalling and had been working on the line for some time. Edwards reported to the LNW Board that he would need to augment these with two carpenters, one labourer and a painter in order to keep things in proper order. This prompted the LNW to ask the GW how many staff they had used. The GW grudgingly admitted that they had had another man but that he sometimes worked at Paddington and was now needed there!

On the 1st of January 1879 the LNW handed the maintenance of the signalling on the West London Line over to the Great Western and on the West London Extension to the London and South Western. The maintenance periods were supposed to be for five years, but it was not until the 1st of July 1886 that both lines were handed back to the LNWR. In August 1890 the LNW suggested that it would be more economical for one Company to be responsible for the maintenance on a permanent basis since the periodic changes caused problems with a variety of equipment. The following year the maintenance was divided: the LNW continued to be responsible for the West London Line while the GW took on the Extension Railway, these arrangements being permanent.

After the grouping the same arrangements were continued. In early BR days practically the whole of the line was transferred to the Western Region and their equipment slowly began to appear. The large LNW cabins at Kensington North and South Main, built in 1892, had their LNW tumbler frames replaced by WR 5 bar vertical tappet 4 inch centres frames. North Main was so treated on 18 April 1954, while the one at South Main was installed on 14 April 1957 and brought into use on 23 February 1958. Rationalisation has changed the appearance of this line considerably over the past 25 years.

THE NORTH LONDON RAILWAY

The North London Railway comes under the category of 'associated lines' being very much a satellite of the LNWR although until 1909 it was operated as an independent Company. A joint line also comes into the picture. The North and South Western Junction Railway from Willesden to Acton and Kew (LNW, Midland and North London Joint) was largely administered by the North London and followed their signalling practice. These notes, therefore, largely apply to the N&SWJR also.

As might be expected of a railway which had to accommodate a dense suburban passenger service, as well as a heavy transfer traffic on its relatively short line, the signalling was something rather special. The district was densely built up, leading to considerable problems in sighting signals due to obstructions from buildings and bridges. There was also the need to cope with operating most of the traffic in the thick fogs which were such a feature of London life. These factors brought the need for additional safety devices to assist the signalmen, and the signalling was fairly advanced in this respect.

The traffic on the NLR built up very rapidly due to the northwards spread of the City and the convenience of the London terminus which had been opened in 1865. By 1870 work was in hand on quadrupling the line between Kentish Town and Dalston. Further widenings between the latter and Broad Street were authorised soon afterwards. Saxby and Farmer were awarded the contract for the signalling at Kentish Town Junction, Maiden Lane and York Road Junction in November 1870 at a price of £1078. At the same time Stevens and Sons tender of £575 for Dalston Western Junction was accepted. In March 1875 McKenzie and Holland were asked to carry out the signalling work on the City Extension line (including Broad Street Station), the signal cabin structures being erected by the North London (**Plate 17.13**). Because of the heavy traffic much pioneering work on the development of signalling practices and equipment took place on the line. Special efforts were made to produce an adequate and safe system of signals for the newly widened lines. The Board of Trade Inspector, Captain Tyler, congratulated the Company on the efforts it had made when he inspected the new work between Kentish Town and Dalston in May 1871.

The NLR was also a pioneer in the adoption of block working and the absolute block system was established throughout the line in 1855. Maintenance of the ordinary telegraphs was undertaken by the Electric Telegraph Company under a long term contract which passed to the Post Office in 1870. Tyer and Company had a contract for the maintenance of the block instruments and associated equipment. When their contract expired at the end of 1875, Tyers offered to maintain the existing block equipment for a further 10 year period at a price of £411, less 10% (equivalent to £370), per annum, and to maintain any additional instruments at a price of £2 per annum, less 10%. This offer was accepted, although the period was reduced to 9 years in order that both telegraph contracts would expire at the end of 1884. When they terminated the North London took on the maintenance work itself.

For some years the signalling work continued to be carried out by contractors, mainly on a competitive tender basis. In April 1877 the General Manager submitted a report to the Board recommending that:

> 'The signals, locking apparatus and machinery connected with the signals be placed in the charge of the Locomotive Department. Signal boxes, switches and crossovers etc., to be continued in the hands of the P.W. Department. That as the several signals require renewal the system recently adopted by the LNW Co. be substituted for the existing arrangements with a view to having a uniform plan. An arrangement by which this anticipates that

Plate 17.8 *Bow Junction in August 1893. The tiny signal cabin must have been practically filled by the lever frame and there can have been very little room for the poor signalman! The zinc roof is an original feature of the cabin which was built in 1870 but the large locking room windows have been added since. The signal and telegraph lineman's boards will be noted just to the right of the nameboard. The large white post near the end of the cabin was once part of a huge double post signal designed to give sight over the Bow Road Bridge (and was, incidentally, well in advance of the points!). The signal has been removed to the other side of the bridge so as to be in the rear of the points. The line straight ahead is the main line to Poplar and near the far end of the erecting shop is Devons Road Up Distant, which is of the 'restricted clearance' type and is showing 'Off'. The curve to the right leads to Gas Factory Junction on the Great Eastern Railway. Something of the problem of signal sighting can be seen from the arrangement and height of the home signals controlling movements from the two lines and restricted clearance arms (home and distant) are visible below the home signal from Devons Road. The distant arm is not reproduced below the top (co-acting) home arm, but only appears below the lower arm. The two arm signal visible above the erecting shop is at Bromley Junction on the London, Tilbury and Southend line, from which another curve comes round to join the NLR at Tilbury Junction, just beyond Bow Station. The Locomotive Works building behind the cabin was converted from the old loco. running shed and erecting shop, the roof of which had become unsafe, in 1882. The walls were extended and the roof placed at a much higher level in order to accommodate two new overhead travelling cranes. The clock on the wall is inscribed 'NLR'.* ▷

Photo: Courtesy National Railway Museum

Plate 17.7 *A Pryce and Ferreira three-wire double needle block instrument of the type used on the North London Railway. This one is from Skinner Street Junction. The nameplate at the bottom reads 'E Tyer Sole Licencee'.*

Courtesy National Railway Museum

Plate 17.9 *A view taken from a similar position to that in* **Plate 17.8** *on 9th July, 1906, after the construction of the new and much larger Bow Junction cabin (45 levers) in 1895. Some interesting changes in the scene can be spotted and the two photographs amply repay careful study. The distant signal for Devons Road has been moved out to the near end of the erecting shop and has become 'splitting'. The arm with the bar on it led to the loco. yard at Devons Road and was actually fixed at danger. The home signals to which these arms apply are illustrated in* **Plate 17.10**. *The main line and branch down home signals can be seen more clearly here and the lower arms on the GER curve signals will be noted as will the vertical bars on the arms. Most noticeable, perhaps, is the forest of ground disc signals which have 'grown' since the last photograph, note also the three vertically mounted point rod compensators in the rodding run just to the left of the cabin steps. The 'S' and 'T' boards (Chapter 15) are clearly seen here as is the use of round point rodding, another subtle difference from the LNW way of doing things! By 1908 LNW type channel rodding was in use for new work.*

Photo: Courtesy National Railway Museum

efficiency will be better maintained and a saving of time effected in repair with an ultimate reduction in expenditure.'

The proposal was accepted and in October 1877 authority was given for the expenditure of £500 for fitting up part of the old engine shed at Bow for the signal work. In November a further £250 for the workshops and £360 for machinery was authorised.

Henry James Pryce was appointed Signal Superintendent of the North London in 1878. He was a clever and able engineer and it was under his direction that the signalling system was developed. He was born on the 29th of April 1852 and was apprenticed at Inchicore Works in Ireland between 1869 and 1874. His name had probably been put forward by the Locomotive Superintendent, James Carter Park (appointed in 1873), who was also an 'Inchicore' man (although trained on the LNWR at Longsight in John Ramsbottom's days). The two men worked quite closely together and patented a number of devices, of which the Park and Pryce train protection bar was, perhaps, the best known and widely used (**Figure 17.9**). These were used extensively on the North London and most stations had at least one example. They were also to be found on other railways, for example the LNWR installed a pair at Weaver Junction in 1884 at a cost of £30.

Pryce also patented a number of electrical signalling devices, of which the Pryce and Ferreira block instrument deserves mention. By 1890 Pryce was becoming increasingly concerned about the limitations of the one-wire, two-position block instruments which were in use on the line. As with the North-Western, these had been installed in the early days in the interests of economy. Pryce, in conjunction with his Telegraph Inspector, Luis de Moraz Gomez Ferreira, set about the task of designing a three-wire instrument which would suit the line's needs and ensure a better standard of safety. The design produced was patented in March 1895. It was a three-wire, three-position instrument and was arranged so that the needles would not 'peg up', or return to 'line blocked' (no matter

Plate 17.10 *This photograph was taken to show the Bow Works Foundry which had been erected in 1892, fortunately several items of signalling equipment seem to have got in the way! Of principle interest is the bracket signal in the foreground which gives a good idea of the 'pseudo LNW' signals used on the NLR. The arms and caps to the posts are of the LNW pattern but the cast iron bracket for the doll is pure North London and nothing like it was used on the LNW. Note the separate ladders provided, one to the bracket platform and main arms and a separate one at the front giving access to the elevated balance levers. Also of interest is the fact that the signal is gas lit and the gas pipes can be seen attached to the back of the post. Although the signalman could only see the back of the signal there are no back-blinders to the signal lamps and indeed there do not appear to be any backlights at all to the lamps for the distant and subsidiary arms. Backlights were not generally provided on the North London until 1887 when a number of signals were fitted up. The general introduction of backlights and backblinders was not begun until 1894. This signal is the up home signal for Devons Road cabin (which was behind the camera) and the arm, with vertical bar, on the left hand bracket (seen on the right here of course!) reads to the up arrival road for the works and loco shed. The lower distant, under the main arm, was for South Bromley cabin. In the foreground is one of the distinctive NLR ground disc signals, these rotated through 90° when pulled 'off'. Many of these were supplied by Dutton and Co., the signalling contractors. A fouling bar is visible in the down main line, just in front of the disc, and it has had to be fitted partly in the narrow space between the running rail and the check rail. This bar was provided to ensure that no vehicles were standing on the main line when the crossing (which led to the up main) was to be used.*

Photo: Courtesy National Railway Museum

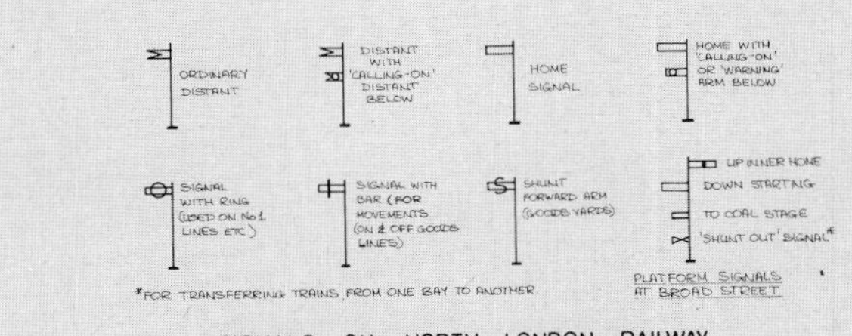

Figure 17.6 *Diagram showing the main types of signals used on the North London Line. These signals are represented by the same symbols as in the signalling diagrams (**Figures 17.8** and **17.9**).*

what position the commutator handle was placed in) until bell signals had been exchanged and transmitted from both ends of the section. A similar arrangement was also found on many Tyers instruments. It is, perhaps, not surprising that the instruments were manufactured by Tyer and Company since their works was practically on top of the NLR, opposite Dalston Junction Station. In December 1895 it was recommended that the block circuits on the North London should be altered from the one-wire to the three-wire system 'now universally adopted by railway companies', at an estimated cost of £2,700. It was further reported that trials of the Pryce and Ferreira

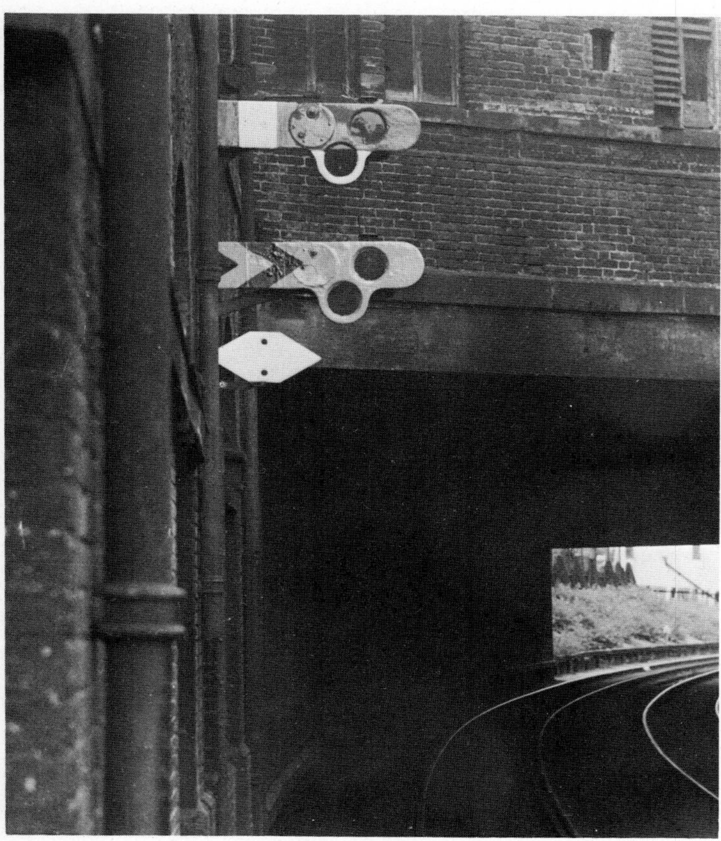

Plate 17.11 *Restricted clearance home and distant arms mounted on a wall just beyond the Eastern Junction curve platform at Dalston Junction Station (signal 8 in* **Figure 17.9***), photographed in 1956. The marks left by the paint from the vertical stripe on the distant arm, when this was painted red, can still be made out. This photograph sums up very well the signal siting problems which beset the North London. This signal was brought into use on the 12th April 1891.*

Photo: G H Platt

Plate 17.12 *Dalston Junction Up No. 1 line home signals in 1946. These are of the restricted clearance type mounted low down to give sight under the platform awnings and footbridge. In NLR days the left hand arm was fitted with a ring and the right hand arm had no white stripe, the description 'No. 1 to No. 2' being painted on it. Just visible beyond the road overbridge are the posts of the three down home signals (reading to No. 2, No. 1 and Eastern Junction lines). These were probably the ultimate in tall signals, the top arms being some 80 feet above rail level and they were designed to give a good early sight to drivers approaching on the viaduct and down the steep gradient from Haggerston. (They are the equivalent of signals 2 and 6 in* **Figure 17.9***). This signal was brought into use on the 15th September 1895.*

Figure 17.7 EXAMPLES OF THE TYPES OF FRAME IN USE ON THE NORTH LONDON AND NORTH AND SOUTH WESTERN JUNCTION RAILWAYS

Signal Cabin	*Type of Lever Frame*	*Number of Levers*	*Date of Frame*
Bow Junction	North London Tappet 5½" centres	55	1895
Broad Street No. 1	" "	75	1890
" " No. 2	Stevens Tappet 4 1/8" centres	73	c1890(1)
Skinner Street Junction	NLR (Webb) Tumbler 5½" centres	84	1892
New Inn Yard	Stevens Tappet 4 1/8" centres	60	1893
Dunloe Street	North London Tappet 5½" centres	35	1892
Dalston Junction	" "	60	1908
" Western Junction	" "	53	1891
Barnsbury	" "	40	1907(2)
York Road Junction	" "	42	1907
Camden Road Junction (Kentish Town)	" "	45	1896
Acton Wells Junction	NLR (Webb) Tumbler 5½" centres	60	1892
" Central	North London Tappet 5½" centres	35	1894
South Acton Junction	" "	35	1897

(1) Cabin constructed 1876, extended to accommodate new frame.
(2) Cabin constructed 1890, extended to accommodate new frame.

instruments had proved satisfactory and that the patentees would be prepared to allow the NLR to use the instruments without payment of royalties. Conversion work was put in hand and by the end of 1896 they had been installed throughout the line. An interlocking pattern of Pryce and Ferreira block was patented in 1899, this giving a form of lock and block. The old one-wire instruments were taken into stock and sold as opportunity offered. The firm of J B Saunders and Company of Cardiff purchased 28 of them in May, 1900 and a further 10 in July, 1902 at a price of £2 15*s* each. This company were electrical contractors to many of the smaller railway companies and no doubt the instruments saw further use on one of these lines.

The career of Henry Pryce is worthy of special mention. In 1884 he took over responsibility for the NLR telegraphs in addition to his signalling duties. Park fell ill in 1892

Plate 17.13 *The next few illustrations give some idea of the variations in signal cabin design that could be found on the North London. This one is Broad Street No. 2 cabin and controlled the No. 2 lines in the station area. Like the other numbered cabins on the quadruple track sections of the line, the numbers referred not to the order in which the cabins occurred but to the pair of lines (No. 1 or No. 2) which they controlled. This cabin was brought into use on 3-9-1876 in connection with the completion of the fourth line to Shoreditch. It had a 37 lever frame when opened, but a 70 lever Stevens frame (extended to 73) was later installed (***Figure 17.7***). The cabin was extended at the right hand end to accommodate this frame. No doubt a Stevens frame with its close lever spacing was used in order to keep the space required to a minimum.*

and in July it was necessary to appoint Pryce to act for him. By the beginning of 1893 it became clear that Park was unlikely to recover sufficiently to resume his duties and it was arranged that he would officially retire on the 30th of April. It was decided that Pryce should be appointed Locomotive Superintendent (which included responsibility for rolling stock) in addition to his existing signal and telegraph duties. Pryce's salary was advanced to £700 per annum (Park had been receiving £1,300 prior to retirement). This situation was probably unique in Britain and almost the reverse of the situation on the LNWR where the Signal Superintendent reported to the Loco. Superintendent! Pryce was given early retirement (from 31/1/1909), after the LNWR reached an agreement with the NLR in December 1908 under which the LNW took over responsibility for the management and engineering work on the line. By this time his salary had risen to £1,100 per annum. He is said to have had little interest in locomotive work, but possessed a bustling personality and had the ability to get work done. He died shortly after the first world war.

Ferreira resigned his post as Telegraph Inspector in April 1900 in order to move into the commercial sector. He subsequently patented a number of electrical devices connected with railway signalling. His place on the North London was taken by G A Brady.

In accordance with the 1877 decision, the NLR adopted, for the majority of its new work, the LNW style of signalling equipment. This was manufactured at Bow Works. In practice the Company did not use the full range of LNW equipment but developed a number of items of its own. These included a distinctive form of cast iron bracket for the signals (**Plate 17.10**) and a rotating ground disc signal. A special form of limited clearance signal arm was also widely used (see Plates). Unlike the LNW, many of the tall signals and gantries had lattice metal posts.

The LNW (Webb) tumbler interlocking frame (**Figure 11.4**) was adopted as standard and a number were manu-

Plate 17.14 *A cabin of altogether different design was this one at Dalston Junction, photographed in 1976. This was originally the No. 2 lines cabin and was opened at the end of 1872. The design was made to match the No. 1 lines cabin which had opened on 27-4-1871. Other cabins of similar design were erected on the line at about this time. In 1908 it was decided to concentrate the working in one cabin. The No. 2 cabin was extended, at the left hand end as seen in the photograph, and a new 60 lever NLR tappet frame installed. This work cost £500.*

MAIDEN LANE JUNCTION

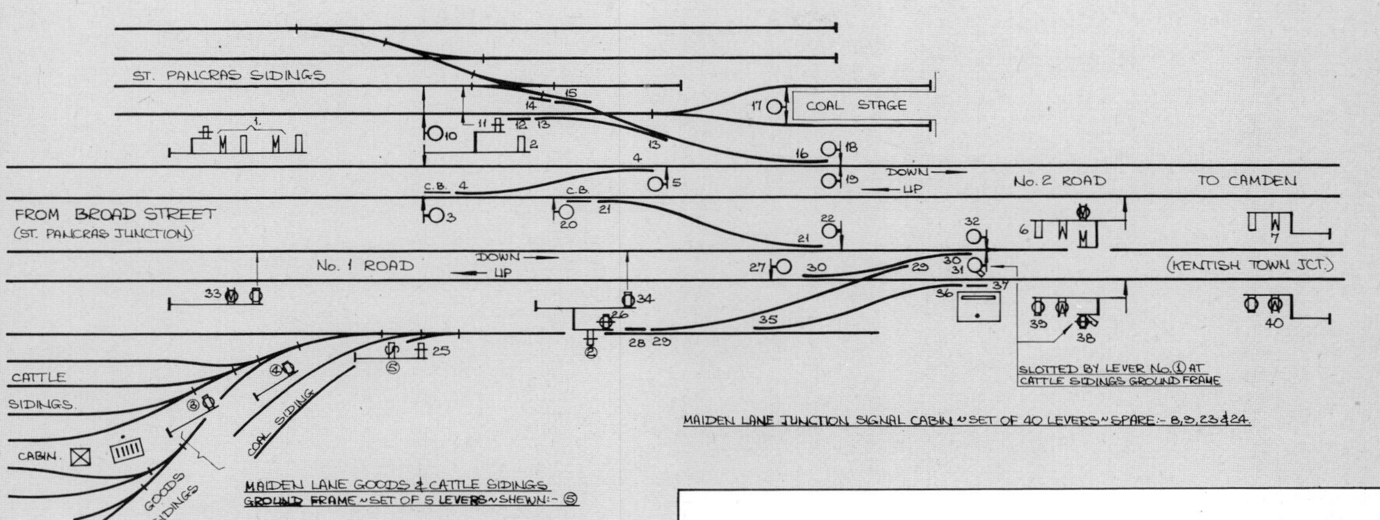

Figure 17.8 *Signalling diagram showing the signalling at Maiden Lane Junction in North London days. This illustrates the use of signal arms with rings and bars. A 'shunt forward' signal, controlled from Maiden Lane Goods and Cattle Sidings Ground Frame is also shown. Note the use of lifting bars at the points leading from the goods lines to the main lines. Clearance bars are used with crossovers 4 and 21 to ensure that a train requiring to cross over is clear of the points before they are changed and the disc cleared for setting back. In the Broad Street direction the cabin worked to St. Pancras Junction on the No. 2 lines and York Road Junction on the No. 1 lines.*

factured at Bow and installed on the line. It is not clear if any of the parts were obtained from Crewe. The terms of the injunction, referred to in Chapter 13, may have been considered to preclude such an arrangement in all but special cases. One of the tumbler frames was installed at Dalston Western Junction and in 1884 Park was able to say that it had given very satisfactory service despite having to handle over 700 trains each day.

From the 1st of July 1878 a separate maintenance of signals account was set up. Pryce began a determined campaign to bring the signalling on the line – which had become rather worn out and outdated – up to standard. During the next four years over £14,000 was expended on the work. From 1882 expenditure on maintenance and renewals was fixed at £2,500 per annum. This was gradually increased over the years and reached a peak of £4,000 p.a. for the period from 1890 to 1904, after which it was reduced to £2,300 p.a. These figures did not include for new installations which were authorised separately.

By the late 1880's Pryce had had considerable experience with the performance in service of a number of different types of lever frame. The patent covering tappet locking had expired and as a result, he introduced a new design of frame for use on the NLR which incorporated the best features of the existing types. As before, this was manufactured at Bow Works. This had the outward appearance of the LNW tumbler frame above floor level and incorporated many of the features of that frame. These included simplicity of construction, and the ability to remove and replace individual components without dismantling the whole frame. LNW loop catch handles were used rather than the more common clasp type handles mounted behind the levers. Below the floor, however, the frame was more akin to Stevens practice. The locking was of the tappet type, mounted in tiers on cast iron brackets which were bolted onto the end standards of the frame (placed, generally, at every tenth lever). The tappet boxes each contained 6 locking bars per channel (three top and three bottom), and had two channels per box. They were not the same as the later LNWR tappet locking boxes which were designed for 5 bars per channel. The frame worked on the 'lever locking' principle and the tappet blades were attached directly to the levers. The locking boxes could be mounted both in front of and behind the frame if required. Unlike the LNW type, these frames rested on

Plate 17.15 *Old Oak Junction on the North and South Western Junction Railway represents a design of cabin which was used at a number of places on the North London system in the early 1890's. Cabins of similar basic design existed, for example, at Barnsbury, Acton Wells Junction and Devons Road.*

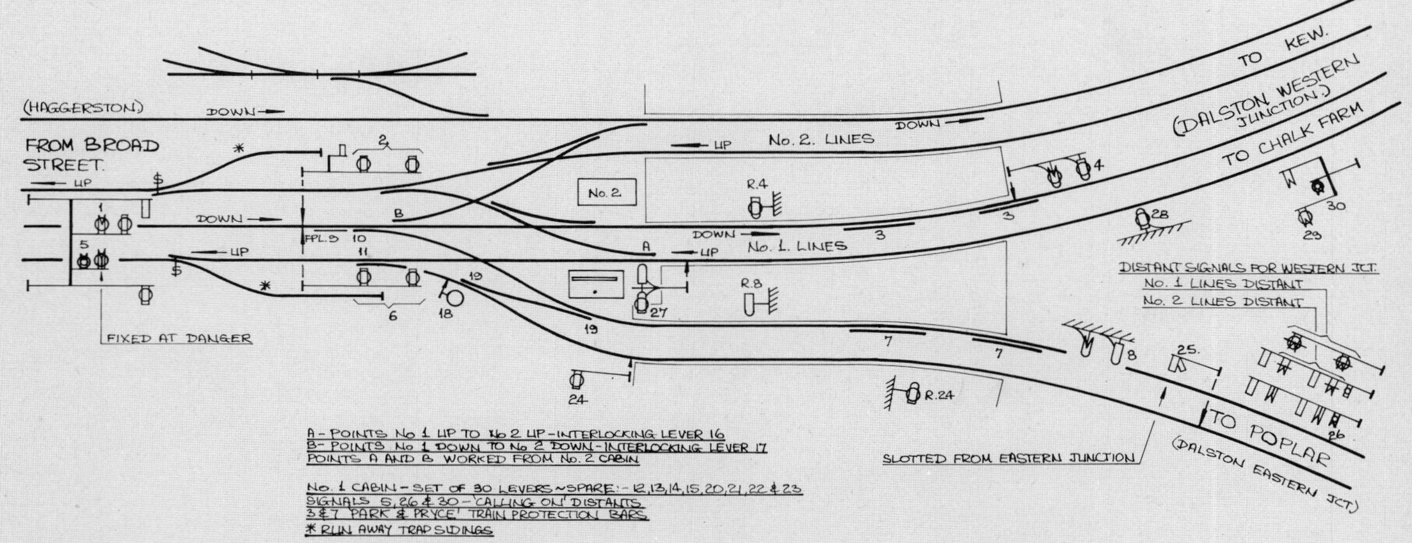

Figure 17.9 *Signalling diagram for Dalston Junction No. 1 cabin. This shows the use of the 'calling-on' distant signals (Nos. 5, 26 and 30) for trains on the No. 1 and Poplar lines, which allowed trains to run forward into the platforms without the delay which would otherwise occur in the train having to be prepared to stop at the home signal. Levers 3 and 7 work 'Park and Pryce' train protection bars. These are effectively the forerunners of track circuits. A train standing on them will hold the lever normal and prevent the signal in the rear being cleared to admit another train into the platform. As can be seen the cabin only worked the No. 1 lines and a separate cabin almost opposite it was provided to work the No. 2 lines. This was a very common feature of the four track section of the NLR and most stations boasted two cabins, one for each set of lines. The cabins were numbered 1 or 2 to coincide with the lines which they controlled rather than the order in which the cabins occurred. In most cases these pairs of cabins were replaced by single cabins controlling both lines, much of the work being done around 1909.*

a 12 inch square sole timber rather than girders and there was, therefore, no 'girder end' spaces in the levers. The sole timber was, however, supported on cast iron uprights like the LNW frames (**Plate 17.17**). The period 1890/3 brought a large number of renewals and resignalling schemes and several lever frames of Stevens design and of the NLR (Webb) tumbler type were installed (**Figure 17.7**).

Like the LNW, the NLR used rings on some signal arms to help drivers distinguish the signals. On the quadruple track section these were used for signals applying to the Number One lines. Not satisfied with this, however, they also used a vertical bar to distinguish signals applying to moves on to and off goods lines and sidings (see diagrams). A signal from the No. 1 line to a goods line would have both of course! On the NLR the rings and bars were painted white on the front and black on the back.

The North London's approach to distant signals was unique and deserves a detailed description. In the 1870's the railway used distant or auxiliary signals in much the same way as the LNW. Drivers were instructed to be prepared to stop at the distant signal, when at danger, whistle, and if he saw the line was clear the train could proceed cautiously to the home signal. The home signal was, however, locked with the starting signal and could not be lowered until the starting signal had been taken off. When the section ahead was blocked and it was necessary for a train to draw forward to the starting signal the signalman authorized the driver to do so by means of a green flag or lamp. This form of locking had been imposed on the NLR back in 1866 by the Board of Trade as an additional precaution in view of the very heavy traffic on the line.

Plate 17.16 *A detail view of the Up No. 2 lines Bay indicators which were used in Skinner Street Junction. These instruments were provided in connection with the station alterations in 1890/2 and they cost about £20. They were worked from No. 2 cabin to control trains approaching the platforms. (See* **Plate 17.18***.)*

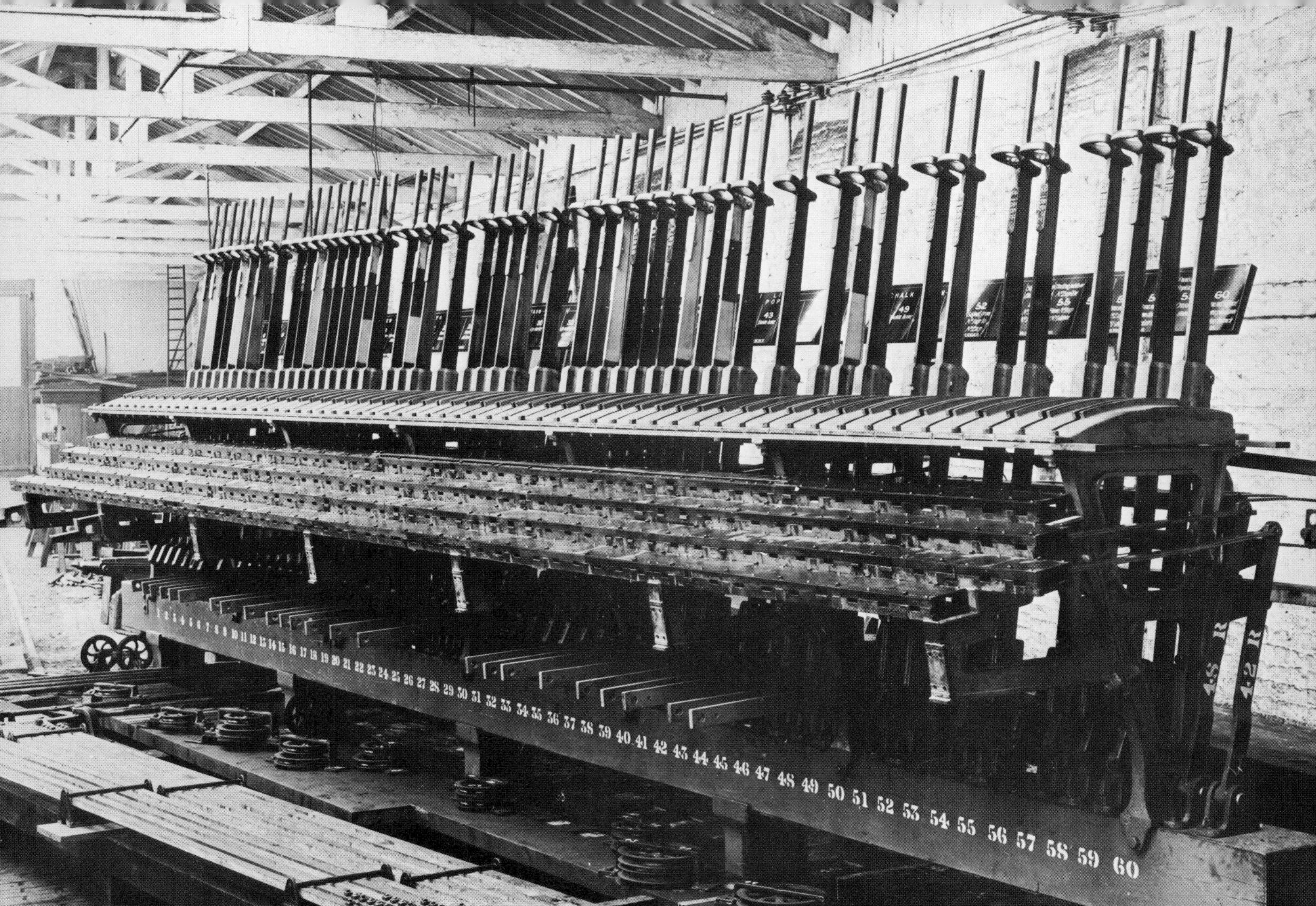

Plate 17.17 *In connection with the concentration of the working of Dalston Nos. 1 and 2 cabins (***Plate 17.14***) a new 60 lever NLR tappet frame was constructed at Bow Works for the enlarged No. 2 cabin. This photograph was taken on 7th July 1908 while the frame was being fitted up in the shops. The construction details of this type of frame should be clear from the photograph and the differences between it and the LNW type frames can be studied by comparing it with* **Plates 11.1** *and* **11.2** *(LNW tumbler) and* **Plates 11.11** *and* **11.13** *(LNW tappet). Above the floor the major differences are the shape of the catch blocks, the quadrant castings, with their double guides, and the flat tops to the levers (this was also a feature of the tumbler frames used by the NLR). Below floor level the frame is supported on a square sole timber which in turn rests on short cast iron uprights. The standards supporting the quadrants are placed at every tenth lever and the brackets for the locking boxes are bolted to them. There are four boxes or tiers of locking fixed on the front of the frame in this photograph but at the far end a couple of brackets have been bolted on to accommodate two more tiers. Three locking boxes have been added at the back of the frame. These are all bracketed off the frame individually, but brackets similar to those on the front could also be used if necessary, where there was sufficient space. The tappets are connected directly to the levers, the frame working on the 'lever locking' principle. The two cranks (labelled 42R and 48R) at the right hand end of the frame work in connection with the train protection bars in the platforms. They are connected with the interlocking by means of tappets at their top end. The light coloured levers (Nos. 2, 5, 13, 36 and 40) are facing point lock levers (blue) and the striped levers (Nos. 18, 22, 42 and 48) work in connection with the train protection bars and are painted blue and black. As with the LNW, spare levers were not provided but spaces have been left in the frame to allow additional levers to be put in later if required. At ground level the uprights rest on horizontal beams running at right angles to the frame and these have been used for fixing the lead off timbers for the point rodding, cranks and wheels. By this time LNW type channel rodding was in use (compare with* **Plate 17.9***). Because the cabin was tapered in section the point rodding run could not be placed parallel to the frame. The NLR followed the LNW system of cast iron number (pull) plates for its levers, but adopted a painted back board for the lever descriptions rather than cast iron name plates.*

Photo: Courtesy Public Record Office

In 1889 the NLR was able to persuade the Board of Trade that this arrangement was no longer necessary and revised regulations came into operation. The Home signal was freed from the Starting signal, and station signal cabins generally had Starting, Home and Distant signals, the Distant being locked with both Home and Starting signals, except at Dalston Junction (No. 1 line and Poplar line) and at Tilbury Junction (Bromley branch) where the Distant was locked only with the Home signal. At these cabins, however, the signalman had instructions not to take off the Distant unless and until both Home and Starting signals had been lowered, except in the case of

Plate 17.18 *Skinner Street Junction cabin contained an NLR tumbler frame as is illustrated in this interior view. Block shelves of the LNW type were not fitted in the cabins in the Broad Street area but instead the instruments were mounted in groups on large vertical boards above the levers as in this photograph. On the right are two Pryce and Ferreira Block instruments with the receiving end of a Tyers train describer between them. The single needle instrument applied to the goods line from New Inn Yard and the double needle instrument to the up and down No. 2 lines between this cabin and New Inn Yard cabin. The remaining instruments mounted along the bottom of the board nearest the camera are special instruments used for controlling movements in the station area. Commencing at the left hand end is a group of four double plunger pegging instruments for signalling trains to Broad Street No. 2 on the down lines from the station, the two position needles displaying 'Down Line Blocked' on the left and 'Down Line Clear' on the right. From left to right the instrument applied to Bay lines 5, 6, 7 and 8. The next single needle double plunger instrument applied to the Bay 9 line, separate instruments being provided for this line because it was constructed as something of an afterthought and was not opened until 1913. The next pair of instruments had miniature semaphore arms showing 'Blocked' in the horizontal position and 'Clear' in the lowered position. They worked to No. 1 cabin and applied respectively to movements from the No. 2 up line to Bay 3 and to Bay 4. The next set of four instruments were worked from Broad Street No. 2 cabin for the up lines approaching the station and applied from left to right to Bays 5, 6, 7 and 8 (see* **Plate 17.16**). *The two position needles displaying 'Bay Blocked' on the left and 'Bay Clear' on the right. Between this instrument and the Pryce and Ferreira double needle block is the corresponding instrument for the Bay 9 line. At the far end of the cabin is another board containing the corresponding instruments for the No. 1 lines.*

Photo: Dr I W Scrimgeour

passenger trains booked to stop at the station, in which case it was the practice to take off Home and Distant only.

This arrangement was also found to be unsatisfactory and it was decided in 1893 to provide supplementary distant signals at certain places. These signals were similar to calling-on arms, which had been introduced on the North London Railway in 1889, but the arm was notched. They were placed underneath the ordinary or through distant signals and showed a small green light when off, but no light when on. In the clear position these signals indicated that the home signal was off but that the starting signal was at danger. They were termed station or calling-on distant signals and the first was installed at Dalston Junction No. 1 (up line) and brought into use on 6th November 1893 (see **Figure 17.9**). This was followed by installations at Bromley Bank and Tilbury Junction in 1894, while Dalston Junction (other lines), Poplar and Victoria Park were equipped in 1895. These signals were particularly useful in foggy or misty weather, and at Dalston where the signals in the tunnels could not readily be seen owing to the curves. During fog the fogsignalmen left detonators on the rail whilst the through distant was on but told the driver if the calling-on distant was off. Calling-on distants remained in use after the grouping, the last being removed in 1940. These signals do not appear to have been adopted by any other railway.

Figure 17.10 MANCHESTER, SOUTH JUNCTION AND ALTRINCHAM RAILWAY – SIGNAL CABINS IN USE 1923

Cabin	*Type*	*Cabin Date*	*Type of Frame*	*Number of Levers*	*Remarks*
London Road MSJ&A	LNW	1915	RSC	30	On narrow base between tracks, replaced Saxby cabin of 1877. The new cabin was of size 'E'.
Oxford Road East	MS&L	1886	S&F	23	Overhead cabin, abolished 1/3/1931.
Oxford Road West	GCR	1897	RSC	40	
Castlefield Junction	GCR		RSC	14W	Demolished in accident 25/1/1940, replaced by new LMS cabin Feb. 1941.
Cornbrook East Junction	LNW		LNW Ta.	25	Replaced Saxby cabin of 1878, this cabin was of size 'E'.
Old Trafford Junction	S&F	1879	S&F Ro.	18	Demolished in accident 24/3/1956.
Old Trafford Station	MS&L	1886	LNW Ta.	30	LNW frame installed 1917.
Warwick Road	RSC	1886	RSC	45	Formerly Old Trafford Cricket Ground.
Stretford	GCR	1898	RSC	42	
Mersey Bridge	RSC	1903	RSC	12	
Sale	RSC	1903	RSC	33	
Brooklands	S&F	1878	S&F Ro.	13	All brick cabin of unusual design.
Timperley Junction	RSC	1897	RSC	40	
Deansgate Junction	S&F	1882	S&F Ro.	16	One loose lever for gates. Replaced by new Cabin 1958.
Navigation Road	S&F	1882	S&F	20	Frame later replaced by one of LMS type in the back of the cabin.
Altrincham North	LNW	1908	LNW	72	Replaced two S&F cabins, this cabin was of size 'O'.
Altrincham South	S&F	1880	S&F	31W	Frame replaced by one of L&Y type May 1958.

KEY TO SYMBOLS:
GCR – Great Central Railway; RSC – Railway Signal Company; S&F – Saxby and Farmer; MS&L – Manchester, Sheffield and Lincolnshire; Ta. – Tappet Frame; Ro. – Rocker Frame; W – Number of working levers; L&Y – Lancashire and Yorkshire Railway. The LNW cabins were all of 'Type 5' design.

MANCHESTER SOUTH JUNCTION AND ALTRINCHAM RAILWAY – PERIODS OF RESPONSIBILITY FOR MAINTENANCE

L&NWR – 1904 to 1907 and 1910 to 1913. The work on the Altrincham North cabin had commenced in 1906 before responsibility was handed over, the job not being completed until 1908.

GCR – 1907 to 1910 and 1913 to 1923. The latter period was extended due to the war.

MANCHESTER, SOUTH JUNCTION AND ALTRINCHAM RAILWAY

This line was the joint property of the LNW and the Manchester, Sheffield and Lincolnshire (later Great Central) Railways, and was managed by a Joint Committee of the two Companies.

The block system was introduced quite early on this busy little line as operations became saturated under the time interval system. The block was introduced on the Altrincham Branch in 1870 and on the South Junction line in 1874. The line was resignalled on 'modern' lines during the 1877 to 1882 period by Saxby and Farmer (see **Plate 17.19**). Among the cabins erected at this time were London Road MSJ&A, in 1877, Cornbrook East and Brooklands (No. 2) in 1878, Old Trafford Junction in 1879 and Altrincham Level Crossing and North in 1880. All seem to have been fitted with the ubiquitous 'Rocker' frames.

After this, the majority of the work was done by the Railway Signal Company, mainly to MSL/GCR standards, but some standard RSC equipment was also installed. Until the adoption of red and green lights in 1893, signals were mainly of the slotted wooden post type with single spectacles (a red glass for the danger position and the white lamp alone for clear – see Chapter 3).

The line between Old Trafford Station and Sale Station was widened to four tracks, between Old Trafford and Stretford in 1897 and between Stretford and Sale in 1904.

From 1904 the responsibility for maintenance was taken alternately by the two owning Companies (see **Figure 17.10**). Altrincham North cabin, opened in April 1908 was, however, an LNW installation since work had commenced on the job in 1906 and extended into a GCR maintenance period. This cabin replaced two Saxby cabins which were a mere 173 yards apart (Altrincham North and Altrincham level crossing).

By the 1920's LNW block instruments and block regulations were in use on the line and by 1930 most of the signals were of the LNW pattern, largely as a result of replacements during the early LMS period.

Electrification in 1930/1 caused alterations to the signals at quite a number of locations in order to clear the overhead equipment and give better sighting. Where signals had to be renewed upper quadrants were installed, some of these being of the short arm type with electric intensified lighting. It is worth mentioning that signal sighting was always a problem on this line due to the numerous bridges and other obstructions, plus the frequent city fogs.

Figure 17.10 lists the signal cabins on the line more or less as they were in 1923. Mention might be made of some of the cabins which had closed earlier. Perhaps the most curious was a small break section cabin named 'Charles Street' which was sited on the viaduct between London Road and Oxford Road. It had 8 levers (4 working – a home and distant each way) and was provided by the Railway Signal Company in September 1890. This and another intermediate cabin at Knott Mill were permanently switched out of circuit by 1905. Later they were both removed.

Brooklands No. 1 had an eight lever Saxby and Farmer Rocker frame and again was out of use by 1905. Brooklands was the last instance on the line of two cabins at an intermediate station, a system which had existed at a number of locations in earlier times. When No. 1 was abolished, No. 2 was renamed 'Brooklands', this cabin retaining its Saxby lever frame until closure in 1971. The pre-quadrupling cabin at Sale had a 19 lever Saxby Rocker frame (5 inch centres), to which a 10 bar, 2 channel, box of Railway Signal Company tappet locking (mounted below the floor) had been added.

After the grouping the line followed LMS signalling practice and it became part of the London Midland Region of British Railways.

Plate 17.19 *The Saxby and Farmer cabin of 1882 at Navigation Road on the Manchester South Junction and Altrincham line. This cabin is of the standard design provided by Saxby and Farmer during the late 1870's and early 1880's on their contracts in the North of England. Cabins of identical design, with the narrow top windows and a further set below the main windows (both are painted over in this example), were quite common on the Lancashire and Yorkshire and Manchester, Sheffield and Lincolnshire lines (see also* **Plate 9.11**).

Plate 17.20 *The Saxby and Farmer rocker frame of 1882 at Deansgate Junction was still in use when photographed in May 1956 (a new cabin to replace this one was provided in 1958). The locking which was mounted above the floor can be seen behind the levers. It was actuated by nibs or studs on the catch blocks which ran in slots in the large cam plates which are mounted on pivots adjacent to the quadrant plates. A delightful feature of joint lines was that equipment of a mixture of origins was often to be found and this is evident in this illustration. The lever number and pull plates are of Railway Signal Company design while the name plates, mounted on a board behind the frame, are of LNW type and their layout follows LNW practice. A pair of LNW pattern face discs can just be seen mounted below the main windows, behind levers 12 to 15. Frames of this type were supplied by Saxby and Farmer for installation in a number of cabins on the LNW itself between about 1876 and the mid 1880's. (Chapter 11.)*

Photo: Dr I W Scrimgeour

Plate 17.21 *Rowrah No. 1 cabin in March 1965. This was one of the Stevens cabins erected in connection with the doubling of the line from here to Marron Junction in the early 1870's. The vertical boarding across the end of the cabin above the windows was typical of early Stevens practice, as was the window design. Note the LNW style signal cabin nameboard with its pointed ends and raised cast iron letters. The Stevens frame was replaced by an LNWR Tappet frame of 32 levers when the line to the north was singled in July 1913.*
Photo: F W Shuttleworth

WHITEHAVEN, CLEATOR AND EGREMONT RAILWAY

This line was originally an independent concern and opened its line in stages from 1855. Much of the original signalling was done by Stevens and Sons, and a number of cabins of their design were erected along the line. This work included the section from Rowrah to Marron signalled between 1871 and 1874 in connection with the doubling of that portion of line (brought into use in 1873).

From 1st July 1877 the line became the property of the LNWR and the signalling work was placed under the charge of the LNWR District Inspector at Lancaster. After some behind the scenes manoeuvring, the line became the joint property of the LNW and Furness Railways from 1st August, 1878. In preparation for this, an LNW Locomotive Committee minute of 16th July, 1878 recorded that:–

> 'Signals and telegraphs on the WC&E; For the sake of uniformity, the signals to be supplied and maintained throughout the joint line by the LNW Co. and the telegraph, block and speaking instruments to be maintained by the Furness Co. The Furness block system to be adopted, the regulations being agreed jointly between Mr Cook and Mr Bedford. The accounts in connection with signals and telegraph to be dealt with in the same way as laid down for permanent way. Mr Webb is attending to this.'

(Mr Bedford was the LNW's West Cumberland District Superintendent, based at Whitehaven and was replaced by Mr Mawby from 1/2/1880).

The first LNW cabin seems to have been erected at Ullock Junction in September 1878. This was put up in connection with the construction of the Gillgarron Branch (Authorised in 1875). This cabin had 30 levers and was of size 'G'. Over the next few years, a number of new cabins were erected, partly as a tidying up exercise on the existing arrangements and partly to accommodate alterations and extensions. As has been mentioned in Chapter 11, the LNW continued to use some Saxby equipment after 1874 and the LNW standard cabins erected at Cleator Moor Junction in 1879 and at Woodend, Clintz and Egremont in 1881 were all fitted with Saxby and Farmer lever frames. No doubt the WC&E received so many of these Saxby frames because it was a relatively unimportant section of line. Keeping the frames together also assisted with maintenance work.

Rather curiously, the Moor Row Nos. 1 and 3 cabins, opened in 1882, both received Railway Signal Company frames. No. 1 cabin was replaced by a new all-timber 'type 5' cabin with an LNW tappet frame in 1907.

In independent days, communication between cabins seems to have been largely by mechanical or electrical gongs (a fairly common arrangement at the time). As mentioned in the LNW minute, the Furness block system was adopted and on the double line sections (and those single lines worked by the ordinary train staff) one-wire two position semaphore block instruments were used.

The LNW West Cumberland lines and the Joint line were physically separated from the remainder of the system, and materials had to be worked into the area over another Company's line. One might have thought the Cockermouth, Keswick and Penrith line would have been used as the shortest route, especially as the LNW worked some of the traffic on this line. This was not so, however, and the Lancaster Inspector was reminded from time to time in the 1880's that materials were to be consigned via the Furness line. A concession was obtained in February 1890 when signal material for Cockermouth was allowed to be sent free over the CK&P. Similar problems arose in respect of Signal Department staff travelling home to the Penrith area, since the CK&P refused to accept their free passes! Relations with the Furness were good at this time, however, and the Inspector was instructed not to charge the Furness for any odd bits of work his men did to assist them, since the Furness did not charge when they provided assistance to the LNW.

Just after the turn of the Century, a welcome increase in traffic occurred in connection with the development of new iron ore mines at Ullcoats and Beckermet. The siding at Ullcoats was controlled by a signal cabin (of size 'C') which was classed as a ground frame and came into use in 1902. The Sellafield to Egremont section was a single line and in connection with the new siding, the method of working was changed from train staff and ticket with the absolute block to the Electric Train Staff system. This worked on a special arrangement with two staff instruments at Egremont. One was the ordinary Egremont to Beckermet section instrument, while the other was a supplementary staff instrument for Egremont to Ullcoats Junction. This was normally out of use and a staff was locked in the main machine to prevent its use. Use of the Ullcoats Junction Staff locked the main machines out of use, but it could be placed in a machine at the ground frame to allow main line traffic to pass while the train was 'shut inside' for shunting. When the work was complete the train collected its staff (if the line was clear of course) and returned to Egremont.

On the section of line north of Moor Row, decline continued, however. First to go was the south to east curve at Marron Junction in 1902. The three cabins (one for each junction) were replaced by a single new one controlling the remaining junction. In the summer of 1913, work began on singling the section from Rowrah to Bridgefoot, and crossing loops were provided at Lamplugh and Ullock Junction, while the Bridgefoot to Marron section remained double. New cabins were provided at Lamplugh and Bridgefoot, together with a new frame for Rowrah No. 1.

CARLISLE

One can hardly produce a book on the LNWR without mentioning Carlisle. Here there were two sections of line in joint ownership and in which the LNW had an interest, these being the Citadel Station Committee (LNW and Caledonian), and the Goods Traffic Committee (LNW, Caledonian, Glasgow & South Western and Midland). However the LNW was deeply involved in the construction of all the new lines in the 1870's and 1880's and provided most of the signalling for them. Because of this and the nature of Carlisle's Railway network it is worth straying a little outside the strict boundaries of the joint sections. It is not possible to give a full history of the signalling in the area here and this section deals principally with the work done during the 1870's and 1880's.

The railways in Carlisle had become somewhat inadequate for the traffic by 1870, while the flat crossing at St Nicholas was both dangerous and restrictive. The usual disagreements between the various Companies involved (in part at least due to the desire on the part of the LNW and Caledonian to maintain their dominant position in the area) delayed action. When the Midland obtained its Act for construction of the Settle and Carlisle line it became clear that something would have to be done. An Act was passed in 1873

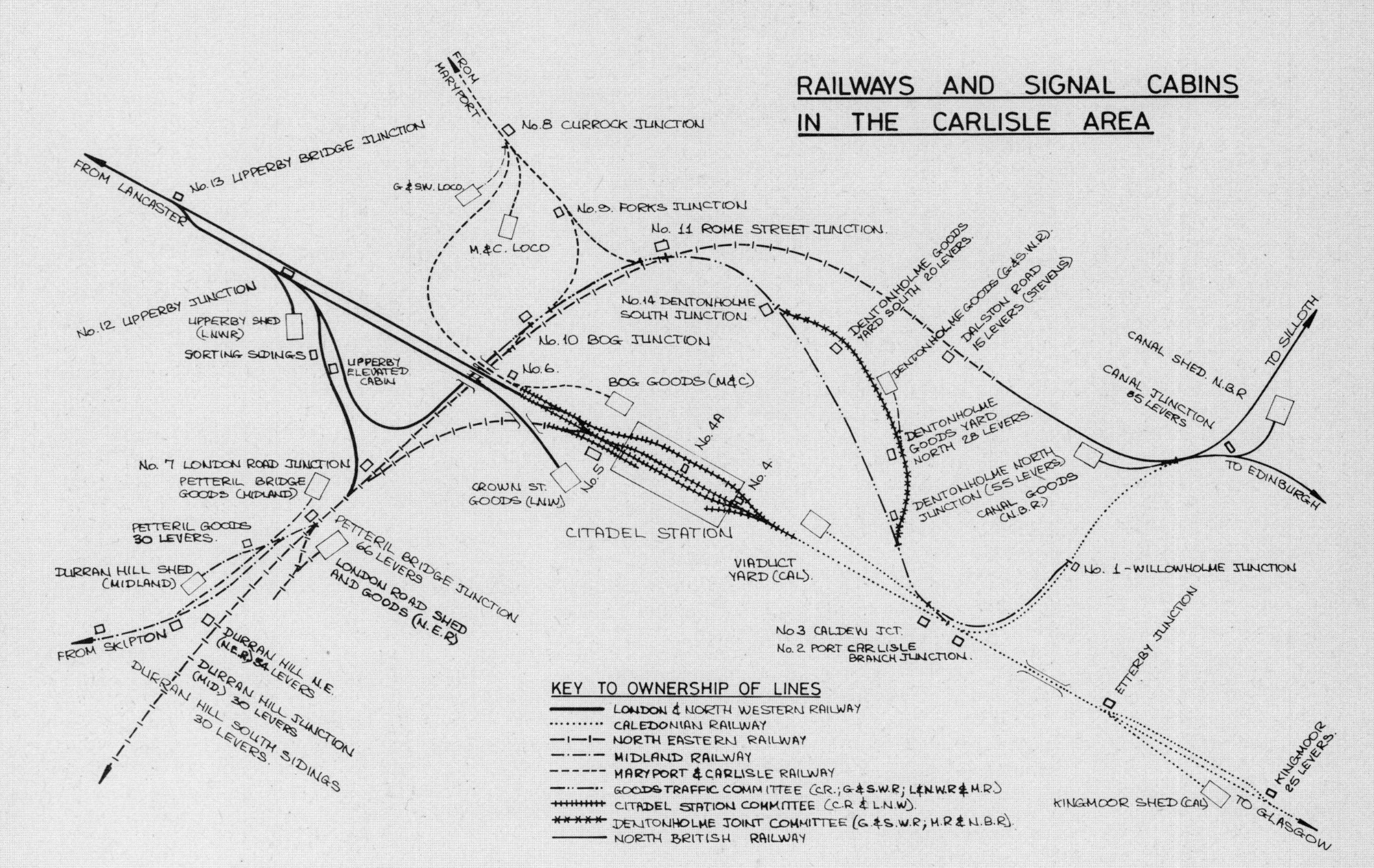

Figure 17.11 *Plan showing the layout and ownership of the lines in the Carlisle area. Also shown are the positions of the 14 numbered cabins and some of the adjacent ones as they were about 1896.*

authorising the necessary enlargements and new lines. The new goods lines were constructed at a cost of £333,284 and were officially opened on the 7th of August 1877, while the much enlarged station opened on the 4th of July 1880, the extensions there having cost £379,135.

The signal cabins on the new and altered lines were given numbers which curiously ran from north to south, the opposite of normal practice, although the numbering sequence itself was fairly logical (see **Figure 17.11**). All but one of the numbered cabins were provided by the LNW and were of its standard design. The exception was No. 2 where an existing Caledonian structure was utilised. The first cabin to open, No. 8, was brought into use in January 1876 concurrently with the Glasgow and South Western locomotive shed. Number 7 cabin, also constructed in 1876, was one of those which Edwards was unable to complete as Crewe works could not provide the interlocking apparatus at the time (Chapters 2 and 11) and it was not completed until March 1877. Those cabins opened in 1876 were fitted with LNW cam-head type frames and those opened in 1877 and thereafter were provided with tumbler frames. The 12 cabins opened in 1876/7 plus the existing No. 5 cabin contained between them 383 levers.

The exact use of distant signals still seems to have been causing the LNW some problems as the majority of those originally provided were not interlocked with the home signals! As was usual at the time the block system

Plate 17.22 *The tall LNW cabin provided in 1877 at Rome Street Junction (Carlisle No. 11) on the Carlisle Goods lines. This cabin was elevated 20 feet above rail level and it was a fair climb up the staircase from rail level to the operating floor. An easier way in was from the road bridge seen behind the cabin, by climbing onto the parapet wall, stepping across onto the window cleaning stage and then climbing in through the window! No doubt that is how the bicycle, visible through the window, got there. As at a number of tall LNW cabins a pulley arrangement is provided near the door to assist the signalman in raising buckets of coal for the stove from the coal pen. In view of the height of the cabin, handrails have been provided around the window cleaning stage.*

Plate 17.23 *An interior photograph of Rome Street Junction Cabin showing the McKenzie and Holland lever frame. This retains the old system of providing small brass badges on the levers which give the lever numbers only, the 'pulls' being painted on the sides of the levers. The lever functions were painted on a description board behind the levers. The block shelf is mounted on cast iron brackets bolted to the lever quadrants, a standard North Eastern Railway practice. Block instruments are of the LNW standard permissive type, although these were a fairly recent addition, Tyers single needle permissive instruments were in use on the goods lines until well into BR days. The Old NER Canal line had been closed by the time this photograph was taken in 1972 and it has been scratched off the illuminated diagram.*

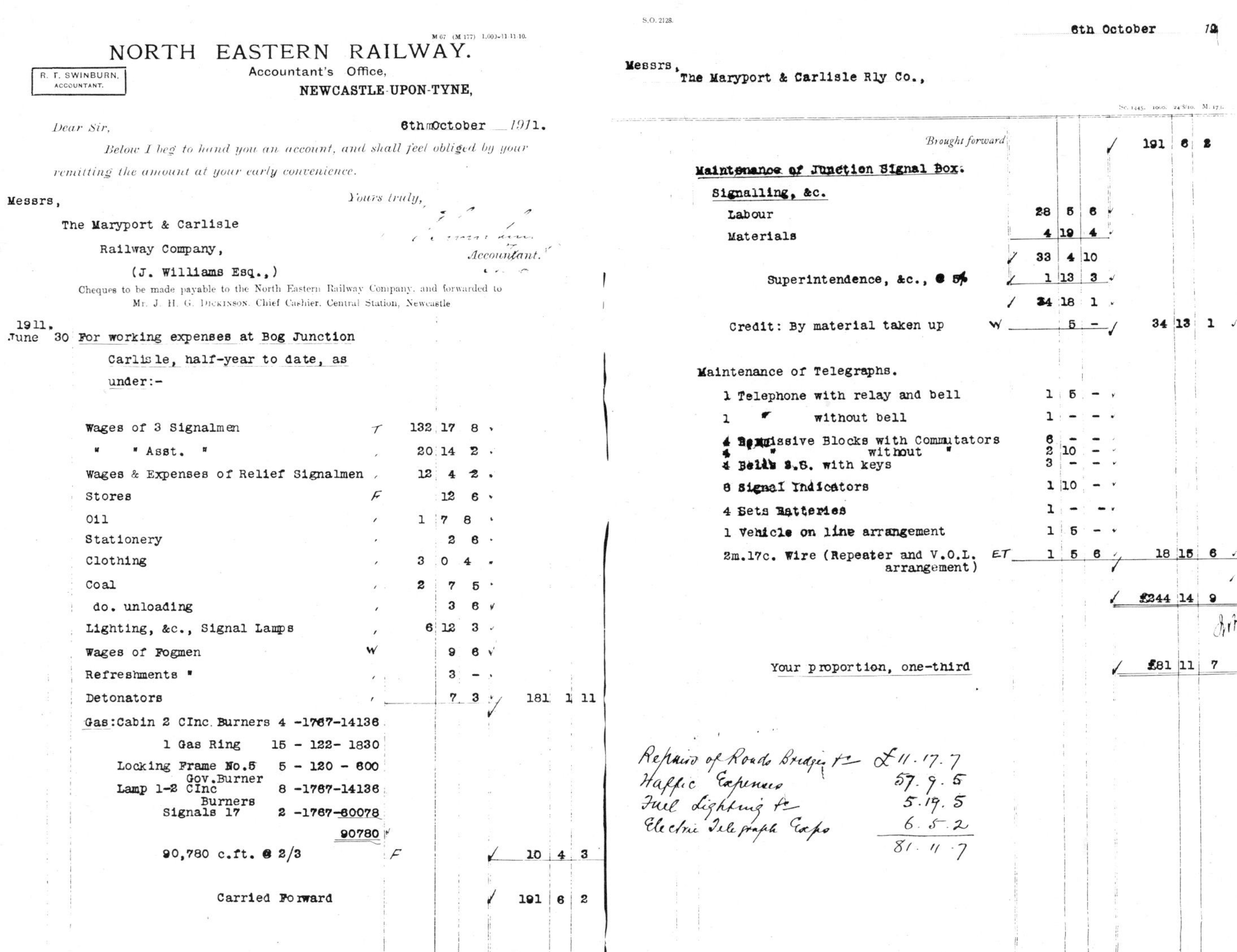

M 67 (M 177) 1,000-11-11-10.

NORTH EASTERN RAILWAY.

R. T. SWINBURN, ACCOUNTANT.

Accountant's Office, NEWCASTLE-UPON-TYNE,

Dear Sir, 6th October 1911.

Below I beg to hand you an account, and shall feel obliged by your remitting the amount at your early convenience.

Messrs, *Yours truly,*

The Maryport & Carlisle Railway Company, (J. Williams Esq.,) *Accountant.*

Cheques to be made payable to the North Eastern Railway Company, and forwarded to Mr. J. H. G. Dickinson, Chief Cashier, Central Station, Newcastle

1911. June 30 For working expenses at Bog Junction Carlisle, half-year to date, as under:-

	£	s	d	£	s	d
Wages of 3 Signalmen	132	17	8			
" " Asst. "	20	14	2			
Wages & Expenses of Relief Signalmen	12	4	2			
Stores		12	6			
Oil	1	7	8			
Stationery		2	6			
Clothing	3	0	4			
Coal	2	7	5			
do. unloading		3	6			
Lighting, &c., Signal Lamps	6	12	3			
Wages of Fogmen		9	6			
Refreshments "		3	-			
Detonators		7	3	181	1	11

Gas: Cabin 2 CInc. Burners 4 -1767-14136
1 Gas Ring 15 - 122- 1830
Locking Frame No.5 5 - 120 - 600
Lamp 1-2 Gov. Burner CInc 8 -1767-14136
Signals 17 Burners 2 -1767-60078
90780

	£	s	d
90,780 c.ft. @ 2/3	10	4	3
Carried Forward	191	6	2

S.O. 2128. 6th October 19[11]

Messrs, The Maryport & Carlisle Rly Co.,

	£	s	d	£	s	d
Brought forward				191	6	2
Maintenance of Junction Signal Box.						
Signalling, &c.						
Labour	28	5	6			
Materials	4	19	4			
	33	4	10			
Superintendence, &c., @ 5%	1	13	3			
	34	18	1			
Credit: By material taken up		5	-	34	13	1
Maintenance of Telegraphs.						
1 Telephone with relay and bell	1	5	-			
1 " without bell	1	-	-			
4 Permissive Blocks with Commutators	6	-	-			
4 " " without "	2	10	-			
4 Bells S.S. with keys	3	-	-			
8 Signal Indicators	1	10	-			
4 Sets Batteries	1	-	-			
1 Vehicle on line arrangement	1	5	-			
2m.17c. Wire (Repeater and V.O.L. arrangement)	1	5	6	18	15	6
				£244	14	9
Your proportion, one-third				£81	11	7

Repairs of Roads Bridges &c	£11.17.7
Traffic Expenses	57.9.5
Fuel Lighting &c	5.19.5
Electric Telegraph Exps	6.5.2
	81.11.7

Figure 17.12 *Copy of an account rendered by the North Eastern Railway to the Maryport and Carlisle Railway, for their proportion of the expenses incurred in operating Carlisle No. 10 signal cabin. The figures give some idea of the cost of operating and maintaining the signalling system at that time. The hand written addition at the end shows the way in which the M and C divided up their proportion of the costs for accounting purposes.*

was not installed in the station area or between numbers 6 & 8, 5 & 7 and 5 & 6 cabins. Absolute block working was instituted between numbers 6 & 8 in 1878 and block working was established between numbers 5 & 7 and 5 & 6 soon after.

In connection with the enlargement of the station and the realignment of the line a 'temporary' No. 4 cabin was provided at the north end of the station. This was a standard LNW all-wood structure and was brought into use on the 1st of June 1876. The permanent No. 4 cabin was brought into use on the 7th of July 1880 and, as on a number of occasions when new signalling was being commissioned, there was an accident during the work (a G&SWR express running into a NBR passenger train). No doubt the temporary cabin was dismantled for re-use elsewhere.

The LNW took over maintenance of the signalling on the joint lines from the 1st of August 1878 under an arrangement whereby the LNW and Caledonian carried out the work for alternate five year periods. Following the 1889 Regulation of Railways Act the maintenance was divided. The CR took responsibility for Nos. 1, 2 & 3 cabins, the North Eastern for Nos. 7, 10 & 11, the Maryport and Carlisle for Nos. 8 & 9, and the LNW for Nos. 12 & 13, while the signalling at No. 14 was maintained by the LNW and the telegraphs by the Caledonian. The LNWR and CR continued to be responsible for the station area as before, an arrangement which continued until the 1st of January 1916 after which the LNW took sole responsibility.

Number 8 cabin was extended by the M&CR in 1895 and was replaced by a new cabin in 1918, while the Caledonian constructed a new No. 3 cabin in about 1911 to replace the existing Nos. 2 and 3 cabins. Number 12 was replaced by an LMS 'ARP' structure in 1940 and Nos. 5 & 6 by a BR mechanical box in 1951.

Special mention might be made of No. 4A cabin which was in the centre of the station and controlled the cross-overs in the middle of the platforms. It seems to have been something of an afterthought (although opened along with the enlarged station in 1880) hence its 'A' designation. The crossovers allowed two trains to use each of the long through platforms and assisted in the process of combining and dividing trains and changing engines. Rather than provide a separate cabin structure the frame was placed high up in the station buildings on the down side island platform. To enable the signalmen to see the layout, small bay windows and balconies were provided on both sides. The frame itself was an LNW SK449 type with the timber wall of the room placed between the frame and the locking rack. The frame was placed at right angles to the tracks across the width of the building so that the windows were at the two ends.

LONDON AND NORTH WESTERN AND GREAT NORTHERN JOINT

This line was constructed in the late 1870's and brought into full use on the 1st of January 1880. Right from the start it was divided into two sections for construction and maintenance purposes. The GNR took charge of the northern section and the LNW the southern, the dividing point being the north end of Melton Station.

The original signalling was carried out by contractors and in December 1878 a contract valued at £4,853 12*s* 4*d* was awarded to Saxby and Farmer to carry out the signalling work on the Great Northern section (Bottesford to Melton and the Bingham Branch). The work was carried out to GN standards with GN style signal cabins containing 5 inch centres Saxby 'Rocker' frames and with somersault signals to control the trains. A party of LNW officers made an inspection of the works in October 1879 and in their report they criticized the GN signals which, at that time worked to a vertical position for the 'clear' indication. They thought that the signals looked unsightly and did not seem to conform with Railway Clearing House Regulations. Despite this, somersault signals were installed throughout the GN sections of the line and many survived into BR days!

Saxby and Farmer also received the contract for signalling the LNW section of the line (Melton to Medbourne Junction), the price being £4,053 17*s* 11*d*. Signalling on this section was to LNW standards and in accordance with normal practice, the signal cabins were of LNW 'Type 4' design fitted with Saxby interlocking frames and with slotted post LNW style signals to control the trains. Saxby and Farmer also installed the signalling at Marefield Junction South in 1882 when a signal cabin was opened there in connection with the Great Northern's Leicester Branch.

Once opened, the Joint Line enjoyed a fairly uneventful life. All the signals on the LNW section were eventually replaced with their 1883 standard signals. In accordance with normal LNW practice, when the Saxby lever frames became due for major repairs they were replaced with standard LNW products. A new cabin of LNW 'Type 5' design was provided at Marefield Junction North and the lever frame at John O'Gaunt replaced in the autumn of 1911. Renewals were carried out at Hallaton Junction, Hallaton Station and East Norton the following year.

The most spectacular renewal occurred in 1914 when the old North and South cabins at Melton Station were closed and replaced by a central cabin of the LNW 'overhead' type. This was fitted with a LNW overhead type tappet frame of 48 levers. In consequence the maintenance boundary was moved to a point just north of the up distant signal. The remaining cabins on the LNW section, Great Dalby and Tilton had their frames renewed in 1919.

Block working on the line also followed the practices of the two Companies. The Great Northern installed its pattern of three-wire block on its section of the line while one-wire two-position Tyers block was installed on the LNW portion, the total cost being £1,395. The latter remained in use until after the grouping and was later replaced with Tyers one-wire three-position block.

LEEDS NEW STATION (LNW AND NORTH EASTERN JOINT)

The signals, telegraphs and electric lighting were maintained by each of the two companies for alternate three year periods, the LNW, for example, covering the three years commencing on the 1st of January 1889. When the LNW's turn came again in January 1895 the NER were in the process of making some alterations to the station both on their own and the Joint account. The maintenance was therefore left with them until the following year. The alterations were still in progress in January 1896 however, and the responsibility was again left with the NER for a further year. The LNW finally took charge for its three-year maintenance period on the 1st of January 1901!

LONDON AND NORTH WESTERN AND LANCASHIRE AND YORKSHIRE JOINT

The various sections of line jointly owned by these two Companies were signalled to one or other of the two Companies Standards. The most important sections were split up as follows:—

North Union and Preston and Longridge	signalled by the LNWR
Preston and Wyre	signalled by the L&YR
Lancashire Union, Southern half	signalled by the LNWR*
Lancashire Union, Northern half	signalled by the L&YR

*L&Y Block.

ASHBY AND NUNEATON JOINT LINE: (LNWR AND MIDLAND JOINT)

The signalling work on this line was taken on by the LNWR from the 1st November, 1875. In later days, however, responsibility was split between the owning Companies. The LNW looked after the Southern end from Nuneaton to Market Bosworth inclusive, while the Midland covered Shackerstone Junction and beyond. The work was all done to the standard designs of the appropriate Company.

LONDON AND NORTH WESTERN RAILWAY
SIGNAL DEPARTMENT – SENIOR STAFF 1873-1923

	Name	*From*	*To*	*Former Position*	*Subsequent Position*
	SIGNAL SUPERINTENDENT				
	Edwards G.	1.7.1873	1.11.1876	Saxby and Farmer	Resigned. Gloucester Wagon Company.
	Dick C.	1.11.1876	1.1.1882	Head Draughtsman Loco. Dept.	Succeeded Mr Worsdell in Crewe Works.
	Thompson A. M.	1.1.1882	1.1.1912	Asst. Signal Supt.	Retired.
	Roberts J.T.	1.1.1912	→	Asst. Signal Supt.	Retired 30.6.1927.
	ASSISTANT SIGNAL SUPERINTENDENT				
	Thompson A. M.	1880	1881	Head Draughtsman	Signal Superintendent.
	Head Draughtsman's Post Redesignated Asst. Signal Supt. and Head Draughtsman July 1883.				
	Dandison W.	1883	1891	Head Draughtsman	Signal Supt. Great Southern and Western Railway Ireland.
	Roberts J. T.	1891	1912	Foreman Crewe Steam Shed	Signal Superintendent.
	Oldham A.	1912	→	Head Draughtsman	
	HEAD DRAUGHTSMAN				
	Thompson A. M.	1877	1880		Asst. Signal Supt.
	Dandison W.	1882	1883	Draughtsman	Asst. Signal Supt.
	Post Redesignated Asst. Signal Superintendent July 1883 (see above). New post created 1893.				
	Bean J. S.	1893	1902	Draughtsman	Asst. Electrical Engineer (Signal Dept.).
	Wayne P. G.	1902	1903	Foreman London Road Power Station	Inspector Electrical Dept.
	Oldham A.	1903	1912	Draughtsman	Asst. Signal Supt.
	Meacher H.	1912	→	Draughtsman	
	HEAD DRAUGHTSMAN – ELECTRICAL DEPARTMENT				
	Baxendale R.	1903	1905	Draughtsman	Draughtsman (not suitable).
	Smith J. E.	1905	1907	New Works	Signal Supt. Egyptian State Railways.
	Post combined with that of Head Draughtsman Signal Department.				
	CHIEF CLERK				
	Faickney J. P.	1874	1881	Initial Appointment	Resigned 30.11.1881.
	Gaskell J.	1881	1882	Correspondence Clerk	Resigned 18.2.1882.
	Brocklehurst G.	1882	1907	Clerk Loco. Works	Retired 31.12.1907.
	Post not filled.				
	Hinton G.	c1915	1922	Correspondence Clerk	Retired 31.3.1922.
	Stevens A.	1922	→	Chief Staff Clerk	
	NEW WORKS INSPECTORS				
(1)	Smith J.	1874	1900	Initial Appointment	Retired 1.1.1901.
	Punter J.	1901	1904	From Ravensthorpe	Signal Supt. Egyptian State Railways 31.5.1904.
	Post not filled.				
(2)	Cade J.	1874	1903	From November 1874	Retired 30.6.1903.
	Starkey J. (1)	1903	1914	From Edge Hill	To Stafford.
	Fidler T.	c1914	→		
(3)	Stothert T.	1875	1875	Initial Appointment May 1875	Dismissed August 1875.
	Bearon W. B.	1875	1885	From Heaton Norris	Retired 30.4.1885.
	Post not filled – Revived 1901.				
	Smith J. E.	1901	1905	Draughtsman	Head Draughtsman (Electrical).
	Post not filled.				
	DISTRICT INSPECTORS – ORIGINAL DISTRICTS				
	Conway				
	Hughes J.	1873	1903	Initial Appointment	Retired 30.6.1903.
	Hinton A.	1903	→	From Abergavenny	
	Craven Arms				
	Gerrard J.	1873	1879	Initial Appointment	Dismissed March 1879.
	Griffiths W.	1879	1883	Sub Inspector, Rugby	To Abergavenny.
	Office and Stores moved to Abergavenny – Autumn 1883.				
	Avergavenny				
	Transferred from Craven Arms – Autumn 1883.				
	Griffiths W.	1883	c1887	From Craven Arms	To Tyldesley.
	Prytherch H.	c1887	1898	From Tyldesley	Died 23.11.1898.
	Hinton A.	1898	1903	Sub Inspector Craven Arms	To Conway 1.7.1903.
	Green G.	1903	1921	Sub Inspector Crewe	Retired 31.12.1921.
	E. Hickman	1922	→	Sub Inspector Rugby	
	Crewe				
	Evers B.	1873	1874	Initial Appointment	Dismissed August 1874.
	Grundy T.	1874	1899		Retired January, 1899.
	Osborne E.	1899	→	Draughtsman	

Name	*From*	*To*	*Former Position*	*Subsequent Position*
Heaton Norris (Stockport)				
Bearon W.B.	1873	1875	Initial Appointment	To New Works 1.5.1875.
Grinham E. (1)	1875	1903	Foreman	Retired 1.7.1903.
Farrall G.	1903	→	From Ravensthorpe	
Lancaster				
Street A.	1873	1877	Initial Appointment	Resigned May, 1877.
Sear T.	1877	1877	Sub Inspector, Rugby	Dismissed November, 1877.
Starkey J. (1)	1877	1886	Sub Inspector, Warrington	To Watford 1.1.1887.
Eves J.	1887	1887	From Watford	Dismissed March, 1887.
Ray J.	1887	1909	Sub Inspector, Tyldesley	Retired 1.3.1909.
Healey G.	1909	1911	Sub Inspector, Rugby	Retired.
Jones H.	1911	→	From Ravensthorpe	
Rugby				
Butcher J.	1873	1909	Initial Appointment	Retired.
Mottram J.	1910	→		
Stafford				
Todd J.	1873	1900	Initial Appointment	Retired 1.1.1901.
Jones W.	1901	1906	Draughtsman	To Watford 31.3.1906.
Hill W.	1906	1914	Sub Inspector, Ravensthorpe	Died 18.9.1914.
Starkey J. (2)	1914	→	From New Works	
Tyldesley				
Prytherch H.	1873	c1887	Initial Appointment	To Abergavenny.
Griffiths W.	c1887	1909	From Abergavenny	Retired 30.9.1909.
McKie P.	1909	1921	From Ravensthorpe	Retired 31.12.1921.
Mackrell T.	1922	→	From Ravensthorpe	
Warrington				
Hodgson J.	1873	1894	Initial Appointment	Died 3.5.1894.
Tonge J.	1894	1912	Sub Inspector	Retired 1.4.1912 (ill health).
District disbanded and divided between adjacent Heaton Norris and Edge Hill Districts.				
District reformed 1.4.1921 by Division of Heaton Norris District.				
Grinham E. (2)	1921	→	Sub Inspector, Tyldesley	
Watford				
Mussell G.	1873	1875	Initial Appointment	Died 12.6.1875.
Eves J.	1875	1886	Sub Inspector	To Lancaster 1.1.1887.
Starkey J. (1)	1887	1906	From Lancaster	Retired 31.3.1906.
Jones W.	1906	→	From Stafford	

DISTRICT INSPECTORS – NEW DISTRICTS

Name	*From*	*To*	*Former Position*	*Subsequent Position*
Craven Arms				
Reopened January 1885 – To cover signalling on Joint Lines and Central Wales Line.				
Greenwood J.	1885	1892	Sub Inspector, Builth Road	To Edge Hill March 1892.
Bullock G.	1892	1904	Sub Inspector, Craven Arms	
Signalling on Joint Line transferred to GWR 1.1.1904.				
Edge Hill				
Formed March 1892 by Division of Warrington District.				
Greenwood J.	1892	1853	From Craven Arms	Retired 25.8.1893 (ill health).
Starkey J. (2)	1893	1903	Sub Inspector	To New Works 30.6.1903.
Ison A.	1903	1921	Sub Inspector	Retired 31.12.1921.
Harding, J.	1922	→	Sub Inspector, Edge Hill	
Walsall				
Formed December 1892 by Division of Stafford District.				
Upstone H.	1892	1918	Sub Inspector, Tyldesley	Retired 28.2.1918.
Dutton F.	1918	→	From Ravensthorpe	
Ravensthorpe				
Formed December 1899 by Division of Heaton Norris District.				
Punter J.	1899	1900	Sub Inspector	To New Works 1.1.1901.
Farrall G.	1901	1903	Sub Inspector, Craven Arms	To Heaton Norris 1.7.1903.
McKie P.	1903	1909	From Workington	To Tyldesley.
Jones H.	1909	1911	Sub Inspector	To Lancaster.
Dutton F.	1911	1918		To Walsall 1.3.1918.
Mackrell T.	1918	1921	Sub Inspector, Heaton Norris	To Tyldesley 1.1.1922.
White W.	1922	→	Sub Inspector, Conway	
Workington				
Formed December 1900 from West Cumberland Portion of Lancaster District.				
McKie P.	1900	1903	Sub Inspector, Tyldesley	To Ravensthorpe 1.7.1903.
Sharp W.	1903	1921	Sub Inspector, Tyldesley	Retired 31.12.1921.
District combined with Lancaster District from 1.1.1922.				

LONDON AND NORTH WESTERN RAILWAY TELEGRAPH DEPARTMENT ORGANISATION - 1897

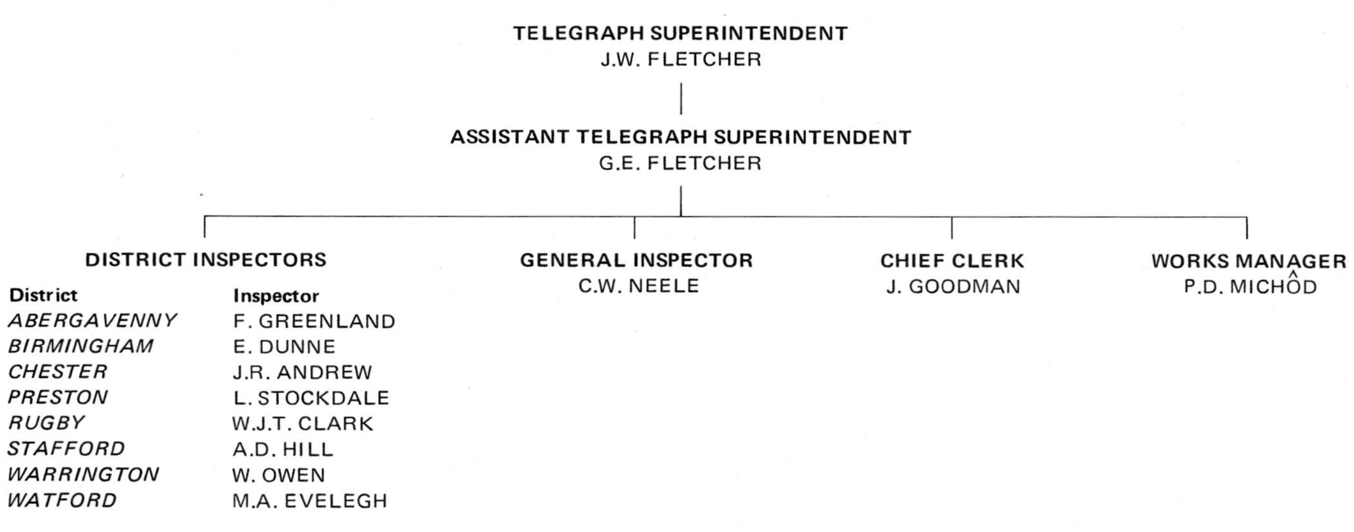

Chapters 1 and 2 contain details of the history of the Telegraph Department and mention is made there of the careers of a number of its members of staff. Brief details are given below of some of the other senior members of the staff whose names appear in the above chart.

F. Greenland moved from Stafford to Abergavenny in 1892 in consequence of an increased workload in the district brought about by the introduction of the Electric Train Staff and other electrical equipment. His salary was increased from £150 to £160 p.a. at the same time.

E. Dunne moved from Stafford to Northampton in 1879. He later returned to Stafford and moved from there to Birmingham in 1896. He died in service in 1903 and was replaced by A.D. Clayton. During his long period of service with the LNWR he patented several electrical devices connected with signalling.

L. Stockdale also died in 1903 and his district was divided. The southern section was placed under the supervision of W.V. Sturgess (formerly the Construction Inspector) with an office at Tyldesley. G.R. Naylor took charge of the northern section and was based at Lancaster.

W.J.T. Clark had been an Inspector at Northampton in the 1870's. He subsequently spent most of his career at Rugby and retired due to ill health in 1907. His salary, which had been £115 p.a. in 1879, had reached £250 p.a. by the time of his retirement. His place at Rugby was taken by G. Clark.

A.D. Hill began his career at Preston and was made a Sub-Inspector there in 1893 on the promotion of W. Owen. He became Inspector at Stafford in 1896 and moved to Chester in 1907.

W. Owen, after a spell as Sub-Inspector at Preston, became Inspector at Rugby in 1893 when C.W. Neele was promoted to the position of General Inspector. Owen moved to Warrington in 1896 on the retirement of G.F. Jones at his existing salary of £170 p.a.

M.A. Evelegh was made Telegraph Inspector, Northern Division, on J.W. Fletcher's promotion in 1879. By 1893 he had been transferred to Watford and was still there in 1911. His was a very senior post and in 1898 his salary reached £300 p.a.

C.W. Neele was formerly Telegraph Inspector at Rugby and moved to Manchester as General Inspector in January 1897. He replaced G.E. Fletcher, who had become the Assistant Telegraph Superintendent. Neele resigned in 1898 to join the GCR as Electrical Engineer. The General Inspector's post was then redesignated Senior General Assistant and P.D. Michôd was promoted to the position. Michod subsequently occupied a number of senior posts with the LNW and LMS Signal and Electrical Departments.

J. Goodman was formerly Chief Telegraph Clerk at Stafford and in 1897 his salary was £190 p.a.

Appendix III Regulations

LONDON AND NORTH WESTERN RAILWAY RULES FOR SIGHTING SIGNALS AND SIGNAL DEPARTMENT REGULATIONS

The LNWR Signal Department issued a set of instructions to its outdoor staff in order to ensure that maintenance work was carried out in a proper and safe manner. Reproduced below are two versions of the Regulations, one issued about 1883 and the other in 1915. They are set out side by side for comparison.

The rules for sighting signals were issued as a separate document originally, but were later incorporated in a new Regulation 19. Two versions are again reproduced to show how practices changed with time.

SIGNAL DEPARTMENT REGULATIONS

circa 1883

All employees of the Signal Department must make themselves thoroughly conversant with the following Regulations, which must be strictly observed, to ensure the safe conduct of the work of the department:—

REGULATION I

Cleaning and Repairing Locking Apparatus, Facing-Points, Locks, & c. When cleaning or repairing a locking apparatus, or the signals and points connected with it, necessitating their disarrangement, the following regulation must be carried out by the signal-fitter or other man sent to do the work.

Before interfering with the locking apparatus, all distant signals must either be disconnected or the levers in the cabin working them fastened in their danger position; and, before interfering with points, signals, and their connections, the distant signals for the roads affected must be fastened in their danger position. When it is necessary to disarrange the locking apparatus at a junction or station where there are facing points, the home or junction signals, as well as the distant signals, must be fastened to danger. When a facing-point or bridge bolt has to be disconnected from the cabin, the home or junction signals for the roads affected must also be fastened to danger, as well as the distant signals. At large junctions, however, where there are a number of facing points, and only one has to be disconnected, the distant signals must be fastened at danger; but special instructions will in each case be issued by the Inspector as regards the fastening of the home signals to danger. When this has been done, the signal fitter or other man must inform the signalman that he is ready to commence the work, when the signalman will, on seeing that the flagmen are properly placed and instructed, enter in the Train Register Book the words "Locking disarranged," with his signature, the fitter adding his signature also.

After this entry has been made the signalman will be responsible for working the frame as if the whole of the locking was absent, and he will do so until the fitter has informed him that the work is completed, when he will enter in the Train Register Book the words "Locking restored," the book again being signed by the signalman and the signal fitter.

When working at a signal box controlling facing-points, the signal fitter must report to his Inspector every case where Rule 149A is not strictly adhered to.

The Signal Inspector will, previous to the work being done, instruct the fitter as to whether any of the facing-points or trap-points may be spiked over during the progress of the work, in which case the fitter must see that the flagman or other man appointed has properly secured the points before he commences his work.

REGULATION II

Locking not to be interfered with except on Sundays. — No locking-frame at a place where there are facing-points, no facing-point, facing-point lock, locking-bar, or bridge bolt, is to be disarranged

1915

REGULATION I

Regulations to be observed when Cleaning or Repairing Locking, Disconnecting and Reconnecting Points, or Repairing Connections, or Signals.

Cleaning and Repairing Locking Apparatus. — When cleaning or repairing a locking apparatus, necessitating the disarrangement or partial disarrangement of the frame, the following Regulation must be carried out:—

Before commencing the work, the fitter must give to the signalman an exact description of the nature of the work he is about to undertake, and disconnect the distant and home signals and other signals for the roads affected, and the signalman will then instruct the flagmen as to their duties and enter in the Train Register Book the words "Locking disarranged" with his signature, the fitter adding his signature also.

Before interfering with the locking the Signal Inspector must satisfy himself that the hand signalmen are at their posts.

When the work is completed the fitter will inform the signalman, who will enter in the Train Register Book the words "Locking restored," the book being again signed by the signalman and signal fitter, a note of the time being also inserted.

The Signal Inspector will, previous to the work being done, instruct the fitter as to whether any facing points or trap points may be spiked over during the progress of the work, in which case the fitter must see that the flagman, or other man appointed, has properly secured the points before he commences the work.

In the case of broken adjusting screws in locking apparatus, the signal fitter must treat the breakage in the same way as a disarrangement of any other portion of the locking, and disconnect the home and distant signals affected; but as the work only, as a rule, occupies a few minutes, it will not be necessary, unless a man is at hand, to appoint a flagman, but where any difficulty arises in carrying out the work, and it is likely to occupy some time a flagman must be appointed as usual.

When cleaning locking, unless it is dismantled, only one backbone must be removed at a time, and then care must be taken that the removal of this backbone does not release any bar.

In the case of a Tappet Locking apparatus only one cover plate must be removed for cleaning or examination purposes at a time and when the cover is removed, a clip or other suitable substitute must be provided to keep the bars in position.

REGULATION II

Locking not to be interfered with except on Sundays. — No locking frame at a place where there are facing-points, no facing-point, facing-point lock, locking-bar, turntable bolt, or bridge bolt, is to be

for the purpose of cleaning, oiling, or ordinary repairs, on a week-day, under any circumstances whatever. Such work must invariably be carried out on a Sunday, and Regulation I strictly adhered to. This Regulation will also apply to places where the traffic is heavy, although there may be no facing-points.

REGULATION III

A list of junctions and stations will be exhibited in each stores-shed, showing where cleaning, oiling, and ordinary repairs, necessitating the disarrangement of locking, & C., may be carried out on week-days. The district Signal Inspector will appoint a day for the work, give the usual slackening notice, and arrange for flagmen; the work may then be carried out, Regulation I being strictly adhered to.

REGULATION IV

When it is absolutely necessary on a week-day to interfere with locking or connections, as mentioned in Regulation II, on account of breakage or failure likely to endanger the safety of the line, the necessary repairs must be carried out without delay. The fitter or chargeman, before commencing work, must apply to the station-master for a flagman, or, if at an intermediate box, application must be made to the signalman on duty, and should a flagman (plate-layer) not be at hand, the fitter or chargeman must send his assistant for a platelayer, who will receive his instructions from the signal-man. The flagman having received his instructions, the work may be commenced, Regulation I being strictly adhered to.

REGULATION V

Under no circumstances must a lever in a signal cabin be moved by Signal Department men, even with the sanction of the signalman on duty. Should a fitter require a lever moved, he must request the signalman to do it; and under no circumstances whatever must a fitter or other person belonging to the Signal Department instruct a flagman.

REGULATION VI

No locking frames, or point or signal connections are to be dis-arranged for the purpose of cleaning, oiling, or ordinary repairs, without the permission of the district Signal Inspector, who will appoint a day, and make arrangements through the Signal Super-intendent for the necessary flagmen, in accordance with Rule 149A, and for the issue of a notice to engine drivers and others.

REGULATION VII

Signal fitters, chargemen, and others, must make themselves specially acquainted with Rules 144, 145, 146, 147, and 149A in the Company's Book of Rules, and see that the instructions contained therein are strictly carried out.

REGULATION VIII

All men belonging to the Signal Department must, before starting work at a signal cabin, enter the time in the Train Register Book and sign their name, and they must again enter the time and sign their name when their work is completed for the day; they must then fill up their time-sheets, entering the date, their name and grade, the description of the work, and the time as given in the Train Register Book, and present it to the signalman on duty for signature, who will sign it after satisfying himself that the entries are correct.

REGULATION IX

Chargemen and their assistants must give special attention to the connections working facing-points, and facing-point locks, which should be carefully examined every time a place is visited, and any weakness or fault at once dealt with.

disarranged for the purpose of cleaning, oiling, or ordinary repairs, on a week-day, under any circumstances whatever, except as provided in Regulation III. Such work must invariably be carried out on a Sunday, and Regulation I strictly adhered to. This Regulation will also apply to places where the traffic is heavy, although there may be no facing points.

REGULATION III

A list of junctions and stations will be exhibited in each stores-shed, showing where cleaning, oiling, and ordinary repairs, necessitating the disarrangement of locking, & C., may be carried out on week-days. The district Signal Inspector will appoint a day for the work, give the usual slackening notice, and arrange for flagmen; the work may then be carried out, Regulation I being strictly adhered to.

REGULATION IV

When it is absolutely necessary on a week-day to interfere with locking or connections, as mentioned in Regulation II, on account of breakage or failure likely to affect the safety of the line, the necessary repairs must be carried out without delay. The fitter or chargeman, before commencing work, must apply to the station-master for a flagman, or, if at an Intermediate box, application must be made to the signalman on duty; and should a flagman (platelayer) not be at hand, the fitter or chargeman must send his assistant for a platelayer, who will receive his instructions from the signalman. The flagman having received his instructions, and the Train Register Book in the cabin being signed, the work may be commenced, Regulation I being strictly adhered to.

REGULATION V

When it is necessary during the carrying out of work for a lever in a signal cabin to be moved, the signalman must be requested to move it; but if there is any special reason for the man in charge of the work to move a lever himself he may do so, subject to the permission of the signalman. Great care must be taken that the lever is moved only at the moment permission is given, and it must only be done by the Inspector, Sub-Inspector, Foreman-in-charge, fitter, or chargeman. Other men in the department must under no circumstances whatever move a lever.

REGULATION VI

No locking-frames, or point or signal connections, are to be dis-arranged for the purpose of cleaning, oiling, or ordinary repairs, without the permission of the district Signal Inspector, who will appoint a day and make arrangements through the Signal Super-intendent for the necessary flagmen, in accordance with Rule 70 of the Company's Book of Rules and Regulations.

REGULATION VII

Signal fitters, chargemen, and others must make themselves specially acquainted with Rules 70, 71, 72, 73, 74 and 273 in the Company's Book of Rules, and see that the instructions contained therein are strictly carried out.

REGULATION VIII

Men not in charge of a Sub-Inspector or Foreman must, before starting work at a signal cabin, enter the time in the Train Register Book and sign their name, and they must again enter the time and sign their name when their work is completed for the day; they must then fill up their time sheets, entering the date, their name and grade, the description of the work and the time as given in the Train Register Book and present it to the signalman on duty for signature, who will sign it after satisfying himself that the entries are correct.

Any man found obtaining the signalman's signature before the particulars have been filled in will be severely dealt with.

REGULATION IX

Chargemen and their assistants, and fitters and their assistants, must give special attention to the connections working facing points and facing-point locks, which should be carefully examined every time a place is visited, and any weakness or fault at once dealt with.

The standard distance a facing-point plunger should be when withdrawn is three-quarters of an inch from the stretcher bar, and when any bolt is found to exceed this distance it must be adjusted.

REGULATION X

Chargemen and their assistants must frequently examine point-rod adjusting screws. Detector-holes are provided in the barrel of each adjusting screw, and the rods are centre-punched, and should the screw be found adjusted beyond the detector-hole, arrangements must be at once made for the rod to be lengthened. The screws for facing-points and facing-point locks must receive special attention.

REGULATION XI

When painting signal arms, painters must be very careful that they do not pull the signal-arm down, as such a practice is liable to lead to serious consequences.

REGULATION XII

Chargemen and their assistants, when cleaning cranks, wheels, & c., are cautioned against leaving the box-lids too close to the line, several mishaps having occurred due to a neglect of the precaution.

REGULATION XIII

All Signal Department men are cautioned against leaving tools or other materials on station platforms, several accidents to passengers, and claims against the Company, resulting from a neglect of the precaution.

REGULATION XIV

In carrying out signal alterations, great care must be taken that the old signals are kept in their danger position until the new signals are brought into use.

REGULATION XV

When it is necessary in hoisting signals or carrying out other work of the department to have guy-ropes across the line, under no circumstances must a train be allowed to pass unless it has previously been brought to a stand; and to avoid delay to passenger trains, such ropes, when practicable, should be cleared away at least ten minutes before the time the train is due.

REGULATION XVI

A diagram is given below which shows the clearance space required for a passenger or goods line and inspectors must see that no signal cabin, signal post, balance weight or other obstruction comes within the space dimensioned and chargemen and others must report to their inspectors any case where the necessary clearance has not been allowed.

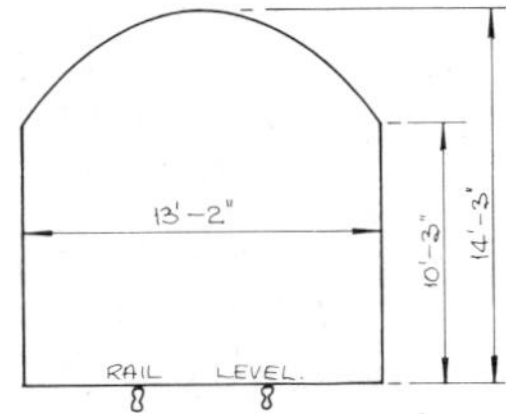

REGULATION XVII

Wooden covers or boxes over facing point locks or other apparatus, in the 4ft must not stand higher than 1 inch above rail level, and if the cover are hinged, they must not stand more than 3 inches above rail level when thrown back. Chargemen must report any case where this regulation has not been adhered to.

REGULATION X

Chargemen and their assistants must frequently examine point-rod adjusting screws. Detector-holes are provided in the barrel of each adjusting screw, and the rods are centre-punched, and should the screw be found adjusted beyond the detector-hole, arrangements must be at once made for the rod to be lengthened. The screws for facing points and facing-point locks must receive special attention.

Testing Points. — Chargemen and their assistants must not only examine points, but must, as far as possible, see the points worked, so as to assure themselves that they are properly fitting on each side, and an entry must be made on the time-sheet showing the numbers of the points at each cabin visited which have been so tested. The chargemen must carry with them a small pinch-bar with which to test the spring of the points on either side. It is desirable that the points should be pulled over slowly, as this is more likely to show a defect.

REGULATION XI

When painting signal arms, painters must be very careful that they do not pull the signal-arm down, as such a practice is liable to lead to serious consequences.

REGULATION XII

Chargemen and their assistants, when cleaning cranks, wheels, & c., are cautioned against leaving the box-lids too close to the line, several mishaps having occurred due to a neglect of the precaution. All material must also be carefully placed clear of the line.

REGULATION XIII

All Signal Department men are cautioned against leaving tools or other materials on station platforms, several accidents to passengers, and claims against the Company, resulting from a neglect of the precaution.

REGULATION XIV

In carrying out signal alterations great care must be taken that the old signals are kept in their danger position until the new signals are brought into use, and where this is not possible the line must be protected by flagmen sent out the usual distances to act in place of the signal, the arrangements for this being made between the Signal Inspector and the Traffic Inspector.

REGULATION XV

When erecting signals the following Regulation must be strictly carried out:—

(see notes at end)

REGULATION XVI

A diagram is given below which shows the clearance space required for a passenger or goods line and inspectors must see that no signal cabin, signal post, balance weight or other obstruction comes within the space dimensioned and chargemen and others must report to their inspectors any case where the necessary clearance has not been allowed.

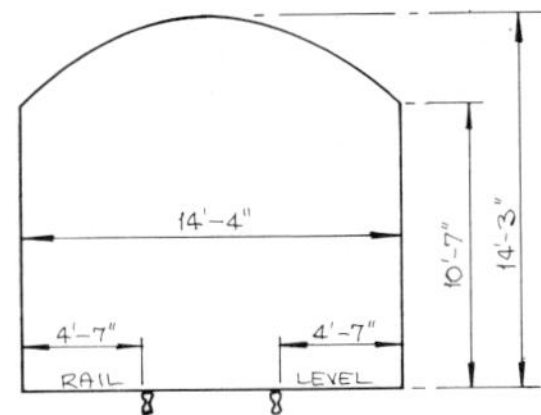

REGULATION XVII

Wooden covers or boxing over facing-point locks, or other apparatus, in the 4 feet, must not stand higher than 1 inch above rail level; and if the covers are hinged, they must not stand more than 3 inches above rail level when thrown back. Chargemen must report any case where this regulation has not been adhered to.

REGULATION XVIII

(see notes at end)

SIGHTING SIGNALS

Instructions to Inspectors

To secure uniformity in the arrangement of signals the following rules must, as far as possible, be observed.

The arrangement of the signals shown on the plan prepared by the Signal Superintendent should be adhered to, and sighted for as nearly as possible as shown on the plan — any modified arrangement suggested by the Inspectors on the ground being sighted for and added to the plan as a rider.

Distant Signals. — These signals should be fixed at an uniform distance of 1,000 yards from the home signal, unless the gradient is a rising one, in which case a distance of 800 yards will be sufficient. In special cases a distant signal may be fixed at a distance of 1,200 yards from the home signal, provided the Signal Inspector agrees that he can obtain a sufficiently direct route for the wire connections to ensure the signal working freely. On no account must a signal be fixed at a greater distance than 1,200 yards from the cabin.

Home Signals. — These signals should be seen by a driver from the distant signals, and must be fixed as close to the cabin as possible, so that a driver whose engine is standing at the signal may be verbally communicated with by the signalman.

Junction Signals. — The same rule applies to the sighting of these signals as for home signals. They must be fixed near the facing points to which they apply, and in no case must they be at a greater distance than 200 yards from the facing points, unless repeater signals or duplicate locking bars are provided.

Junction signals for protecting a junction in the trailing direction should be fixed so far from the fouling point as to afford a margin for a driver should he accidentally draw past the signal.

Junction signals must not in any case be placed on the same post one above the other, but a separate post must be provided for each signal.

This rule need not apply to bay starting or other subordinate signals; in these cases the signals may be placed on a single post, one signal above the other. The top signal must then apply to the road leading off to the left-hand, the second signal to the next left-hand road, and so on.

Platform Starting-Signals. — These must be sighted at a height of about 15 feet above rail level, and it will be sufficient if they be seen by a driver the length of the platform.

This rule will not apply if the starting signal post carries the distant signal of a cabin in advance, or if the starting signal acts as a home signal for a cabin in advance; in these cases the signals must be sighted as distant and home signals respectively.

Advanced Starting-Signals. — These signals may be sighted of an uniform height with platform starting-signals, of 15 feet above the rail level; they should be seen by a driver from the platform starting-signal, and must not be at a greater distance from the cabin than 350 yards. If an engine or other obstruction standing at the advanced starting-signal cannot be clearly seen by the signalman, the signal must not be provided, and it will then be necessary for the sidings in advance of the platform starting signal to be worked in the block.

Bay starting and other subordinate signals should be of an uniform height of 15 feet above rail level, have short arms, and *be provided with purple lights*.

A distant signal for a cabin in advance must never overlap a home or starting signal for a cabin in the rear, but must be fixed on the same post 7 feet below the home or starting signal, and be controlled by the home or starting signal, to prevent the distant arm being off when the home or starting arm is at danger. When a distant signal is placed below a home or starting signal, no other signal must be placed on the same post, excepting "fog" or "calling-on" arms.

When the distant signals for a junction have to be combined with the home or starting signals for a cabin in the rear, then the starting signal post must be nearest the line with the distant arm for the right-hand junction placed under it, and the distant signal for the left-hand junction must be carried by a separate post to the left of the home or starting post. Both distant arms must be controlled by the home or starting signal. This rule will not apply if the junction to the right is a goods loop or other subordinate line; in this case, the distant signal must be carried on a separate post to the right of the home or starting post.

SIGHTING SIGNALS

REGULATION XIX

To secure uniformity in the arrangement of signals, the following rules must, as far as possible, be observed:—

The arrangement of the signals shown on the plan prepared by the Signal Superintendent should be adhered to, and sighted for as nearly as possible as shown on the plan — any modified arrangement suggested by the Inspectors on the ground being sighted for and added to the plan as a rider.

Distant Signals. — These signals should be fixed at a uniform distance of 1,000 yards from the home signal, unless the gradient is a rising one, in which case a distance of 800 yards will be sufficient. In special cases distant signals can be worked at a greater distance if necessary, but when so sighted the Inspector must report at the same time if he sees any difficulty in working the signal in the ordinary way, so that the method of working may be considered.

These signals should only be sighted of sufficient height to get the best sight for a driver and high signals should not be sighted to enable the signalman to see them, but be electrically repeated.

Home Signals. — These signals should be seen by a driver from the distant signals, and must be fixed as close to the cabin as possible, so that a driver whose engine is standing at the signal may be verbally communicated with by the signalman.

Junction Signals. — The same rule applies to the sighting of these signals as for home signals. They must be fixed near the facing points to which they apply and in no case must they be at a greater distance than 150 yards from the facing points, unless repeater signals or duplicate locking-bars are provided.

Junction signals for protecting a junction in the trailing direction should be fixed so far from the fouling point as to afford a margin for a driver should he accidentally draw past the signal.

Junction signals must not in any case be placed on the same post one above the other, but a separate post must be provided for each signal.

This rule need not apply to bay starting or other subordinate signals; in these cases the signals may be placed on a single post, one signal above the other. The top signal must then apply to the road leading off to the left hand, the second signal to the next in order from the left-hand road, and so on.

Platform Starting Signals. — These must be sighted at a height of about 15 feet above rail level, and it will be sufficient if they be seen by a driver the length of the platform.

This rule will not apply if the starting signal post carries the distant signal of a cabin in advance, or if the starting signal acts as a home signal for a cabin in advance; in these cases the signals must be sighted as distant and home signals respectively.

Advanced Starting Signals. — These signals should be sighted of a uniform height of 15 feet above rail level wherever possible; they should be seen by a driver from the platform starting signal and should not be sighted further out than necessary to meet the length of the trains to be dealt with.

If an engine or other obstruction standing at the advanced starting signal cannot be clearly seen by the signalman, attention must be drawn to the fact when reporting the sighting, so that track circuiting or other means may be provided to remind the signalman of a train drawn up at such a signal.

Bay Starting and other subordinate signals should be of a uniform height of 15 feet above rail level and be provided with short arms.

A distant signal for a cabin in advance must never overlap a home or starting signal for a cabin in the rear, but must be fixed on the same post 7 feet below the home or starting signal, and be controlled by the home or starting signal, to prevent the distant arm being off when the home or starting arm is at danger. When a distant signal is placed below a home or starting signal, no other signal must be placed on the same post, excepting "fog" or "calling-on" arms.

When the distant signals for a junction have to be combined with the home or starting signals for a cabin in the rear, then the starting signal post must be nearest the line with the distant arm for the right-hand junction placed under it, and the distant signal for the left-hand junction must be carried by a separate post to the left of the home or starting post. Both distant arms must be controlled by the home or starting signal. This rule will not apply if the junction to the right is a goods loop or other subordinate line; in this case the distant signal must be carried on a separate post to the right of the home or starting post.

Lamps must never be placed nearer together than 7 feet, with the exception of bay starting or other subordinate signals, for which the lamps may be fixed closer together.

Back Lights, which cannot be seen by the signalman working the signals, must be dispensed with unless they can be seen from a station platform; in this case they may be retained if it is considered desirable.

Signals elevated more than 45 feet above rail level must have a lower or fog arm, worked in connection with the top arm at an elevation of 15 feet above rail level, but a single lamp only is necessary, to be opposite the bottom arm when practicable.

Signal Cabins should be so placed that the signalman can see all points and signals from the levers working them, especially facing points, which must be in all cases clearly seen.

Electric Repeaters must be avoided, as far as possible, even at the expense of higher signals. If a repeater cannot be avoided, then the signals should be only sighted at such an elevation as to give a driver a good sight.

All Signals should be fixed on the left-hand side of, and as near as possible to, the road to which they apply.

A signal cabin or signal placed on a passenger platform must not be at a less distance then 6 feet from the nosing of the platform, and a cabin or signal must not be erected at a less distance than 4 feet 6 inches from a passenger line.

The Inspectors must each consider the general arrangement of the signalling. It will be the special duty of the *Traffic Inspector* to see that the signal cabin is suitably placed, and that the signals are seen by the Signalman. It will be the special duty of the *Locomotive Inspector* to see that the drivers' sight of signals is good, and that the signals are fixed at a suitable distance from the fouling points. It will be the duty of the *Signal Inspector* to see that the points and signals are placed in such a position as to be satisfactorily worked, are suitably arranged, and in accordance with the plan.

Lamps must be fixed at arm level in all cases. If there are any special circumstances necessitating any different arrangement a special report to be made.

Backlights which cannot be seen by the signalman working the signals must be dispensed with unless such backlights are required to enable any other signalman or station staff to see them.

Signals elevated more than 40 feet above rail level must have a lower or fog arm worked in connection with the top arm at an elevation of 15 feet above rail level, but it is not necessary in all such cases to provide a lamp for each arm where the lamp fixed at the lower arm can be well seen.

Signal Cabins should be so placed that the signalman can see all points and signals from the levers working them, especially facing points, which must be in all cases clearly seen.

Electric Repeaters should be provided in all cases where distant signals would otherwise have to be at a greater height, but in the case of home and starting signals repeaters should be avoided if possible, even if somewhat higher signals have to be provided. Where repeaters are absolutely necessary, the signals to be kept as low as possible to suit the driver's sight.

All Signals should be fixed on the left-hand side of, and as near as possible to, the road to which they apply.

A signal cabin or signal placed on a passenger platform must not be at less distance than 6 feet from the nosing of the platform, and a cabin or signal must not be erected at a less distance than 4 feet 7 inches from a passenger line.

The Inspectors must each consider the general arrangement of the signalling. It will be the special duty of the *Traffic Inspector* to see that the signal cabin is suitably placed, and that the signals are seen by the signalman. It will be the special duty of the *Locomotive Inspector* to see that the drivers' sight of signals is good, and that the signals are fixed at a suitable distance from the fouling points. It will be the duty of the *Signal Inspector* to see that the points and signals are placed in such a position as to be satisfactorily worked, are suitably arranged, and in accordance with the plan.

1915 REGULATIONS – ADDITIONAL ITEMS

In addition to the above the 1915 regulations contained further instructions as follows:

REGULATION I

To this was added instructions on the maintenance of points, bolts, bars, train stops, signals and level crossings.

REGULATION XV

When erecting signals the following Regulations must be strictly carried out:—

Before the derrick is placed in position, or ropes carried across, or in close proximity to the Railway, all signals must be fastened in their danger position which apply to the line or lines so obstructed, or liable to be obstructed, if the derrick or the signal which is being erected should fall, and in addition flagmen must be sent out to a point at least 800 yards on a rising gradient, and 1,000 yards on a falling gradient, from the point where the obstruction exists. These men will be provided with detonators, and will warn drivers of all trains during such time as ropes are across the lines, or signals being erected. Three flagmen will consequently be required, i.e., distant men in each direction and a man with the working party.

The signals, which may include distant, home, starting and advanced starting signals, can be fastened in their danger position by disconnecting them as given in Regulation I. When this is done, and an entry made in the Train Register Book, and signed in accordance with Regulation I, and when the flagmen are posted by the Traffic Department, the work may proceed.

When the signal has been erected and made secure, the derrick pole lowered to the ground, and all ropes obstructing the line cleared away, the signals should without delay, be reconnected, this work being entered in the Train Register Book, which must be again signed, after which the flagman may be withdrawn.

In some cases where there are four lines of rails, it may be possible to erect a signal without fear of some of the lines being obstructed should the signal or derrick post fall, but in every case of doubt it is desirable to err on the side of safety.

In the case of the erection of a distant signal for say, the up line, as there will be no signal protecting the up line, it will be necessary to place a flagman out as usual, with detonators: but, in addition to this, the down signals must be fastened in their danger position to carry out the above Regulation. The same rule will apply to the erection of a down distant, the up signals being fastened to danger.

When arranging for the hoisting of signals, the Inspector, Sub-Inspector, or other person in charge must be careful to choose his time, so as to avoid all unnecessary interference with the running of important trains.

REGULATION XVIII

Accidents. — In cases of accident, chargemen and other men in charge of stations or sections of line must immediately report by telegraph to the Signal Superintendent and their Inspector brief particulars of the case. In any cases where on arrival on the ground the chargeman finds that the mishap has been caused, or alleged to have been caused, by a defect in the signal apparatus, he must immediately make a thorough examination of everything in connection with them, and note, in case it should be required for any future enquiry, the exact position of affairs. He must then get the signalman to test the working of the signals in his presence, and note carefully the result.

Where it is probable that some enquiry may be held as to the cause of a mishap, no alteration must, prior to such enquiry, be made to the signals or connections at the place in question, unless there is reason to fear that any obstruction or defect discovered may lead to the signals working improperly, but full particulars must be at once sent by the chargeman to the District Inspector, who will visit the place and arrange what he considers best.

Should any vehicles be off the line and fouling other lines the signals referring to all lines fouled must be disconnected.

Repairing Signal Cabins. — In carrying out renewal of signal cabin steps and landing the man in charge of the work must, before removing the old landing or steps, nail a batten on the outside of the signal cabin door frame, as a reminder to the signalman that the steps or landing have been taken away.

REGULATION XX

Protection for Men Working in Dangerous Positions. — In the case of men working in dangerous positions a look-out man must be appointed, either from the gang, or a platelayer obtained from the Permanent Way Department. In the case of fitters and chargemen with assistants, one of the men must act as look-out man while the other is working in any dangerous position.

A further unnumbered section contained instructions to cover the repair of the 'Crewe System' Power Signalling.

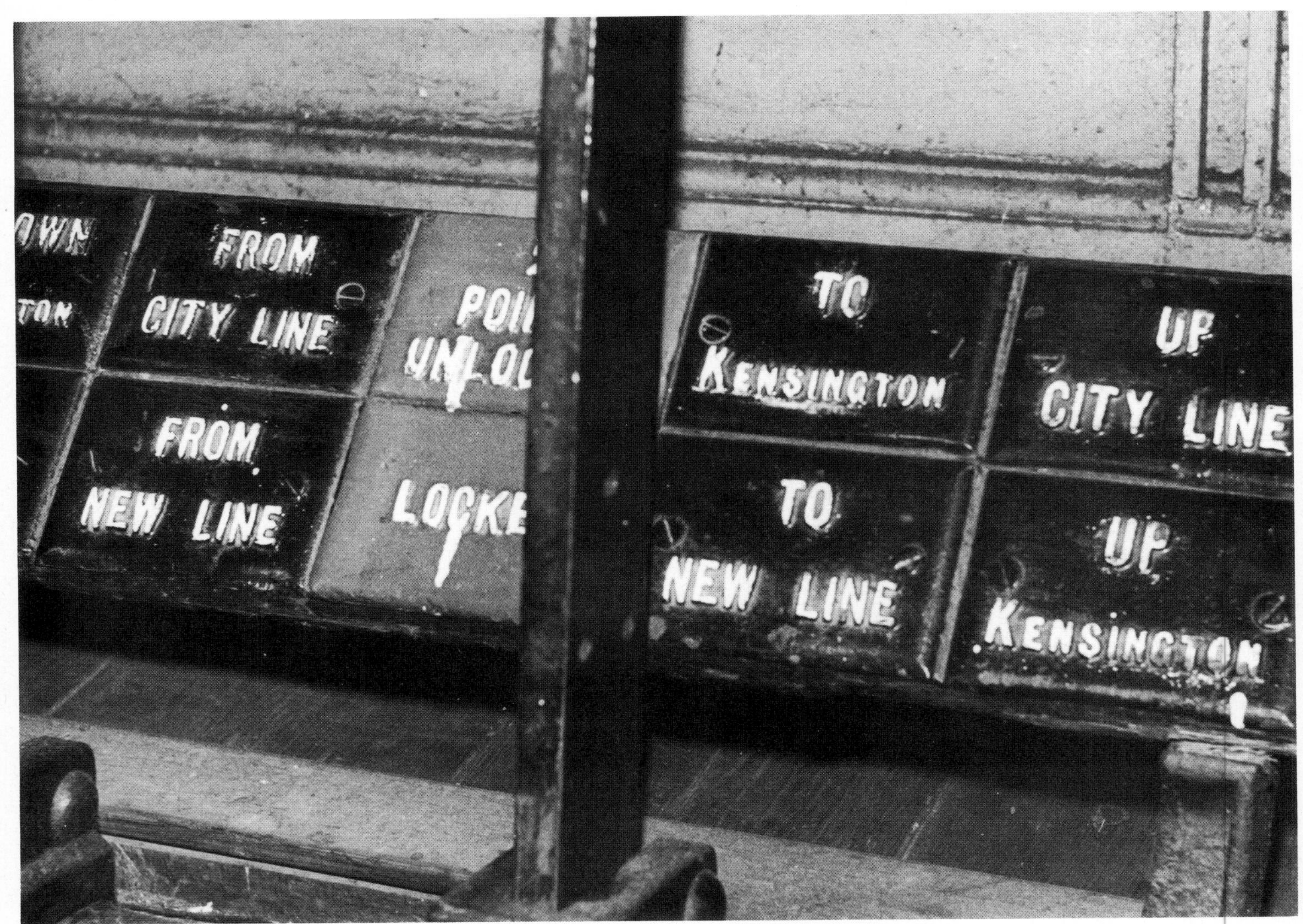

Appendix IV Costs

1 - L.N.W. SIGNAL DEPARTMENT

In order to give an idea of the costs incurred by the LNWR in carrying out signalling work some examples of actual costs are given below. As will be seen from the instances quoted the installed costs were largely dependent on the work necessary on the ground. This would depend on the length and ease of installation of point rod and signal wire runs and the amount of preparation necessary for the installation. The foundation work necessary to prepare for a new signal cabin could vary considerably from one place to another.

1) **COST OF SIGNALS AT THE WORKS, 1884**

New Pattern Ground Disc Signal	£2.9s 8d
New Pattern 20 ft Signal Post and Arm	£6.15s 0d
Posts between 20 and 30 ft	2/- per foot extra
Posts between 30 and 40 ft	2/6d per foot extra
Posts over 40 ft in length	3/- per foot extra
New Pattern 2 Arm Signal on 20 ft posts	£9 5s 0d
Posts between 20 and 30 ft	3/- per foot extra
Posts between 30 and 40 ft	2/6d per foot extra
Posts above 40 ft	3/- per foot extra
Guy Posts	14/7d

2) **PAINTERS WORK**

1878. Painters paid 2½d per foot for scraping and painting signal posts.
1879. Instructions issued that painters were not to be allowed to do any more work in a week than would give them a total wage of £2. (i.e. Time + a third).
1880 : Painters rates for painting signal cabins to be:—

Size N Cabin	£6.15s 0d
Size O Cabin	£8 2s 6d
Size P Cabin	£9 12s 0d

1881: Painting new pattern Disc Signals 4d per coat.

3) **COST OF NEW SCHEMES**

1877:	Lilbourne. New size 'C' cabin at platform level, 15 levers (9 working)	£539
	Theddingworth: New size E cabin, 20 levers (15 working)	£791
1881:	Wrenbury. New size 'C' cabin, 20 levers, all working plus 7 lever ground frame for yard	£780
1884:	Pentre Siding (Flint). New cabin, connecting up existing signalling plus new signals and gates	£540
1889:	Smethwick Rolfe Street. New overhead cabin size 'F, 36 levers (27 working) to work new layout	£906
1895:	Ledsham Station. New size 'G' cabin, 34 levers, provided in connection with quadrupling of line	£993
1897:	Carwardine Cutting. Intermediate cabin size 'C' with 4 working levers	£145
1905:	Connahs Quay No. 1. New cabin size 'G' (all wood), 36 levers, for quadrupling of line and new yard	£951

4) **RENEWAL OF SIGNAL CABINS AND APPARATUS**

1892:	Widnes No. 7. Renew signal cabin with all-wood size 'D' cabin, 20 levers (13 working), connecting new crossover	£265
1893:	Queensferry. New cabin size 'D' to control existing layout	£408
1894:	Widnes No. 4 Dock Junction, New size 'J' cabin, 45 levers	£934
1896:	British Alkali. New size 'D' cabin	£206
1898:	Brandon Ballast Pit. New size 'D' cabin, 20 levers	£396
1920:	Penkridge Goods. New size 'F' cabin and new signal	£906
1889:	Llanfairfechan: Provide second hand cabin and apparatus from Abergele No. 2 to work existing signalling	£57
1882:	Weaver Bank. New 10 lever apparatus in existing cabin, connect up new crossover	£82

5) **GROUND FRAMES**

1877:	Husband's Bosworth Level Crossing. Provide Webb 'right angle' frame, 4 signals, gate lock and train indicators	£142
1880:	Whitehall Road (Leeds). New 9 ft square hut plus 9 working levers for new goods yard	£390
1889:	Spring Vale (Deepfields). New ground frame, slot to existing running signals and bolt lock from signal cabin	£244
1902:	Treborth. New platform G.F. and new siding points locked by Annetts key	£78
1902:	Llanerch-y-Mor (Holywell). 6 lever G.F. and connections	£108

6) **RUNNING SIGNALS**

1881:	Widnes No. 3. Provide and connect up new signal	£22
1888:	Lichfield No. 3 (TV). Provide new down starting signal, new lever in cabin and connect up	£34
1890:	Penrhyn Sidings. New starting signal with lower distant	£37
1891:	Weedon No. 2. Provide and connect up new signal	£30
1892:	Pochin Pits (Abernant). New starting signal with lower distant for next cabin	£43
1900:	Portobello Junction. New distant signal, 250 yards further from cabin	£25

7) **SUBSIDIARY AND DISC SIGNALS**

1882:	Stafford No. 5. Four new call-on arms on existing post	£26
1883:	Crewe No. 2. Call-on arm on existing post	£6
1889:	Llandudno Junction. Call-on signal on existing post, connections plus additional lever	£26
1890:	Soho Soap Works. New tall siding signal	£15
1898:	New Street No. 6. Two shunt arms on existing posts plus one set back disc	£45
1880:	Chequerbent. New disc signal working with points	£8
1883:	Hindley Green. Two new disc signals from yard	£19
1886:	Lime Street. Two new disc signals	£27
1897:	Polesworth. New Disc signal in sidings	£14

8) **POINTS AND GONGS**

1882:	Soho Soap Works. New crossover and discs	£25
1884:	Tilton. Connect up one point outside cabin	£11
1891:	Bangor No. 2. Connect up one new pair of points	£12
1902:	Stechford No. 2. Connect up new trap point to cabin	£26
1897:	Soho. Provide gong and gong lever on ground, 40 yards apart	£16
1902:	Stechford. Provide 2 gongs and levers for working them on ground about 200 yards apart	£20

9) **MISCELLANEOUS**

1883:	Weaver Junction. Move two signals and install two 'Park and Pryce' patent locking bars on down lines.	£30
1884:	Crewe. Provide and fix 2 face discs lettered 'Up Platform Line Clear' and 'Up Main Line Clear' in No. 3 cabin, connect up and work from No. 2 cabin.	£26
1892:	Garndiffaith Junction. Remove rings from 5 signal arms applying to branch to Golynos. Remove FPL's from branch points and install shunt forward signal arm on existing up main home, less allowance for materials taken up.	£20

2 - SAXBY AND FARMER'S CONTRACT OF 1867

On 25th August 1867 Saxby and Farmer submitted a new Schedule of Prices for signalling work on the LNW. They stated that they would be prepared to enter into a Contract to supply signalling equipment at these prices provided the LNWR would agree to obtain all of its signalling equipment from Saxby and Farmer during the period covered by the Contract (this was not to apply at junctions with other lines, on joint lines or at places where special arrangements existed). The offer was accepted and a contract was signed in September 1867. It was agreed that the new prices would be back-dated to 30th June. These prices were a reduction on those charged under the 1862 Contract and other arrangements. As explained in Chapter 1, further substantial reductions were negociated in 1870. The prices offered under the 1867 Contract are listed below.

Signal Cabins

Bricked and braided down to ground level. Floor elevated 6 ft above rail level as per specification in tender.
10 ft x 10 ft – £80; 14 ft x 14 ft – £100; Others in proportion.

Junction or station semaphore signals

Twenty feet above ground – wood posts	£18
" " " " – wrought iron posts	£26

Additional and reduced heights to be charged or allowed for at the rate of; wood posts – 5/6d per foot; wrought iron posts 9/- per foot.

Patent Apparatus (interlocking frames)

Machinery for working points and signals by levers (as approved by the Board of Trade) per lever, including labour for fixing etc.	£7
Spare levers in the apparatus, each	£4-10s
Frames and levers without locking, per lever	£3-10s

Point Connections

Point connections etc.	each 4/8d
Extra rods	per yard 3/8d
Corresponding levers for long point connections	each 15/-
Right and Left hand adjusting screws	each 12/6d
Wrought iron pedestal cranks	each 18/-
" " 9" side cranks	each 15/-
Half crank and double joints	each 15/-

Signal connections

Quadrant wheel and lever for working distant and gongs	each £3
Wood frame for fixing ditto	each 12/-
Oak frame for fixing ditto	each 25/-
Connections to distant signals, fixing etc.	per yard 5/-
Adjusting coupling for ditto	each 5/6d
Wood trunking for wire connections	per yard 2/-
Ground disc signals	each £9
Extra arm and lamp complete, being one additional signal	each £6
Single crab for distant signals	each £4-10s
Double ditto with repeater	each £5-15s
Wooden frame for fixing crab and repeaters	each 12/-
Oak frame for ditto	each 25/-
Chain connections	per foot 4d
Lever wheel on iron plate for working repeating signals	each 45/-
Point indicators (fixing timber extra)	each £9
Distant signals, additional wire on the same stumps	per yard 4d

Miscellaneous equipment

Discs	each £4
Gongs	each £5
Repeaters into cabins	each £7
Crossing wheels 10 inch	each 6/-
" " 14 inch	each 8/-
Wood boxes for ditto	each 6/-

General conditions

Signals etc. for unopened lines to be conveyed on such new lines to the ground at the purchasers cost.
Free conveyance to be provided for Saxby and Farmer's workmen and Superintendents on the authority of the LNW Co.'s Engineers.

3 - COST OF SIGNALS MANUFACTURED BY THE L.N.W.R. IN 1867

For comparison with the above, the cost of signals manufactured and fixed by the LNW Permanent Way Department in October 1867 were as follows:

Mr. Woodhouse's District	25 ft signal, 2 arms complete	£16-16s 7d
	20 ft distant signal, one arm	£14-13s 9d
Mr. Worthington's District	25 ft signals, 2 arms complete	£16- 7s 7d
	20 ft distant signal, one arm	£14- 0s 0d
Mr. Lee's District	30 ft semaphore	£17- 0s 0d
	20 ft auxiliary	£12- 4s 6d
Mr. Smith's District	Non manufactured.	

CONVERSION FACTORS
12 (old) pence (d) = 1 shilling (s) = 5 (new) pence (p); 20 shillings = £1; 1 foot = 305 millimetres; 1 inch = 25.4 millimetres; 1 pound (weight) = 0.454 kilogrammes; 1 Ton = 1016 kilogrammes; 1 ounce (oz.) = 28.35 grammes.

Appendix V Electric Lock

REGULATIONS FOR WORKING FLETCHER'S ELECTRIC LOCK FOR INTERMEDIATE SIDINGS–1884

London and North Western Railway

Instruction to signalmen and others working the points and electrical apparatus between A and B.

Electric gong code from Station A to Station B.

Call attention and acknowledgement	1 Stroke on the gong.
Points unlocked	6 (2-2-2)
Clear '. . . Line' at siding for train to pass	7
Special train entering section signal	8 (2-2-2-2 or 4-4)

Codes B to A

Call attention and acknowledgement	1 Stroke
Unlock points	6 (2-2-2)
'. . . line' cleared points replaced and indicator changed to siding locked signals unlocked	7

Codes . . . siding to B

Call attention and acknowledgement	1 Stroke
Unlock points	6 (2-2-2)
Engine gone forward to stn. B	3 (2-1)
Train " " " " "	4 (3-1)
Signal in error	5*
'. . . line' cleared, points replaced and indicator changed to 'siding locked, signals unlocked'.	7
Inspector's signal for testing apparatus	16*

Electric gong code from station 'B' to 'siding' –

Call attention and acknowledgement	1 Stroke on the gong.
Points unlocked	6 Strokes (2-2-2)
Signal in error	5* "
Clear '. . . line' for train to pass	7 "
Inspector's signal for testing apparatus	16*

*Signals marked thus must be repeated before they can be considered as understood.

The system of working will be as follows:–

1. Before a train leaves station 'A' which has to call at the 'siding' the signalman must signal it on to station 'B', as laid down in the rules for absolute block working, giving, however, the special signal of eight strokes on the gong (thus, 2-2-2-2) as 'train entering section' signal, for the information of station 'B' signalman that the train is calling at the siding.

2. The signalman at station 'A' will then allow the train to proceed to the 'siding', and, as soon as it has passed his signals, will electrically release the points at the 'siding', and thus lock his own signal levers.

3. If during the time the train is occupied at the siding the signalman at station 'A' receives the 'be ready' for an important train approaching on the '. . . line', he will advise station 'B' by giving seven strokes on the gong, station 'B' transmitting the same (seven strokes) to the 'siding', this signal being acknowledged by one stroke in each case; and the shunter or brakesman must, as soon as possible, finish his work and send forward the train to station 'B', or shunt his train into the 'siding'.

4. When the shunter or brakesman has completed the shunting at the 'siding', and the engine or train is ready to start towards station 'B', he must call the attention of the signalman at station 'B' by giving one stroke on the gong, and, having obtained an acknowledgement, he must give the code of three strokes (thus, 2-1) or four strokes (thus, 3-1), as the case may be. After this has been acknowledged by the signalman at station 'B', the shunter or brakesman must close the points, give seven strokes on the gong, and then proceed on his way. On the engine or train passing station 'B', the signalman at that place will transmit this signal (seven strokes) to station 'A', and turn his indicator to 'siding locked, signals unlocked', which station 'A' will acknowledge by one stroke on the gong, and the section to station 'A' is then to be cleared, in accordance with the rules laid down for absolute block working.

5. If the train is one which is going to remain at the siding for any purpose the signalman at station 'A' must signal it on to station 'B' as laid down in the rules for absolute block working, giving, however, the special signal of eight strokes on the gong (thus, 4-4) as 'train entering section' signal, for the information of the station 'B' signalman that the train is going into the siding to remain. The signalman at station 'A' will then proceed to act as directed in paragraph 2.

6. As soon as the whole train has been put into the siding, and the main line is clear, the shunter or brakesman must close the points and give seven strokes on the gong to station 'B', who will acknowledge by giving one stroke on the gong, transmit the same (seven strokes) to station 'A' and turn his indicator to 'siding locked, signals unlocked', which station 'A' will acknowledge by giving one stroke on the gong. The signalman at station 'B' will then clear the section to station 'A', in accordance with the rules laid down for absolute block working.

7. When the train is ready to proceed from the 'siding' towards station 'B', the shunter or brakesman must call the attention of the signalman at station 'B' by giving one stroke on the gong, and, having obtained an acknowledgement, he must give six strokes on the gong (thus, 2-2-2), 'unlock points', which station 'B' will transmit to station 'A' (providing he has not accepted a 'be ready' signal for another train on the '. . . line', in which case he will wait until the section is clear); and if the signalman at station 'A' has no other train on hand to send forward, he will electrically release the points at the 'siding' (thus locking his own signal levers), and will reply to station 'B' by giving six strokes on the gong (thus, 2-2-2), 'points unlocked'. Station 'B' will then proceed to block the '. . . line', as laid down in the rules for absolute block working, and then transmit the signal, six strokes on the gong (thus, 2-2-2), 'points unlocked', to the 'siding'. The shunter or brakesman will then open the points and despatch the train, advising the signalman at station 'B' that he has done so by giving four strokes on the gong (thus, 3-1). After this has been acknowledged, the shunter or brakesman must close the points and give seven strokes on the gong. On the train passing station 'B', the signalman at that place will transmit this signal (seven strokes) to station 'A', and turn his indicator to 'siding locked, signal unlocked', which station 'A' will acknowledge by one stroke on the gong, and the section to Station 'A' is then to be cleared, in accordance with the rules laid down for absolute block working.

N.B. – When the work is being done by the brakesman, the engine-driver must allow him to get into the brake before starting away.

The rules were drawn up so as to meet all the requirements, the arrangement being worked in different ways, i.e.:

(a) Between the block-post in rear and siding.
(b) Between two block-posts, with siding intermediate.
(c) When the train could be put into the siding, and the main line cleared.
(d) When both up and down lines were obstructed as in the case of Weedon Drawbridge.

Summary of Contents

In a detailed work such as this it is not possible to provide a full index. The list below is intended to locate for the reader the FIRST or MAIN mention of the subject concerned.

Contents	*Page*
Accidents — Ditton Junction	55
Northampton	187
Quintinshill	188
Watford	189
Wigan	14, 214
To S&T Staff	25
Annetts Locks	112, 166, 195
Arm Repeaters	178
Ashby & Nuneaton Joint	257
Bell Codes, Routing	180
Bells, Platform, Cabin, etc.	218
Birkenhead Joint Lines	235
Bishop's Castle Railway	235
Black's Lock	112
Block — Instruments	173
Introduction of	4, 10
Pryce & Ferreira	242
Shelves	184
Systems in use, 1869	7
2 — Wire	192
Carbinoleumed Cabins	145
Carlisle Joint Lines	254
Chester & Holyhead Cabins	114
Clark 2-mile Telegraph	4, 6
Clark-Webb Chain Brake	200
Clearance Bars	214, 216
Coal and Ash Pens	145
Costs, Samples of	16, 267
Cranks	215
Crossovers, Use of 2 Levers	130
Dick, Charles	16
District Inspectors	20, 258
Edwards, George	14, 16
Electric — Lock, Fletcher's	183,269
Signalling	160, 200
Train Staff	193
Electrical Dept.	18, 22
Face Discs	221
Fireman's Call Box	186
Fletcher, J.W.	18, 22
Fletcher — Arm Repeaters	178
Blocks	22, 176
Electric Lock	183, 269
Train Describer	183
Fog — Regulations for	227
Special Equipment	224
Gates — Painting	112
Stops	105, 107
Wheels	103, 109
Gongs	218
GN & LNW Joint	257
Granary Junction, GER	202
Ground Frames	166
GW & LNW Joint	235
GWR, Early Signals	1
Hereford, Enlargement at	236
Hydraulic Systems	201
Interlocking — Early	8
Interlocking Frames	12, 148
— Brackets	162
Cam-Head	148
Girders	154, 156, 202
Key	166
North London	247
Overhead	155, 163
Power	200
Racks	148, 158
Right Angle	166
Tappet	160
Tumbler	149
Uprights	154, 163, 202
Johnson, R.E.	235
Key Interlocking	112, 166, 195
L&Y & LNW Joint	257
Lamps — Gate	108
Signal	31,44
Lancaster & Carlisle Cabins	115
Leeds, LNW & NE Joint	257
Level Crossings	101
— Levers Required	110
Lever Collars	186
Levers — LNW Totals	17
Fog	224
Light Repeaters	178
Lineman's Boards	217
Link	186
LMS Standard Frame	160
Manchester, South Junction and Altrincham Railway	251
Midway Release	216
MR & LNW Joint	257
MR — Rotary Block	187
Tappet Frames	160
Nameboards	115, 142
NER & LNW Joint, Leeds	257
North & South Western Junction Railway	242
North London Railway	242
Northampton Locks	186
One Engine in Steam System	192
Overhead Cabins	132, 144
— Special Frames	155
Painting — Cabins	141
Gates	112
LMS & BR Colours	145
Signals	55
Park, J.C.	244
Park & Pryce Train Bars	244
Pedley Street Power House	206
Pilot Engines	191
Points — Electric	206
Facing, Locks	214
Maximum Distances	214
Rodding	213
Police Huts	114

Power Signalling 200
Pryce, H.J. 244
Pryce & Ferreira Block 242

Railway Signal Co. 195, 211
Roberts, J.T. 18, 23, 188, 198
Route (Train) Indicators 180
Rugby Gantry 80
Rules — Signal Dept. 261
    1860 Extracts 2, 5

Saxby & Farmer —
    Early Associations 8, 11
    Early Cabins 115, 199, 123
    Lever Frames 8, 13, 165
Severus Junction, NER 211
Shrewsbury Joint Lines 235
Signals —
    1874 Types 27
    1876 Types 29
    1883 Types 39
    Arrangement of Arms 59
    Automatic Release 94
    Auxiliaries 3
    Bracket 28, 58
    Bridge 38, 91
    Calling-On 37, 94
    Co-Acting 44, 51
    Colour Light 100
    Concrete Posts for 57
    Distant 1, 29, 54
        — Multiple Levers for 224
        North London 248
        Special Locking 159
    Disc (and Crossbar) 1
    Disc (Ground & Miniature) 38, 85
    Draw Ahead of 1877 37
    Early History of 1, 26
    Gantries 72
    Guying 48
    Heights 45, 60
    Heights of Arms 59, 234
    Ladders 51
    Lamps 31, 44
    Lights 39, 87
    Loop Line 98
    North London 246
    Painting 55
    Pinnacles & Caps 29, 43
    Power 203
    Rings on 47
    Route Indicating 99
    Shunt Ahead 38, 94
    Shunting 36, 97
    Sighting 30, 44. 261
    Slotting 34, 49
Signal Department 14
    — 1902 to 1923 22
    District Inspectors 20, 258
    Heaton Norris 14
    LMS Changes 25
    Move to Crewe 16, 23
    Staff Structure 15, 24, 258

Signal, Electrical & Telegraph Dept. 22
Signal Cabins —
    ARP 212
    Cleaning Stages 129
    Elevation 129, 132
    Extensions 135
    Fires 136, 210
    Heating 135
    LNW Designs 123
    Overhead 132, 144
    Painting 141
    Pre-1874 Designs 113
    — Surviving Examples 121
    Siting of 132
Signal Huts 146
Signalling Layouts 228
Signalmen — Reminders to 183
Single Lines 191
    — Irregular Working 196
Solenoid Motors 203
Station Working 176
Stockport Works 22, 177
Sykes Lock and Block 187

Tappet Frames 160, 246
Telegraph Dept. —
    1870-1903 20
    Formation 9
    Staff 260
Thompson, A.M. 18
    — Key Interlocking 166
    Power Signalling 200
    Train Staff 193
Time Interval System 3
Track Circuits 188
Train on Line Indicators 188
Train Registers 183
Train Staff — and Ticket 191
    Electric 193
    Exchangers 197
Tumbler Frames 149
Tunnel Gongs 220
Turntable Bolts 213
Tyer — Blocks 173
    Train Describer 181
    Train Tablet 193

Webb, F.W. 14, 148
    — Frames 148, 200
    Train Staff 193
Wellington Type Cabin 240
Welshpool Station 241
Westinghouse 200
West London Railway 241
West London Extension Rly. 241
Whitehaven, Cleator & Egremont Rly. 253
Wicket Gates 111
Windows 123, 126, 137
Wire Adjusters 221

Vale of Towy Joint 241
Vehicle on Line Indicators 189

Zinc Roofs 118

Acknowledgements

The task of putting together a work which sets out to describe events which began over 130 years ago and relate to a Company which itself ceased to exist nearly 60 years ago would not have been possible without the kind assistance of a number of individuals and organisations. I would like to express my grateful thanks to the following for their assistance.

Particular thanks are due to Messrs J T Howard-Turner, Executive Consultant to the National Railway Museum, on Signalling and Telecommunications, Permanent Way, and Train Operating; M J Addison; M Christensen; M R L Instone and the late G H Platt for taking the trouble to read through the manuscript (in some cases several times!) and providing me with a number of helpful comments and suggestions.

The following have also given me assistance in some form or another, over the last few years, during the preparation of this volume and my grateful thanks should be recorded to them: The National Railway Museum, York (the photographs credited 'National Railway Museum' are reproduced by Courtesy of Dr J A Coiley, Keeper of the Museum); Divisional Signal and Telecommunications Engineers, British Rail, London Midland Region, Crewe and Birmingham and their staff; Public Record Office Kew and Ashridge; W F Hardman; J Cooper; P A Millard; The late J K Nelson; J Edgington; R Owen, formerly Public Relations Officer, British Rail, Stoke Division; H M Roocroft; The Manager, British Rail Engineering Ltd., Wolverton Works; P J Fisher; P Churchman; J M Hammond; D Ibbotson; Dr I W Scrimgeour; B E Timmins; M N Bland; Dr P H Spriggs; F W Shuttleworth; The Institution of Railway Signal Engineers; The Institution of Electrical Engineers; J Harding; L G Warburton; A Roberts; S Robinson; R Clavell; R J Talbot; J Whitaker; Mrs E M Foster, I C Foster; Museum of Science and Industry, Birmingham; J S Earnshaw; F Collinge; P Jordan; J R Hinson; T L Guest; J M Boyes; M J Borrowdale; D Powell; G K Fox; R Anderson; B D Matthews; D Hanson; J Dixon; R Newman; The Central Reference Library, Birmingham.

Much of the historical information in this book is based on extensive reading of the Minute Books, and other documents relating to the LNW, NL, N&SWJ Railways and the LNW & GW Joint Committee. These records are held by the Public Record Office, Kew, under Group reference RAIL, Classes 410, 529, 521 and 404 respectively. **Plate 17.17** forms part of Document ref. RAIL. 529/128.

In a book like this it is impossible to cover in detail all aspects of the subject let alone any more general details of the LNWR itself. Those who would like to know more about the LNW in general or in a particular field might consider membership of the LNWR Society (enquiries: 7, Walnut Grove, Winchester, Hants., SO22 5HR). Those interested in signalling may find membership of the Signalling Record Society (enquiries: 178, Birmingham Road, Kidderminster, DY10 2SJ) will assist them in the pursuit of their interests.

BIBLIOGRAPHY

The following titles are referred to in the text or may be useful as reference works or as additional reading. (Not all are currently in print.)

British Railway Pre-Grouping Atlas	Ian Allan Ltd.
British Railways Signalling by Kitchenside and Williams	Ian Allan Ltd.
A Pictorial Record of LMS Signals by L G Warburton	O.P.C.
A Pictorial Record of Southern Signals by G A Pryer	O.P.C.
A Pictorial Record of Great Western Signalling by A Vaughan	O.P.C.
LNWR Portrayed by J K Nelson	Peco Publishing
LNWR Miscellany by E Talbot (two volumes)	O.P.C.
Railway Reminiscences by G P Neele	Reprinted by E.P. Publishing
North London Railway: A Pictorial Record	H.M.S.O.
The London Brighton and South Coast Railway (3 Volume history) by J T Howard-Turner	Batsford
The Bishop's Castle Railway by E Griffith	Author